# INTRODUCTION TO
# ENGINEERING MECHANICS

*by*

JOHN V. HUDDLESTON

*Yale University*

ADDISON-WESLEY PUBLISHING COMPANY, INC.

READING, MASSACHUSETTS, U.S.A.

LONDON, ENGLAND

# PREFACE

This book is designed for a first course in engineering mechanics. It emphasizes the fundamentals of mechanics, but it differs from the many other introductory books on the subject in the selection and sequence of topics.

Rather than presenting mechanics as it developed historically, I have attempted to treat the subject logically and lucidly in its present-day state, tying together the various parts and using the most up-to-date mathematical tools consistent with the beginner's ability to understand. Thus, I have divided the subject on the basis of particles, rigid bodies, and deformable bodies, as opposed to the traditional separation of statics and dynamics that makes little mention of deformable bodies. And, since most of the quantities dealt with in mechanics are vectors, I have included a general vector algebra and have used vector notation freely for those parts of the theory in which such notation seemed advantageous.

I have given priority to the objectives of clarity and rigor and left it to the instructor to provide additional fulfillment of the objectives of motivation and detail. I feel that this is the most effective way to divide responsibilities between author and instructor.

The book is intended for a one-year course. By unifying statics, dynamics, and strength of materials, it allows the student of electrical or chemical engineering to cover the fundamentals of these subjects in two semesters instead of the usual three or four. At the same time it gives the student of civil engineering, mechanical engineering, metallurgy, or engineering science enough background so that, in his second year of engineering mechanics, he can study topics normally classified as advanced mechanics (e.g., Lagrange's equations) or advanced strength of materials (e.g., theory of elastic stability). Too often the engineering curriculum treats mechanics and strength of materials as separate subjects, establishing their connecting ties only vaguely. The student must then wait for advanced courses in vibrations, elasticity, etc., to see the unity of mechanics. In this book I have tried to show at the beginning the intimate relationship between Newtonian mechanics and mechanics of materials.

Although the book presupposes some knowledge of calculus and physics, its preliminary versions have been used successfully at Yale by students who have had no college physics and who take college calculus concurrently with engineering mechanics. Many of this group have been introduced to calculus in secondary school, but, to accommodate those who have not and to make the material of the later chapters comprehensible, part of our course must be devoted to filling in the elements of scalar calculus. I have included an appendix in the book for that purpose. (Direct references to the appendix have been avoided in the body of the text in order not to distract readers already familiar with the calculus.) Although topics such as vibrations and elastic stability which require solution of differential equations are not discussed in detail, all the basic laws and assumptions needed to set up such differential equations are presented, and the instructor of a class with the required background can add these topics.

Excluding the appendix, there are 120 solved examples and 341 problems for the student. I have chosen the examples to be as illustrative as possible without being so numerous or so lengthy that the reader becomes bored with a mass of computations. Many of the examples and problems are "classical" problems of mechanics for which I could devise no suitable substitutes, but many are also "new" problems. All or part of the answer is given for most of the even-numbered problems.

Where curriculum arrangements preclude an integrated approach to engineering mechanics, this book may be used for courses that separate statics, dynamics, and strength of materials by taking the chapters in the following order:

Statics: 1, 2, 3, 4, 7, 8, 9, 10, 11

Dynamics: 5, 6, 12, 13, 19, 20

Strength of materials: 14, 15, 16, 17, 18, 21

I acknowledge the help of the numerous authors of books on mechanics, especially Synge and Griffith, to whom I am most indebted. There is a list of modern books at the end of my book which I suggest for different viewpoints of or further study in the general areas covered herein. The list does not go beyond intermediate-level treatments and does not include books on specific topics of mechanics.

The course on which this book is based was composed by a committee consisting of John E. Griffith, Joel I. Abrams, and me. I wish to thank the other two members of this committee for the many ideas of theirs that I have incorporated into the book. I am also grateful to Messrs. Abrams, Christensen, Corr, DeLeeuw, Gray, Kalnins, Kiely, Kuo, McDonald, Schultz, Smith, and Vreeland, presently or formerly at Yale, who tested the preliminary versions in their classrooms.

A significant contribution was made by the student assistants who worked on various phases of the book, including Richard G. Bruce, James L. Paterson, and Daniel G. Schweikert, and especially John N. Dirga and

Elbert D. Manchester, whose devotion and generosity deserve the highest praise. Among other things, Messrs. Dirga and Manchester proofread the entire book.

Finally, I offer my thanks to all the engineering students at Yale who learned mechanics from the preliminary versions of the book, especially the Class of 1962, who received the poorly reproduced first draft in irregular installments and, despite the confusion, mastered the subject and first proved that the book was worthy of publication.

J. V. H.

*New Haven, Connecticut*
*March, 1961*

# CONTENTS

## PART 1.  MECHANICS OF A PARTICLE

## PART 2.   MECHANICS OF RIGID BODIES

## PART 3. MECHANICS OF DEFORMABLE BODIES

*Part 1*

# MECHANICS OF A PARTICLE

# CHAPTER 1

## INTRODUCTION

**1.1 Nature of mechanics.** What is the subject of mechanics? In its broad sense, mechanics is the study of the effect of forces on portions of the physical universe. The portion considered may be very large, such as a galaxy, or very small, such as an atomic particle. With a free interpretation of the word "forces," this definition gives the subject of mechanics an important, underlying role in nearly all the physical sciences.

In a narrower sense, mechanics is the study of forces and motion in "medium-sized" parts of the universe, i.e., in objects that we can see around us, such as machines, projectiles, clouds, or the moon. In this sense the subject is the oldest and most fundamental branch of physics. It is the oldest because man's earliest attempts to understand his surroundings were studies of the behavior of bodies which he could see and feel. It is the most fundamental because much of the later work in physics, including such abstruse developments as atomic physics and the theory of relativity, was either based on the earlier discoveries in mechanics or made possible by the experience man had gained from them.

The mechanics of medium-sized objects consists of a few basic physical laws on which the entire subject is built. Even before these laws were discovered, however, man had been attempting to control the forces of nature and to put them to work for his own benefit. For example, levers were used for raising heavy objects long before there were any laws of mechanics to explain why the objects were "heavy" or how the levers were able to overcome their "heaviness." As man's knowledge of physics grew, he began using more and more of that knowledge to improve his crafts. It is this application of physical theories to practical problems which is known as "engineering." Much of engineering requires the direct application of the laws of mechanics, and hence the subject of "engineering mechanics." The purpose of this book is to introduce the basic theory of mechanics in a form which will serve as a foundation for further study in mechanics and in all branches of engineering.

**1.2 Methods of mechanics.** The theory of mechanics is developed by starting with fundamental propositions of three different types: basic physical *laws*, as mentioned in Art. 1.1 and discussed more fully in subsequent parts of this book; arbitrary *definitions* introduced purely for convenience; and simplifying *assumptions* which limit the applicability of the

1

theory but which are justified by generations of experience and experimentation. The italicized words above are used often throughout this book to emphasize the correct status of the various propositions employed. A better understanding of the differences among the three types of proposition can come only after studying mechanics and other branches of physics extensively.

By deductive reasoning which is primarily mathematical, various results are derived from the fundamental propositions. These results are called *theorems, principles* (although this word is also used to describe some physical laws), *formulas*, or *equations*. Many examples of these derived results are given in this book.

With the theory available, a complete investigation of the behavior of any portion of the universe includes four steps:

(1) *Isolation.* The portion selected, called the *mechanical system*, is imagined to be detached from its surroundings. The reason for this step is that the theory of mechanics distinguishes between effects on the system that come from within the system and effects that are exerted by its surroundings. Some examples of mechanical systems are the following: (a) the piston of an automobile engine, (b) the entire engine, (c) the entire automobile. The system may be one that actually exists or one that is imaginary (e.g., an automobile engine to be designed); the engineer is frequently concerned with the latter type.

(2) *Idealization.* The laws of mechanics and the theory based on them apply only under ideal conditions which never exist in nature. Because of this, the mechanical system must be idealized to make it conform to the assumptions used in developing the theory, i.e., the physical problem must be translated into a mathematical problem. As an example, consider a mechanical system composed of the shaft and block shown in Fig. 1.1. If the hole in the upper end of the shaft is fitted over a peg, the object can be used as a pendulum which swings back and forth in the plane of

the paper. Some idealizations which could be made here for the purpose of predicting the motion of the pendulum are the following: (a) The shaft is "weightless," remains perfectly straight, and does not change in length. (b) The block has weight but "no size." (c) The entire pendulum is supported at a "point." The system resulting from such idealizations is called, because of the abstractions involved, a "mathematical model" of the real system. The theory of mechanics gives exact results for the mathematical model but only approximate results for the real

FIGURE 1.1        pendulum represented by the model. The accuracy of the approximation depends on how closely the model resembles the real system. Different kinds of idealizations lead to models of varying degrees of complexity, but no model is as complex as the real system.

(3) *Mathematical analysis.* This step is the solution of the mathematical problem resulting from the preceding step. The calculations usually involve a straightforward application of the theory, as illustrated in the examples appearing throughout this book.

(4) *Interpretation.* The results are explained in physical terms, which means that the mathematical solution is translated back into a solution of the physical problem. Experimental observations on the real system can often be used to verify results predicted by the analysis. Many such experiments have been performed in the history of mechanics, and these reveal, for many types of systems, the size of errors introduced by various idealizations.

The foregoing description of a mechanical analysis is summarized in the following chart:

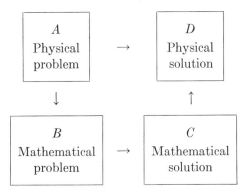

To proceed directly from $A$ to $D$ might be called the "intuitive" approach, while proceeding from $A$ to $D$ by way of $B$ and $C$ would be the "scientific" approach. The latter procedure is generally more reliable and is the one advocated by this book.

The subject of mechanics may be subdivided in the following manner:

A. *Statics*, the study of stationary systems.
B. *Dynamics*, the study of moving systems.
  1. *Kinematics*, the study of motion without reference to its cause, e.g., determining the path of a point on the rim of a rolling wheel.
  2. *Kinetics*, the study of the relationship between motion and its cause, e.g., finding out what makes a wheel roll.

The material in the mechanical system may be in either of the two commonly experienced states, solid or fluid, and hence mechanics is also divided into mechanics of solids and mechanics of fluids. This book is devoted primarily to the mechanics of solids.

**1.3 Basic concepts.** The basic physical laws of mechanics and the principles derived from them relate quantities such as length, time, and force. One of the difficulties of mechanics is to define these basic quantities precisely. Also, in stating the laws and principles, we frequently find it necessary to use the words "particle," "rigid body," etc., which are another group of concepts difficult to define. The following discussion of these basic concepts, while far from giving precise definitions, should help explain their meaning. With that background, the theory of mechanics can be built up in a very precise manner.

(1) *Space.* Intuition gives us a crude idea of what space is, since we live and move in it constantly. It is possible to imagine a one-dimensional space (a straight line) and a two-dimensional space (a plane). Since the space that we occupy is one step more complex than the latter, it is said to be three-dimensional.

(2) *Length.* To measure distance in any direction in space requires a basic unit of length, and nature does not provide any absolute unit. For example, if everything in the universe suddenly increased to a thousand times its original size, there would be no way of detecting the change. From this example it can be seen that length is a relative quantity. To measure length, a scale is established by making two marks on a bar of metal and defining the distance between the marks as a unit of length. Other distances are then measured in these units.

(3) *Position.* Position is another relative concept, since it is possible to locate points in space only relatively to some arbitrary reference point. If everything in the universe suddenly moved a million miles in unison, the new location could not be distinguished from the old one. The laws of mechanics assume a "fixed" reference point, but such a point is artificial in our universe. Astronomers frequently use the sun as a fixed reference point, even though they know that the sun moves relatively to the other stars. Engineers frequently use a point on the earth as a fixed reference point, in spite of the known motion of the earth. The errors introduced into any analysis by such idealizations can be checked by experiment.

Once a reference point is chosen, the position of any other point can be described by its distance and direction from the "fixed" point. But direction, like distance, is relative. Suppose that the entire universe suddenly rotated 90° about a line through the reference point. Again the change could not be detected. It follows that more than a fixed point is needed;

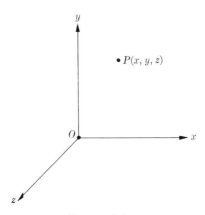

FIGURE 1.2

some lines through the point which are arbitrarily assumed to have "fixed" directions are also needed.  Intuition indicates that two perpendicular lines (although nonperpendicular lines would also suffice) through the point would be adequate; one would be insufficient since rotation about it would still go unnoticed.  Three perpendicular lines are more desirable than two, since they provide a convenient *coordinate system*, as shown in Fig. 1.2.  By specifying the three coordinates $x$, $y$, $z$ of a point $P$ (its distance from the three coordinate planes, the $yz$-, $zx$-, and $xy$-planes, respectively), we can completely define its exact relative location and hence both its distance and direction from the fixed point $O$ (called the *origin* of the coordinate system).  The set of three intersecting lines is called a *frame of reference*, and the laws of mechanics assume a fixed frame of reference. Since there is no fixed frame in the universe, one must be imagined if the laws of mechanics are to be regarded as exact.

In practical problems various frames of reference are used.  For example, three intersecting corners of a room would provide a suitable frame of reference for some problems.  But to assume that the frame is fixed would be to imply that the earth is stationary and all the heavenly bodies are moving around it, a theory that was long ago abandoned in favor of the idea that the stars remain stationary while the earth rotates.  Since the frame of reference is arbitrary, it appears superficially that the old theory was just as plausible as the new one.  A closer investigation, however, reveals some important conclusions.  Since the pattern of stars observed in the sky does not change during ordinary time intervals, it is often convenient to use these stars as a frame of reference.  The laws of mechanics then predict events in the solar system with great accuracy, whereas assuming that the earth is fixed leads to discrepancies between observed phenomena (such as the path of a comet) and theoretical predictions. One is thus led to believe that the stars come closer to forming a fixed frame of reference than the earth.

(4) *Time.* Time is measured in units defined by the duration of some occurrence involving motion, such as one rotation of the earth or one oscillation of the pendulum of a clock. Since all motion is relative, time is also relative, and all the difficulties encountered in defining position follow through into the definition of time.

(5) *Force.* Although we experience forces continually through such muscular activity as pushing, pulling, lifting, and breathing, force is a most elusive concept to define. Rather than attempting an extensive analysis of this concept, let us simply say that force is a quantity whose magnitude is measurable in some units. The measurement is accomplished by using the laws of mechanics (which are concerned with forces). For example, mechanics says that the magnitude of the force on an ideal spring is proportional to the change in length of the spring. A standard change in length of a standard spring can be used to define a unit of force, and any force can be measured by the number of these standard changes in length it produces in the standard spring.

(6) *Mass.* Mass is that property of a body which gives it *inertia* (resistance to starting and stopping) and which makes it attracted by other bodies. For example, a body is attracted by the earth, and the magnitude of the force that the earth exerts on it is called its weight. The weight of a body varies slightly at different points on the earth's surface, but its mass remains constant. In fact, the mass of a body would manifest itself far out in space (where it would have no weight) by the inertia it always possesses. This inertia could be perceived by shaking the body back and forth and noting its resistance to starting and stopping. The unit of mass can be defined by selecting a standard body and specifying that its mass is unity. The mass of any other body is then found by an experiment (such as weighing) in which enough of the standard masses are used so that the behavior of the unknown mass is exactly the same as that of the group of standard masses. The number of standard masses (or the fraction of a standard mass) required is then the mass of the other body.

(7) *Particle.* This is a mathematical model of a piece of matter. The piece has no size at all but has a position in the frame of reference and has mass. A particle is also called a "mass point." It is not an atomic particle, but rather a more abstract type of particle. A body of any size or shape may be idealized as a particle when its size and shape are irrelevant. When this is not the case, the body can be studied by subdividing it into small portions and treating the subdivisions as particles.

(8) *Rigid body.* All real bodies are deformable, but in many cases a real body is idealized into a rigid body, one in which all points of the body remain at fixed distances from each other.

(9) *Displacement.* A displacement is a change in position of a particle from one point in the frame of reference to another point. The path followed by the particle between the two points, although important in itself in many cases, is not included in the meaning of the word "displacement."

The difficulties encountered in establishing the foregoing concepts should not be allowed to cast doubt on the validity of mechanics. Engineering achievements based on mechanics stand as a monument to its reliability.

**1.4 Units.** The units used in this book for the various measurable quantities are:

> *Length:* foot, inch, yard, mile.
> *Time:* second, minute, hour.
> *Force:* pound (or poundal).
> *Mass:* pound (or slug).

The units of length and time and the pound unit of force are assumed to be familiar units. All the other units mentioned are discussed in detail in Chapter 6.

**1.5 Brief history of mechanics.** With a long history dating back to the early Greek philosophers, mechanics has received contributions from countless men down through the ages. Even today there are thousands of people doing research in this field. The subject is still very much alive and is growing at a remarkable rate.

The great milestones in the development of mechanics, however, are few. The experimental background on which the subject rests is attributable largely to Galileo Galilei (1564–1642), who discovered patterns in the behavior of freely falling bodies, and Johannes Kepler (1571–1630), who, by observing the motion of the planets, was able to set down several experimental laws to describe their behavior. Starting with Galileo's and Kepler's laws and adding some experimental work of his own, Isaac Newton (1642–1727) first stated the fundamental laws of mechanics. His ingenuity and perspicacity in arriving at these laws have been a marvel to every generation of scientists since his time, even up to the present day. It is fitting that the classical mechanics based on his laws has come to be known as "Newtonian" mechanics, since he was unquestionably the greatest single contributor to the subject.

The three laws of Newton, stated approximately in the language used by Newton, are as follows:

(1) *Every body continues in the state of rest, or of uniform motion in a right line, unless it is compelled to change that state by forces impressed upon it.*

(2) *The change of motion is proportional to the motive force impressed and is made in the direction of the right line in which the force is impressed.*

(3) *To every action there is always opposed an equal reaction; or, the mutual actions of two bodies upon each other are always equal and directed to contrary parts.*

These laws, after translation into modern language and notation, are used as the starting point for the theory of mechanics as developed in this book.

Using the experimental laws of Kepler and his own second law, Newton then discovered his famous law of gravitation, which states that the magnitude of the force of attraction between two particles is directly proportional to the product of their masses and inversely proportional to the square of the distance between them. This law is discussed more fully in Chapter 6.

After Newton, the subject of mechanics received valuable contributions from several more men, two of whom were Lagrange (1736–1813) and Hamilton (1805–1865). These men formulated the basic laws of mechanics in new and different ways, using the concepts of potential and kinetic energy. This gave the subject of Newtonian mechanics several different starting points from which the theory could be developed. The new approaches had some advantages and some disadvantages when compared with Newton's laws, but Newton's laws still appear to be the best way to introduce mechanics to students of engineering.

Most of the work done today in solid mechanics is concerned with deformable bodies. This great branch of mechanics was begun by Robert Hooke (1635–1702) when he formulated his law of perfect elasticity by stating that the magnitude of the force on the ends of a rod is proportional to the change in length of the rod. The generalized theory of deformation produced in solid bodies by more general forces was then developed by Navier (1785–1836), Poisson (1781–1840), and Cauchy (1789–1857), who knew and used Newton's laws in their investigations.

In recent times researchers have concerned themselves with the statics of deformable bodies which are not elastic and with the dynamics of all types of deformable bodies.

## CHAPTER 2

## ELEMENTARY VECTOR ALGEBRA

**2.1 Introduction.** There are certain physical quantities which require specification of both *magnitude* and *direction* to fully describe one of the quantities or to completely determine its effect upon a mechanical system. Such a quantity is called a *vector*. Two examples of vectors are force and displacement. If a book is standing on edge on a table and a force of one-pound magnitude is applied to it in the various ways indicated by the arrows in Fig. 2.1, the book behaves differently for each different direction of the force. If a ship could travel through a displacement of 100 miles in either of the two directions indicated in Fig. 2.2, the ship would have a different final position in each case.

Other physical quantities, such as mass, volume, and temperature, are completely specified by magnitude only. A quantity of this type is called a *scalar*. Some scalars are inherently positive (e.g., mass), while others, known as algebraic scalars, may be either positive or negative (e.g., temperature).

Another property of vectors which is frequently given separate attention is *sense*. To describe the sense of a vector means to state which of two opposite ways it actually "goes." For example, a 100-mile displacement from south to north (Fig. 2.2) has a direction along a north-south line and a sense from south to north. In this book the property of direction is always understood to include sense when the sense is not mentioned specifically. Thus, in the above example, the direction would be described as "from south to north" or "toward the north," and another displacement of

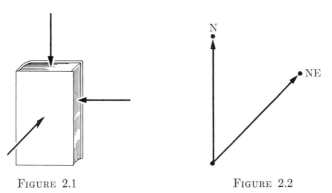

FIGURE 2.1　　　　　　　　FIGURE 2.2

9

100 miles from north to south would be said to have opposite direction from the preceding one (rather than same direction and opposite sense).

It is convenient to represent a vector by an imaginary *directed line segment* in space, where the direction of the line is the same as that of the vector and the length of the segment signifies the magnitude of the vector to some convenient scale. For example, using a scale of 1 in. = 100 lb, a 600-lb force is represented by a line segment which has the same direction as the force and a length of 6 in. The directed line segment may then be shown on a drawing of the mechanical system by an arrow like those in Figs. 2.1 and 2.2. Note that the arrowhead is used to indicate the sense of the vector. If the force on top of the book in Fig. 2.1 were reversed so that it "pulled" on the book instead of "pushing," the arrowhead would be placed at the other end of the arrow. Since the effect of the force would be quite different after this change, care must be exercised in placing the arrowhead on an arrow which represents a vector. Arrows are used to represent vectors in many of the figures appearing throughout this book.

For some vectors, e.g., forces, the actual line in space along which the vector lies (called the "line of action") is also important in determining its physical effect. Furthermore, the actual point along the line where the vector acts (called the "point of application") may be important too in some cases. The branch of mathematics known as vector algebra, however, is not concerned with these other aspects of the vectors. All its operations are defined in terms of the two basic properties of vectors, magnitude and direction (including sense).

A vector is distinguished from a scalar by the use of a special kind of symbol. In print, it is customary to use a bold-faced symbol, e.g.,

$$\mathbf{A}, \mathbf{B}, \mathbf{a}, \mathbf{F}, \mathbf{r}.$$

The magnitude of the vector (a scalar which is always positive) is then denoted by absolute value signs, e.g.,

$$|\mathbf{A}|, |\mathbf{B}|, |\mathbf{a}|, |\mathbf{F}|, |\mathbf{r}|.$$

Whenever there will be no confusion with other scalars that have sign, the magnitude may be written more simply, e.g.,

$$A, B, a, F, r.$$

Since mechanics deals with many quantities which are vectors, it is desirable to establish a general vector algebra with rules that apply to all different types of vectors.

**2.2 Equality of vectors.** By definition, equality between two vectors of the same type (e.g., two displacements) means that the two vectors have

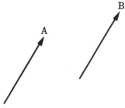

FIGURE 2.3

the *same magnitude and direction*. This situation is represented sym-
bolically by the equation

$$A = B$$

and graphically by two arrows with the same length and the same direction
(which means that the two arrows are parallel), as shown in Fig. 2.3. For
example, if two ships start from two different points and both travel northeast for a distance of 100 miles, then their displacements are equal (neglecting the curvature of the earth's surface).

It follows from the foregoing definition of equality that, if $A = C$ and
$B = C$, then $A = B$.

**2.3 Addition of vectors.** The definition of addition involves the directed
line segments which represent the vectors. For the sum of two vectors,
i.e.,

$$S = A + B, \tag{2.1}$$

S is determined either by the *Triangle Rule* or by the *Parallelogram Rule*,
as depicted in Figs. 2.4 and 2.5, respectively. To use the Triangle Rule,
the "tail" of the arrow representing **B** is connected to the "head" of that
representing **A**, and an arrow from the tail of **A** to the head of **B** then
represents the sum **S**. For the Parallelogram Rule, the two tails are connected, and a parallelogram is formed with **A** and **B** as two adjacent sides.
The sum **S** is then represented by that diagonal which goes from the tails
of **A** and **B** to the opposite corner of the parallelogram. The vectors **A** and

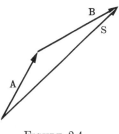

FIGURE 2.4

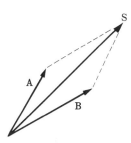

FIGURE 2.5

**B**, of course, must be of the same type (e.g., two forces) if they are to be added, and the arrows must be drawn to scale to make the operation meaningful. The result **S** clearly has both magnitude (to the same scale as used for **A** and **B**) and direction and is the same regardless of which of the two rules is used.

It is obvious that the addition of two vectors is *commutative*, i.e.,

$$\mathbf{A} + \mathbf{B} = \mathbf{B} + \mathbf{A}, \tag{2.2}$$

since connecting the tail of **A** to the head of **B** gives the same **S** as connecting the tail of **B** to the head of **A**. If a ship travels 100 miles north and then 100 miles east in the vicinity of the equator (where, for the distances involved, the earth's surface may be assumed flat), the total displacement (not the total distance traveled, which is 200 miles and is a scalar) is 141.4 miles toward the northeast, and this result is independent of the order in which the two displacements are added together.

Addition of three vectors,

$$\mathbf{S} = \mathbf{A} + \mathbf{B} + \mathbf{C}, \tag{2.3}$$

is defined by the *Polygon Rule*, an extension of the Triangle Rule, as shown in Fig. 2.6. (The four intersection points in this figure do not necessarily lie in the same plane.) By considering the dashed arrows in Fig. 2.6, we can see that addition of three vectors is *associative*, i.e.,

$$(\mathbf{A} + \mathbf{B}) + \mathbf{C} = \mathbf{A} + (\mathbf{B} + \mathbf{C}). \tag{2.4}$$

Since the addition of two vectors is commutative, the right-hand side of the foregoing equation can be rewritten to give

$$(\mathbf{A} + \mathbf{B}) + \mathbf{C} = (\mathbf{B} + \mathbf{C}) + \mathbf{A}.$$

Hence, dropping the parentheses, it follows that

$$\mathbf{S} = \mathbf{A} + \mathbf{B} + \mathbf{C} = \mathbf{B} + \mathbf{C} + \mathbf{A}. \tag{2.5}$$

In a similar way it can be shown that the same result is obtained for any order of addition of the three vectors.

Addition of any number of vectors,

$$\mathbf{S} = \mathbf{A} + \mathbf{B} + \mathbf{C} + \mathbf{D} + \cdots, \tag{2.6}$$

is still defined by the Polygon Rule, and it can again be shown that the order of addition is immaterial.

Note that the plus sign, when written between two vectors, has a different meaning than when written between two scalars.

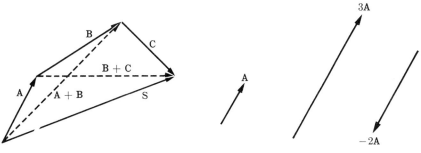

FIGURE 2.6                     FIGURE 2.7

**2.4 Multiplication of a vector by a scalar.** If $M$ is an algebraic scalar and **A** is a vector, the product $M$**A** is defined as a vector with magnitude $|M||\mathbf{A}|$ and with direction the same as that of **A** if $M > 0$ and opposite that of **A** if $M < 0$. The case where $M = 0$ is considered later. Examples of multiplication of a vector by a scalar are shown in Fig. 2.7.

Multiplication of a vector by a scalar can be shown to be *distributive*, i.e.,

$$(M + N)\mathbf{A} = M\mathbf{A} + N\mathbf{A} \tag{2.7}$$

and

$$M(\mathbf{A} + \mathbf{B}) = M\mathbf{A} + M\mathbf{B}, \tag{2.8}$$

and *associative*, i.e.,

$$M(N\mathbf{A}) = (MN)\mathbf{A} = MN\mathbf{A}. \tag{2.9}$$

A negative vector is defined in terms of multiplication of a vector by a scalar as follows:

$$-\mathbf{A} = (-1)\mathbf{A}. \tag{2.10}$$

From this it follows that $-\mathbf{A}$ is a vector with the same magnitude as **A** but with opposite direction, as shown in Fig. 2.8. The division of a vector **A** by a scalar $M$ is also defined in terms of multiplication of a vector by a scalar, i.e.,

$$\frac{\mathbf{A}}{M} = \left(\frac{1}{M}\right)\mathbf{A}. \tag{2.11}$$

FIGURE 2.8

One important distinction between a scalar and a vector which should be understood is the following: A symbol (such as $M$ or $N$) for an algebraic scalar stands for a quantity which may take on negative values as well as positive (so that $-M$ may actually be a positive number), while a symbol (such as **A**) for a vector stands for a quantity which has magnitude and direction *but no sign*. The minus sign in front of a vector means simply that the direction of the vector is reversed.

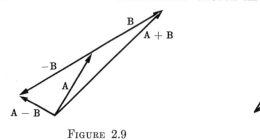

FIGURE 2.9                    FIGURE 2.10

**2.5 Subtraction of vectors.** By definition,

$$A - B = A + (-B), \tag{2.12}$$

the meaning of $-B$ being in accordance with Eq. (2.10). Thus, to subtract $B$ from $A$, the direction of $B$ is reversed and the new vector is added to $A$. This operation is depicted in Figs. 2.9 and 2.10, which show two different ways of performing the operation and also compare the sum $A + B$ with the difference $A - B$.

**2.6 Null vector.** The null vector **0** is obtained by the operation of subtraction of a vector from itself,

$$A - A = 0, \tag{2.13}$$

or by multiplying a vector by the scalar 0,

$$0A = 0. \tag{2.14}$$

The null vector occupies in vector algebra a position similar to that of the scalar 0 in scalar algebra. It is obvious that, if $B = 0$, then $B = 0$, where $B$ is the magnitude of $B$. This situation is described by saying that $B = 0$ is a *sufficient condition* for (implies, leads to) $B = 0$. The converse is also true, i.e., if $B = 0$, then $B = 0$. Thus, $B = 0$ is also a *necessary condition* for (is implied by, follows from) $B = 0$. The question of necessity and sufficiency comes up often in mathematics and in those branches of physics (such as mechanics) which use mathematics. Another way of stating the above combination of necessity and sufficiency is to say that $B = 0$ if (necessary) and only if (sufficient) $B = 0$.

Since null vectors have no magnitude, the concept of direction is meaningless for them, and all null vectors are considered equal to one another.

The equation

$$A = B$$

can now be written

$$A - B = 0,$$

and vice versa, and hence the rules of transposition for scalar equations also apply to vector equations.

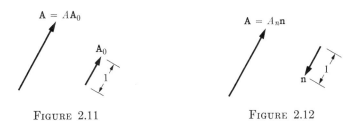

FIGURE 2.11                          FIGURE 2.12

**2.7 Unit vector.** A unit vector is a vector with magnitude of unity. It is symbolized by a subscript zero or by a small letter, e.g.,

$$\mathbf{A}_0, \quad \mathbf{a}_0, \quad \mathbf{i}, \quad \mathbf{n}.$$

The subscript zero usually means that the unit vector is in the same direction as the corresponding vector without the subscript. Being a means of identifying direction, the unit vector is a useful and powerful tool in mechanics.

From the definition of multiplication of a vector by a scalar, we find that any vector may be written as the product of its magnitude and a unit vector in its direction, i.e.,

$$\mathbf{A} = A\mathbf{A}_0. \tag{2.15}$$

Any vector may also be written as the product of an algebraic scalar and a unit vector parallel to the given vector but not necessarily with the same sense, i.e.,

$$\mathbf{A} = A_n\mathbf{n}, \tag{2.16}$$

where the subscript is used to denote an algebraic scalar. For a graphical representation of these results, see Figs. 2.11 and 2.12. It is customary to consider the unit vector as dimensionless and to assign the proper units (e.g., lb or ft) to $A$ or $A_n$ in order to give the vector $\mathbf{A}$ its required dimensions.

**2.8 Components of a vector.** For any given vector it is always possible to find a group of two or more vectors (of the same type as the given vector) whose sum is the given vector. Each one of the group is called a *vector component* of the given vector. In Fig. 2.13, a vector $\mathbf{A}$ is shown "resolved" into a set of three vector components $\mathbf{A}'$, $\mathbf{A}''$, $\mathbf{A}'''$. Inasmuch as there are any number of ways in which a vector can be resolved into vector components, the components have little significance unless other conditions are imposed on the operation. A frequently encountered restriction is that one of the vector components must be parallel to a given line, i.e., have a specified direction but an unspecified sense. In Fig. 2.14, the vector component $\mathbf{A}'$ has been taken parallel to the directed line $L$ (which does not necessarily intersect the line of action of $\mathbf{A}$), and a unit vector $\mathbf{n}$ has been placed on the line $L$ to identify its direction and sense. Using the

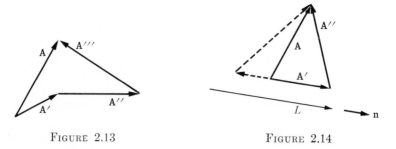

FIGURE 2.13                              FIGURE 2.14

results of Art. 2.7, we can write the component **A′** as the product of an algebraic scalar $A_L$ and the unit vector **n** as follows:

$$\mathbf{A'} = A_L\mathbf{n}. \tag{2.17}$$

This is simply the application of Eq. (2.16) to the special vector **A′**. The algebraic scalar $A_L$ is referred to as the *scalar component* of **A** in the *L*-direction, or more simply as the "*L*-component" of **A**. It has a negative value when **A′** is taken with a direction opposite to that of **n**, as illustrated by the dashed arrows in Fig. 2.14.

The restriction of parallelism to a given line for one component still does not lead to a unique set of vector components for **A**, since (1) the component **A′** can be taken in either of two opposite directions and with any desired magnitude (i.e., $A_L$ may be assigned any positive or negative value), and (2) the remainder of the polygon after **A′** is chosen is still arbitrary. The second ambiguity is removed whenever the total number of vector components is required to be two, for in that case **A″** is found by connecting the head of **A′** to the head of **A**. To then remove the first ambiguity, let it be required either (a) that **A′** have a given magnitude and direction (including sense), or (b) that both **A′** and **A″** have given directions (but unspecified senses).

---

EXAMPLE 2.1. Resolve **u**, a displacement of 100 miles toward the northeast, into two components such that: (a) one is 100 miles toward the west, and (b) one is in a northwest-southeast direction and the other is in a north-south direction.

*Solution.* This problem may be solved either graphically or by trigonometry. The trigonometric solution is illustrated here, using Figs. 2.15(a) and 2.15(b) for parts (a) and (b), respectively. (All known magnitudes are shown in parentheses in these figures.) The graphical solution would consist of drawing the figures to scale in accordance with the given information and measuring unknown magnitudes and directions by means of scale and protractor.

(a) It is clear that the triangle of Fig. 2.15(a) is isosceles and has a base angle of 22.5°. Thus,

$$|\mathbf{u''}| = 2(100) \cos 22.5° = 2(100)(0.924) = 184.8 \text{ miles.}$$

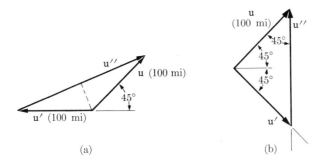

FIGURE 2.15

The angle that **u**″ makes with a north-south line is 90° − 22.5°, or 67.5°. The component **u**″ is therefore fully described by saying that it has a magnitude of 184.8 miles and a direction of N67.5°E. (Specifying a direction in this manner is sometimes referred to as giving the "bearing.") It is important to note that both the magnitude and direction of an unknown vector must be reported. Giving only the magnitude *does not constitute a complete answer*.

(b) This part of the problem is solved by drawing a northwest-southeast line through the tail of **u** and a north-south line through the head of **u**. The intersection point of the two lines is the third vertex of the triangle. Analyzing the triangle by trigonometry, we find that **u**′ is 100 miles toward the southeast and **u**″ is 141.4 miles toward the north. Note that the sense of neither component can be specified in the statement of part (b) of the problem; both senses must be found as part of the solution. Had the problem required that **u**′ be toward the northwest, a solution would have been impossible.

A more elaborate restriction is often imposed on one of the vector components of a vector, namely that the component must be parallel to a given line and have magnitude and sense as determined by two planes through the ends of the vector, where the planes are taken parallel to a given plane. This type of component for a vector **A** is shown in Fig. 2.16. If the arrowhead ends of both **A** and **A**′ are made to lie in the same one of

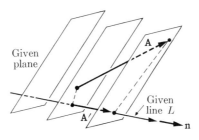

FIGURE 2.16

the planes, it is clear that the component $\mathbf{A}'$ is fully determined by the operation. Equation (2.17) still holds, but now both the value and the sign of the scalar component $A_L$ are determined by the parallel planes.

The type of component discussed in the preceding paragraph, which can be used regardless of how many additional vector components the vector is being resolved into, takes on a special importance when the planes through the ends of the vector are made perpendicular to the given line, as illustrated in Fig. 2.17. If the angle $\phi_L$ between the vector $\mathbf{A}$ and the vector $\mathbf{n}$ is known, the scalar component $A_L$ can be found by the following equation:

$$A_L = A \cos \phi_L. \tag{2.18}$$

This important equation follows from an application of elementary trigonometry to the right triangle $PQR$ in Fig. 2.17. The angle $\phi_L$ is measured in the plane defined by $\mathbf{A}$ and $\mathbf{n}$ (when $\mathbf{n}$ is moved parallel to itself so that it intersects $\mathbf{A}$), and, for convenience, it is always taken as the smaller angle between the positive direction of $\mathbf{A}$ and the positive direction of $\mathbf{n}$. Hence, its value is always in the interval

$$0 \leq \phi_L \leq 180°,$$

and Eq. (2.18) is valid for any $\phi_L$ in this interval. The sign of $A_L$ is automatically given by the sign of $\cos \phi_L$ (which is negative when $\phi_L$ is between 90° and 180°), since $A$, the magnitude of $\mathbf{A}$, is always positive.

If two vectors $\mathbf{A}$ and $\mathbf{B}$ have vector components $\mathbf{A}'$ and $\mathbf{B}'$ in the $L$-direction, respectively, and if these components are determined by two sets of planes all parallel to each other, it follows from geometry that the equation

$$\mathbf{A} = \mathbf{B}$$

is a sufficient condition but not a necessary condition that

$$\mathbf{A}' = \mathbf{B}' \quad \text{and} \quad A_L = B_L,$$

since two parallel lines of the same length have projections of the same length on any one line. The condition is not necessary because any number of nonparallel lines can be found which have the same projection on a given line.

If $\mathbf{S}$ is the sum of three vectors $\mathbf{A}$, $\mathbf{B}$, $\mathbf{C}$, then it follows from Fig. 2.18, a view which shows all the parallel planes edgewise, that

$$\mathbf{S}' = \mathbf{A}' + \mathbf{B}' + \mathbf{C}' \tag{2.19}$$

and

$$S_L = A_L + B_L + C_L, \tag{2.20}$$

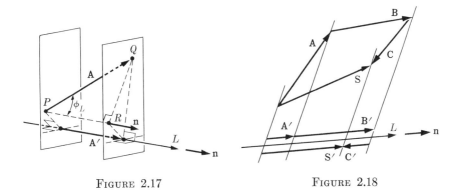

FIGURE 2.17                        FIGURE 2.18

and similar equations hold for any number of vectors. For the particular group of vectors shown in Fig. 2.18, $C_L$ is a negative quantity (equal to $-|\mathbf{C}'|$), and hence the sign before $C_L$ in Eq. (2.20) must be a plus sign to properly express the fact that, from Fig. 2.18,

$$|S_L| = |A_L| + |B_L| - |C_L|,$$

i.e., that the length of $\mathbf{S}'$ is obtained by subtracting the length of $\mathbf{C}'$ from the combined length of $\mathbf{A}'$ and $\mathbf{B}'$. Equation (2.19) illustrates a special kind of vector addition in which all the vectors involved are parallel; nevertheless, the addition still uses the Polygon Rule discussed in Art. 2.3.

In light of the foregoing discussion, two important derived principles can be stated:

(1) The vector component in the $L$-direction of the sum of several vectors equals the sum of the vector components of those vectors in the $L$-direction.

(2) The scalar component in the $L$-direction of the sum of several vectors equals the (algebraic) sum of the scalar components of those vectors in the $L$-direction.

**2.9 Vectors in rectangular coordinate systems.** The use of coordinates is virtually indispensable in mechanics. Even though many different types of coordinate systems (e.g., cylindrical coordinates, spherical coordinates) can be attached to a frame of reference and used in special applications, this book emphasizes the simplest and most basic system, namely, a rectangular system such as that shown in Fig. 1.2 (frequently called a "cartesian" coordinate system). The use of coordinates is known as the "analytical" approach to mechanics.

The $x$-, $y$-, and $z$-directions of the rectangular coordinate system are identified by a set of three unit vectors $\mathbf{i}$, $\mathbf{j}$, $\mathbf{k}$, respectively, as shown in

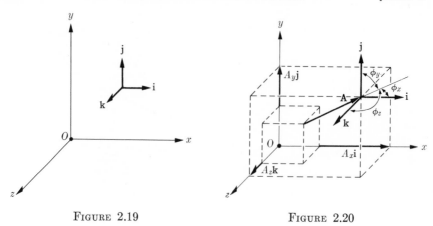

FIGURE 2.19                    FIGURE 2.20

Fig. 2.19. The coordinate system employed is usually made to be "right-handed," which means that, when the fingers of the right hand describe the 90° rotation about the $x$-axis required to have the $y$-axis move into the position of the $z$-axis, the thumb of the right hand points in the $x$-direction and that similar statements hold when the letters $x$, $y$, $z$ are replaced by $y$, $z$, $x$, respectively, and when these in turn are replaced by $z$, $x$, $y$, respectively. If one axis of a right-handed system is reversed in direction, the system becomes "left-handed," which means that the left hand must be used in the above rules instead of the right hand. Keeping the coordinate systems uniform (i.e., right-handed) is mostly a matter of convenience, but in some instances (discussed in Chapter 7) it is essential that they be kept uniform.

When the directed line segment which represents a vector is located in a rectangular coordinate system, planes may be passed through the ends of the segment as in Fig. 2.20 to find the *rectangular components* of the vector in the directions of the three axes. The vector components are $A_x\mathbf{i}$, $A_y\mathbf{j}$, $A_z\mathbf{k}$, and the scalar components are $A_x$, $A_y$, $A_z$. All the discussion of components in Art. 2.8 applies to these rectangular components, and the vector **A** may be written as the sum of the vector components, i.e.,

$$\mathbf{A} = A_x\mathbf{i} + A_y\mathbf{j} + A_z\mathbf{k}. \tag{2.21}$$

This is a most important equation. It shows that, once the coordinate system is established, specification of the three scalar components $A_x$, $A_y$, $A_z$ *fully* describes the vector **A**. Describing the vector in this manner is usually more convenient than attempting to describe its magnitude and direction.

In advanced mathematics and mechanics, a scalar is defined as a quantity which does not change when the coordinate system is rotated. If the vector **A** in Fig. 2.20 is fixed, for example, while the coordinate system is rotated about some line through $O$, the magnitude $A$ does not change, but each of the three components $A_x$, $A_y$, $A_z$ does. If a scalar is defined by its invariance, then, $A_x$, $A_y$, $A_z$ are not scalars but are simply components of a vector. In this book, any quantity which is not a vector is called a scalar, so that each one of the three rectangular components is considered an algebraic scalar.

The three angles $\phi_x$, $\phi_y$, $\phi_z$ (Fig. 2.20) which **A** makes with **i**, **j**, **k**, respectively, are called the *direction angles* of **A**, and the three cosines $\cos \phi_x$, $\cos \phi_y$, $\cos \phi_z$ are called the *direction cosines* of **A**. From Eq. (2.18),

$$
\begin{aligned}
A_x &= A \cos \phi_x, \\
A_y &= A \cos \phi_y, \\
A_z &= A \cos \phi_z,
\end{aligned} \tag{2.22}
$$

where $A$ is the magnitude of **A**. Thus, if the magnitude and three direction cosines of a vector are known, its three scalar components can be computed from Eqs. (2.22).

It follows from the three-dimensional Pythagorean theorem that

$$
A = \sqrt{A_x^2 + A_y^2 + A_z^2}, \tag{2.23}
$$

and, therefore, by Eqs. (2.22) and (2.23),

$$
\begin{aligned}
\cos \phi_x &= \frac{A_x}{\sqrt{A_x^2 + A_y^2 + A_z^2}}, \\[2mm]
\cos \phi_y &= \frac{A_y}{\sqrt{A_x^2 + A_y^2 + A_z^2}}, \\[2mm]
\cos \phi_z &= \frac{A_z}{\sqrt{A_x^2 + A_y^2 + A_z^2}}.
\end{aligned} \tag{2.24}
$$

Thus, if the three scalar components of a vector are known, its magnitude and three direction cosines can be computed from Eqs. (2.23) and (2.24).

Since the scalar components, three independent quantities, fully describe a vector, it must be true that the magnitude and three direction cosines, a total of four quantities, cannot all be independent. The interdependence of the four quantities is seen by substituting Eqs. (2.22) into Eq. (2.23) to obtain the following relation:

$$
\cos^2 \phi_x + \cos^2 \phi_y + \cos^2 \phi_z = 1. \tag{2.25}
$$

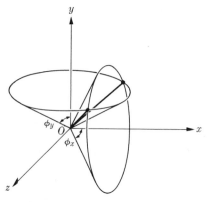

FIGURE 2.21

Hence the magnitude of a vector can be specified arbitrarily, but only two of the direction cosines can; the absolute value of the third is then determined by Eq. (2.25). For example, suppose that $\phi_x$ and $\phi_y$ are given and that

$$\phi_x + \phi_y > 90°.$$

The two possible directions, corresponding to the two values of $\phi_z$ given by Eq. (2.25), are along the intersection lines of the two cones of Fig. 2.21. (If $\phi_x + \phi_y = 90°$, there is one line of intersection, $\phi_z$ being 90°; if $\phi_x + \phi_y < 90°$, no direction exists.) Inasmuch as Eq. (2.25) does not give the sign of $\cos \phi_z$, it is of limited usefulness. Equations (2.24) automatically give the correct sign for each direction cosine.

To find the sum **S** of several vectors **A, B, C,** ... by analytical methods, the vectors are first expressed in terms of their $x$-, $y$-, and $z$-components, i.e.,

$$\mathbf{A} = A_x\mathbf{i} + A_y\mathbf{j} + A_z\mathbf{k},$$
$$\mathbf{B} = B_x\mathbf{i} + B_y\mathbf{j} + B_z\mathbf{k},$$
$$\mathbf{C} = C_x\mathbf{i} + C_y\mathbf{j} + C_z\mathbf{k},$$
$$\vdots$$

Then, using the distributive property of multiplication of a vector by a scalar,

$$\begin{aligned}
\mathbf{S} &= \mathbf{A} + \mathbf{B} + \mathbf{C} + \cdots \\
&= (A_x + B_x + C_x + \cdots)\mathbf{i} \\
&\quad + (A_y + B_y + C_y + \cdots)\mathbf{j} \\
&\quad + (A_z + B_z + C_z + \cdots)\mathbf{k},
\end{aligned}$$

or, to restate this result,

$$S_x = A_x + B_x + C_x + \cdots,$$
$$S_y = A_y + B_y + C_y + \cdots, \qquad (2.26)$$
$$S_z = A_z + B_z + C_z + \cdots.$$

Equations (2.26), of course, agree with Eq. (2.20).

---

EXAMPLE 2.2.   A ship undergoes two displacements, $u_1$, which is 100 miles toward the west, and $u_2$, which is 184.8 miles N67.5°E.  Taking the $x$-axis toward the east and the $y$-axis toward the north (which makes the $z$-axis vertical), express the two vectors analytically and add them together.

*Solution.*  Let $\phi_{1x}$, $\phi_{1y}$, $\phi_{1z}$ be the direction angles of $u_1$. Then

$$\phi_{1x} = 180°, \qquad \cos \phi_{1x} = -1,$$
$$\phi_{1y} = 90°, \qquad \cos \phi_{1y} = 0,$$
$$\phi_{1z} = 90°, \qquad \cos \phi_{1z} = 0,$$

and

$$u_1 = -100i \text{ miles.}$$

Let $\phi_{2x}$, $\phi_{2y}$, $\phi_{2z}$ be the direction angles of $u_2$. Then

$$\phi_{2x} = 22.5°, \qquad \cos \phi_{2x} = 0.924,$$
$$\phi_{2y} = 67.5°, \qquad \cos \phi_{2y} = 0.383,$$
$$\phi_{2z} = 90°, \qquad \cos \phi_{2z} = 0,$$

and

$$u_2 = (184.8)(0.924)i + (184.8)(0.383)j$$
$$= 170.7i + 70.7j \text{ miles.}$$

Thus, adding the two displacements,

$$u_1 + u_2 = 70.7i + 70.7j \text{ miles.}$$

Since expressing a vector in terms of $i$, $j$, $k$ fully describes the vector, it is normally unnecessary in solving problems to compute the magnitude and direction cosines unless these quantities are explicitly required by the statement of the problem.

---

To express a unit vector $n$ (with direction angles $\phi_{nx}$, $\phi_{ny}$, $\phi_{nz}$) in terms of rectangular components, note that, from Eqs. (2.22),

$$n_x = \cos \phi_{nx}, \qquad n_y = \cos \phi_{ny}, \qquad n_z = \cos \phi_{nz},$$

and, from Eq. (2.21),

$$\mathbf{n} = (\cos \phi_{nx})\mathbf{i} + (\cos \phi_{ny})\mathbf{j} + (\cos \phi_{nz})\mathbf{k}.$$

The foregoing shows that the rectangular components of any unit vector are its direction cosines.

**2.10   The position vector of a particle.**  The *position vector* $\mathbf{r}$ of a particle (or, more generally, of any point in space) is a vector from the origin of the coordinates to the particle (or the point), as shown in Fig. 2.22.  This is a very important vector in mechanics because it fully describes the "position," a concept discussed in Art. 1.3.  The scalar components of $\mathbf{r}$ are simply the coordinates of the particle, i.e.,

$$r_x = x, \qquad r_y = y, \qquad r_z = z,$$

so that

$$\mathbf{r} = x\mathbf{i} + y\mathbf{j} + z\mathbf{k}. \qquad (2.27)$$

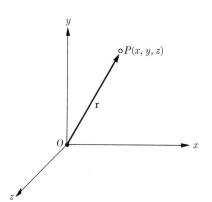

The *displacement* $\mathbf{u}$ of a particle from a position $P_1$ (with position vector $\mathbf{r}_1$) to a position $P_2$ (with position vector $\mathbf{r}_2$) can now be defined as the difference between $\mathbf{r}_2$ and $\mathbf{r}_1$, that is,

$$\mathbf{u} = \mathbf{r}_2 - \mathbf{r}_1, \qquad (2.28)$$

from which it follows that

FIGURE 2.22

$$\mathbf{u} = (x_2 - x_1)\mathbf{i} + (y_2 - y_1)\mathbf{j} + (z_2 - z_1)\mathbf{k}. \qquad (2.29)$$

Restating this result,

$$u_x = x_2 - x_1, \qquad u_y = y_2 - y_1, \qquad u_z = z_2 - z_1. \qquad (2.30)$$

**2.11   Discussion.**  In the foregoing articles of this chapter, forces, displacements, and position vectors are used as examples to illustrate the various operations defined for the general class of quantities known as vectors.  It should be emphasized, however, that the operations are all defined in mathematical terms whereas the vectors themselves are physical quantities.  It does not follow that the operations have any physical significance.  For example, two vectors of the same type occurring in a physical situation may not have a total effect which is the same as that of their sum, where the sum is obtained by the mathematical operation of addition. Each type of vector must be checked to make sure that all the operations are valid physically for that type. It is clear from the way in which they are defined that displacements and position vectors add, subtract, etc., in a physical way which agrees with the mathematical way. Forces are discussed in subsequent chapters and are shown to follow the rules also. But another type of vector, the rotation vector, which arises in advanced treatments of mechanics, does not. Physically speaking, addition of rotation vectors is not commutative; in fact, the operation of addition has no physical significance whatever for rotation vectors.

## PROBLEMS

2.1 Using a scale of 1 in. = 50 miles, find by graphical construction the sum of a displacement of 100 miles toward the southwest and a displacement of 50 miles toward the west. Label the arrow representing the sum with the magnitude of the total displacement.

2.2 Show graphically that the order of addition of the following three displacements is immaterial:

**u**: 100 miles toward northeast,

**v**: 50 miles toward south,

**w**: 150 miles toward west.

To do this, start from the same point on the paper and add the vectors in all possible orders.

2.3 If **A** = 3**P**, **B** = −2**P**, **C** = 2**P**, find: (a) **A** + **B** + **C**, and (b) **A** + **B** − **C**, both in terms of **P**.

2.4 Find by trigonometry the sum **P** + **Q** and the difference **P** − **Q** of the forces **P** and **Q** shown in Fig. 2.23. Specify the directions of the results by giving the angles that they make with **Q**.

[*Ans.:* **P** + **Q**: 2240 lb, 63.4°CCW; **P** − **Q**: 2240 lb, 116.6°CCW.]

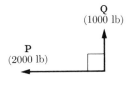

FIGURE 2.23

**2.5** If **S** and **D** are two known vectors and

$$\mathbf{S} = \mathbf{A} + \mathbf{B}, \qquad \mathbf{D} = \mathbf{A} - \mathbf{B},$$

show how **A** and **B** can be found: (a) graphically, and (b) by solving the two simultaneous vector equations in two unknowns.

**2.6** Given:

$$2\mathbf{A} + \mathbf{B} = 3\mathbf{C}, \qquad \mathbf{A} - 3\mathbf{B} = -4\mathbf{C},$$

where **C** is a known vector. Find **A** and **B**.

[*Ans.:* $\mathbf{A} = \frac{5}{7}\mathbf{C}, \mathbf{B} = \frac{11}{7}\mathbf{C}.$]

**2.7** If **R** is a known vector and

$$\mathbf{P} + 2\mathbf{Q} = \mathbf{R}, \qquad \mathbf{P} - 3\mathbf{Q} = 2\mathbf{R},$$

show by solving for **P** and **Q** that **P** has the same direction as **R** and that **Q** has the opposite direction. What must **Q** be if the 2 in the second equation is replaced by 1?

**2.8** Show that multiplication of a vector by a scalar is distributive, i.e., that

$$(M + N)\mathbf{A} = M\mathbf{A} + N\mathbf{A}, \qquad M(\mathbf{A} + \mathbf{B}) = M\mathbf{A} + M\mathbf{B}.$$

**2.9** Using trigonometry, resolve **u**, a displacement of 100 miles with direction N30°W, into two components such that one is 100 miles toward the east.

**2.10** The arrows representing three vectors **A**, **B**, **C** are drawn from one vertex of a parallelogram to the other three vertices as shown in Fig. 2.24. Find, in terms of **C**, (a) $\mathbf{A} + \mathbf{B} + \mathbf{C}$, and (b) $\mathbf{A} + \mathbf{B} - \mathbf{C}$.

[*Ans.:* (a) 2**C**; (b) **0**.]

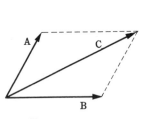

FIGURE 2.24

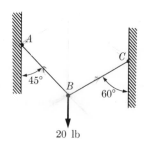

FIGURE 2.25

**2.11** A vertical force of 20-lb magnitude is applied as shown in Fig. 2.25 at point *B* of a string *ABC*. Using trigonometry, resolve the force into two components: (a) parallel to *AB* and *BC*, (b) parallel and perpendicular to *BC*.

2.12 (a) If $4\mathbf{A} = -\mathbf{B}$ and the scalar component of $\mathbf{B}$ along a directed line $L$ is $-6$, find the scalar component of $\mathbf{A}$ in the $L$-direction. (b) If three vectors $\mathbf{A}, \mathbf{B}, \mathbf{C}$ have scalar components in an $L$-direction of 100, $-75$, $-40$, respectively, what is the $L$-component of their sum $\mathbf{S}$?

[*Ans.:* (a) $\frac{3}{2}$; (b) $-15$.]

2.13 Find $\mathbf{A} + \mathbf{B}, \mathbf{A} - \mathbf{B}$, and $-2\mathbf{A}$ if: (a) $\mathbf{A} = 3\mathbf{i} + 2\mathbf{j} + 5\mathbf{k}$ and $\mathbf{B} = 2\mathbf{i} + \mathbf{j}$; (b) $\mathbf{A} = 2\mathbf{i} - 3\mathbf{j} + \mathbf{k}$ and $\mathbf{B} = -\mathbf{i} + 3\mathbf{j} + 4\mathbf{k}$.

2.14 Given:
$$\mathbf{v} = 3\mathbf{i} + 4\mathbf{j} - 5\mathbf{k}, \qquad \mathbf{w} = 4\mathbf{i} + 4\mathbf{j} + 4\mathbf{k}.$$
Find:

(a) $3(\mathbf{v} - \mathbf{w})$,     (b) $\dfrac{\mathbf{v} - \mathbf{w}}{3}$,     (c) $-4\mathbf{v} + 3\mathbf{w}$.

[*Ans.:* (a) $-3\mathbf{i} - 27\mathbf{k}$; (b) $-\frac{1}{3}\mathbf{i} - 3\mathbf{k}$; (c) $-4\mathbf{j} + 32\mathbf{k}$.]

2.15 A hiker undergoes two displacements, $\mathbf{u}_1$, which is 2000 yards NE, and $\mathbf{u}_2$, which is 3000 yards WNW (i.e., N67.5°W). Let the $x$-axis be toward the east and the $y$-axis toward the north. (a) Express the two vectors analytically and add them together. (b) Find the magnitude and direction cosines of the total displacement. (c) How far and in what direction must the hiker walk to return to his starting point?

2.16 Given:
$$\mathbf{A} + \mathbf{B} = 4\mathbf{i} + 13\mathbf{j} - 10\mathbf{k}, \qquad A_x = -3, \qquad A_y = 8, \qquad A_z = 10.$$
Find $\mathbf{B}$.

[*Ans.:* $7\mathbf{i} + 5\mathbf{j} - 20\mathbf{k}$.]

2.17 Given:
$$\mathbf{A} - \mathbf{B} = 2\mathbf{i} - 4\mathbf{j} + 7\mathbf{k}, \qquad A_x = 2, \qquad A_y = -14, \qquad |\mathbf{A}| = 15.$$
Find two possible vectors $\mathbf{B}$.

2.18 Express analytically a displacement from $(-2, 1, 0)$ to $(3, -3, 1)$. What are its magnitude and three direction cosines?

[*Ans.:* $\mathbf{u} = 5\mathbf{i} - 4\mathbf{j} + \mathbf{k}$.]

CHAPTER 3

## CONCURRENT FORCE SYSTEMS

**3.1 Introduction.** The forces which act on a body may ordinarily be classified as two types: *surface forces* and *body forces*. The first type arises from "contact" of the body with its surroundings, e.g., pressure from an adjacent body or an enveloping fluid. The second type acts "at a distance," e.g., the gravitational attraction exerted on the body by the earth or some other body. In a real situation forces of either type are *distributed forces*, the surface forces being distributed over some portion of the surface area of the body, and the body forces being distributed over some portion (usually all) of the volume of the body. For the forces on a body to have clearly defined properties of magnitude and direction, and hence to be vectors, it is desirable that they be *concentrated forces*, each acting at one specific point of the body. This is achieved by idealization when the surface area or volume over which a force is distributed is small as compared with the total surface area or volume of the body. When that is not the case, it becomes necessary to replace the actual distributed force by an imaginary concentrated force which would have the same effect on the body as the real force. The latter procedure must be used with caution; the rules governing its validity are discussed in later chapters.

When the size and shape of a body are unimportant, as they might be for example when the given body is very small as compared with distances to other bodies exerting forces on the given body, the body is often idealized as a particle. In that case, since the particle has no size, all the forces acting on it are concentrated forces. Furthermore, they form a *concurrent* force system (i.e., all their lines of action intersect at a common point), and they all have the same point of application.

**3.2 Resultant of a group of forces.** By definition, the *resultant* $\mathbf{R}$ of any group of forces $\mathbf{F}_1$, $\mathbf{F}_2$, $\mathbf{F}_3$, ... is their vector sum, i.e.,

$$\mathbf{R} = \mathbf{F}_1 + \mathbf{F}_2 + \mathbf{F}_3 + \cdots. \tag{3.1}$$

The addition is accomplished by the Polygon Rule in the same way as for any other vectors and thus does not depend upon the lines of action or points of application of the forces but only upon their magnitudes and directions. And, as usual, the operation yields only the magnitude and direction of the resultant.

28

In some situations it is necessary to imagine a system of forces to be replaced by its resultant, and it is sometimes possible to fulfill the requirement that the resultant alone have the same physical effect as the original forces. The physical effect of the resultant, however, depends not only upon its magnitude and direction, properties given by the adding operation, but also upon where it is placed on the mechanical system, i.e., upon its line of action and point of application. Thus, to achieve the sameness of effect, it is necessary to assign the secondary properties of a line of action (based on the lines of action of the contributing forces) and, in some cases, a point of application (based on the points of application of the contributing forces) to the resultant. This is possible only for certain types of mechanical systems acted upon by particular kinds of force systems.

The way in which the secondary properties are assigned to the resultant for various kinds of force systems is discussed in this and later chapters.

**3.3 Concurrent forces in a plane.** For a group of $N$ concurrent forces $\mathbf{F}_1, \mathbf{F}_2, \ldots, \mathbf{F}_N$ all lying in the same plane, the resultant $\mathbf{R}$ described by Eq. (3.1) is found by a plane polygon and assigned a line of action through the point of concurrency, as shown for three forces in Fig. 3.1. If the forces act on a particle $P$, as in Fig. 3.2, $\mathbf{R}$ is also given the particle itself as a point of application. (For forces, it is customary to place either the head or the tail of the arrow representing the force at the point of application.)

The resultant $\mathbf{R}$ discussed in the preceding paragraph may be found either graphically by drawing to scale the polygon illustrated in Fig. 3.1(b) or analytically by establishing an $xy$-system of coordinates in the plane and adding the rectangular components of the individual forces. To use the latter method, it is first necessary to find the $x$- and $y$-components of each force. Let $\mathbf{F}_i$ be any one of the group of forces (i.e., $i$ may be any

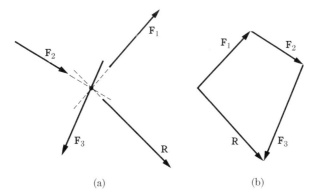

(a)                                        (b)

FIGURE 3.1

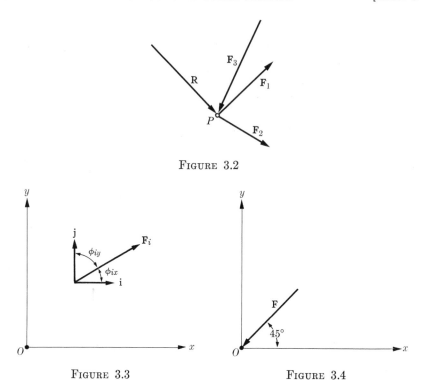

FIGURE 3.2

FIGURE 3.3                              FIGURE 3.4

integer from 1 to $N$). Let $F_{ix}$ and $F_{iy}$ be the $x$- and $y$-components, respectively, of $\mathbf{F}_i$, and let $\phi_{ix}$ and $\phi_{iy}$ be the angles that $\mathbf{F}_i$ makes with $\mathbf{i}$ and $\mathbf{j}$, respectively, as shown in Fig. 3.3. Then, by Eqs. (2.22),

$$F_{ix} = F_i \cos \phi_{ix}, \qquad F_{iy} = F_i \cos \phi_{iy}, \qquad (3.2)$$

where $F_i$ is the magnitude of $\mathbf{F}_i$. Since all the forces lie in the $xy$-plane, all the $z$-components are zero (that is, $\phi_{iz} = 90°$ for all $i$). The cosines in Eqs. (3.2) automatically give the correct signs to $F_{ix}$ and $F_{iy}$ for a force $\mathbf{F}_i$ in any direction in the plane. For example, the force $\mathbf{F}$ in Fig. 3.4 is such that $\phi_x = \phi_y = 135°$. Hence, $\cos \phi_x = \cos \phi_y = -0.707$, and $F_x = F_y = -0.707F$.

If both $F_{ix}$ and $F_{iy}$ are positive, as in Fig. 3.3, and if $\phi_{ix}$ has a value $\alpha$ (between 0 and 90°), then $\phi_{iy} = 90° - \alpha$ and $\cos \phi_{iy} = \sin \alpha$. In that case,

$$F_{ix} = F_i \cos \alpha, \qquad F_{iy} = F_i \sin \alpha.$$

In many problems in mechanics in which the rectangular components of a force $\mathbf{F}$ are needed, the direction of $\mathbf{F}$ is given (as in Fig. 3.5) by two

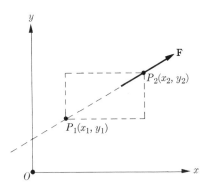

FIGURE 3.5

known points $P_1$ and $P_2$ on its line of action instead of by $\phi_x$ and $\phi_y$. Using the dashed right triangles in Fig. 3.5, we may express the direction cosines of $\mathbf{F}$ in terms of the coordinates of $P_1$ and $P_2$ as follows:

$$\cos \phi_x = \frac{x_2 - x_1}{d}, \qquad \cos \phi_y = \frac{y_2 - y_1}{d},$$

where $d$ is the distance between $P_1$ and $P_2$. By the Pythagorean theorem,

$$d = \sqrt{(x_2 - x_1)^2 + (y_2 - y_1)^2}, \tag{3.3}$$

and, by Eqs. (3.2),

$$F_x = F\frac{x_2 - x_1}{d}, \qquad F_y = F\frac{y_2 - y_1}{d}. \tag{3.4}$$

In Eqs. (3.4), $F$ and $d$ are always positive, and the correct signs of $F_x$ and $F_y$ are therefore given automatically by the signs of the coordinates, provided, of course, that $P_2$ is toward the positive end of the force from $P_1$. The foregoing statement can be verified by considering forces with all different directions and lines of action.

Once the components of each of the forces in a group to be added have been found, the forces may be written in terms of their components as follows:

$$\mathbf{F}_1 = F_{1x}\mathbf{i} + F_{1y}\mathbf{j},$$
$$\mathbf{F}_2 = F_{2x}\mathbf{i} + F_{2y}\mathbf{j},$$
$$\vdots$$
$$\mathbf{F}_N = F_{Nx}\mathbf{i} + F_{Ny}\mathbf{j},$$

and they may be added as in Art. 2.9:

$$\mathbf{R} = \mathbf{F}_1 + \mathbf{F}_2 + \cdots + \mathbf{F}_N$$
$$= (F_{1x} + F_{2x} + \cdots + F_{Nx})\mathbf{i} + (F_{1y} + F_{2y} + \cdots + F_{Ny})\mathbf{j}.$$

Restating this result,

$$R_x = F_{1x} + F_{2x} + \cdots + F_{Nx} = \sum_{i=1}^{N} F_{ix},$$

$$(3.5)$$

$$R_y = F_{1y} + F_{2y} + \cdots + F_{Ny} = \sum_{i=1}^{N} F_{iy}.$$

EXAMPLE 3.1. Find the resultant of the three concurrent forces shown in Fig. 3.6. (Note that the arrows in Fig. 3.6 are not drawn to scale; instead, the magnitudes are labeled in parentheses.)

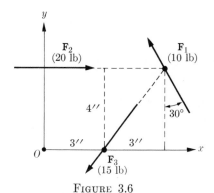

FIGURE 3.6

*Solution.* For the force $\mathbf{F}_1$, since direction angles are measured between the positive directions of the axes and the positive direction of the force,

$$\phi_{1x} = 120°, \qquad \cos \phi_{1x} = -0.500,$$
$$\phi_{1y} = 30°, \qquad \cos \phi_{1y} = 0.866,$$

and, by Eqs. (3.2),

$$\mathbf{F}_1 = -5\mathbf{i} + 8.66\mathbf{j} \text{ lb.}$$

For the force $\mathbf{F}_2$,

$$\phi_{2x} = 0, \qquad \cos \phi_{2x} = 1,$$
$$\phi_{2y} = 90°, \qquad \cos \phi_{2y} = 0,$$

and

$$\mathbf{F}_2 = 20\mathbf{i} \text{ lb.}$$

(This result could have been obtained by inspection.)  For the force $\mathbf{F}_3$,

$$x_1 = 6 \text{ in.}, \qquad x_2 = 3 \text{ in.},$$
$$y_1 = 4 \text{ in.}, \qquad y_2 = 0,$$
$$d = \sqrt{(3 - 6)^2 + (0 - 4)^2} = 5 \text{ in.},$$

and hence, by Eqs. (3.4),

$$F_{3x} = 15 \left( \frac{3 - 6}{5} \right) = 15 \left( -\frac{3}{5} \right) = -9 \text{ lb,}$$

$$F_{3y} = 15 \left( \frac{0 - 4}{5} \right) = 15 \left( -\frac{4}{5} \right) = -12 \text{ lb.}$$

Thus,

$$\mathbf{F}_3 = -9\mathbf{i} - 12\mathbf{j} \text{ lb.}$$

Since we have all three forces expressed in terms of $\mathbf{i}$ and $\mathbf{j}$, the vector addition is accomplished by Eqs. (3.5) to obtain

$$\mathbf{R} = 6\mathbf{i} - 3.34\mathbf{j} \text{ lb.}$$

---

For a group of nonconcurrent forces in a plane, the system may be analyzed in stages by starting with any two of the forces, since any two forces in a plane form, by themselves, a concurrent system.  In Fig. 3.7, the sum $\mathbf{R}'$ of $\mathbf{F}_1$ and $\mathbf{F}_2$ alone is assigned a line of action through the intersection point of $\mathbf{F}_1$ and $\mathbf{F}_2$.  The pair of forces $\mathbf{R}'$ and $\mathbf{F}_3$ are then added in the same way to obtain the magnitude, direction, and line of action of $\mathbf{R}''$, which, since addition is associative, is the sum of $\mathbf{F}_1$, $\mathbf{F}_2$, and $\mathbf{F}_3$.  The procedure can be continued for any number of forces and yields the resultant of all the forces with its line of action located.

The foregoing method of adding forces in pairs is suitable for graphical determination of the resultant of a plane, nonconcurrent force system when

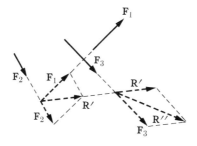

FIGURE 3.7

it is required that the line of action of the resultant be located. It is not convenient, however, when the line of action is to be found without using graphical construction. The analytical method of locating the resultant of a nonconcurrent system in a plane is discussed in Chapter 8.

**3.4 Concurrent forces in space.** For a group of concurrent forces $\mathbf{F}_1$, $\mathbf{F}_2$, ..., $\mathbf{F}_N$ in three dimensions, the resultant $\mathbf{R}$ described by Eq. (3.1) is defined by a space polygon, which means that there is no practical way to find the magnitude and direction of $\mathbf{R}$ by a graphical method on a plane sheet of paper. The three-dimensional analytical method, being only slightly more complicated than the two-dimensional, thus assumes an unquestionable position of importance.

As in two dimensions, the resultant $\mathbf{R}$ is assigned a line of action through the point of concurrency. Also, if the force system acts on a particle, the resultant is considered to have the particle as its point of application. These results for a group of three forces may be pictured by visualizing Figs. 3.1(a) and (b) and 3.2 as drawings with depth.

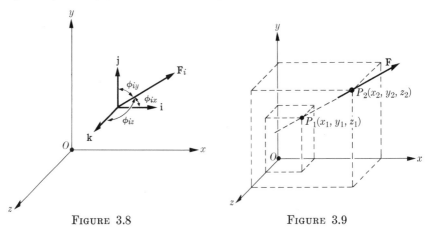

FIGURE 3.8                    FIGURE 3.9

Once an $xyz$-system of coordinates is established, the rectangular components of each force can be found, as in Art. 3.3, by the use of Eqs. (2.22). Let $\mathbf{F}_i$ be any one of the group as before, with $F_{ix}$, $F_{iy}$, $F_{iz}$ the scalar components and $\phi_{ix}$, $\phi_{iy}$, $\phi_{iz}$ the direction angles. (See Fig. 3.8.) Then, by Eqs. (2.22),

$$F_{ix} = F_i \cos \phi_{ix}, \qquad F_{iy} = F_i \cos \phi_{iy}, \qquad F_{iz} = F_i \cos \phi_{iz}, \quad (3.6)$$

where $F_i$ is the magnitude of $\mathbf{F}_i$.

In the event that the direction of a force $\mathbf{F}$ is given by two known points on its line of action, as shown in Fig. 3.9, the direction cosines of $\mathbf{F}$ may be expressed in terms of the coordinates of $P_1$ and $P_2$ as follows:

$$\cos \phi_x = \frac{x_2 - x_1}{d}, \qquad \cos \phi_y = \frac{y_2 - y_1}{d}, \qquad \cos \phi_z = \frac{z_2 - z_1}{d},$$

where $d$ is again the distance between $P_1$ and $P_2$. By the three-dimensional Pythagorean theorem,

$$d = \sqrt{(x_2 - x_1)^2 + (y_2 - y_1)^2 + (z_2 - z_1)^2}, \qquad (3.7)$$

and, by Eqs. (3.6),

$$F_x = F \frac{x_2 - x_1}{d}, \qquad F_y = F \frac{y_2 - y_1}{d}, \qquad F_z = F \frac{z_2 - z_1}{d}. \qquad (3.8)$$

Equations (3.8) automatically give the correct signs for $F_x$, $F_y$, $F_z$, provided, again, that $P_2$ is toward the positive end of the force from $P_1$.

Expressing the forces in the group in terms of their components as follows:

$$\mathbf{F}_1 = F_{1x}\mathbf{i} + F_{1y}\mathbf{j} + F_{1z}\mathbf{k},$$
$$\mathbf{F}_2 = F_{2x}\mathbf{i} + F_{2y}\mathbf{j} + F_{2z}\mathbf{k},$$
$$\vdots$$
$$\mathbf{F}_N = F_{Nx}\mathbf{i} + F_{Ny}\mathbf{j} + F_{Nz}\mathbf{k},$$

the addition is performed as usual to obtain

$$\begin{aligned}
\mathbf{R} = \mathbf{F}_1 + \mathbf{F}_2 + \cdots + \mathbf{F}_N \\
= (F_{1x} + F_{2x} + \cdots + F_{Nx})\mathbf{i} \\
+ (F_{1y} + F_{2y} + \cdots + F_{Ny})\mathbf{j} \\
+ (F_{1z} + F_{2z} + \cdots + F_{Nz})\mathbf{k}.
\end{aligned}$$

Restating this result,

$$R_x = F_{1x} + F_{2x} + \cdots + F_{Nx} = \sum_{i=1}^{N} F_{ix},$$

$$R_y = F_{1y} + F_{2y} + \cdots + F_{Ny} = \sum_{i=1}^{N} F_{iy}, \qquad (3.9)$$

$$R_z = F_{1z} + F_{2z} + \cdots + F_{Nz} = \sum_{i=1}^{N} F_{iz}.$$

Since a group of concurrent forces in a plane is merely a special case of the more general problem of a group of concurrent forces in space, Eqs. (3.2), (3.3), (3.4), and (3.5), which govern the former, can be derived, respectively, from Eqs. (3.6), (3.7), (3.8), and (3.9), which govern the latter, by taking $\phi_{iz} = 90°$ and $F_{iz} = 0$ for all $i$ and by letting $z_1 = z_2$.

Once the resultant $\mathbf{R}$ is known in terms of $\mathbf{i}$, $\mathbf{j}$, $\mathbf{k}$, its magnitude and direction cosines, if needed, may be found by using Eqs. (2.23) and (2.24).

---

EXAMPLE 3.2. Find the resultant of the three concurrent forces shown in Fig. 3.10. Compute the magnitude and direction cosines of the resultant.

*Solution.* For the force $\mathbf{F}_1$, since direction angles are measured between the positive directions of the axes and the positive direction of the force,

$$\phi_{1x} = 120°, \quad \cos \phi_{1x} = -0.500,$$
$$\phi_{1y} = 120°, \quad \cos \phi_{1y} = -0.500,$$
$$\phi_{1z} = 135°, \quad \cos \phi_{1z} = -0.707,$$

and

$$\mathbf{F}_1 = -5\mathbf{i} - 5\mathbf{j} - 7.07\mathbf{k} \text{ lb.}$$

Note that Eq. (2.25) is satisfied by the direction angles given for $\mathbf{F}_1$. For the force $\mathbf{F}_2$,

$$\phi_{2x} = 90°, \quad \cos \phi_{2x} = 0,$$
$$\phi_{2y} = 180°, \quad \cos \phi_{2y} = -1,$$
$$\phi_{2z} = 90°, \quad \cos \phi_{2z} = 0,$$

and

$$\mathbf{F}_2 = -16\mathbf{j} \text{ lb.}$$

(This result could have been obtained by inspection.) For the force $\mathbf{F}_3$,

$$x_1 = 4 \text{ in.}, \quad x_2 = 2 \text{ in.},$$
$$y_1 = 0, \quad y_2 = 6 \text{ in.},$$
$$z_1 = 0, \quad z_2 = 3 \text{ in.},$$
$$d = \sqrt{(2 - 4)^2 + (6 - 0)^2 + (3 - 0)^2} = 7 \text{ in.},$$

and hence, by Eqs. (3.8),

$$F_{3x} = 21 \left( \frac{2 - 4}{7} \right) = 21 \left( -\frac{2}{7} \right) = -6 \text{ lb,}$$

$$F_{3y} = 21 \left( \frac{6 - 0}{7} \right) = 21 \left( \frac{6}{7} \right) = 18 \text{ lb,}$$

$$F_{3z} = 21 \left( \frac{3 - 0}{7} \right) = 21 \left( \frac{3}{7} \right) = 9 \text{ lb.}$$

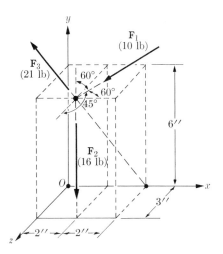

FIGURE 3.10

Thus,

$$\mathbf{F}_3 = -6\mathbf{i} + 18\mathbf{j} + 9\mathbf{k} \text{ lb,}$$

and

$$\mathbf{R} = -11\mathbf{i} - 3\mathbf{j} + 1.93\mathbf{k} \text{ lb.}$$

By Eq. (2.23),

$$R = \sqrt{121 + 9 + 3.72} = 11.56 \text{ lb,}$$

and, by Eqs. (2.24),

$$\cos \phi_x = \frac{-11}{11.56} = -0.952,$$

$$\cos \phi_y = \frac{-3}{11.56} = -0.260,$$

$$\cos \phi_z = \frac{1.93}{11.56} = 0.167.$$

Finally, therefore,

$$\phi_x = 162°, \qquad \phi_y = 105°, \qquad \phi_z = 80.4°.$$

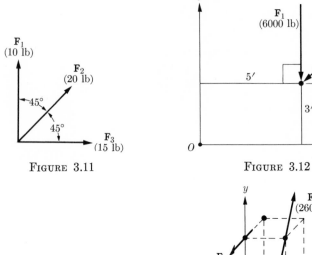

FIGURE 3.11

FIGURE 3.12

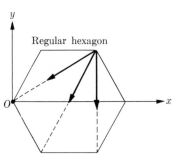

FIGURE 3.13

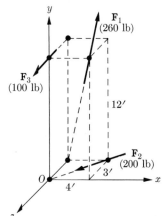

FIGURE 3.15

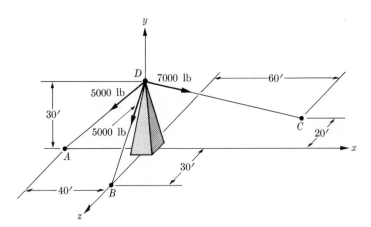

FIGURE 3.14

## Problems

3.1 Add graphically the three plane, concurrent forces shown in Fig. 3.11. Label the magnitude of the resultant on the arrow representing it.

3.2 Find analytically the resultant of the two forces shown in Fig. 3.12. Give the coordinates of a point on the line of action of the resultant.

[*Ans.:* $\mathbf{R} = -6130\mathbf{i} - 11{,}140\mathbf{j}$ lb.]

3.3 Each of the three forces shown in Fig. 3.13 has a magnitude $M$. Find their resultant analytically. Compute the magnitude and direction cosines of the resultant.

3.4 Find the resultant of the following two forces:

$$F_1 = 100 \text{ lb}, \quad \phi_{1x} = 60°, \quad \phi_{1y} = 120°, \quad \phi_{1z} = 45°,$$
$$F_2 = 200 \text{ lb}, \quad \phi_{2x} = 50°, \quad \phi_{2y} = 100°, \quad \phi_{2z} > 90°.$$

Compute the magnitude and direction angles of the resultant.

[*Ans.:* $\mathbf{R} = 178.6\mathbf{i} - 84.7\mathbf{j} - 78.5\mathbf{k}$ lb.]

3.5 The following four forces concur at the origin. Find their resultant.

$$F_1 = 50 \text{ lb}, \quad \phi_{1x} = 90°, \quad \phi_{1y} = 150°, \quad \phi_{1z} = 120°,$$
$$F_{2x} = 30 \text{ lb}, \quad \cos \phi_{2y} = 0.6, \quad \cos \phi_{2z} = -0.5,$$
$$F_{3z} = -20 \text{ lb}, \quad \phi_{3x} = 50°, \quad \phi_{3y} = 75°,$$
$$F_4 = 100 \text{ lb}, \quad F_{4y} > 0, \quad (3, -2, -4) \text{ is a point on } \mathbf{F}_4.$$

3.6 Three guy wires attached to the top of a tower as shown in Fig. 3.14 exert forces on the tower in the directions of the wires. Find the resultant of the three forces. (Points $A$, $B$, and $C$ all lie in the $zx$-plane.)

[*Ans.:* $2000\mathbf{i} - 9540\mathbf{j} + 1540\mathbf{k}$ lb.]

3.7 Find the resultant of the nonconcurrent force system shown in Fig. 3.15.

# CHAPTER 4

## EQUILIBRIUM OF A PARTICLE

**4.1 Introduction.** To say that a particle is in *equilibrium* means that it is either stationary or moving in a straight line with constant speed (i.e., at a constant number of feet per second). Newton called these two states "rest" and "uniform motion," respectively. (See Art. 1.5.) Neither of the states can be achieved in an absolute sense or observed with certainty because of the lack of fixed reference points and fixed reference lines in the universe. It is possible, however, for the particle to be at rest or in uniform motion with respect to the frame of reference being used. An example of the former state is a particle occupying a fixed position on one of the three axes, and an example of the latter is a particle traveling along one of the axes at constant speed. The amount of deviation from true equilibrium then depends on the amount of motion and type of motion of the frame of reference. As an example, consider a particle fixed on the surface of the earth. In most practical problems such a particle is considered to be in equilibrium. Strictly speaking, however, the particle is neither at rest nor moving on a straight line. If the distant stars are used as a frame of reference, as suggested in Art. 1.3, the particle is moving in some complicated way which is influenced by the following factors:

(1) Rotation of the earth.
(2) Revolution of the earth about the sun.
(3) Motion of the solar system with respect to the distant stars.

The effect of (1) is very small in most cases; it is investigated quantitatively in Chapter 6 after some background is established in the dynamics of a particle. The effect of (2) is even smaller than that of (1), and there appears to be a trend toward less and less effect as the scale of size grows larger. Hence, even though very little is known about the large-scale movements in the universe, such movements are presumed to occur slowly (considering the distances involved) and to have a negligible effect on Newtonian mechanics as applied to "small" portions of the universe.

**4.2 Newton's First Law.** Using the terminology and notation introduced in Chapters 2 and 3 and the present chapter, we may state Newton's First Law (Art. 1.5) as follows: A particle is in equilibrium if the resultant of the forces acting on it is a null vector, i.e., $\mathbf{R} = \mathbf{0}$ is a sufficient condition for equilibrium. Although Newton was explicit concerning the sufficiency

40

of the condition only, it is generally agreed that $\mathbf{R} = \mathbf{0}$ is also a necessary condition for equilibrium. Thus, the law may be amplified and restated as follows:

NEWTON'S FIRST LAW: *A particle is in equilibrium if and only if*

$$\mathbf{R} = \mathbf{0}, \tag{4.1}$$

*where* $\mathbf{R}$ *is the resultant of all the forces acting on the particle.*

The forces on a particle may be classified as: *active forces*, which are those forces tending to set the particle into motion (e.g., the weight force); and *reactive forces*, which are those forces set up by the surroundings to prevent motion. Both types of forces must be included in Eq. (4.1).

The graphical meaning of Eq. (4.1) is that the force polygon is a closed figure, as illustrated in Figs. 4.1(a) and (b). A very simple example of this situation is a particle subjected to two forces with equal magnitudes but opposite directions.

In Art. 2.8 it is shown that equality between two vectors is a sufficient condition for equality of their scalar components in any given direction. When we apply this principle to the vectors $\mathbf{R}$ and $\mathbf{0}$, it is clear that, when $\mathbf{R} = \mathbf{0}$ in accordance with Eq. (4.1), the scalar component of $\mathbf{R}$ in any direction $L$ is zero, i.e.,

$$R_L = 0,$$

and the scalar components of $\mathbf{R}$ along the three coordinate axes are all zero, i.e.,

$$R_x = 0, \qquad R_y = 0, \qquad R_z = 0. \tag{4.2}$$

Equality of two vectors is not a necessary condition for equality of their scalar components in a given direction because it is always possible to find two nonparallel lines which have the same projection on a given line.

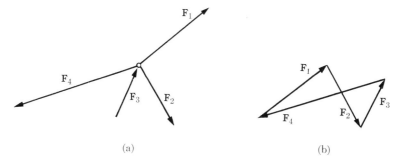

(a)                                                (b)

FIGURE 4.1

(This lack of necessity can be seen for the vectors $\mathbf{R}$ and $\mathbf{0}$ by considering a line perpendicular to $\mathbf{R}$; the vector $\mathbf{R}$ need not be a null vector to make its component on this line zero.) It is obvious, however, that no two non-parallel lines can be found which have the same projections on each of the three coordinate axes simultaneously. Therefore, Eq. (4.1) is both a necessary and a sufficient condition for Eqs. (4.2) taken as a group. Since the orientation of the coordinate axes is arbitrary, Eq. (4.1) is a necessary and sufficient condition that the components of $\mathbf{R}$ in any three perpendicular directions are zero. (More generally, the statement holds for any three directions not all in the same plane.)

In general, any vector equation such as Eq. (4.1) is equivalent to a set of three scalar equations such as Eqs. (4.2).

**4.3 Equilibrium in a plane.** For a particle subjected to a system of forces all lying in the $xy$-plane, the third of Eqs. (4.2) is satisfied automatically, and the other two are then an analytical expression of the fact that the plane polygon is a closed figure. Substituting Eqs. (3.5) into the first two of Eqs. (4.2) leads to the following *equations of equilibrium of a particle in a plane:*

$$\sum_{i=1}^{N} F_{ix} = 0, \qquad \sum_{i=1}^{N} F_{iy} = 0.$$

It is customary to write these equations in a still more abbreviated form, namely,

$$\sum F_x = 0, \qquad \sum F_y = 0, \tag{4.3}$$

with the understanding that the summations are to be taken over all the forces which act on the particle, including the weight force. (In this book the expression "weight force" is used to describe the gravitational force exerted on the particle by the earth; the magnitude of this force is called simply the "weight" of the particle.) Equations (4.3) are both necessary and sufficient conditions for equilibrium of a particle subjected to a plane force system.

From the two equations of equilibrium it is possible to find two unknowns, e.g., the magnitude and direction (or $x$- and $y$-components) of one of the forces acting on the particle, or the magnitudes of two forces having known directions. In solving problems involving the equilibrium of a particle, it is strongly advisable to draw a *free-body diagram*, which is a sketch showing the particle isolated from its surroundings and showing all the forces which act on the particle. The purpose of the free-body diagram is to ensure that all contributions to the left-hand sides of Eqs. (4.3) will be included when the equations are written out.

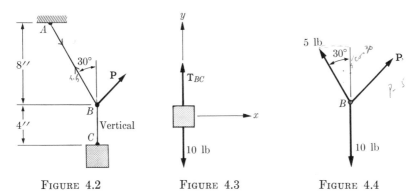

FIGURE 4.2              FIGURE 4.3              FIGURE 4.4

EXAMPLE 4.1.  A block weighing 10 lb is supported by an ideal string $ABC$ as shown in Fig. 4.2.  A force $\mathbf{P}$ is applied to the string at $B$ in such a way that the block is held in equilibrium in the position shown and the tension in portion $AB$ of the string is 5 lb.  Find $\mathbf{P}$.

*Solution.*  An ideal string is one which is perfectly flexible and weightless, so that the force exerted by the string on any body to which it is tied is in the direction of the string.  (Such a string can be in tension only, never in compression.)  Drawing a free-body diagram of the block first, as shown in Fig. 4.3, we can use Eqs. (4.3) to find the unknown magnitude $T_{BC}$ of the reactive force exerted on the block by the string.  Let the $x$-axis be to the right and the $y$-axis be upward.  Then the first of Eqs. (4.3) is satisfied identically (i.e., all terms on both sides of the equation are zero), and the second gives

$$\sum F_y = T_{BC} - 10 = 0,$$

from which it follows that

$$T_{BC} = 10 \text{ lb.}$$

The magnitude of the force (i.e., the tension) in the string $BC$ is thus 10 lb, and it is a consequence of Newton's Third Law (stated in its original form in Art. 1.5 and discussed more fully in Chapter 11) that every part of the string $BC$ pulls with a force of 10-lb magnitude on adjacent parts and that the upper end of the string $BC$ pulls down with a force of 10-lb magnitude on point $B$.

Drawing next a free-body diagram of the "particle" $B$ of the string, as shown in Fig. 4.4, we can again use Eqs. (4.3) to find $\mathbf{P}$:

$$\sum F_x = P_x - 5(0.500) = 0,$$
$$\sum F_y = P_y + 5(0.866) - 10 = 0.$$

Finally, therefore,

$$P_x = 2.50 \text{ lb,} \qquad P_y = 5.67 \text{ lb,}$$

and

$$\mathbf{P} = 2.50\mathbf{i} + 5.67\mathbf{j} \text{ lb.}$$

Since, in the foregoing example, the forces acting on the block form a concurrent system, the size and shape of the block are unimportant (i.e., its dimensions do not affect the solution), and hence it is permissible to treat the block as a particle. Even if the forces acting on a body are not all concurrent, it is still possible to analyze the body as a particle, the justification for this being that Eq. (4.1) holds for any body in equilibrium, as is shown in Chapter 11, where the meaning of equilibrium for a rigid body is discussed. (One case of equilibrium is when the body is stationary.) It must be emphasized, however, that, when the forces are not concurrent, Eq. (4.1) is only a necessary condition for equilibrium, not a sufficient condition. If the forces are not concurrent, they must, in addition to satisfying Eq. (4.1), be arranged with certain lines of action in order to hold the body in equilibrium. The only type of problem involving nonconcurrent forces which is solvable by the theory of this chapter, therefore, is the type in which it is a given fact that the body is in equilibrium and some of the unknown quantities are to be found.

---

EXAMPLE 4.2. The large block in Fig. 4.5 weighs 400 lb and is held stationary on a smooth, inclined plane by two flexible ropes attached at $A$ and $B$. The ropes run over ideal pulleys at $C$ and $D$, with the rope over pulley $C$ carrying a vertical force of 100-lb magnitude. Find the magnitude $T$ of the unknown vertical force on the other rope and the magnitude $N$ of the total force exerted on the block by the plane. (The line of action of the latter force is an unknown which cannot be found by the methods of this chapter.)

*Solution.* Two new kinds of idealizations are introduced in this example. One is the ideal pulley, which means that the tension in the rope is the same on either side of the pulley. The other is the smooth surface, which means that

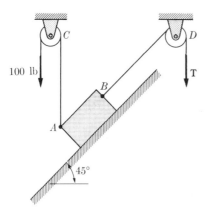

FIGURE 4.5

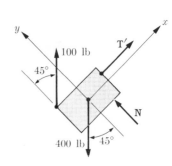

FIGURE 4.6

the force exerted on any body in contact with the surface is perpendicular to the surface. With these idealizations, the present problem is that type which requires finding the magnitudes of two forces with known directions.

Taking the $x$-axis parallel and the $y$-axis perpendicular to the inclined plane, the free-body diagram of Fig. 4.6 is drawn, the sketch showing clearly all the known forces as well as the two forces with unknown magnitudes. (The force $\mathbf{T}'$ has the same magnitude $T$ as the force $\mathbf{T}$.) Writing the equations of equilibrium,

$$\Sigma F_x = T + 100(0.707) - 400(0.707) = 0,$$

$$\Sigma F_y = N + 100(0.707) - 400(0.707) = 0,$$

we find that

$$T = N = 212 \text{ lb.}$$

**4.4 Equilibrium in space.** For a particle subjected to a general system of forces, all three of Eqs. (4.2) must be used to express the fact that the space polygon is a closed figure. Substituting Eqs. (3.9) into Eqs. (4.2) leads to the following *equations of equilibrium of a particle in space:*

$$\Sigma F_x = 0, \qquad \Sigma F_y = 0, \qquad \Sigma F_z = 0. \tag{4.4}$$

Equations (4.4) are both necessary and sufficient conditions for equilibrium of a particle in space. If all the forces lie in the $xy$-plane, the third of Eqs. (4.4) is satisfied identically, and the equations reduce to Eqs. (4.3).

From the three equations of equilibrium it is possible to find three unknowns, and it is again advisable to draw a free-body diagram. An equation of equilibrium may be written by adding components in any direction, but the total number of *independent* equations (and hence the number of unknowns which can be found) is three (two in the plane case), since it takes only three equations (two in the plane case) to specify that the resultant force is a null vector.

---

EXAMPLE 4.3. A block weighing 224 lb is supported by three ropes tied at points $A$, $B$, $C$ in the $zx$-plane, as shown in Fig. 4.7. (Point $D$ is on the negative $y$-axis.) Find the tension in each rope.

*Solution.* The tension in rope $DE$ is 224 lb, and the free-body diagram of particle $D$ is superimposed on the drawing of Fig. 4.7. In this problem the direction of each of the three unknown forces is given by two known points on its line of action. By Eq. (3.7),

$$d_A = \sqrt{(7-0)^2 + (0+4)^2 + (-4-0)^2} = 9 \text{ ft,}$$

$$d_B = \sqrt{(-8-0)^2 + (0+4)^2 + (-1-0)^2} = 9 \text{ ft,}$$

$$d_C = \sqrt{(0-0)^2 + (0+4)^2 + (3-0)^2} = 5 \text{ ft,}$$

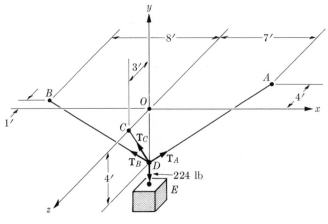

FIGURE 4.7

and, by Eqs. (3.8),

$$T_{Ax} = \tfrac{7}{9}T_A, \qquad T_{Bx} = -\tfrac{8}{9}T_B, \qquad T_{Cx} = 0,$$
$$T_{Ay} = \tfrac{4}{9}T_A, \qquad T_{By} = \tfrac{4}{9}T_B, \qquad T_{Cy} = \tfrac{4}{5}T_C,$$
$$T_{Az} = -\tfrac{4}{9}T_A, \qquad T_{Bz} = -\tfrac{1}{9}T_B, \qquad T_{Cz} = \tfrac{3}{5}T_C.$$

Thus, using Eqs. (4.4),

$$\sum F_x = \tfrac{7}{9}T_A - \tfrac{8}{9}T_B = 0,$$
$$\sum F_y = \tfrac{4}{9}T_A + \tfrac{4}{9}T_B + \tfrac{4}{5}T_C - 224 = 0,$$
$$\sum F_z = -\tfrac{4}{9}T_A - \tfrac{1}{9}T_B + \tfrac{3}{5}T_C = 0.$$

This system of three simultaneous equations in three unknowns can be solved by using the first equation to express $T_A$ in terms of $T_B$ as follows:

$$T_A = \tfrac{8}{7}T_B.$$

Substituting this into the second and third equations gives:

$$\tfrac{4}{9}(\tfrac{8}{7})T_B + \tfrac{4}{9}T_B + \tfrac{4}{5}T_C - 224 = 0,$$
$$-\tfrac{4}{9}(\tfrac{8}{7})T_B - \tfrac{1}{9}T_B + \tfrac{3}{5}T_C = 0,$$

or

$$\tfrac{60}{63}T_B + \tfrac{4}{5}T_C - 224 = 0,$$
$$-\tfrac{39}{63}T_B + \tfrac{3}{5}T_C = 0.$$

These two remaining equations in two unknowns can be solved by using the latter one to express $T_C$ in terms of $T_B$ as follows:

$$T_C = \tfrac{5}{3}(\tfrac{39}{63})T_B = \tfrac{65}{63}T_B.$$

Substituting this into the former one gives:

$$\tfrac{60}{63}T_B + \tfrac{4}{5}(\tfrac{65}{63})T_B - 224 = 0,$$

or

$$\tfrac{112}{63}T_B - 224 = 0,$$

from which

$$T_B = 126 \text{ lb.}$$

Hence,

$$T_A = \tfrac{8}{7}(126) = 144 \text{ lb,}$$

and

$$T_C = \tfrac{65}{63}(126) = 130 \text{ lb.}$$

---

In the foregoing example, three unknown tensions are found by using the three equations of equilibrium. If the three ropes supporting a block all lie in the same plane, say the $xy$-plane, as shown in Fig. 4.8, one of the equations of equilibrium, namely

$$\sum F_z = 0,$$

is satisfied identically, leaving only two usable equations. In this case the three unknown tensions cannot be found, even though two equations relating them can be written. A system in which there are more unknowns than usable equations of equilibrium is said to be *statically indeterminate*. The system in Fig. 4.8 is indeterminate to the first degree, since the number of unknowns is one more than the number of equations. Adding $n$ ropes more than the two in which the tensions can be found by the equations of equilibrium would make the system indeterminate to the $n$th degree.

Statically indeterminate problems can be solved if deformations are taken into account. If in the system shown in Fig. 4.8, for example, the assumption of inextensibility of the ropes is discarded, the ropes will

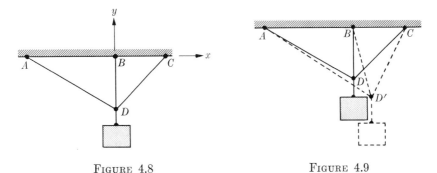

FIGURE 4.8                    FIGURE 4.9

stretch slightly when the load is applied and cause point $D$ to move to a new position $D'$ such as that shown in Fig. 4.9 (in which the displacement is greatly exaggerated). The tensions in the ropes determine their elongations, and the three elongations must be of such relative magnitudes that all three of the ropes still terminate at the same point (namely $D'$) after stretching. This, in effect, gives another relation among the three tensions and makes it possible to solve for them. The solution of statically indeterminate problems is illustrated in Chapter 18.

**4.5 Static friction.** The idealization of a smooth surface, introduced in Art. 4.3, simplifies many equilibrium problems by giving a known direction (perpendicular to the surface) to the reactive force exerted on a body in contact with the surface. In some problems, however, the deviation of the reactive force from the normal direction due to "roughness" of the surface is an essential part of the problem, so that the idealization of "smoothness" must be discarded. Consider a stationary body $A$ in contact with a fixed surface $B$, and let the $xy$-plane be a vertical plane perpendicular to the surface (or, if the surface is not a plane, perpendicular to the tangent plane at the point of contact). Figure 4.10 is a view which shows the $xy$-plane in the plane of the paper. If the total force exerted on the body by the surface is $Q$, then $Q$ can be resolved into two vector components: $N$, which is normal to the surface (or to the tangent plane at the point of contact) and is called the "normal force"; and $F$, which is parallel to the surface (or to the tangent plane) and is called the "friction force."

Consider first the case in which all the forces acting on the body other than $Q$ are parallel to the $xy$-plane. Since $N$ is perpendicular to the surface, it also is parallel to the $xy$-plane. Thus, by the third equation of equilibrium, $F$ is parallel to the $xy$-plane as well. (All the forces actually lie within the $xy$-plane if the body $A$ is a particle.) The angle $\psi$ shown in

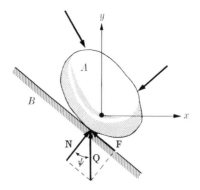

FIGURE 4.10

Fig. 4.10 is the angle by which **Q** deviates from the normal direction. Whereas a smooth surface can introduce only one unknown (that is, $N$) into an equilibrium problem, a rough surface can introduce two (that is, $N$ and $F$ or, equivalently, $Q$ and $\psi$). If the problem is that type in which both $N$ and $F$ are unknown, the two equations of equilibrium are spent in finding $N$ and $F$. The friction force **F**, however, is a type of force which may have, despite its known direction, unknown sense as well as unknown magnitude, and the sense can be found at the same time that $N$ and $F$ are solved for. To accomplish this, we *assume* a sense for **F** and show the force on the free-body diagram with its assumed sense. When the equations of equilibrium are solved, the assumed sense is correct if the magnitude $F$ comes out positive. If it comes out negative (which it cannot actually be), the correct sense is opposite that assumed. Because of the uncertainty of the sense of **F**, the answers to an equilibrium problem involving friction should include a clear stipulation of the sense of **F**, as illustrated in the following example.

---

EXAMPLE 4.4. A block of known weight $W$ rests on a plane with known inclination $\alpha$ as shown in Fig. 4.11. Find the magnitude $N$ of the normal force and the magnitude $F$ and sense of the friction force.

*Solution.* Taking the $x$-axis parallel and the $y$-axis perpendicular to the plane, the free-body diagram of Fig. 4.12 is drawn, with the sense of **F** assumed up the plane. Writing the equations of equilibrium,

$$\sum F_x = F - W \sin \alpha = 0,$$
$$\sum F_y = N - W \cos \alpha = 0,$$

we find that

$$N = W \cos \alpha, \qquad F = W \sin \alpha.$$

Since $F$ comes out positive, the sense of **F** is up the plane.

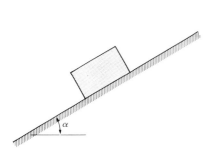

FIGURE 4.11

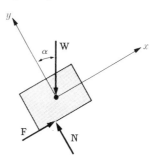

FIGURE 4.12

Some systems, such as the one in the foregoing example, cannot be in equilibrium without the presence of friction. (Note in Fig. 4.12 that the force **F** is needed to balance the $x$-component of **W**; if the surface were smooth, the block would slide down the plane. Note also that **F** acts in a direction opposite to the direction in which motion would occur if there were no friction.) Other systems, such as the one in Example 4.2, would be indeterminate if there were friction.

Referring again to Fig. 4.10, if all the forces other than **Q** are not parallel to the $xy$-plane, the contact force **Q** may have two friction components: **F**, parallel to the $xy$-plane, and **F'** (not shown), perpendicular to the $xy$-plane. The magnitude $F'$ is then an additional unknown, but there is an additional equation of equilibrium (i.e., $\sum F_z = 0$) available for finding it.

---

EXAMPLE 4.5. The block shown in Fig. 4.13 weighs 100 lb and rests on a horizontal plane. If a force with magnitude of 30 lb is applied in the direction shown, find the magnitude $N$ of the normal force and the magnitudes and senses of the two friction forces **F** and **F'** (parallel and perpendicular to the $xy$-plane, respectively).

*Solution.* On the free-body diagram of Fig. 4.14, **F** and **F'** are assumed to be in the positive $x$- and $z$-directions, respectively. By the equations of equilibrium,

$$\sum F_x = F - 30(0.707) = 0,$$
$$\sum F_y = N + 30(0.500) - 100 = 0,$$
$$\sum F_z = F' + 30(0.500) = 0,$$

from which it follows that

$$N = 85 \text{ lb}, \qquad F = 21.2 \text{ lb} \quad (\textbf{F in the positive } x\text{-direction}),$$
$$F' = -15 \text{ lb} = 15 \text{ lb} \quad (\textbf{F' in the negative } z\text{-direction}).$$

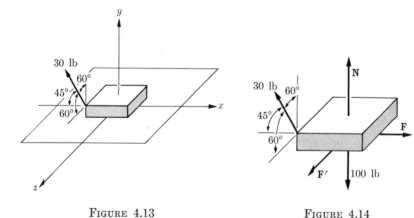

FIGURE 4.13                    FIGURE 4.14

One of the basic laws of mechanics, called the *law of static friction*, states that there is a limited attainable value of the ratio between the magnitude of the total friction force and the magnitude of the normal force. For the two-dimensional force system, this law may be written mathematically as follows:

$$\frac{F}{N} \leq \mu_s. \tag{4.5}$$

The limiting value $\mu_s$, called the *coefficient of static friction*, is assumed in the elementary theory to depend only on the nature of the two surfaces in contact. Its dependence upon the contact area, the magnitude of the normal force, etc., is neglected.

The dimensionless coefficient $\mu_s$ is a measure of the "roughness" of the two surfaces, which is influenced by the material of which the body and the fixed surface are made, by the extent to which the surfaces have been sanded, ground, or polished, by the amount of lubrication, etc. Varying ordinarily between $\frac{1}{4}$ and $\frac{1}{2}$ for wood on wood and between $\frac{1}{2}$ and unity for rubber on concrete, the actual value of $\mu_s$ must ordinarily be determined by experiment for each given set of contact conditions.

By definition, the *angle of static friction* $\psi_s$ is given by

$$\tan \psi_s = \mu_s. \tag{4.6}$$

Hence, referring to Fig. 4.10,

$$\tan \psi = \frac{F}{N} \leq \mu_s = \tan \psi_s,$$

from which it follows that

$$\psi \leq \psi_s. \tag{4.7}$$

Thus, $\psi_s$ is the largest value of the angle $\psi$ by which **Q** can deviate from the normal direction. For a smooth surface, $\mu_s = 0$, from which it follows that $\psi_s = 0$, and therefore $F = \psi = 0$.

For a three-dimensional force system acting on the body, the law of static friction is generalized as follows:

$$\frac{|\mathbf{F} + \mathbf{F'}|}{N} \leq \mu_s. \tag{4.8}$$

Any one of the inequalities (4.5), (4.7), and (4.8) may be thought of as a necessary condition for equilibrium, so that if any one of them is violated by values of $F$, $N$, etc., given by the equations of equilibrium, then equilibrium is impossible. Hence, values of $F$, $N$, etc., computed by the equations of equilibrium should be checked to make sure that the appropriate inequality is satisfied. For example, if $\mu_s = 2 \tan \alpha$ in Example 4.4, the block will remain stationary, since

$$\frac{F}{N} = \tan \alpha < 2 \tan \alpha.$$

On the other hand, if $\mu_s = \frac{1}{4}$ in Example 4.5, the block cannot remain stationary, since

$$\frac{|\mathbf{F} + \mathbf{F}'|}{N} = \frac{\sqrt{(21.2)^2 + (15)^2}}{85} = \frac{\sqrt{675}}{85} = 0.306 > \frac{1}{4}.$$

**4.6 Impending motion.** In some problems it is known that the body is at "impending motion," which means that the ratio of $F$ to $N$ has achieved its largest possible value and the body is about to slide on the surface. In this case the law of static friction becomes an equation instead of an inequality, i.e.,

$$\frac{F}{N} = \mu_s, \tag{4.9}$$

thereby making it possible to solve for an additional unknown. The sense of $\mathbf{F}$ is opposite the direction of the impending motion. Equation (4.9) must not be used unless it is definitely given that the body is at impending motion.

---

EXAMPLE 4.6. Find the largest value of the inclination $\alpha$ which can be given to the plane of Fig. 4.11 without causing the block to slide down the plane. Assume that $\mu_s$ is known.

*Solution.* In this problem there are three unknowns, $F$, $N$, and $\alpha$, but the condition of impending motion gives a relation between $F$ and $N$, Eq. (4.9), which, when used with the two equations of equilibrium, yields all three unknowns. Using the free-body diagram of Fig. 4.12, the three equations are:

$$\sum F_x = F - W \sin \alpha = 0,$$
$$\sum F_y = N - W \cos \alpha = 0,$$
$$F = \mu_s N.$$

Substituting the third equation into the first and rewriting the first two,

$$\mu_s N = W \sin \alpha, \qquad N = W \cos \alpha.$$

Having eliminated $F$, we may solve the last two equations for $N$ and $\alpha$ by dividing the first by the second to obtain

$$\tan \alpha = \mu_s.$$

Hence, using Eq. (4.6),

$$\alpha = \psi_s.$$

This is the maximum possible value of the angle $\alpha$. To find the other two unknowns, this value of $\alpha$ can now be substituted back into previous equations to give

$$N = W \cos \psi_s = \frac{W}{\sqrt{1 + \mu_s^2}},$$

$$F = \mu_s W \cos \psi_s = \frac{\mu_s W}{\sqrt{1 + \mu_s^2}}.$$

---

In Art. 4.5 it is mentioned that $\mu_s$ must be determined by experiment for any given pair of surfaces. Any problem in which $\mu_s$ is one of the unknowns may be regarded as an experiment conducted to measure $\mu_s$.

---

EXAMPLE 4.7. A block resting on a horizontal plane is used in an experiment to measure $\mu_s$. The weight of the block is 200 lb, and a force **P** is applied as shown in Fig. 4.15. If the force **P** can have its magnitude increased to 42.4 lb before the block moves, find $\mu_s$.

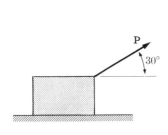

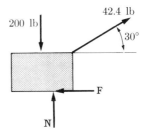

FIGURE 4.15                              FIGURE 4.16

*Solution.* Using the free-body diagram of Fig. 4.16, we find that the equations of equilibrium are:

$$\sum F_x = 42.4(0.866) - F = 0,$$
$$\sum F_y = N + 42.4(0.500) - 200 = 0,$$

from which

$$F = 36.7 \text{ lb}, \qquad N = 178.8 \text{ lb}.$$

By Eq. (4.9), which is valid because the block is at impending motion,

$$\mu_s = \frac{36.7}{178.8} = 0.205.$$

## PROBLEMS

**4.1** Find the force **P** required to hold the particle shown in Fig. 4.17 in equilibrium.

**4.2** Find the tensions in portions $AB$ and $BC$ of the string $ABC$ shown in Fig. 4.18.

[*Ans.:* $T_{AB}$ = 17.93 lb, $T_{BC}$ = 14.64 lb.]

**4.3** A 3000-lb beam (Fig. 4.19) is suspended by a sling $ABC$ to which a force of 3000 lb is applied at $B$. Find the tensions in portions $AB$ and $BC$ of the sling.

**4.4** Two bodies are held in equilibrium by flexible ropes and an ideal pulley, as shown in Fig. 4.20. Find the tensions in ropes $AB$ and $AC$.

[*Ans.:* $T_{AB}$ = 112.5 lb, $T_{AC}$ = 12.5 lb.]

**4.5** A block of weight $W$ is held in equilibrium by the arrangement of ideal strings and ideal pulleys shown in Fig. 4.21. Find $P$. (Assume that weightlessness is one of the properties of an ideal pulley.)

**4.6** The airplane in Fig. 4.22 is climbing on a straight line at an angle of 20° with the horizontal. The plane weighs 25,000 lb and is traveling at a constant speed of 750 mph. (This motion is a state of equilibrium.) If the magnitude $D$ of the drag force is 5000 lb at this speed, determine the magnitude $T$ of the thrust force and the magnitude $L$ of the lift force.

[*Ans.:* $T$ = 13,550 lb, $L$ = 23,500 lb.]

**4.7** The particle at $A$ in Fig. 4.23 is held by three strings fixed at $B$, $C$, and $D$. It carries a force of 7 lb directed along the diagonal $EA$. Find the tension in each of the three strings.

**4.8** An equilateral triangular platform of weight $W$ is held in equilibrium by a force of magnitude $W$ applied as shown in Fig. 4.24 to the top of a sling consisting of three ropes of equal length $L$. Find the tension in each rope.

$$\left[ Ans: \frac{W}{3\sqrt{1 - \frac{1}{3}(b/L)^2}} \text{ in each rope.} \right]$$

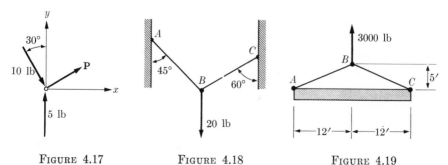

FIGURE 4.17          FIGURE 4.18          FIGURE 4.19

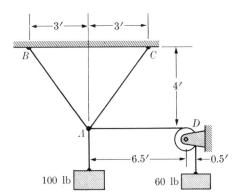

FIGURE 4.20

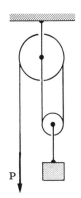

FIGURE 4.21

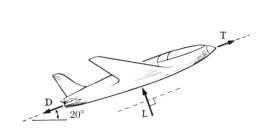

FIGURE 4.22

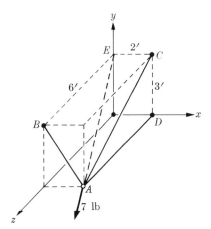

FIGURE 4.23

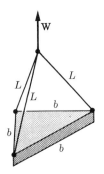

FIGURE 4.24

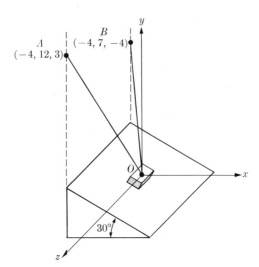

FIGURE 4.25

4.9 The smooth plane on which a 100-lb block rests (Fig. 4.25) is parallel to the $z$-axis and makes an angle of 30° with the $zx$-plane. Two strings fixed at $A$ and $B$ help support the block. Find the tension in string $OA$.

4.10 Two bodies are held in equilibrium by flexible ropes and a small pulley, as in Fig. 4.26. Find the tensions in ropes $AB$ and $AC$. How would this system be classified if $AE$ were fixed at $E$ instead of being over the pulley?

[$Ans.$: $T_{AB}$ = 193 lb, $T_{AC}$ = 450 lb.]

4.11 The block in Fig. 4.5 weighs 400 lb, and the coefficient of static friction between it and the plane is 0.30. Find the magnitude of the normal force and

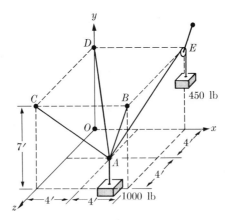

FIGURE 4.26

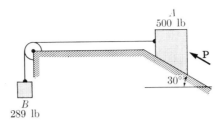

FIGURE 4.27

the magnitude and sense of the friction force acting on the block if: (a) $T =$ 160 lb, (b) $T = 260$ lb.

4.12 The block in Fig. 4.5 weighs 400 lb, and the coefficient of static friction between it and the plane is 0.25. Find the magnitude $T$ required for impending motion: (a) up the plane, (b) down the plane.

[*Ans.*: (a) 265 lb; (b) 159 lb.]

4.13 The apparatus of Fig. 4.5 is used to measure the coefficient of static friction between the 400-lb block and the plane. With the block stationary, the magnitude of the force **T** is increased gradually until, at a value of 296 lb, the block begins to move. Find: (a) $\mu_s$, and (b) the values of $N$ and $F$ just before the block moves.

4.14 To facilitate the moving of the 500-lb block $A$, a counterweight $B$ is attached by an ideal cable as in Fig. 4.27. The coefficient of static friction between $A$ and the inclined plane is 0.1. Find the magnitude of the force **P** for impending motion up the plane: (a) with the counterweight, (b) without the counterweight.

[*Ans.*: (a) 57.7 lb; (b) 293.3 lb.]

# CHAPTER 5

## KINEMATICS OF A PARTICLE

**5.1 Introduction to vector calculus.** A vector **V** is said to be a *vector variable* if it can change in either magnitude or direction or both. Let $S$ be an independent scalar variable which can assume any value in an interval $A \leq S \leq B$. If each value of $S$ in the interval determines, according to some definite law, a magnitude and a direction for a vector variable **V**, then **V** is said to be a *vector function* of $S$. This relationship is symbolized by writing the vector equation

$$\mathbf{V} = \mathbf{f}(S), \tag{5.1}$$

or, more simply, by writing

$$\mathbf{V}(S).$$

The vector **V** determined by a specific value $S_0$ of $S$ is represented by the symbols $\mathbf{f}(S_0)$ or $\mathbf{V}(S_0)$.

As an example of a vector function, consider a particle $P$ which is constrained to move along a line $L$, as shown in Fig. 5.1. If the particle is attached to an ideal spring which has one end fixed at $Q$, the force **F** exerted on the particle by the spring varies in both magnitude and direction as the particle assumes different positions on the line, as shown by the dashed arrows in Fig. 5.1. If $x$ is the directed distance to $P$ from a fixed reference point $O$, then

$$\mathbf{F} = \mathbf{f}(x).$$

Returning to the general function $\mathbf{V} = \mathbf{f}(S)$, if a change $\Delta S$ is imagined to occur in $S$, there are corresponding changes in the magnitude and direction of **V**. To avoid complications, only those vector functions which

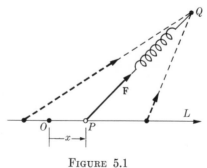

FIGURE 5.1

58

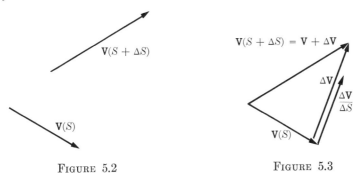

FIGURE 5.2  FIGURE 5.3

are "single-valued" (which means that each value of $S$ determines a unique vector $\mathbf{V}$) and "continuous" (which means that the changes in magnitude and direction of $\mathbf{V}$ caused by $\Delta S$ can be made arbitrarily small by letting $|\Delta S|$ be small enough) are considered in this introduction to vector calculus. Figure 5.2 shows the vectors $\mathbf{V}(S)$ and $\mathbf{V}(S + \Delta S)$. By definition, the "increment" $\Delta \mathbf{V}$ of $\mathbf{V}$ which corresponds to the increment $\Delta S$ of $S$ is a vector given by

$$\Delta \mathbf{V} = \mathbf{V}(S + \Delta S) - \mathbf{V}(S). \tag{5.2}$$

By use of the rule for vector subtraction (Art. 2.5), the vector $\Delta \mathbf{V}$ is determined as in Fig. 5.3. Dividing the vector $\Delta \mathbf{V}$ by the scalar $\Delta S$ gives (according to Art. 2.4) another vector, $\Delta \mathbf{V}/\Delta S$, which is parallel to $\Delta \mathbf{V}$, and this other vector is also shown in Fig. 5.3 (although it is a different type of vector from $\Delta \mathbf{V}$ and its arrow must be imagined drawn according to a new scale). Using Eq. (5.2),

$$\frac{\Delta \mathbf{V}}{\Delta S} = \frac{\mathbf{V}(S + \Delta S) - \mathbf{V}(S)}{\Delta S}. \tag{5.3}$$

If $\Delta S$ is now imagined to approach zero, the vector $\Delta \mathbf{V}$ approaches the null vector, but the vector $\Delta \mathbf{V}/\Delta S$ approaches a new vector which, except for certain special functions, is not in general a null vector (although it is usually a function of $S$ and may be null for particular values of $S$). If the limit of $\Delta \mathbf{V}/\Delta S$ exists and is the same regardless of the manner in which $\Delta S$ is made to approach zero, the vector function is said to be *differentiable*, and the *derivative* of $\mathbf{V}$ with respect to $S$, symbolized by $d\mathbf{V}/dS$, $d\mathbf{f}/dS$, $\mathbf{V}'(S)$, or $\mathbf{f}'(S)$, is defined as a vector given by

$$\frac{d\mathbf{V}}{dS} = \lim_{\Delta S \to 0} \frac{\Delta \mathbf{V}}{\Delta S}. \tag{5.4}$$

The symbol $d\mathbf{V}/dS$ is not to be interpreted as the quotient of a vector and a scalar but rather as a single symbol denoting the vector defined by Eq. (5.4).

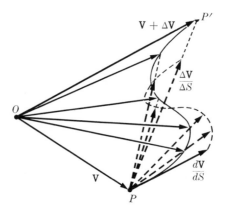

FIGURE 5.4

As the increment $\Delta S$ approaches zero, the vector $\mathbf{V} + \Delta \mathbf{V}$ varies in some manner, and a space figure can be drawn (Fig. 5.4) in such a way that the tail of $\mathbf{V} + \Delta \mathbf{V}$ is always at the same point $O$. The head of $\mathbf{V} + \Delta \mathbf{V}$ then traces out a curve in space (the solid curve $P'P$ in Fig. 5.4) as $\Delta S$ approaches zero. If the vector $\Delta \mathbf{V}/\Delta S$ is drawn from $P$ (as shown by the dashed arrows), its head traces out another curve in space (the dashed curve). The vector $\Delta \mathbf{V}/\Delta S$ approaches a limiting line which is called the *tangent* to the space curve at $P$, and $d\mathbf{V}/dS$, if drawn from $P$, lies along the tangent.

From Eqs. (5.3) and (5.4),

$$\frac{d\mathbf{V}}{dS} = \lim_{\Delta S \to 0} \frac{\mathbf{V}(S + \Delta S) - \mathbf{V}(S)}{\Delta S}. \tag{5.5}$$

Since the derivative is itself a vector function of $S$, it can be differentiated with respect to $S$ to obtain what is called the *second derivative* of $\mathbf{V}$ with respect to $S$, symbolized by $d^2\mathbf{V}/dS^2$, $d^2\mathbf{f}/dS^2$, $\mathbf{V}''(S)$, or $\mathbf{f}''(S)$. By definition,

$$\frac{d^2\mathbf{V}}{dS^2} = \frac{d}{dS}\left(\frac{d\mathbf{V}}{dS}\right). \tag{5.6}$$

Similarly, by definition,

$$\frac{d^n\mathbf{V}}{dS^n} = \frac{d}{dS}\left(\frac{d^{n-1}\mathbf{V}}{dS^{n-1}}\right). \tag{5.7}$$

The derivative of various types of vector functions can be found by a procedure called the "$\Delta$-process," which involves the application of Eq. (5.5) to the particular function in question. For example, if $\mathbf{A}$ is a "constant" vector (i.e., neither its magnitude nor its direction changes with $S$), then

$$\frac{d}{dS}(\mathbf{A}) = \lim_{\Delta S \to 0} \frac{\mathbf{A} - \mathbf{A}}{\Delta S} = \lim_{\Delta S \to 0} \mathbf{0}.$$

Hence,

$$\frac{d}{dS}(\mathbf{A}) = \mathbf{0}. \tag{5.8}$$

For the sum of two vector functions $\mathbf{V}_1(S)$ and $\mathbf{V}_2(S)$,

$$\frac{d}{dS}(\mathbf{V}_1 + \mathbf{V}_2) = \lim_{\Delta S \to 0} \frac{[\mathbf{V}_1(S + \Delta S) + \mathbf{V}_2(S + \Delta S)] - [\mathbf{V}_1(S) + \mathbf{V}_2(S)]}{\Delta S}$$

$$= \lim_{\Delta S \to 0} \left[ \frac{\mathbf{V}_1(S + \Delta S) - \mathbf{V}_1(S)}{\Delta S} + \frac{\mathbf{V}_2(S + \Delta S) - \mathbf{V}_2(S)}{\Delta S} \right].$$

It can be shown that the limit of the sum of two vectors equals the sum of the limits of the two vectors. Thus,

$$\frac{d}{dS}(\mathbf{V}_1 + \mathbf{V}_2) = \frac{d\mathbf{V}_1}{dS} + \frac{d\mathbf{V}_2}{dS}, \tag{5.9}$$

and a similar equation holds for any number of vector functions. For the product of a scalar function $U(S)$ and a vector function $\mathbf{V}(S)$,

$$\frac{d}{dS}(U\mathbf{V}) = \lim_{\Delta S \to 0} \frac{[(U + \Delta U)(\mathbf{V} + \Delta \mathbf{V})] - [U\mathbf{V}]}{\Delta S}$$

$$= \lim_{\Delta S \to 0} \left( U \frac{\Delta \mathbf{V}}{\Delta S} + \frac{\Delta U}{\Delta S} \mathbf{V} + \Delta U \frac{\Delta \mathbf{V}}{\Delta S} \right)$$

$$= \lim_{\Delta S \to 0} \left( U \frac{\Delta \mathbf{V}}{\Delta S} \right) + \lim_{\Delta S \to 0} \left( \frac{\Delta U}{\Delta S} \mathbf{V} \right) + \lim_{\Delta S \to 0} \left( \Delta U \frac{\Delta \mathbf{V}}{\Delta S} \right).$$

It can be shown that the limit of a product of a scalar and a vector equals the product of the limits of the scalar and the vector. Thus,

$$\lim_{\Delta S \to 0} \left( \Delta U \frac{\Delta \mathbf{V}}{\Delta S} \right) = \lim_{\Delta S \to 0} (\Delta U) \lim_{\Delta S \to 0} \frac{\Delta \mathbf{V}}{\Delta S} = (0) \left( \frac{d\mathbf{V}}{dS} \right) = \mathbf{0},$$

and

$$\frac{d}{dS}(U\mathbf{V}) = U \frac{d\mathbf{V}}{dS} + \frac{dU}{dS} \mathbf{V}. \tag{5.10}$$

If $\mathbf{V}$ is a function of a scalar $R$ which in turn is a function of a scalar variable $S$,

$$\frac{d}{dS}\{\mathbf{V}[R(S)]\} = \lim_{\Delta S \to 0} \frac{\mathbf{V}(R + \Delta R) - \mathbf{V}(R)}{\Delta S}$$

$$= \lim_{\Delta S \to 0} \left[\frac{\mathbf{V}(R + \Delta R) - \mathbf{V}(R)}{\Delta R} \frac{\Delta R}{\Delta S}\right].$$

Therefore, since the limit of a product equals the product of the limits,

$$\frac{d}{dS}\{\mathbf{V}[R(S)]\} = \frac{d\mathbf{V}}{dR}\frac{dR}{dS}. \tag{5.11}$$

By definition, the *differential* $d\mathbf{V}$ of the vector function $\mathbf{V} = \mathbf{f}(S)$ is given by

$$d\mathbf{V} = \mathbf{f}'(S)\,\Delta S, \tag{5.12}$$

where $\Delta S$ is an arbitrarily chosen increment of $S$ (which produces a change $\Delta\mathbf{V}$ in $\mathbf{V}$). Both $d\mathbf{V}$ and $\Delta\mathbf{V}$ are functions of the two independent variables $S$ and $\Delta S$, but, in general,

$$d\mathbf{V} \neq \Delta\mathbf{V}.$$

In fact, Eq. (5.12) shows that the differential $d\mathbf{V}$ is parallel to the derivative, so that it differs from $\Delta\mathbf{V}$ in both magnitude and direction, as shown in Fig. 5.5. (In some cases $d\mathbf{V}$ may be a suitable approximation to $\Delta\mathbf{V}$ for small $\Delta S$.) By Eq. (5.12),

$$\mathbf{f}'(S) = \frac{d\mathbf{V}}{\Delta S},$$

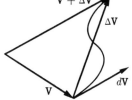

FIGURE 5.5

which means that the derivative may be expressed as the quotient of $d\mathbf{V}$, the differential of $\mathbf{V}$, and $\Delta S$, the increment of $S$.

It is customary to write $dS$ instead of $\Delta S$ for the increment of $S$, so that Eq. (5.12) becomes

$$d\mathbf{V} = \mathbf{f}'(S)\,dS,$$

and thus

$$\mathbf{f}'(S) = \frac{d\mathbf{V}}{dS},$$

where $d\mathbf{V}/dS$ is now the quotient of the differential $d\mathbf{V}$ (not the increment $\Delta\mathbf{V}$) and the increment $dS$. It can now be seen that the symbol used for the derivative may be considered a quotient, provided that the correct interpretation is placed on the numerator and denominator.

The operation of *integration* is the inverse of finding the differential. If $\mathbf{W}$ is a function of $S$ such that

$$\frac{d\mathbf{W}}{dS} = \mathbf{V},$$

then, by definition, the *indefinite integral* of $\mathbf{V}(S)\,dS$, symbolized by $\int \mathbf{V}(S)\,dS$, is given by

$$\int \mathbf{V}(S)\,dS = \mathbf{W}(S) + \mathbf{C}, \tag{5.13}$$

where $\mathbf{C}$ is an arbitrary constant vector. If $\mathbf{W}_1$ and $\mathbf{W}_2$ are two functions of $S$ such that

$$\frac{d\mathbf{W}_1}{dS} = \mathbf{V}_1, \qquad \frac{d\mathbf{W}_2}{dS} = \mathbf{V}_2,$$

then

$$\int [\mathbf{V}_1(S) + \mathbf{V}_2(S)]\,dS = \int \left( \frac{d\mathbf{W}_1}{dS} + \frac{d\mathbf{W}_2}{dS} \right) dS.$$

By Eq. (5.9), therefore,

$$\int [\mathbf{V}_1(S) + \mathbf{V}_2(S)]\,dS = \mathbf{W}_1(S) + \mathbf{W}_2(S) + \mathbf{C},$$

only one constant of integration being required. Thus,

$$\int [\mathbf{V}_1(S) + \mathbf{V}_2(S)]\,dS = \int \mathbf{V}_1(S)\,dS + \int \mathbf{V}_2(S)\,dS, \tag{5.14}$$

and a similar equation holds for any number of vector functions.

Equation (5.5) is not convenient for the actual evaluation of the derivative of specific vector functions other than a constant vector, since these functions cannot be expressed by a simple mathematical equation as in scalar calculus. In the application of vector calculus to mechanics, therefore, it is necessary to employ a coordinate system and resolve the vector function into components. Using a rectangular coordinate system, we can resolve the vector $\mathbf{V}$ into scalar components $V_x$, $V_y$, $V_z$ each of which is a scalar function of $S$. That is,

$$\mathbf{V}(S) = V_x(S)\mathbf{i} + V_y(S)\mathbf{j} + V_z(S)\mathbf{k}.$$

Then, by Eqs. (5.8), (5.9), and (5.10),

$$\frac{d\mathbf{V}}{dS} = \frac{dV_x}{dS}\mathbf{i} + \frac{dV_y}{dS}\mathbf{j} + \frac{dV_z}{dS}\mathbf{k}, \tag{5.15}$$

since **i**, **j**, **k** are constant in magnitude and direction. Similarly, by Eq. (5.6),

$$\frac{d^2 \mathbf{V}}{dS^2} = \frac{d^2 V_x}{dS^2}\,\mathbf{i} + \frac{d^2 V_y}{dS^2}\,\mathbf{j} + \frac{d^2 V_z}{dS^2}\,\mathbf{k}, \tag{5.16}$$

and the process can be repeated until any desired order of derivative is obtained. Also, it can be shown by Eqs. (5.10) and (5.14) that

$$\int \mathbf{V}(S)\,dS = \mathbf{i}\int V_x(S)\,dS + \mathbf{j}\int V_y(S)\,dS + \mathbf{k}\int V_z(S)\,dS. \tag{5.17}$$

**5.2 Velocity and acceleration.** Kinematics is concerned only with the *description* of the motion of various mechanical systems and may therefore be called a study of the "geometry" of motion. Consider a particle $P$ moving on a path in a fixed, three-dimensional frame of reference as in Fig. 5.6. Let the particle be located by a position vector **r** from a fixed origin $O$. If $t$ is the time, then

$$\mathbf{r} = \mathbf{f}(t),$$

where the function is single-valued (because the particle can occupy only one position at a time). Only those cases in which the function is also continuous and differentiable are considered. By definition, the *velocity* **v** of the particle is given by

$$\mathbf{v} = \frac{d\mathbf{r}}{dt}, \tag{5.18}$$

and the *acceleration* **a** of the particle is given by

$$\mathbf{a} = \frac{d\mathbf{v}}{dt}. \tag{5.19}$$

Substituting Eq. (5.18) into Eq. (5.19),

$$\mathbf{a} = \frac{d^2\mathbf{r}}{dt^2}. \tag{5.20}$$

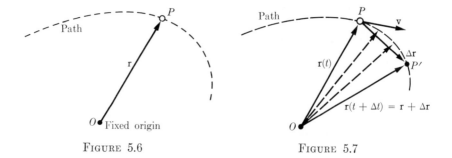

FIGURE 5.6                    FIGURE 5.7

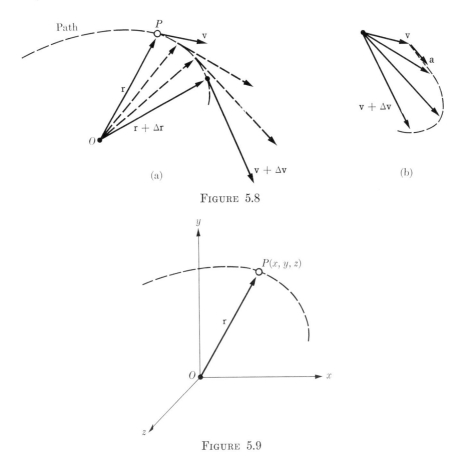

FIGURE 5.8

FIGURE 5.9

An increment $\Delta t$ of $t$ is accompanied by a displacement $\Delta\mathbf{r}$ of the particle as shown in Fig. 5.7, and the curved line joining all the points through which the head of $\mathbf{r} + \Delta\mathbf{r}$ passes as displacements $\Delta\mathbf{r}$ of diminishing magnitude are considered is the path itself (since the tail of $\mathbf{r} + \Delta\mathbf{r}$ is always at point $O$). Because of this, the vector $\mathbf{v}$ is tangent to the path at $P$. The vector $\mathbf{a}$, on the other hand, is not in general tangent to the path, because the acceleration is a measure of the change in direction as well as the change in magnitude of the velocity. Figure 5.8(a) shows the velocity vector $\mathbf{v} + \Delta\mathbf{v}$ for various values of $\Delta t$, while Fig. 5.8(b) shows all the velocity vectors with their tails at the same point. The vector $\mathbf{a}$ is tangent to the dashed curve in Fig. 5.8(b), but this curve is not the path of the particle.

If a rectangular coordinate system with origin at $O$ is used for locating the particle $P$ as shown in Fig. 5.9, then, as in Art. 2.10,

$$\mathbf{r} = x\mathbf{i} + y\mathbf{j} + z\mathbf{k}. \tag{5.21}$$

In this case, since the particle is in motion, $x$, $y$, and $z$ are functions of $t$; that is,

$$x = f_1(t), \qquad y = f_2(t), \qquad z = f_3(t). \tag{5.22}$$

If the functions of Eqs. (5.22) can be expressed as mathematical equations, the equations are called the *parametric equations* of the path, since each value of the parameter $t$ determines the three coordinates of a point on the path.

By Eq. (2.29), the displacement $\Delta\mathbf{r}$ (Fig. 5.7) may be written as follows:

$$\Delta\mathbf{r} = \Delta x\mathbf{i} + \Delta y\mathbf{j} + \Delta z\mathbf{k}.$$

The velocity $\mathbf{v}$, by Eqs. (5.15), (5.18), and (5.21), is

$$\mathbf{v} = \frac{dx}{dt}\mathbf{i} + \frac{dy}{dt}\mathbf{j} + \frac{dz}{dt}\mathbf{k}.$$

The acceleration $\mathbf{a}$, by Eqs. (5.16), (5.20), and (5.21), is

$$\mathbf{a} = \frac{d^2x}{dt^2}\mathbf{i} + \frac{d^2y}{dt^2}\mathbf{j} + \frac{d^2z}{dt^2}\mathbf{k}.$$

A concise and convenient notation for time derivatives is the use of a dot over a dependent variable for the first derivative with respect to time, two dots for the second derivative, three for the third, etc. Rewriting the equations for $\mathbf{v}$ and $\mathbf{a}$ in this notation, we have

$$\mathbf{v} = \dot{x}\mathbf{i} + \dot{y}\mathbf{j} + \dot{z}\mathbf{k} \tag{5.23}$$

and

$$\mathbf{a} = \ddot{x}\mathbf{i} + \ddot{y}\mathbf{j} + \ddot{z}\mathbf{k}. \tag{5.24}$$

All the foregoing results can be restated in the following form:

$$v_x = \frac{dx}{dt}, \qquad v_y = \frac{dy}{dt}, \qquad v_z = \frac{dz}{dt}, \tag{5.25}$$

and

$$a_x = \frac{dv_x}{dt} = \frac{d^2x}{dt^2}, \qquad a_y = \frac{dv_y}{dt} = \frac{d^2y}{dt^2}, \qquad a_z = \frac{dv_z}{dt} = \frac{d^2z}{dt^2}. \tag{5.26}$$

Equations (5.25) and (5.26) are to be regarded as results derived from the definitions of Eqs. (5.18) and (5.19). The units of $v_x$, $v_y$, $v_z$ are length/time (e.g., ft/sec), and those of $a_x$, $a_y$, $a_z$ are length/time$^2$ (e.g., ft/sec$^2$).

By definition, the *speed* of the particle is the magnitude of the velocity, which, according to Eq. (2.23), is given by

$$v = \sqrt{v_x^2 + v_y^2 + v_z^2}. \tag{5.27}$$

By Eq. (2.28), the displacement $\mathbf{u}$ of a particle between time $t_1$ and time $t_2$ is given by

$$\mathbf{u} = \mathbf{r}(t_2) - \mathbf{r}(t_1). \tag{5.28}$$

**5.3 Rectilinear motion.** A particle is in rectilinear motion, by definition, if its path is a straight line. Since the orientation of the coordinate axes is arbitrary, the $x$-axis can be taken along the straight line of the motion. In that case Eqs. (5.22) reduce to

$$x = f_1(t),$$

and

$$y = z = 0$$

at all times. Hence, by Eqs. (5.25) and (5.26),

$$v_x = \frac{dx}{dt} \tag{5.29}$$

and

$$a_x = \frac{dv_x}{dt} = \frac{d^2x}{dt^2}, \tag{5.30}$$

while

$$v_y = v_z = a_y = a_z = 0$$

at all times. The speed is now given by

$$v = |v_x|. \tag{5.31}$$

The significance of the foregoing equations is that, for rectilinear motion along the $x$-axis, the vectors $\mathbf{r}$, $\mathbf{v}$, and $\mathbf{a}$ are all parallel to the $x$-axis at all times, so that only $x$-components need be considered. For this reason, it is customary when dealing with rectilinear motion to call $v_x$ the "velocity" and $a_x$ the "acceleration."

Some clarification of the meaning of velocity in rectilinear motion is achieved by considering a time $t$ when the particle is at a point $P$ (Fig. 5.10). If, during a subsequent increment of time $\Delta t$, the particle travels a distance $\Delta x$ (to a point $P'$), the "average" velocity between $P$ and $P'$ is $\Delta x/\Delta t$. By Eq. (5.29), the velocity $v_x$ at time $t$ is then the limit of this average velocity as the increment used in computing the average approaches zero.

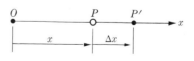

FIGURE 5.10

The examples which follow illustrate various types of problems which can be solved by Eqs. (5.29) and (5.30).

EXAMPLE 5.1. A particle travels on the $x$-axis in such a way that

$$x = t^3 - 6t^2 + 9t - 2,$$

where $x$ is in ft and $t$ is in sec. Find $v_x(t)$ and $a_x(t)$ and draw graphs of $x$, $v_x$, and $a_x$ vs. $t$ for positive values of $t$.

*Solution.* By Eqs. (5.29) and (5.30),

$$v_x = 3t^2 - 12t + 9,$$

$$a_x = 6t - 12.$$

Figure 5.11(a) shows the particle $P$ and the physical line along which it is traveling, while Fig. 5.11(b) shows the required graphs. Plotting the graphs is greatly facilitated by the fact that the $v_x$-$t$ curve represents the slope of the $x$-$t$ curve and the $a_x$-$t$ curve represents the slope of the $v_x$-$t$ curve. Awareness of this, combined with some knowledge of the properties of curves from analytic geometry, makes it possible to draw sketches of the curves without actually computing very many ordinates.

The graphs of Fig. 5.11(b) give a complete picture of the motion of this example. In the $x$-$t$ graph, any value of the abscissa $t$ determines a point on the curve with ordinate $x$. For example, at $t = 3$ sec the ordinate $x$ is $-2$ ft, expressed by the equation

$$x(3) = -2.$$

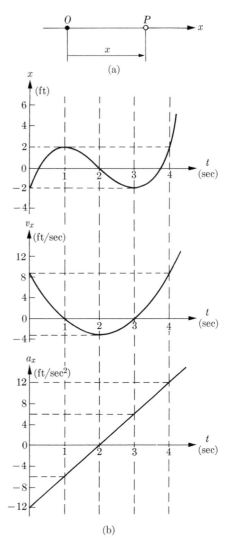

(a)

(b)

FIGURE 5.11

But $x$ is not only the ordinate of the graph; it is also the coordinate of the particle, so that the actual location of the particle at this time is 2 ft to the left of point $O$ on the line in Fig. 5.11(a). As $t$ increases from zero, the point on the graph travels along the curve, and, if the point on the graph is projected to the $x$-axis of the graph, the pattern of motion of the particle itself can be visualized.

The signs of $v_x$ and $a_x$ have a simple physical significance. Between $t = 0$ and $t = 1$, $v_x$ is positive and $a_x$ is negative. This means that the particle is moving in the positive $x$-direction with decreasing velocity (and decreasing speed). Between $t = 1$ and $t = 2$, both $v_x$ and $a_x$ are negative, which happens when the motion is in the negative $x$-direction with decreasing velocity (but increasing speed). For $2 < t < 3$, $v_x$ is negative and $a_x$ is positive. This means that the particle is moving in the negative $x$-direction with increasing velocity (and decreasing speed). Finally, for $t > 3$, both $v_x$ and $a_x$ are positive, and this happens when the motion is in the positive $x$-direction with increasing velocity (and increasing speed).

Some important features of the motion in this example are the relative maximum on $x$ at $t = 1$ sec and the relative minimum on $x$ at $t = 3$ sec. These values of $t$ are found analytically by setting $v_x$ equal to zero, i.e.,

$$3t^2 - 12t + 9 = 0,$$

and solving for $t$ by the quadratic formula:

$$t = \frac{12 \pm \sqrt{36}}{6} = 1 \text{ sec or } 3 \text{ sec.}$$

The minimum velocity occurs when the acceleration is zero, i.e., when

$$6t - 12 = 0,$$

from which

$$t = 2 \text{ sec.}$$

For this value of $t$,

$$v_x = 3(2)^2 - 12(2) + 9 = -3 \text{ ft/sec.}$$

For rectilinear motion along the $x$-axis, the displacement $\mathbf{u}$, like $\mathbf{r}$, $\mathbf{v}$, and $\mathbf{a}$, is always parallel to the $x$-axis, so that only its $x$-component need be considered. That is, from Eq. (5.28),

$$u_x = x(t_2) - x(t_1), \tag{5.32}$$

and the scalar $u_x$ can, for rectilinear motion, be called the "displacement." Equation (5.32) can be used, for example, to find the displacement of the particle in Example 5.1 between $t = 0$ and $t = 4$ sec:

$$u_x = x(4) - x(0) = 2 - (-2) = 4 \text{ ft.}$$

The displacement is significant as the net change in $x$ in a time interval.

Another important quantity in rectilinear motion is the distance $d$ traveled during an interval of time, $d$ being a positive scalar. To find $d$ for any interval, it is necessary to determine all values of $t$ in the interval at which $v_x = 0$. The sum of the absolute values of the displacements during the subintervals is then the distance traveled. To find the distance traveled by the particle of Example 5.1 between $t = 0$ and $t = 4$ sec, note that $v_x = 0$ at $t = 1$ sec and at $t = 3$ sec.  Thus,

$$d = |x(1) - x(0)| + |x(3) - x(1)| + |x(4) - x(3)|$$
$$= |2 - (-2)| + |-2 - (2)| + |2 - (-2)|$$
$$= |4| + |-4| + |4| = 12 \text{ ft.}$$

The foregoing results could have been obtained readily by studying the $x$-$t$ graph of Fig. 5.11(b), which shows that the particle moves 4 ft out on the $x$-axis, then 4 ft back, and then 4 ft out again during the first four seconds, giving a displacement of 4 ft and a distance traveled of 12 ft.

In many problems involving the kinematics of rectilinear motion, the velocity $v_x$, rather than the coordinate $x$, is given as a function of $t$, in which case, by Eq. (5.29), it is necessary to integrate in order to find $x(t)$.

---

EXAMPLE 5.2.  A particle travels on the $x$-axis in such a way that

$$v_x = k,$$

where $k$ is a constant with units of ft/sec.  Find $x(t)$ and $a_x(t)$ and draw graphs of $x$, $v_x$, and $a_x$ vs. $t$.

*Solution.*  By Eq. (5.29),

$$dx = v_x(t) \, dt,$$

and hence

$$x = \int v_x(t) \, dt.$$

In this example,

$$x = \int k \, dt = kt + C,$$

where $C$ is an arbitrary constant.  Thus, there exists a family of $x$-$t$ curves (corresponding to all different values of $C$) all of which have the same $v_x$-$t$ curve. The constant $C$ can be evaluated only by considering the physical conditions of the problem.  For example, if the physical location of the particle at some specific time is known, say

$$x(t_1) = x_1,$$

where $x_1$ is a known value, this equation can be substituted into the equation for $x$ to obtain

$$x_1 = kt_1 + C,$$

from which

$$C = x_1 - kt_1.$$

Hence,

$$x = kt - kt_1 + x_1,$$

and this is the equation of the specific curve in the family which represents the motion. In many problems the location of the particle is known at $t = 0$, that is,

$$x(0) = x_0,$$

where $x_0$ is a known value; this type of equation is called an *initial condition*. Substituting the initial condition into the equation for $x$,

$$x_0 = (k)(0) + C,$$

from which

$$C = x_0.$$

Hence,

$$x = kt + x_0.$$

From Eq. (5.30),

$$a_x = \frac{dv_x}{dt} = 0.$$

The graphs for this example are shown in Fig. 5.12.

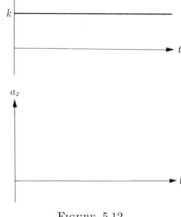

FIGURE 5.12

The foregoing example illustrates the "uniform" type of motion which is a state of equilibrium, as discussed in Art. 4.1. For this motion the speed can be seen to be the ratio of the distance traveled in any time interval and the time elapsed.

The most common type of rectilinear-motion problem is that in which the acceleration $a_x$ is known as a function of $t$ and $v_x(t)$ and $x(t)$ are to be found. This type of problem gives rise to two arbitrary constants $C_1$ and $C_2$ and therefore requires two initial conditions, one on $v_x$ and one on $x$.

EXAMPLE 5.3. A particle starts at the origin with an initial velocity of 9 ft/sec and travels on the $x$-axis in such a way that

$$a_x = 6t - 12,$$

where $a_x$ is in ft/sec$^2$ and $t$ is in sec. Find $v_x(t)$ and $x(t)$.

*Solution.* By Eq. (5.30),

$$dv_x = a_x(t) \, dt,$$

and hence

$$v_x = \int a_x(t) \, dt.$$

In this example,

$$v_x = \int (6t - 12) \, dt = 3t^2 - 12t + C_1.$$

Substituting $v_x(0) = 9$,

$$9 = 3(0)^2 - 12(0) + C_1,$$

from which

$$C_1 = 9.$$

Hence,

$$v_x = 3t^2 - 12t + 9.$$

From Eq. (5.29),

$$x = \int v_x \, dt = \int (3t^2 - 12t + 9) \, dt = t^3 - 6t^2 + 9t + C_2.$$

Substituting $x(0) = 0$,

$$C_2 = 0,$$

and hence

$$x = t^3 - 6t^2 + 9t.$$

Comparing the motion of this example with that of Example 5.1, we can see that the only difference is in the constant term of the $x$-$t$ equation. Thus, the $a_x$-$t$ and $v_x$-$t$ curves for this example are exactly those of Fig. 5.11(b), and the only modification required in the $x$-$t$ curve of Fig. 5.11(b) is that it be displaced upwardly until the ordinate at $t = 0$ is zero. This represents a change in position for any given time, but $u_x$ and $d$ in any time interval are unchanged.

———————

In the foregoing example, $a_x$ is given as a function of $t$. It frequently happens that $a_x$ is known as a function of $x$ rather than $t$. For example, if

$$a_x = -kx,$$

then finding $x(t)$ consists of finding a function which satisfies the initial conditions and the equation

$$\ddot{x} + kx = 0.$$

An equation of this type, which involves a function $x(t)$ and its derivatives, is called a *differential equation*. The solution of differential equations is beyond the scope of this book, although a method of solving problems in which

$$a_x = f(x)$$

is given in Chapter 20.

In some kinematics problems it is necessary to derive the equation for $x$ in terms of $t$ before differentiating to find $v_x$ and $a_x$.

EXAMPLE 5.4. The block $A$ in Fig. 5.13 rests on the floor, and the string $ABC$ runs over a small pulley at $B$. If starting at $t = 0$, the end $C$ of the string is moved to the right with a constant speed $v_0$, find the velocity and acceleration of the block as functions of time.

*Solution.* Figure 5.14 shows the block and string at some time $t$ later than $t = 0$. Measuring $x$ in the vertical direction and letting $L$ be the variable length of the portion $BC$ of the string, it is clear from Fig. 5.14 that

$$L = \sqrt{h^2 + d^2}.$$

Since $x$ is the length of string that has passed over the pulley, it follows that

$$x = L - h,$$

and therefore

$$x = \sqrt{h^2 + d^2} - h.$$

The last equation gives $x$ as a function of the variable $d$, and $d$ must now be expressed in terms of $t$. Since the speed of point $C$ is constant,

$$d = v_0 t,$$

so that

$$x = \sqrt{h^2 + v_0^2 t^2} - h.$$

Once the $x$-$t$ equation is known, the solution is completed in the usual way by differentiation.

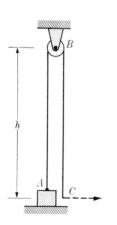

FIGURE 5.13

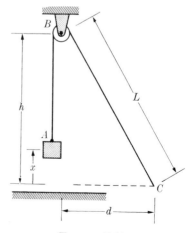

FIGURE 5.14

**5.4 Curvilinear motion in a plane.** For a particle moving on a curved path in a plane, it is desirable to make the $xy$-plane coincide with the plane of the motion. In this case Eqs. (5.22) reduce to

$$x = f_1(t), \qquad y = f_2(t), \tag{5.33}$$

and

$$z = 0$$

at all times. If the parameter $t$ can be eliminated from Eqs. (5.33) to obtain an expression for $y$ in terms of $x$, the resulting equation,

$$y = f(x), \tag{5.34}$$

is called the *explicit equation* of the path.

Motion in the $xy$-plane is characterized by the following reductions of the general equations of Art. 5.2: Eq. (5.21) reduces to

$$\mathbf{r} = x\mathbf{i} + y\mathbf{j}; \tag{5.35}$$

Eq. (5.23) reduces to

$$\mathbf{v} = \dot{x}\mathbf{i} + \dot{y}\mathbf{j}; \tag{5.36}$$

and Eq. (5.24) reduces to

$$\mathbf{a} = \ddot{x}\mathbf{i} + \ddot{y}\mathbf{j}. \tag{5.37}$$

The foregoing equations show that the vector character of $\mathbf{r}$, $\mathbf{v}$, and $\mathbf{a}$ is no longer superfluous as it is in rectilinear motion. There is, however, an important resemblance between rectilinear motion and curvilinear motion, which can be seen in a restatement of Eqs. (5.36) and (5.37) in terms of scalar rectangular components:

$$v_x = \frac{dx}{dt}, \qquad v_y = \frac{dy}{dt}, \tag{5.38}$$

and

$$a_x = \frac{dv_x}{dt} = \frac{d^2x}{dt^2}, \qquad a_y = \frac{dv_y}{dt} = \frac{d^2y}{dt^2}. \tag{5.39}$$

These equations show that the $x$-components of $\mathbf{r}$, $\mathbf{v}$, and $\mathbf{a}$ are related to one another by the same equations as those applicable to rectilinear motion on the $x$-axis, Eqs. (5.29) and (5.30), while the $y$-components are related by a completely separate set of similar equations. Consequently, all the methods of problem-solving developed in Art. 5.3 apply separately to $x$- and $y$-components when the particle is moving in the $xy$-plane.

EXAMPLE 5.5. A particle in the $xy$-plane is moving along the curve

$$y = 2x^2 - 2 \qquad (x \text{ and } y \text{ in in.})$$

in such a way that

$$x = 4t \qquad (x \text{ in in., } t \text{ in sec}).$$

(a) Find its velocity and acceleration when $t = \frac{1}{4}$ sec. (b) Find its displacement between $t = 0$ and $t = \frac{1}{4}$ sec.

*Solution.* (a) Substituting the equation for $x$ into the equation of the path gives $y$ as a function of $t$, that is,

$$y = 32t^2 - 2.$$

Hence,

$$\dot{x} = 4, \qquad \dot{y} = 64t,$$

and

$$\ddot{x} = 0, \qquad \ddot{y} = 64.$$

Therefore,

$$\mathbf{v}(t) = 4\mathbf{i} + 64t\mathbf{j},$$

and

$$\mathbf{a}(t) = 64\mathbf{j}.$$

At $t = \frac{1}{4}$ sec,

$$\mathbf{v}(\tfrac{1}{4}) = 4\mathbf{i} + 16\mathbf{j} \text{ in./sec},$$

and

$$\mathbf{a}(\tfrac{1}{4}) = 64\mathbf{j} \text{ in./sec}^2.$$

(b) By Eq. (5.28),

$$\mathbf{u} = \mathbf{r}(\tfrac{1}{4}) - \mathbf{r}(0).$$

But

$$\mathbf{r}(t) = 4t\mathbf{i} + (32t^2 - 2)\mathbf{j},$$

and thus

$$\mathbf{r}(\tfrac{1}{4}) = \mathbf{i} + 0\mathbf{j} \text{ in.}$$

and

$$\mathbf{r}(0) = 0\mathbf{i} - 2\mathbf{j} \text{ in.}$$

Finally, then,

$$\mathbf{u} = \mathbf{i} + 2\mathbf{j} \text{ in.}$$

Figure 5.15 shows the path of the particle and the location of the particle at $t = \frac{1}{4}$ sec. The vectors $\mathbf{r}$, $\mathbf{v}$, and $\mathbf{a}$ at $t = \frac{1}{4}$ sec and the vector $\mathbf{u}$ between $t = 0$ and $t = \frac{1}{4}$ sec are also shown in the figure.

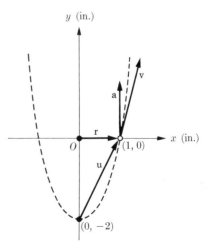

FIGURE 5.15

The slope of the vector **v** at any time is given by

$$\tan \theta = \frac{v_y}{v_x} = 16t = 4x,$$

while the slope of the curve is

$$\frac{dy}{dx} = 4x,$$

and this shows that **v** is tangent to the curve for all locations of the particle.

---

Many curvilinear-motion problems involve integration, but, if rectangular coordinates are used, the integration can be accomplished in a simple manner by dealing with $x$- and $y$-components separately.

---

EXAMPLE 5.6.  A particle travels in the $xy$-plane in such a way that

$$\dot{x} = -\frac{x_0}{t_0} \sin \frac{t}{t_0},$$

$$\ddot{y} = -\frac{v_0}{t_0} \sin \frac{t}{t_0},$$

where $x_0$, $v_0$, and $t_0$ are known positive constants. If $x(0) = x_0$, $y(0) = 0$, and $\dot{y}(0) = v_0$, (a) find $\mathbf{a}(t)$ and $\mathbf{a}(0)$, (b) find $\mathbf{v}(t)$ and $\mathbf{v}(0)$, and (c) write the equation of the path.

*Solution.*  (a) By Eq. (5.37),

$$\mathbf{a}(t) = -\frac{x_0}{t_0^2} \cos \frac{t}{t_0} \mathbf{i} - \frac{v_0}{t_0} \sin \frac{t}{t_0} \mathbf{j},$$

and therefore

$$\mathbf{a}(0) = -\frac{x_0}{t_0^2} \mathbf{i}.$$

(b) By integration of $\ddot{y}$,

$$\dot{y} = v_0 \cos \frac{t}{t_0} + C_1,$$

and, substituting $\dot{y}(0) = v_0$,

$$C_1 = 0.$$

Thus, by Eq. (5.36),

$$\mathbf{v}(t) = -\frac{x_0}{t_0} \sin \frac{t}{t_0} \mathbf{i} + v_0 \cos \frac{t}{t_0} \mathbf{j},$$

and therefore

$$\mathbf{v}(0) = v_0 \mathbf{j}.$$

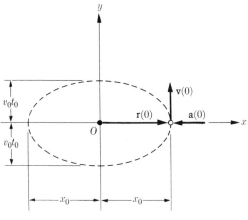

FIGURE 5.16

(c) Integrating $\dot{x}$ gives

$$x = x_0 \cos \frac{t}{t_0} + C_2,$$

and, by substitution of $x(0) = x_0$,

$$C_2 = 0.$$

Integrating $\dot{y}$ gives

$$y = v_0 t_0 \sin \frac{t}{t_0} + C_3,$$

and, by substitution of $y(0) = 0$,

$$C_3 = 0.$$

Hence,

$$\frac{x}{x_0} = \cos \frac{t}{t_0},$$

$$\frac{y}{v_0 t_0} = \sin \frac{t}{t_0}.$$

An easy way to eliminate the parameter $t$ from these equations is to square both equations and add them together to obtain

$$\frac{x^2}{x_0^2} + \frac{y^2}{v_0^2 t_0^2} = 1.$$

This, since $y$ is not given explicitly in terms of $x$, is called the *implicit equation* of the path. It is the equation of an ellipse with semiaxes of lengths $x_0$ and $v_0 t_0$, as shown in Fig. 5.16. (The vectors $\mathbf{r}$, $\mathbf{v}$, and $\mathbf{a}$ at $t = 0$ are shown in this figure.) In this case $y$ is not a single-valued function of $x$, but $x$, $y$, and $\mathbf{r}$ are all single-valued functions of $t$.

**5.5 Curvilinear motion in space.** If the path of the particle is a space curve, the general equations of Art. 5.2 must be used in analyzing the motion, since all three components of $\mathbf{r}$, $\mathbf{v}$, and $\mathbf{a}$ must be included.

---

EXAMPLE 5.7. A particle travels in such a way that

$$a_x = 6, \qquad a_y = 0, \qquad a_z = \frac{\pi^2}{2} \cos \frac{\pi}{3} t,$$

where the acceleration components are in ft/sec$^2$ and $t$ is in sec. If $v_x(0) = v_y(0) = -5$ ft/sec, $v_z(0) = 0$, and $x(0) = y(0) = z(0) = 0$, find the position vector at $t = 3$ sec.

*Solution.* By integration,

$$v_x = 6t + C_1, \qquad v_y = C_2, \qquad v_z = \frac{3\pi}{2} \sin \frac{\pi}{3} t + C_3.$$

Using the initial conditions on the velocity components,

$$v_x = 6t - 5, \qquad v_y = -5, \qquad v_z = \frac{3\pi}{2} \sin \frac{\pi}{3} t.$$

Integrating again,

$$x = 3t^2 - 5t + C_4, \qquad y = -5t + C_5, \qquad z = -\frac{9}{2} \cos \frac{\pi}{3} t + C_6,$$

and, using the initial conditions on the coordinates,

$$x = 3t^2 - 5t, \qquad y = -5t, \qquad z = -\frac{9}{2} \cos \frac{\pi}{3} t + \frac{9}{2}.$$

Hence,

$$x(3) = 3(3)^2 - 5(3) = 12 \text{ ft},$$
$$y(3) = -5(3) = -15 \text{ ft},$$
$$z(3) = -\tfrac{9}{2} \cos \pi + \tfrac{9}{2} = 9 \text{ ft},$$

and

$$\mathbf{r}(3) = 12\mathbf{i} - 15\mathbf{j} + 9\mathbf{k} \text{ ft}.$$

**5.6 Cylindrical coordinates.** Another useful coordinate system for specifying the position of a particle $P$ in a frame of reference is the *cylindrical coordinate system*. This system can be defined in relation to the basic cartesian system as shown in Fig. 5.17. The coordinate $\rho$ is the distance from the $z$-axis to $P$ and is given, according to the Pythagorean theorem, by

$$\rho = \sqrt{x^2 + y^2} \,.$$

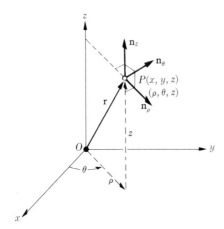

FIGURE 5.17

The coordinate $\theta$ is the angle in radians measured from the $zx$-plane to a plane through $P$ and the $z$-axis (the dashed plane in Fig. 5.17). From trigonometry,

$$\theta = \arctan \frac{y}{x},$$

$\theta$ being measured counterclockwise from the $x$-axis when viewed in the negative $z$-direction. The coordinate $z$ is the distance from the $xy$-plane to $P$ and is the same as the $z$-coordinate in the rectangular system.

The three independent coordinates of a point in space are now $\rho$, $\theta$, $z$ instead of $x$, $y$, $z$. In terms of analytic geometry, $\rho =$ constant is the equation of a circular cylinder whose axis is the $z$-axis, this property of the coordinate system being the source of its name. Similarly, $\theta =$ constant is the equation of a plane through the $z$-axis, and $z =$ constant is the equation of a plane parallel to the $xy$-plane. The specific equation $z = 0$ is the equation of the $xy$-plane itself, and points in this plane are located by the two coordinates $\rho$ and $\theta$, which are called *polar coordinates* when $z = 0$.

Three unit vectors $\mathbf{n}_\rho$, $\mathbf{n}_\theta$, $\mathbf{n}_z$ are established at each point for the purpose of expressing vectors in terms of their components in the new coordinate system. At any given point (such as $P$ in Fig. 5.17), the three unit vectors are tangent to the lines of intersection of the three surfaces

$$\rho = \text{constant}, \quad \theta = \text{constant}, \quad z = \text{constant}$$

passing through the point. Hence $\mathbf{n}_\rho$ is a unit vector in the "radial" direction, $\mathbf{n}_\theta$ is one in the "transverse" direction (i.e., perpendicular to the plane $\theta =$ constant), and $\mathbf{n}_z$ is the same vector as $\mathbf{k}$ in the rectangular system. As $P$ changes its location, the vectors $\mathbf{n}_\rho$ and $\mathbf{n}_\theta$ change in direction while $\mathbf{n}_z$

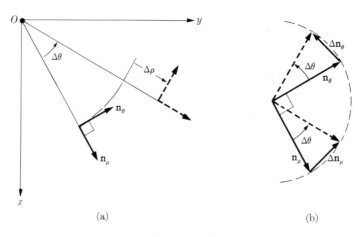

FIGURE 5.18

remains constant. Any vector associated with the moving point $P$ can be resolved into three components in the directions of the unit vectors, even though the lines to which the vector must be projected are constantly changing in direction.

If $P$ is a moving particle, $\rho$, $\theta$, and $z$ are functions of $t$, that is,

$$\rho = f_1(t), \qquad \theta = f_2(t), \qquad z = f_3(t). \tag{5.40}$$

Using Fig. 5.17 and the rules for addition of vectors and multiplication of a vector by a scalar, we can express the position vector $\mathbf{r}$ in terms of its components by

$$\mathbf{r} = \rho\mathbf{n}_\rho + z\mathbf{n}_z.$$

(The dependence of $\mathbf{r}$ on $\theta$ is implicit in its dependence on $\mathbf{n}_\rho$, which is a function of $\theta$.) Therefore,

$$\mathbf{v} = \frac{d\mathbf{r}}{dt} = \rho\,\frac{d\mathbf{n}_\rho}{dt} + \dot\rho\mathbf{n}_\rho + \dot z\mathbf{n}_z,$$

the derivative of $\mathbf{n}_z$ being a null vector. This equation for $\mathbf{v}$ can be put into a more useful form by expressing the derivative of $\mathbf{n}_\rho$ in terms of the unit vectors $\mathbf{n}_\rho$, $\mathbf{n}_\theta$, $\mathbf{n}_z$. To accomplish this, consider the changes produced in $\rho$, $\theta$, $\mathbf{n}_\rho$, and $\mathbf{n}_\theta$ by an increment of time $\Delta t$, as shown in Fig. 5.18(a). Figure 5.18(b) shows the unit vectors from Fig. 5.18(a) with their tails all at the same point. Since $\mathbf{n}_\rho$ is a function of $\theta$, and $\theta$ in turn is a function of $t$, Eq. (5.11) can be used to introduce the variable $\theta$ into the derivation as follows:

$$\frac{d\mathbf{n}_\rho}{dt} = \frac{d\mathbf{n}_\rho}{d\theta}\,\dot\theta.$$

But, by definition,

$$\frac{d\mathbf{n}_\rho}{d\theta} = \lim_{\Delta\theta\to 0} \frac{\Delta\mathbf{n}_\rho}{\Delta\theta}.$$

As the limit is approached, $\Delta\mathbf{n}_\rho$ approaches the direction of the tangent to the circle of Fig. 5.18(b), which is the direction of $\mathbf{n}_\theta$, and the magnitude of $\Delta\mathbf{n}_\rho$ approaches the arc length $(1)(\Delta\theta)$, since the radius of the circle is unity and $\Delta\theta$ is in radians. Hence, using Eq. (2.16),

$$\frac{d\mathbf{n}_\rho}{d\theta} = \lim_{\Delta\theta\to 0} \frac{(1)(\Delta\theta)\mathbf{n}_\theta}{\Delta\theta} = \lim_{\Delta\theta\to 0} \mathbf{n}_\theta = \mathbf{n}_\theta,$$

and therefore

$$\frac{d\mathbf{n}_\rho}{dt} = \dot\theta\mathbf{n}_\theta.$$

Substituting this equation into the expression for $\mathbf{v}$ gives

$$\mathbf{v} = \dot\rho\mathbf{n}_\rho + \rho\dot\theta\mathbf{n}_\theta + \dot z\mathbf{n}_z, \tag{5.41}$$

or, to restate this result,

$$v_\rho = \frac{d\rho}{dt}, \qquad v_\theta = \rho\frac{d\theta}{dt}, \qquad v_z = \frac{dz}{dt}. \tag{5.42}$$

The speed $v$ of the particle is given by

$$v = \sqrt{v_\rho^2 + v_\theta^2 + v_z^2}.$$

Equation (5.41) can now be differentiated to find $\mathbf{a}$:

$$\mathbf{a} = \left(\dot\rho\frac{d\mathbf{n}_\rho}{dt} + \ddot\rho\mathbf{n}_\rho\right) + \left[(\rho\dot\theta)\frac{d\mathbf{n}_\theta}{dt} + (\rho\ddot\theta + \dot\rho\dot\theta)\mathbf{n}_\theta\right] + (\ddot z\mathbf{n}_z).$$

To express $d\mathbf{n}_\theta/dt$ in terms of the unit vectors, Fig. 5.18(b) and Eq. (2.16) are used again to obtain

$$\frac{d\mathbf{n}_\theta}{d\theta} = \lim_{\Delta\theta\to 0} \frac{\Delta\mathbf{n}_\theta}{\Delta\theta} = \lim_{\Delta\theta\to 0} \frac{-(1)(\Delta\theta)\mathbf{n}_\rho}{\Delta\theta} = -\mathbf{n}_\rho.$$

Thus,

$$\frac{d\mathbf{n}_\theta}{dt} = -\dot\theta\mathbf{n}_\rho.$$

The equations for $d\mathbf{n}_\rho/dt$ and $d\mathbf{n}_\theta/dt$ can also be derived by expressing $\mathbf{n}_\rho$ and $\mathbf{n}_\theta$ (Fig. 5.17) in terms of $\mathbf{i}$ and $\mathbf{j}$ as follows:

$$\begin{aligned} \mathbf{n}_\rho &= \cos\theta\mathbf{i} + \sin\theta\mathbf{j}, \\ \mathbf{n}_\theta &= -\sin\theta\mathbf{i} + \cos\theta\mathbf{j}. \end{aligned} \tag{5.43}$$

(Note the dependence of $\mathbf{n}_\rho$ on $\theta$ referred to previously.) Differentiating,

$$\frac{d\mathbf{n}_\rho}{dt} = -\dot{\theta} \sin \theta \mathbf{i} + \dot{\theta} \cos \theta \mathbf{j} = \dot{\theta}\mathbf{n}_\theta,$$

$$\frac{d\mathbf{n}_\theta}{dt} = -\dot{\theta} \cos \theta \mathbf{i} - \dot{\theta} \sin \theta \mathbf{j} = -\dot{\theta}\mathbf{n}_\rho.$$

Substituting into the expression for $\mathbf{a}$ and regrouping terms gives

$$\mathbf{a} = (\ddot{\rho} - \rho\dot{\theta}^2)\mathbf{n}_\rho + (\rho\ddot{\theta} + 2\dot{\rho}\dot{\theta})\mathbf{n}_\theta + \ddot{z}\mathbf{n}_z, \qquad (5.44)$$

or, stated alternatively,

$$a_\rho = \frac{d^2\rho}{dt^2} - \rho\left(\frac{d\theta}{dt}\right)^2, \qquad a_\theta = \rho\frac{d^2\theta}{dt^2} + 2\frac{d\rho}{dt}\frac{d\theta}{dt}, \qquad a_z = \frac{d^2z}{dt^2}. \qquad (5.45)$$

Equations (5.42) and (5.45) show that the $\rho$- and $\theta$-components of $\mathbf{v}$ and $\mathbf{a}$ cannot be analyzed separately by different sets of equations, as was true for rectangular components. If the components of $\mathbf{a}$ are given as functions of $t$, the components of $\mathbf{v}$ and $\mathbf{r}$ cannot be found by simple integration. On the other hand, if the coordinates of the particle are given as functions of $t$, both $\mathbf{v}$ and $\mathbf{a}$ can be found by differentiating in accordance with Eqs. (5.41) and (5.44).

---

EXAMPLE 5.8. A particle moves in space in such a way that

$$\rho = 6, \qquad \theta = \pi t, \qquad z = 2t,$$

where $\rho$ and $z$ are in in., $\theta$ is in radians, and $t$ is in sec. Find $\mathbf{v}(t)$ and $\mathbf{a}(t)$.

*Solution.* By Eq. (5.41),

$$\mathbf{v}(t) = 6\pi\mathbf{n}_\theta + 2\mathbf{n}_z,$$

and, by Eq. (5.44),

$$\mathbf{a}(t) = -6\pi^2\mathbf{n}_\rho.$$

The units of $v_\theta$ and $v_z$ are in./sec, while those of $a_\rho$ are in./sec$^2$.

---

A very common type of motion is that of a particle on a circular path parallel to the $xy$-plane, as shown in Fig. 5.19. If the radius of the circle is $b$ and the constant height above the $xy$-plane is $h$, Eqs. (5.40) reduce to

$$\rho = b, \qquad \theta = f_2(t), \qquad z = h.$$

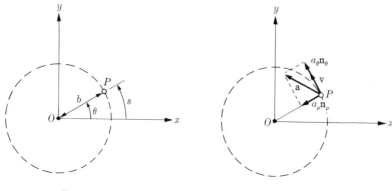

FIGURE 5.19                          FIGURE 5.20

By Eqs. (5.42),

$$v_\rho = 0, \qquad v_\theta = b\dot\theta, \qquad v_z = 0, \tag{5.46}$$

and, by Eqs. (5.45),

$$a_\rho = -b\dot\theta^2, \qquad a_\theta = b\ddot\theta, \qquad a_z = 0. \tag{5.47}$$

The vectors **v** and **a** for this motion are shown in Fig. 5.20. Referring again to Fig. 5.19, we see that the angle $\theta$ can be expressed in terms of the distance $s$ measured counterclockwise along the circle from the $zx$-plane by

$$\theta = \frac{s}{b},$$

from which

$$\dot\theta = \frac{\dot s}{b} \tag{5.48}$$

and

$$\ddot\theta = \frac{\ddot s}{b}. \tag{5.49}$$

Substituting Eq. (5.48) into Eqs. (5.46), we have

$$v_\rho = 0, \qquad v_\theta = \dot s, \qquad v_z = 0. \tag{5.50}$$

The speed $v$ is thus given by

$$v = |\dot s|. \tag{5.51}$$

Substituting Eqs. (5.48), (5.49), and (5.51) into Eqs. (5.47),

$$a_\rho = -\frac{\dot s^2}{b} = -\frac{v^2}{b}, \qquad a_\theta = \ddot s, \qquad a_z = 0. \tag{5.52}$$

A special case of circular motion occurs when $\dot{s} = k$, where $k$ is a known constant. This means that $\dot{\theta} = k/b$ and $\ddot{\theta} = 0$, and hence, by Eqs. (5.47) and (5.52),

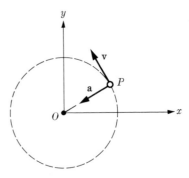

FIGURE 5.21

$$a_\rho = -\frac{k^2}{b} = -\frac{v^2}{b},$$
$$a_\theta = 0, \qquad a_z = 0.$$

(5.53)

The vectors **v** and **a** for this special case are shown in Fig. 5.21. Note that $v$ and $a$ are constant scalars, but **v** and **a** are not constant vectors.

---

EXAMPLE 5.9. A car starts from rest and travels on a circular track with a radius of 100 ft in accordance with the equation

$$s = 6t^2,$$

where $s$ is the distance measured counterclockwise along the track from the starting point in ft and $t$ is the time in sec. Find the velocity and acceleration of the car when $s = 150$ ft.

*Solution.* By Eqs. (5.50),
$$\mathbf{v}(t) = 12t\mathbf{n}_\theta,$$

and, by Eqs. (5.52),

$$\mathbf{a}(t) = -\frac{144t^2}{100}\mathbf{n}_\rho + 12\mathbf{n}_\theta.$$

When $s = 150$ ft, the given equation for $s$ yields

$$t = \sqrt{150/6} = 5 \text{ sec},$$

and, at this time,
$$\mathbf{v}(5) = 60\mathbf{n}_\theta \text{ ft/sec}$$

and
$$\mathbf{a}(5) = -36\mathbf{n}_\rho + 12\mathbf{n}_\theta \text{ ft/sec}^2.$$

The results of this problem are in terms of $\mathbf{n}_\rho$ and $\mathbf{n}_\theta$. This means that the absolute directions (relative to a fixed frame of reference) of the vectors $\mathbf{v}(5)$ and $\mathbf{a}(5)$ are not yet known, since the directions of $\mathbf{n}_\rho$ and $\mathbf{n}_\theta$ at $t = 5$ have not been explicitly determined. To transform the results to the basic cartesian coordinate system, it is necessary to substitute Eqs. (5.43) into them. Then, evaluating $\theta(5)$, the vectors may be specified in terms of **i** and **j**.

PROBLEMS

5.1 Show that the derivative of a vector with constant magnitude is perpendicular to the vector and that the derivative of a vector with constant direction is parallel to the vector.

5.2 Show: (a) by the $\Delta$-process, and (b) by using Eq. (5.10), that, if $C$ is a scalar constant and $\mathbf{V}$ is a vector function of $S$, then

$$\frac{d}{dS}(C\mathbf{V}) = C\frac{d\mathbf{V}}{dS}.$$

5.3 Given:
$$\mathbf{F} = 3xy\mathbf{i} + 5y\mathbf{j} - 5xyz\mathbf{k},$$
$$x = 2t, \quad y = 4t^2, \quad z = 0.$$

Find $d\mathbf{F}/dt$.

5.4 A particle travels on the $x$-axis in such a way that

$$x = t^3 - 12t + 5,$$

where $x$ is in ft and $t$ is in sec. (a) Find $v_x(t)$ and $a_x(t)$. (b) Considering only positive values of $t$, determine the values of $x$ and $a_x$ when $v_x = 0$. (c) Find the displacement and the distance traveled between $t = 1$ sec and $t = 3$ sec.

[*Ans.:* (b) $x = -11$ ft, $a_x = 12$ ft/sec$^2$; (c) $u_x = 2$ ft, $d = 12$ ft.]

5.5 An elevator travels upward in such a way that its height $h$ is given, during the first three seconds of motion, by

$$h = 3t^2 + 2t^3,$$

where $h$ is in ft and $t$ is in sec. Find its velocity and acceleration as functions of $t$ for the first three seconds. Draw graphs of height, velocity, and acceleration vs. $t$ for the first three seconds.

5.6 A particle travels on the $x$-axis in such a way that

$$v_x = -6t + 4,$$

where $v_x$ is in ft/sec and $t$ is in sec. If $x(0) = -3$ ft, (a) find $x(t)$ and $a_x(t)$, (b) find the maximum value of $x$, and (c) draw graphs of $x$, $v_x$, and $a_x$ vs. $t$.

[*Ans.:* (b) $-1.67$ ft.]

5.7 A particle travels on the $x$-axis in such a way that

$$v_x = -A\omega \sin \omega t,$$

where $A$ and $\omega$ are constants. If $x(0) = x_0$, find $x(t)$ and $a_x(t)$. Express $a_x$ as a function of $x$.

5.8 A particle moves on the $x$-axis in such a way that

$$a_x = -10 \text{ ft/sec}^2$$

at all times. If, when $t = 5$ sec, $v_x = -30$ ft/sec and $x = 0$, (a) find the speed when $t = 3$ sec, (b) find the displacement between $t = 0$ and $t = 5$ sec, (c) find the maximum value of $x$.

[*Ans.:* (a) 10 ft/sec; (b) $-25$ ft; (c) 45 ft.]

5.9 A car starts from rest at $t = 0$ and $x = 0$ and travels with a constant acceleration, i.e.,

$$a_x = k,$$

until a time $t_1$ when $v_x = v_{x1}$ and $x = x_1$. Derive the two equations for:

(a) $v_{x1}$, $x_1$ in terms of $k$, $t_1$,     (b) $v_{x1}$, $t_1$ in terms of $k$, $x_1$,
(c) $x_1$, $t_1$ in terms of $k$, $v_{x1}$,     (d) $k$, $v_{x1}$ in terms of $x_1$, $t_1$,
(e) $k$, $x_1$ in terms of $v_{x1}$, $t_1$,     (f) $k$, $t_1$ in terms of $v_{x1}$, $x_1$.

5.10 A car is traveling in a straight line with a constant speed of 30 ft/sec when the brakes are applied. Assuming a constant acceleration of $-10$ ft/sec$^2$, find: (a) the time it takes after the brakes are applied for the car to stop, and (b) the distance the car travels before stopping.

[*Ans.:* (a) 3 sec; (b) 45 ft.]

5.11 A particle is in rectilinear motion along the $x$-axis. If $a_x = k$ (a constant), $v_x(0) = v_{x0}$, and $x(0) = x_0$, show that

$$v_x^2 = v_{x0}^2 + 2k(x - x_0).$$

5.12 A particle travels on the $x$-axis in such a way that

$$a_x = 10t,$$

where $a_x$ is in ft/sec$^2$ and $t$ is in sec. If $v_x(0) = -5$ ft/sec and $x(3) = 20$ ft, find $v_x(t)$ and $x(t)$. What is the distance traveled between $t = 0$ and $t = 2$ sec?

[*Ans.:* $d = 10$ ft.]

5.13 An aircraft carrier uses an arresting device which imparts a linearly varying acceleration to a landing aircraft, that is, $a_x = kt$. (a) What must be the value of $k$ if the device is to stop a plane going 300 ft/sec in the positive $x$-direction in 5 sec? (b) How much distance is required for the landing? (c) What is the greatest magnitude achieved by the acceleration during the landing?

5.14 The acceleration of a rocket weighing 5000 lb is given, during the first 20 sec of motion, by

$$a_x = -15t^2 + 300t,$$

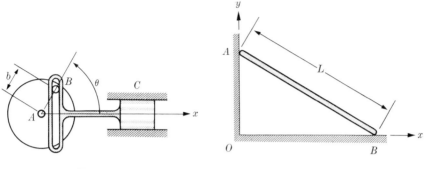

FIGURE 5.22                                    FIGURE 5.23

where $a_x$ is in ft/sec$^2$ and $t$ is in sec. (a) If the rocket starts from rest, what is its speed after 10 sec of motion? (b) How far does the rocket travel during the first 10 sec of motion?

[*Ans.:* (a) 10,000 ft/sec; (b) 37,500 ft.]

5.15 The mechanism in Fig. 5.22 consists of a flywheel mounted on a fixed shaft at $A$ and a piston $C$ which is constrained to move on the $x$-axis. The peg $B$ is attached to the flywheel and drives a slotted arm connected rigidly to the piston. If the flywheel turns in such a way that $\theta = kt$, where $k$ is a positive constant, select an origin and derive, for the piston, an equation for $x$ as a function of $t$. Then differentiate twice to find $v_x(t)$ and $a_x(t)$ for the piston. Sketch curves to show the variation of $v_x$ and $a_x$ with $t$ during the first revolution of the flywheel.

5.16 A slender rod $AB$ of length $L$ moves in such a way that end $A$ remains in contact with a vertical wall and end $B$ remains in contact with a horizontal floor (Fig. 5.23). Starting with the rod in a horizontal position at $t = 0$, end $A$ is moved up the wall with a constant speed $v_0$. Find $x$, $v_x$, and $a_x$ of end $B$ as functions of time, and draw $x$-$t$ and $v_x$-$t$ curves for the period of time between $t = 0$ and the time $B$ arrives at $O$.

$$\left[ Ans.:\ x = (L^2 - v_0^2 t^2)^{1/2}, \right.$$

$$v_x = - \frac{v_0^2 t}{(L^2 - v_0^2 t^2)^{1/2}},$$

$$\left. a_x = - \frac{v_0^2 L^2}{(L^2 - v_0^2 t^2)^{3/2}}. \right]$$

5.17 A particle moves in the $xy$-plane in such a way that

$$x = 2(1 + t)^2, \qquad y = -3(1 - t)^2,$$

where $x$ and $y$ are in ft and $t$ is in sec. (a) Find its velocity and acceleration when $t = 1$ sec. (b) Find its displacement between $t = 0$ and $t = 2$ sec.

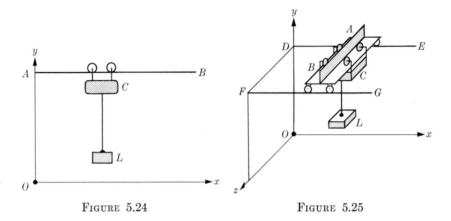

FIGURE 5.24                    FIGURE 5.25

5.18 A particle moves in the $xy$-plane in such a way that

$$a_x = 0, \qquad a_y = -g,$$

where $g$ is a known positive constant. If $v_x(0) = v_{x0}$, $v_y(0) = v_{y0}$, and $x(0) = y(0) = 0$, find the equation of the path and sketch the path.

$$\left[ Ans.: y = -\frac{1}{2} \frac{g}{v_{x0}^2} x^2 + \frac{v_{y0}}{v_{x0}} x. \right]$$

5.19 A particle starts from rest at the origin and moves in the $xy$-plane in such a way that

$$v_x = 6 \sin 2t, \qquad a_y = -3t + 2,$$

where $v_x$ is in ft/sec, $a_y$ is in ft/sec$^2$, and $t$ is in sec. (a) Find the acceleration of the particle when $t = 0$. (b) Find the $x$- and $y$-coordinates of the particle as functions of $t$.

5.20 The crane $C$ shown in Fig. 5.24 picks up a load $L$ at $O$ and moves along the track $AB$ in the positive $x$-direction at a constant speed of 5 ft/sec. In the meantime the rate at which the crane takes in cable starts from zero, and, during each second, this rate increases uniformly by 2 ft of cable per second. Assuming that the cable always remains vertical, find the velocity and acceleration of the load after 3 sec. If the crane is 25 ft above the floor (the $x$-axis), when and where will the load reach the crane?

[Ans.: $\mathbf{v}(3) = 5\mathbf{i} + 6\mathbf{j}$ ft/sec, $\mathbf{a}(3) = 2\mathbf{j}$ ft/sec$^2$.]

5.21 A particle moves in space in such a way that

$$x = 2(1 + t)^2, \qquad y = -3(1 - t)^2, \qquad z = 5t,$$

where $x$, $y$, and $z$ are in ft and $t$ is in sec. (a) Find its velocity and acceleration when $t = 1$ sec. (b) Find its displacement between $t = 0$ and $t = 2$ sec.

5.22 The crane $C$ in Fig. 5.25 is supported on a beam $AB$ which rolls on the tracks $DE$ and $FG$. The crane picks up a load $L$ at $O$ and moves along the

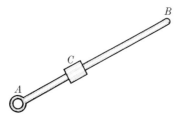

FIGURE 5.26

beam from $A$ to $B$ at a constant rate of 5 ft of beam per second while the beam moves with a constant speed of 3 ft/sec in the positive $x$-direction. In the meantime the rate at which the crane takes in cable starts from zero, and, during each second, this rate increases uniformly by 2 ft of cable per second. Assuming that the cable always remains vertical, find the velocity and acceleration of the load after 3 sec. If the crane is 25 ft above the floor (the $zx$-plane), when and where will the load reach the crane?

[*Ans.:* $\mathbf{v}(3) = 3\mathbf{i} + 6\mathbf{j} + 5\mathbf{k}$ ft/sec, $\mathbf{a}(3) = 2\mathbf{j}$ ft/sec$^2$.]

5.23 A particle moves in the $\rho\theta$-plane in such a way that

$$\rho = 6t^2 - t^3, \qquad \theta = \frac{\pi}{6} t,$$

where $\rho$ is in in., $\theta$ is in rad, and $t$ is in sec. (a) Find the velocity when $t = 6$ sec. (b) Find the acceleration when $t = 6$ sec.

5.24 The horizontal shaft $AB$ in Fig. 5.26 rotates about a vertical axis at $A$ with a constant angular speed of one revolution per second (counterclockwise). At the same time the small block $C$ moves from $A$ to $B$ at a constant rate of 5 in. of shaft per second. Find the velocity and speed of the block when it is 10 in. from $A$.

[*Ans.:* $\mathbf{v} = 5\mathbf{n}_\rho + 20\pi\mathbf{n}_\theta$ in./sec, $v = 63.0$ in./sec.]

5.25 A particle moves on a circular path of 10-ft radius in such a way that $\dot{s} = -4t + 8$, where $s$ is the distance in ft measured CCW along the path from the starting point and $t$ is the time in sec measured from the starting time. (a) Find the velocity and acceleration when $t = 3$ sec. (b) Find the velocity after the particle has traveled 40 ft.

# CHAPTER 6

## KINETICS OF A PARTICLE

**6.1 Introduction.** Most of the particles considered in Chapter 5 are not in equilibrium, and the question arises as to what forces must be applied to a particle to produce the various types of motion discussed there. The converse question, what type of motion is produced by a given set of forces, is equally important.

**6.2 Newton's Second Law.** By definition, the *momentum* of a particle is the product of its mass $m$ (a positive scalar) and its velocity $\mathbf{v}$ (a vector). Thus, the momentum $m\mathbf{v}$ is a vector which is parallel to $\mathbf{v}$ and therefore is tangent to the path of the particle.

Using the terminology and notation introduced in Chapters 2, 3, 5, and the present chapter, Newton's Second Law (Art. 1.5) may be stated as follows:

NEWTON'S SECOND LAW: *The resultant force acting on a particle is equal to the derivative of the momentum with respect to time, i.e.,*

$$\mathbf{R} = \frac{d}{dt}(m\mathbf{v}). \tag{6.1}$$

This is a fundamental physical law first postulated by Newton and verified countless times since by experiment. Like any other physical law, it applies in an exact sense only to idealized situations and is useful only for a limited group of phenomena. The area of applicability is very broad in this case, however, and practically all motion problems in engineering can be solved with sufficient accuracy by this law and the equations derived from it.

In Newtonian mechanics the mass of a particle, $m$, is assumed to be a constant quantity. (In the theory of relativity, $m$ changes with the speed of the particle and approaches infinity as the speed approaches the speed of light, but for all ranges of speed encountered in engineering applications this change in $m$ is completely negligible.) By Eq. (5.10), therefore,

$$\mathbf{R} = m\frac{d\mathbf{v}}{dt},$$

and, substituting Eq. (5.19),

$$\mathbf{R} = m\mathbf{a}. \tag{6.2}$$

This form of Newton's Second Law is
the one most often used and remembered. It implies that the acceleration **a** induced by a resultant force **R**
is always parallel to **R**, even if the
direction of **R** is changing with time.
Figure 6.1 shows the parallelism between **R** and **a** for a particle moving
under the action of three forces. By
Eqs. (3.1), (5.20), and (6.2),

$$\mathbf{F}_1 + \mathbf{F}_2 + \mathbf{F}_3 = m\,\frac{d^2\mathbf{r}}{dt^2}.$$

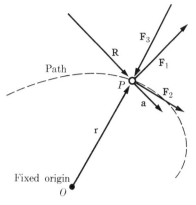

FIGURE 6.1

Equation (6.2) implies also that the vectors **R** and $m\mathbf{a}$ have equal magnitudes, i.e.,

$$R = ma. \tag{6.3}$$

Although Eq. (6.3) follows from Eq. (6.2), it is only a partial statement of
Newton's Second Law.

In the English-speaking countries, engineers use two systems of units,
called the *British absolute system* and the *British gravitational system*. In
the absolute system, the unit of mass is the pound, and the mass of the
standard body mentioned in Art. 1.3 is defined as 1 lb. To make Eq. (6.3)
dimensionally correct, $R$ must be measured in lb-ft/sec², a unit which is
called a *poundal* (so that one poundal is the magnitude of the force required to give the standard body an acceleration with magnitude of 1
ft/sec²). In the gravitational system, the unit of force is the pound, and
1 lb is defined as the force exerted by the earth on the standard body at a
certain location on the surface of the earth. Equation (6.3) now requires
that $m$ be measured in lb-sec²/ft, a unit which is called a *slug* (so that one
slug is the mass of a particle which would be given an acceleration with
magnitude of 1 ft/sec² by a force with magnitude of 1 lb). The two systems of units derive their names from the fact that the former system
would be usable anywhere in the universe, while the latter depends on
the attraction of the earth for its definition. In spite of this, engineers
usually employ the gravitational system.

To obtain an idea of the size of the units of poundals and slugs, it is
helpful to study the behavior of the standard body as it falls freely in the
earth's gravitational field. Galileo discovered that, neglecting air resistance, all bodies fall with the same constant acceleration at the same location on the earth's surface. The magnitude of this acceleration is about
32.2 ft/sec² (although it varies slightly at different points on the earth's
surface and changes with large changes in altitude). Calling the magnitude

TABLE 6.1

| | Body A | | Body B (standard body) | | Body C | |
|---|---|---|---|---|---|---|
| | Absolute system | Gravitational system | Absolute system | Gravitational system | Absolute system | Gravitational system |
| Mass | $\dfrac{1}{32.2}$ lb | $\dfrac{1}{(32.2)^2}$ slugs | 1 lb* | $\dfrac{1}{32.2}$ slugs | 32.2 lb | 1 slug* |
| Magnitude of force required for acceleration with magnitude of 1 ft/sec² | $\dfrac{1}{32.2}$ pdl | $\dfrac{1}{(32.2)^2}$ lb | 1 pdl* | $\dfrac{1}{32.2}$ lb | 32.2 pdl | 1 lb* |
| Weight, i.e., magnitude of force required for acceleration with magnitude of 32.2 ft/sec² | 1 pdl* | $\dfrac{1}{32.2}$ lb | 32.2 pdl | 1 lb* | $(32.2)^2$ pdl | 32.2 lb |

* The units of force and mass mentioned in Art. 1.4.

of the acceleration due to gravity $g$ and the magnitude of the weight force $W$, we find that Eq. (6.3) requires that

$$W = mg. \tag{6.4}$$

In the absolute system, $m$ is 1 lb for the standard body, so that the weight of the standard body is

$$W = mg = (1)(32.2) = 32.2 \text{ poundals}.$$

In the gravitational system, $W$ is 1 lb for the same standard body, so that its mass is

$$m = \frac{W}{g} = \frac{1}{32.2} \text{ slugs}.$$

Table 6.1 describes in both systems of units three different bodies: Body $A$, which has a mass of $1/32.2$ lb in the absolute system; Body $B$, which is the standard body; and Body $C$, which has a mass of 32.2 lb in the absolute system. If each of the three bodies were placed on a spring scale calibrated in lb, the scale readings would be the weights appearing in the last row of the table under "Gravitational system."

Referring again to Eq. (6.1), we can see that the equation

$$\mathbf{v} = \mathbf{C},$$

where $\mathbf{C}$ is a constant vector (which means that the motion is on a straight line with constant speed), is a necessary and sufficient condition for the equation

$$\mathbf{R} = \mathbf{0},$$

and hence Newton's First Law (Art. 4.2) is a special case of Newton's Second Law. Even if the velocity is not constant, Eq. (6.2) can be rewritten as

$$\mathbf{R} - m\mathbf{a} = \mathbf{0}, \tag{6.5}$$

and, provided a fictitious force

$$-m\mathbf{a}$$

is assumed to be acting on the particle, the particle can be treated as if it were in equilibrium. This fact is known as *D'Alembert's principle*.

Since equality between two vectors is a necessary and sufficient condition for equality between their two scalar components in every direction, a rectangular coordinate system can be used to obtain the following set of three scalar equations, which are equivalent to Eq. (6.2):

$$R_x = ma_x, \qquad R_y = ma_y, \qquad R_z = ma_z. \tag{6.6}$$

Substituting Eqs. (3.9) and (5.26) into Eqs. (6.6) leads to the following *equations of motion of a particle:*

$$\sum F_x = m\ddot{x}, \quad \sum F_y = m\ddot{y}, \quad \sum F_z = m\ddot{z}. \quad (6.7)$$

As discussed in Chapter 13, these equations can be applied without modification to a rigid body if all points in the body have the same motion (a type of rigid-body motion called *translation*), since **a** may then be regarded as the acceleration of any point in the body.

Equations (6.7) can be used to solve many problems involving motion. In general the three equations make possible the determination of three unknowns, but additional unknown quantities can usually be found by writing kinematical equations, as illustrated in the examples of this chapter.

In solving motion problems it is again advisable to draw a free-body diagram of the particle or body to ensure that all contributions to the left-hand sides of Eqs. (6.7) will be included when the equations are written out.

**6.3 Rectilinear motion.** If a particle is in rectilinear motion on the $x$-axis, the equations of motion reduce to

$$\sum F_x = m\ddot{x}, \quad \sum F_y = 0, \quad \sum F_z = 0, \quad (6.8)$$

the last two equations being the same as the last two equations of equilibrium of a particle in space. Either of these last two equations may be satisfied identically in a given problem, thereby reducing the number of unknowns that can be found. For example, if all the forces lie in the $xy$-plane, only the first two equations are usable.

---

EXAMPLE 6.1. Under the action of a horizontal force **P**, a particle weighing 16.1 lb slides along a smooth horizontal wire in such a way that its distance $x$ from a fixed point is given by

$$x = 10t^2 + 5t + 15,$$

where $x$ is in ft and $t$ is in sec. Find the magnitude of **P**.

*Solution.* Drawing the free-body diagram of Fig. 6.2, we can see that the two unknowns are $N$ and $P$, the former of which is equal to $W$ and the latter of which can be found after $\ddot{x}$ is obtained. Differentiating $x$ twice,

$$\dot{x} = 20t + 5, \quad \ddot{x} = 20 \text{ ft/sec}^2.$$

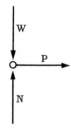

FIGURE 6.2

The mass of the particle, according to Eq. (6.4), is

$$m = \frac{W}{g} = \frac{16.1}{32.2} = \frac{1}{2} \text{ slugs.}$$

Hence, by the first of Eqs. (6.8),

$$P = \tfrac{1}{2}(20) = 10 \text{ lb.}$$

The foregoing example illustrates the type of problem in which the motion is completely known and certain unknown forces are to be found. Another class of problems is that in which some aspects of the motion itself are unknown.

EXAMPLE 6.2. A block of known weight $W$ is released from rest on a smooth plane having known inclination $\alpha$. (See Fig. 4.11.) Find the time it takes for the block to travel a distance $d$ down the plane.

*Solution.* Taking the $x$-axis parallel and the $y$-axis perpendicular to the plane, we draw the free-body diagram of Fig. 6.3. The two unknowns which can be found by the first two of Eqs. (6.8) are $N$ and $\ddot{x}$. Writing the equations,

$$\sum F_x = -W \sin \alpha = \frac{W}{g} \ddot{x},$$

$$\sum F_y = N - W \cos \alpha = 0,$$

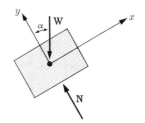

we find that

$$N = W \cos \alpha, \qquad \ddot{x} = -g \sin \alpha.$$

Integrating the acceleration and using the initial condition on velocity,

FIGURE 6.3

$$\dot{x} = -g (\sin \alpha)t.$$

Taking the origin at the point where the block is released, an initial condition on $x$ is obtained, and, by a second integration,

$$x = -\tfrac{1}{2}g (\sin \alpha)t^2.$$

The value of $x$ after the unknown time has elapsed is $-d$. Thus, from the equation

$$-d = -\tfrac{1}{2}g (\sin \alpha)t^2,$$

the time required for the motion is given by

$$t = \sqrt{(2d)/(g \sin \alpha)}.$$

Another problem of the preceding type arises when the following question is considered: Is the motion given in the statement of Example 6.1 the only motion which a force **P** of 10-lb magnitude can produce for the particle described there? If $P$ is given as 10 lb, then $\ddot{x}$ is found from the equations of motion to be the same as in the solution of Example 6.1, namely, 20 ft/sec². But, using two integrations, only the first term on the right-hand side of the $x$-$t$ equation is determined by the magnitude of 10 lb; the other two terms depend on the initial conditions on velocity and position. Hence, the motion produced by a force of 10-lb magnitude is not unique.

**6.4 Kinetic friction.** To analyze the motion of a body on a rough surface, it is necessary to distinguish between rolling motion and sliding motion. Consider a body $A$ on a fixed surface $B$ as shown in Fig. 4.10, and let the total force **Q** exerted on the body by the surface again be divided into vector components **N** and **F**. If the point of $A$ in contact with $B$ slides with respect to $B$ (as it would, for example, if $A$ were in translation), another basic law of mechanics, called the *law of kinetic friction*, states that the force **F** acting on $A$ is in a direction opposite to the direction of motion of the point of $A$ in contact with $B$ and that $F$ is directly proportional to $N$, that is,

$$F = \mu_k N, \qquad (6.9)$$

where $\mu_k$ is a property of the surfaces called the *coefficient of kinetic friction*. This law differs from the law of static friction in that it gives an equation instead of an inequality, but it does not apply if $A$ is rolling without sliding on $B$.

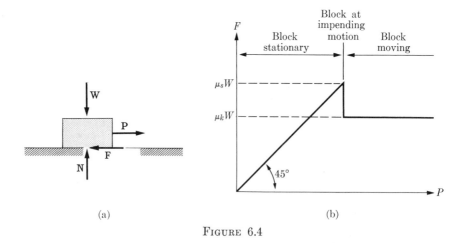

(a)                                          (b)

FIGURE 6.4

The coefficient $\mu_k$ is assumed in the elementary theory to depend only on the nature of the two surfaces in contact, not on the speed or the magnitude of the acceleration of the moving body or on the contact area. Thus, the theory is not applicable when the surfaces are lubricated (i.e., it is a theory of "dry friction"), since the speed then affects $\mu_k$. It is known from experiment that, for most contact conditions other than smooth contact,

$$\mu_k < \mu_s,$$

which means that friction offers a greater resistance to motion when the body is stationary than it does after motion has begun. To illustrate this phenomenon, consider the stationary block in Fig. 6.4(a). As the magnitude of **P** is gradually increased, $F$ also increases and remains equal to $P$, as shown in the graph of $F$ vs. $P$ in Fig. 6.4(b). At impending motion,

$$F = \mu_s W.$$

If $P$ is increased further, the block begins to move, causing $F$ to decrease abruptly and then remain constant at a value given by

$$F = \mu_k W.$$

By definition, the *angle of kinetic friction* $\psi_k$ is given by

$$\tan \psi_k = \mu_k. \qquad (6.10)$$

Hence, referring to Fig. 4.10, we have

$$\tan \psi = \frac{F}{N} = \mu_k = \tan \psi_k$$

during sliding motion, from which it follows that

$$\psi = \psi_k$$

during the motion. For a smooth surface, $\mu_k = 0$, from which it follows that $\psi_k = 0$, and therefore $F = \psi = 0$.

In solving kinetics problems with friction or constant-velocity equilibrium problems with friction, Eq. (6.9) is an additional equation that can be used to find an additional unknown.

---

EXAMPLE 6.3. A block of known weight $W$ is released from rest on a rough plane having known inclination $\alpha$ and known coefficient of kinetic friction $\mu_k$. (See Fig. 4.11.) Find the time it takes for the block to travel a distance $d$ down the plane.

*Solution.* Taking the $x$-axis parallel and the $y$-axis perpendicular to the plane, we draw the free-body diagram of Fig. 6.5. By Eqs. (6.8),

$$\sum F_x = F - W \sin \alpha = \frac{W}{g}\ddot{x}, \qquad \sum F_y = N - W \cos \alpha = 0,$$

and, by Eq. (6.9),

$$F = \mu_k N.$$

Hence,

$$F = \mu_k W \cos \alpha,$$

and

$$\ddot{x} = -g\,(\sin \alpha - \mu_k \cos \alpha).$$

Integrating twice and using initial conditions on $v_x$ and $x$,

$$x = -\tfrac{1}{2}g\,(\sin \alpha - \mu_k \cos \alpha)t^2.$$

Hence, substituting $x = -d$,

$$t = \sqrt{(2d)/[g\,(\sin \alpha - \mu_k \cos \alpha)]}.$$

This, of course, reduces to the solution of Example 6.2 when $\mu_k = 0$. Note that, from Example 4.6, the largest value which can be given to $\alpha$ without motion of the block is given by

$$\tan \alpha = \mu_s.$$

Thus, since $\mu_k < \mu_s$,

$$\mu_k < \tan \alpha,$$

and

$$\mu_k \cos \alpha < \sin \alpha.$$

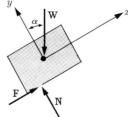

FIGURE 6.5

Therefore the acceleration $\ddot{x}$ of the present example is negative (and cannot be zero) when $\alpha$ is great enough to cause motion starting from rest.

**6.5 Curvilinear motion in a plane.** For a particle moving on a curved path in the $xy$-plane, the equations of motion become:

$$\sum F_x = m\ddot{x}, \qquad \sum F_y = m\ddot{y}, \qquad \sum F_z = 0. \qquad (6.11)$$

---

EXAMPLE 6.4. After being fired with an initial velocity $\mathbf{v}_0$ having both horizontal and vertical components, a projectile travels over a short enough range so that its weight force may be assumed not to change in magnitude or direction. Neglecting air resistance, find the path described by the projectile.

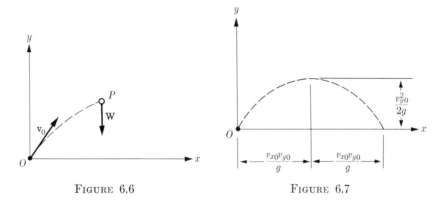

FIGURE 6.6                    FIGURE 6.7

*Solution.* If the $xy$-plane is taken as the vertical plane containing the initial velocity, there will be no forces and no motion outside the $xy$-plane. In Fig. 6.6, the origin of the coordinate system is taken at the point where the projectile is fired. The free-body diagram, included in Fig. 6.6, shows the only force acting on the particle, the weight force. From the free-body diagram,

$$\sum F_x = 0, \qquad \sum F_y = -W,$$

and, therefore, from Eqs. (6.11),

$$\ddot{x} = 0, \qquad \ddot{y} = \frac{g}{W}(-W) = -g.$$

Letting $v_{x0}$ and $v_{y0}$ be the components of $\mathbf{v}_0$, and integrating,

$$\dot{x} = v_{x0}, \qquad \dot{y} = -gt + v_{y0}.$$

By a second integration,

$$x = v_{x0}t, \qquad y = -\tfrac{1}{2}gt^2 + v_{y0}t.$$

Solving the first of these two equations for $t$ and substituting into the second gives

$$y = -\frac{g}{2v_{x0}^2}x^2 + \frac{v_{y0}}{v_{x0}}x,$$

which is the explicit equation of the path. This path, a parabola, is pictured in Fig. 6.7. The time at which the projectile reaches its maximum height is given by

$$t = \frac{x}{v_{x0}} = \frac{1}{v_{x0}}\left(\frac{v_{x0}v_{y0}}{g}\right) = \frac{v_{y0}}{g},$$

while the time at which it falls back to the ground is given by

$$t = \frac{1}{v_{x0}}\left(\frac{2v_{x0}v_{y0}}{g}\right) = \frac{2v_{y0}}{g}.$$

In some plane problems the motion of the particle is completely known (i.e., the path and location on the path at all times are known) and some or all of the forces acting on the particle must be found.

EXAMPLE 6.5. The particle in Example 5.5 is traveling on a smooth, horizontal plane (the $xy$-plane) under the action of its weight force and an unknown force $\mathbf{P}$ in the $xy$-plane. If the weight of the particle is 96.6 lb, find $\mathbf{P}$ and the magnitude $N$ of the normal force exerted on the particle by the plane.

*Solution.* By the equations of motion and the results of Example 5.5,

$$\sum F_x = P_x = ma_x = 0,$$

$$\sum F_y = P_y = ma_y = \left(\frac{96.6}{32.2}\right)\left(\frac{64}{12}\right) = 16 \text{ lb}.$$

(The factor of 12 is required to put $a_y$ in ft/sec$^2$.) Hence,

$$\mathbf{P} = 16\mathbf{j} \text{ lb}.$$

By the third of Eqs. (6.11),

$$\sum F_z = N - 96.6 = 0,$$

from which

$$N = 96.6 \text{ lb}.$$

**6.6 Curvilinear motion in space.** For a particle moving in three-dimensional space, all three equations of motion must be used to analyze the motion.

EXAMPLE 6.6. A particle with mass of 2 slugs is acted upon by a resultant force $\mathbf{R}$ such that

$$R_x = 0, \qquad R_y = -10, \qquad R_z = 4t,$$

where the force components are in lb and $t$ is in sec. If $v_x(0) = 20$ ft/sec and $v_y(0) = v_z(0) = x(0) = y(0) = z(0) = 0$, find the parametric equations of the path of the particle.

*Solution.* By the equations of motion,

$$\ddot{x} = 0, \qquad \ddot{y} = -5, \qquad \ddot{z} = 2t.$$

By integration,

$$\dot{x} = 20, \qquad \dot{y} = -5t, \qquad \dot{z} = t^2,$$

and hence, by a second integration,

$$x = 20t, \qquad y = -\tfrac{5}{2}t^2, \qquad z = \tfrac{1}{3}t^3.$$

**6.7 Cylindrical coordinates.** If, instead of using a cartesian coordinate system to express Eq. (6.2) in terms of scalar components, we use the cylindrical coordinates described in Art. 5.6, the following three equations result:

$$R_\rho = ma_\rho, \qquad R_\theta = ma_\theta, \qquad R_z = ma_z. \tag{6.12}$$

By Eq. (2.20),

$$R_\rho = \sum F_\rho, \qquad R_\theta = \sum F_\theta, \qquad R_z = \sum F_z,$$

and, substituting these equations and Eqs. (5.45) into Eqs. (6.12),

$$\sum F_\rho = m(\ddot\rho - \rho\dot\theta^2),$$

$$\sum F_\theta = m(\rho\ddot\theta + 2\dot\rho\dot\theta), \tag{6.13}$$

$$\sum F_z = m\ddot z.$$

Equations (6.13) are called the *equations of motion of a particle in cylindrical coordinates.* If the motion of the particle is known completely, these equations can be used to find as many unknown force components as there are usable equations.

For motion of a particle on a circular path parallel to the $xy$-plane, let $b$ be the radius of the circle and use Eqs. (5.48), (5.49), and (5.51). Equations (6.13) then become

$$\sum F_\rho = -mb\dot\theta^2 = -\frac{m\dot s^2}{b} = -\frac{mv^2}{b},$$

$$\sum F_\theta = mb\ddot\theta = m\ddot s, \tag{6.14}$$

$$\sum F_z = 0.$$

Equations (6.14) can be used in general to find three unknowns, some of which may be kinematical quantities such as $v$ and $\ddot s$. The following example illustrates a problem in which the second of Eqs. (6.14) is satisfied identically.

---

EXAMPLE 6.7. A "conical pendulum" consists of a particle $P$ of weight $W$ attached to one end of an ideal string 4 ft long, with the other end of the string at a fixed point $O$ (as in Fig. 6.8). If the particle travels freely and with constant speed on a circular path about a vertical axis through $O$, and if the angle between the string and the axis is 30°, find the tension in the string in terms of $W$. What must the speed of the particle be to maintain the angle of 30°?

*Solution.* The free-body diagram of Fig. 6.9 is a view taken in the direction of $\mathbf{n}_\theta$. By the third of Eqs. (6.14),

$$\sum F_z = T\left(\frac{\sqrt3}{2}\right) - W = 0,$$

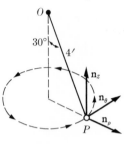

FIGURE 6.8

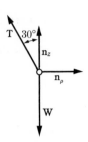

FIGURE 6.9

from which

$$T = \frac{2}{\sqrt{3}} W.$$

By the first of Eqs. (6.14),

$$\Sigma F_\rho = -T\left(\frac{1}{2}\right) = -\frac{W}{\sqrt{3}} = -\frac{W}{g}\frac{v^2}{4(\frac{1}{2})}.$$

Hence,

$$v^2 = \frac{2g}{\sqrt{3}} = 37.2,$$

and

$$v = 6.10\ \text{ft/sec.}$$

The following example shows another type of problem which can be solved by the equations of this article.

EXAMPLE 6.8. A small ball of weight $W$ is supported by two strings $AP$ and $BP$ as shown in Fig. 6.10. String $BP$ is vertical, so that there is no tension in string $AP$. If string $BP$ is suddenly cut, find the tension in $AP$ and the acceleration of the ball immediately after $BP$ is cut.

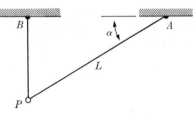

FIGURE 6.10

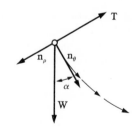

FIGURE 6.11

*Solution.* The free-body diagram of the ball just after $BP$ is cut is shown in Fig. 6.11. Since $v = 0$ at this instant, it follows from the first of Eqs. (6.14) that

$$\sum F_\rho = W \sin \alpha - T = 0,$$

and thus

$$T = W \sin \alpha.$$

By the second of Eqs. (6.12),

$$a_\theta = \frac{g}{W} R_\theta = \frac{g}{W} (W \cos \alpha) = g \cos \alpha,$$

and therefore

$$\mathbf{a} = g (\cos \alpha) \mathbf{n}_\theta.$$

Note that the length $L$ of string $AP$ affects neither of the answers.

Although the particle is easily analyzed at the instant the string $BP$ is cut, the subsequent motion along the circular path is complicated and cannot be found by the elementary methods of this book.

---

The expressions "centripetal force" and "centrifugal force" are often used in discussing motion on a circular path. Normally, the former means $-R_\rho \mathbf{n}_\rho$ (i.e., the resultant force toward the center of the circle), while the latter is an opposite force $R_\rho \mathbf{n}_\rho$. Considering the particle of the preceding example, we see that neither of these is an actual individual force on the particle, although, in some usage, the expressions refer, respectively, to the reactive force $\mathbf{T}$ on the particle and the opposite force $-\mathbf{T}$ acting on point $A$.

**6.8 Gravitation.** The universal law of gravitation (Art. 1.5), derived by Newton from Kepler's laws, states that the force of attraction $\mathbf{F}$ exerted by either one of any two particles on the other acts along the line joining the two particles and has a magnitude $F$ given by

$$F = G \frac{m_1 m_2}{r^2}, \tag{6.15}$$

where $m_1$ and $m_2$ are the masses of the two particles, $r$ is the distance between them, and $G$ is a constant which depends only on the system of units employed. In the British absolute system, $G$ has been found by experiment to be approximately 10.69 $(10^{-10})$ ft$^3$/lb-sec$^2$. Because this constant is so small, the gravitational force is perceptible only if one of the particles has a very large mass.

If one of the two particles is replaced by a solid sphere having its mass distributed symmetrically about its center and having a total mass $M$, the gravitational force $\mathbf{W}$ exerted on the remaining particle can be shown to be along the line joining the particle and the center of the sphere, as depicted in Fig. 6.12, and to have a magnitude given by

$$W = G \frac{Mm}{r^2}, \tag{6.16}$$

where $r$ is the distance from the center of the sphere to the particle.

If the sphere is stationary and there are no other forces acting upon the particle, the force $\mathbf{W}$ gives the particle an acceleration $\mathbf{g}$ (with magnitude $g$) toward the center of the sphere, and, by Eq. (6.3),

$$W = mg.$$

Substituting this into Eq. (6.16),

$$g = \frac{GM}{r^2}, \tag{6.17}$$

which means that the magnitude of the acceleration is a function of the distance $r$.

Letting $r_0$ be the radius of the sphere, $W_0$ the value of $W$ at the surface of the sphere, and $g_0$ the value of $g$ at the surface, it follows from Eqs. (6.3) and (6.16) that

$$W_0 = mg_0 = G \frac{Mm}{r_0^2},$$

and hence that

$$W = \frac{r_0^2}{r^2} W_0 = \frac{r_0^2}{r^2} mg_0 \tag{6.18}$$

and

$$g = \frac{r_0^2}{r^2} g_0. \tag{6.19}$$

Equations (6.18) and (6.19) give $W$ and $g$ in terms of $W_0$ and $g_0$ and the distance $r$.

An approximate solution to problems involving the earth and bodies in the vicinity of the earth can be obtained by using the model of sphere and particle discussed in the preceding paragraphs. The quantity $W$ is then the weight of the object, and $W$ varies with altitude in accordance with Eq. (6.18), $W_0$ being the weight of the object at the surface and $g_0$ being the magnitude of the acceleration of gravity at the surface. For example, the motion of long-range missiles, high-altitude rockets, and earth satellites (including the moon) can be studied. In fact, the motion of any satellite about a planet or star can be investigated quantitatively with this model. In most cases it must be remembered that $\mathbf{W}$ changes in direction as well as magnitude, so that the motion is much more complicated

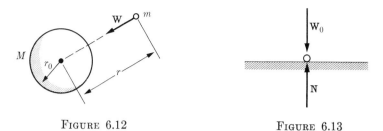

FIGURE 6.12                    FIGURE 6.13

than that of the simple projectile discussed in Art. 6.5. In problems in which the earth is the parent body, an average value of $g_0$ such as 32.2 ft/sec² is ordinarily used.

In refined analyses of objects near the earth, such as artificial satellites, or in high-accuracy experiments conducted on the surface of the earth, it is often necessary to take into account the fact that the earth is not truly spherical but rather "bulges" slightly at the equator and resembles an *oblate spheroid* more closely than it does a sphere. This causes objects at the surface to be at different distances from the center at different latitudes and explains partially the variations with latitude of weight and magnitude of acceleration due to gravity.

Another imperfection in the model, however, is contributed by the rotation of the earth. To obtain an idea of the error introduced into an equilibrium problem by this rotation, assume that the earth is a perfect sphere of 3960-mile radius with a constant angular speed $\dot{\theta}$ of 1 revolution per day, and let $g_0$ be 32.2 ft/sec². If a particle of weight $W_0$ is resting on a horizontal plane at the equator, as shown in Fig. 6.13, the first of Eqs. (6.14) can be written for the particle as follows:

$$\Sigma F_\rho = N - W_0 = -\frac{W_0}{g_0} r_0 \dot{\theta}^2.$$

Hence,

$$N = W_0 \left(1 - \frac{r_0}{g_0} \dot{\theta}^2\right) = W_0 \left\{1 - \left[\frac{(3960)(5280)}{32.2}\right]\left[\frac{2\pi}{(24)(60)(60)}\right]^2\right\}$$

$$= 0.997 W_0.$$

If the particle rests on a horizontal plane at one of the poles,

$$\Sigma F_\rho = N - W_0 = 0.$$

In this case, then,

$$N = W_0.$$

The following example illustrates a simple type of problem which can be solved using the law of gravitation in conjunction with the equations of motion in polar coordinates.

EXAMPLE 6.9. A satellite travels with constant speed $v_0$ on a circular path of radius $b$. Find the speed.

*Solution.* Figure 6.14 shows the path of the satellite and includes a free-body diagram. By Eq. (6.18),

$$W = \frac{r_0^2}{b^2} mg_0,$$

and, by the first of Eqs. (6.14),

$$\sum F_\rho = -\frac{r_0^2}{b^2} mg_0 = -\frac{mv_0^2}{b}.$$

Hence,

$$v_0^2 = \frac{r_0^2 g_0}{b}.$$

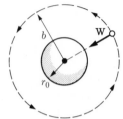

FIGURE 6.14

The circular motion of the foregoing example is one type of motion which the gravitational force can produce. It is not the only type, however. The path of a satellite can be elliptical, parabolic, or hyperbolic; only the proper combination of speed and altitude produces a circular path.

## PROBLEMS

6.1 Express D'Alembert's principle in the form of three scalar equations on rectangular components.

6.2 An elevator weighing 3220 lb starts from rest and travels upward in such a way that its height $h$ above the starting point is given, during the first two seconds of motion, by

$$h = 3t^2 - \frac{t^3}{2},$$

where $h$ is in ft and $t$ is in sec. Find the tension in the cable: (a) as a function of $t$ during the first two seconds of motion, and (b) when $t = 2$ sec.

[*Ans.:* (b) 3220 lb.]

6.3 A bullet weighing 1.5 oz is fired straight up with an initial speed of 1288 ft/sec. Neglecting air resistance, find: (a) the amount of time it takes the bullet to reach its maximum height, (b) the maximum height to which it rises, (c) the amount of time it takes the bullet to fall back to the ground from its maximum height, and (d) the speed with which it strikes the ground.

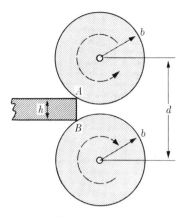

FIGURE 6.15

6.4 A particle of weight $W$ starts from rest at the origin and moves on the $x$-axis in such a way that

$$R_x = (6 - 2t)W,$$

where $R_x$ and $W$ are in lb and $t$ is in sec. (a) When will the particle again be at the origin? (b) How far will it have traveled in the interim?

[*Ans.:* (a) $t = 9$ sec; (b) 2320 ft.]

6.5 The skid marks on a level road indicate that an automobile slid 150 ft to a stop after the brakes were applied. If $\mu_k$ is 0.6 for the tires and road involved, determine what the speed of the automobile was in mph when the brakes were applied.

6.6 A block of weight $W$ slides on a rough plane of inclination $\alpha$. If $\mu_s = 0.5$ and $\mu_k = 0.4$, find the angle $\alpha$ required for a constant speed $v_0$. Compare this with the value required for impending motion.

[*Ans.:* $\alpha_k = 21.8°$, $\alpha_s = 26.6°$.]

6.7 An automobile is traveling down a plane hill of inclination $\alpha$ with a speed $v_0$ when the brakes are suddenly applied. If the car slides to a stop and the coefficient of kinetic friction is $\mu_k$, derive a formula for the time it takes the car to stop after the brakes are applied.

6.8 A rolling mill consists of two rollers mounted on fixed shafts and turning in opposite directions as shown in Fig. 6.15. A bar of height $h$ is to be drawn into the rollers when it touches them at $A$ and $B$ (i.e., the total forces exerted on the bar at $A$ and $B$ must have horizontal components to the right). If the coefficient of kinetic friction is $\mu_k$, what, in terms of $h$, $b$, and $\mu_k$, is the minimum value of $d$?

$$\left[ Ans.:\ h + \frac{2b}{\sqrt{1 + \mu_k^2}}. \right]$$

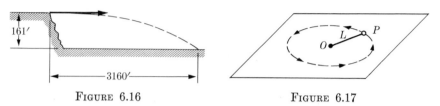

FIGURE 6.16                                    FIGURE 6.17

6.9 The muzzle speed of a gun is to be determined by firing it horizontally from a cliff 161 ft high (Fig. 6.16). If the shell travels 3160 ft in a horizontal direction before striking the ground, determine the muzzle speed of the gun. Neglect air resistance.

6.10 The range of a projectile is defined as the straight-line distance from the point of launching to the point of landing, and the launching angle is defined as the angle that the initial velocity makes with the horizontal. (a) For a given initial speed $v_0$, find the range of a projectile as a function of the launching angle if the projectile is launched on horizontal ground. (b) What launching angle is required for maximum range?

[*Ans.*: (b) 45°.]

6.11 If, for the particle of Example 5.6,

$$t_0 = \sqrt{m/k},$$

where $m$ is the mass and $k$ is a positive constant, (a) find the resultant force as a function of time, (b) find $R_x$ and $R_y$ as functions of $x$ and $y$, (c) find the magnitude $R$ of the resultant as a function of the distance $r$ from $O$ to the particle, (d) name a point which is always on the line of action of the resultant.

6.12 A particle $P$ of weight $W$ is attached to one end of a string of length $L$, with the other end of the string at a fixed point $O$ on a rough, horizontal plane (Fig. 6.17). If the particle is projected into a circular path on the plane, find the tension in the string as a function of the speed $v$.

$$\left[ Ans.:\ T = \frac{W}{gL} v^2. \right]$$

6.13 At the bottom of a dive, an airplane is traveling on a vertical circle of 2-mile radius at a speed of 1050 mph. If the weight of the pilot is 160 lb, find the magnitude of the vertical force exerted on him by the seat. How many times $g$ is the vertical component of the acceleration of the pilot?

6.14 An airplane is traveling on the top part of a vertical circle of 10,000-ft radius. (a) What must the speed of the airplane be if there is to be no force exerted on the pilot by the seat at the instant the plane passes the highest point of the circle? (b) What path is required if this so-called "weightlessness" is to persist over the entire range of travel on the path?

[*Ans.*: (a) 567 ft/sec.]

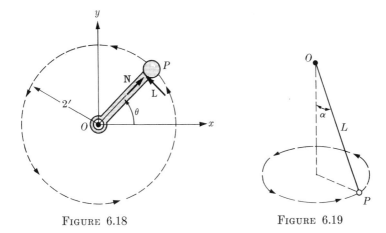

FIGURE 6.18                    FIGURE 6.19

6.15 A small ball $P$ weighing 3.22 lb is attached to the end of a light, rigid rod $OP$ which is 2 ft long. The rod rotates in a vertical plane about a fixed point $O$ in such a way that the ball travels with a constant speed of 7 ft/sec, and the rod exerts forces $\mathbf{N}$ and $\mathbf{L}$ on the ball as in Fig. 6.18. (a) Find the magnitude and sense of the force $\mathbf{N}$ when the ball is at the highest point on its path. (b) Find the values of $\theta$ at which the magnitude of $\mathbf{N}$ is zero. (c) Find the magnitude of $\mathbf{L}$ for these values of $\theta$.

6.16 A "conical pendulum" consists of a particle $P$ of weight $W$ attached to one end of an ideal string of length $L$, with the other end of the string at a fixed point $O$ (Fig. 6.19). If the particle travels freely and with constant speed on a circular path about a vertical axis through $O$, and if the angle between the string and the axis is $\alpha$, derive equations for the tension $T$ in the string and the speed $v_0$.

$$\left[ Ans.:\ T = \frac{W}{\cos \alpha},\ v_0 = \sqrt{gL \sin \alpha \tan \alpha}. \right]$$

6.17 An airplane flying 1500 mph is to make a horizontal turn of 5-mile radius. If the reaction $\mathbf{N}$ of the air on the plane is perpendicular to the wings, as in Fig. 6.20, find the angle of bank $\alpha$ required. How many times $g$ is the horizontal acceleration of the pilot?

6.18 A car of weight $W$ travels around a curve of radius $b$ on a roadway which is banked at an angle $\alpha$ as shown in Fig. 6.21. The speed of the car is $v_0$, a constant. (a) Derive equations for the magnitudes of the two forces $\mathbf{N}$ and $\mathbf{F}$ exerted on the car by the roadway. (b) Obtain an equation for the "rated" speed of a curve, which is the speed at which $F$ is zero. (c) Find the value of $\alpha$ required to make $F$ zero when $v_0 = 60$ mph and $b = 1000$ ft.

$[Ans.:$ (b) $v_0 = \sqrt{gb \tan \alpha}$; (c) 13.5°.]

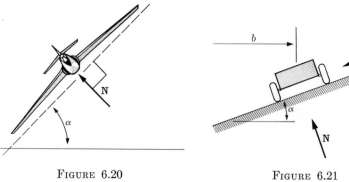

FIGURE 6.20                              FIGURE 6.21

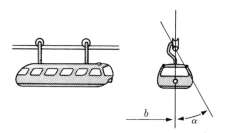     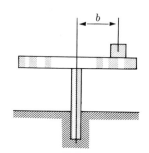

FIGURE 6.22                              FIGURE 6.23

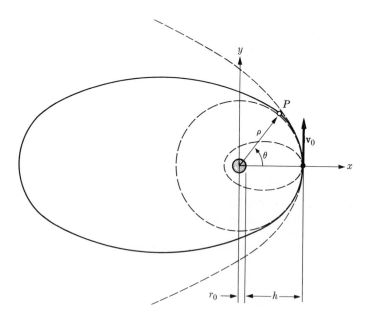

FIGURE 6.24

6.19 The monorail car in Fig. 6.22 rounds a curve of radius $b$ at a constant speed $v_0$. Assuming that there is no friction between the wheels and the rail, find an expression for the angle $\alpha$ by which the car swings out during the turn. (Neglect the change in $b$ due to the swing.) Show that the direction of the reaction force of a flat seat on a passenger is perpendicular to the seat (i.e., there is no tendency for the passenger to slide on the seat) regardless of the speed with which a curve is taken.

6.20 A small block of weight $W$ rests on a horizontal turntable which rotates at constant angular speed. The block is at a distance $b$ from the axis of rotation, as shown in Fig. 6.23. If the coefficient of static friction between the block and the surface of the turntable is $\mu_s$, find the maximum permissible angular speed in revolutions per second if the block is not to slip off.

$$\left[ Ans.: \ \frac{1}{2\pi} \sqrt{(\mu_s g)/b} \ . \right]$$

6.21 The coefficient of kinetic friction between the particle and plane of Problem 6.12 is $\mu_k$. If the particle is projected with an initial speed $v_0$, find the time it takes for the particle to come to rest.

6.22 Assuming that the moon travels on an approximately circular path about the earth and takes 28 days to complete one revolution, find the distance from the center of the earth to the center of the moon.

[$Ans.:$ 242,000 miles.]

6.23 A satellite weighing 2000 lb at the earth's surface is launched horizontally at an altitude of 1000 miles. (a) If the path is to be circular, determine the initial speed required. (b) Show that the speed of the satellite is constant after launching.

6.24 If a satellite $P$ of mass $m$ is launched horizontally at an altitude $h$ and with an initial speed $v_0$ as shown in Fig. 6.24, it is found under ideal conditions that the satellite travels on a path given by

$$\frac{1}{\rho} = \left[ \frac{1}{r_0 + h} - \frac{r_0^2 g_0}{v_0^2 (r_0 + h)^2} \right] \cos\theta + \frac{r_0^2 g_0}{v_0^2 (r_0 + h)^2}$$

such that

$$\rho^2 \dot{\theta} = v_0 (r_0 + h),$$

where $g_0$ is the magnitude of the acceleration of gravity at the earth's surface. Derive Newton's law of gravitation, i.e., show that the resultant force $\mathbf{R}$ on the particle has components as follows:

$$R_\rho = -\frac{r_0^2}{\rho^2} m g_0, \qquad R_\theta = 0.$$

*Part* 2

# MECHANICS OF RIGID BODIES

CHAPTER 7

PRODUCTS OF VECTORS

**7.1 Multiplication of two vectors.** The only type of multiplication involving vectors which is discussed in Chapter 2 is the product of a scalar $M$ and a vector $\mathbf{A}$. In many physical situations it is convenient to employ the concept of multiplication of two vectors $\mathbf{A}$ and $\mathbf{B}$, and meaning must be assigned to this type of multiplication.

Two completely different kinds of products are commonly defined. One, symbolized by $\mathbf{A} \cdot \mathbf{B}$, is by definition a scalar and is called the *scalar product*. The other, $\mathbf{A} \times \mathbf{B}$, is by definition a vector and is called the *vector product*. As suggested by their symbols, the scalar product and vector product are frequently called the *dot product* and *cross product*, respectively.

**7.2 Scalar product of two vectors.** By definition, the scalar product of two vectors $\mathbf{A}$ and $\mathbf{B}$ is an algebraic scalar which is the product of the two magnitudes and the cosine of the angle $\phi$ between the vectors, i.e.,

$$\mathbf{A} \cdot \mathbf{B} = AB \cos \phi. \tag{7.1}$$

Figure 7.1 shows the plane defined by the two arrows representing the vectors when their tails are connected. The angle $\phi$ is always measured in this plane, it is always measured between the positive directions of the two arrows, and its value is always in the interval

$$0 \leq \phi \leq 180°.$$

The sign of the product, of course, depends only on the sign of $\cos \phi$, which is negative when $\phi$ is greater than $90°$.

An important geometrical significance of the dot product comes from Eq. (2.18). Using that equation, we can see that $\mathbf{A} \cdot \mathbf{B}$ is equal to the product of $A$ and the scalar component of $\mathbf{B}$ in the direction of $\mathbf{A}$. It is also equal to the product of $B$ and the scalar component of $\mathbf{A}$ in the direction of $\mathbf{B}$.

The following properties of the scalar product follow from the definition of Eq. (7.1):

(1) The scalar product is commutative, i.e.,

$$\mathbf{A} \cdot \mathbf{B} = \mathbf{B} \cdot \mathbf{A}, \tag{7.2}$$

since scalar multiplication is commutative, i.e., since

$$AB = BA.$$

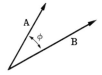

FIGURE 7.1

(2) Since the cosine of zero is unity, it follows that

$$\mathbf{A} \cdot \mathbf{A} = A^2, \tag{7.3}$$

where $A$ is the magnitude of $\mathbf{A}$, and hence $\mathbf{A} \cdot \mathbf{A}$ is zero if and only if $\mathbf{A}$ is a null vector.

(3) If $\mathbf{A} \neq \mathbf{0}$ and $\mathbf{B} \neq \mathbf{0}$, then $\mathbf{A} \cdot \mathbf{B} = 0$ is a necessary and sufficient condition for perpendicularity between $\mathbf{A}$ and $\mathbf{B}$, since $\cos 90°$ is zero and since $90°$ is the only angle between zero and $180°$ with cosine of zero.

(4) The scalar product is distributive, i.e.,

$$\mathbf{A} \cdot (\mathbf{B} + \mathbf{C}) = \mathbf{A} \cdot \mathbf{B} + \mathbf{A} \cdot \mathbf{C}, \tag{7.4}$$

since the scalar component of $\mathbf{B} + \mathbf{C}$ in the direction of $\mathbf{A}$ is equal to the algebraic sum of the scalar components of $\mathbf{B}$ and $\mathbf{C}$ in the direction of $\mathbf{A}$ (from Art. 2.8).

(5) The scalar product is associative, i.e.,

$$(M\mathbf{A}) \cdot (N\mathbf{B}) = MN(\mathbf{A} \cdot \mathbf{B}) \tag{7.5}$$

or

$$(M\mathbf{A}) \cdot (N\mathbf{B}) = (MN\mathbf{A}) \cdot (\mathbf{B}) = (\mathbf{A}) \cdot (MN\mathbf{B}).$$

To verify these equations, let $\phi$ be the angle between $\mathbf{A}$ and $\mathbf{B}$ and use the properties of multiplication of a vector by a scalar:

$$(M\mathbf{A}) \cdot (N\mathbf{B}) = (MA)(NB) \cos \phi = MN(AB \cos \phi)$$
$$= (MNA)(B) \cos \phi = (A)(MNB) \cos \phi.$$

The evaluation of the scalar product is accomplished readily by expressing the vectors $\mathbf{A}$ and $\mathbf{B}$ in terms of their components in a cartesian coordinate system, i.e.,

$$\mathbf{A} = A_x\mathbf{i} + A_y\mathbf{j} + A_z\mathbf{k},$$
$$\mathbf{B} = B_x\mathbf{i} + B_y\mathbf{j} + B_z\mathbf{k},$$

so that

$$\mathbf{A} \cdot \mathbf{B} = (A_x\mathbf{i} + A_y\mathbf{j} + A_z\mathbf{k}) \cdot (B_x\mathbf{i} + B_y\mathbf{j} + B_z\mathbf{k}).$$

Expanding the right-hand side of this equation by means of Eqs. (7.4) and (7.5),

$$\mathbf{A} \cdot \mathbf{B} = A_xB_x\mathbf{i} \cdot \mathbf{i} + A_xB_y\mathbf{i} \cdot \mathbf{j} + A_xB_z\mathbf{i} \cdot \mathbf{k}$$
$$+ A_yB_x\mathbf{j} \cdot \mathbf{i} + A_yB_y\mathbf{j} \cdot \mathbf{j} + A_yB_z\mathbf{j} \cdot \mathbf{k}$$
$$+ A_zB_x\mathbf{k} \cdot \mathbf{i} + A_zB_y\mathbf{k} \cdot \mathbf{j} + A_zB_z\mathbf{k} \cdot \mathbf{k}.$$

By properties (2) and (3) of the scalar product,

$$\mathbf{i} \cdot \mathbf{i} = \mathbf{j} \cdot \mathbf{j} = \mathbf{k} \cdot \mathbf{k} = 1, \qquad \mathbf{i} \cdot \mathbf{j} = \mathbf{j} \cdot \mathbf{k} = \mathbf{k} \cdot \mathbf{i} = 0. \qquad (7.6)$$

Hence,

$$\mathbf{A} \cdot \mathbf{B} = A_x B_x + A_y B_y + A_z B_z. \qquad (7.7)$$

This very important relation can be expressed verbally as follows: The scalar product of two vectors equals the algebraic sum of the three products of their corresponding scalar rectangular components.

The existence of Eq. (7.7) gives the scalar product several useful applications in geometry and mechanics. One of these applications is that of finding scalar components. If one of the vectors in the product is a unit vector, the product is then the scalar component of the other vector in the direction of the unit vector. For example,

$$A_x = \mathbf{A} \cdot \mathbf{i}, \qquad A_y = \mathbf{A} \cdot \mathbf{j}, \qquad A_z = \mathbf{A} \cdot \mathbf{k},$$

so that the vector **A** may be written as follows:

$$\mathbf{A} = (\mathbf{A} \cdot \mathbf{i})\mathbf{i} + (\mathbf{A} \cdot \mathbf{j})\mathbf{j} + (\mathbf{A} \cdot \mathbf{k})\mathbf{k}.$$

If the vector **A** is now replaced by a unit vector **n** with components $n_x$, $n_y$, $n_z$ and direction angles $\phi_{nx}$, $\phi_{ny}$, $\phi_{nz}$, then

$$n_x = \mathbf{n} \cdot \mathbf{i} = \cos \phi_{nx},$$
$$n_y = \mathbf{n} \cdot \mathbf{j} = \cos \phi_{ny}, \qquad (7.8)$$
$$n_z = \mathbf{n} \cdot \mathbf{k} = \cos \phi_{nz},$$

so that

$$\mathbf{n} = (\cos \phi_{nx})\mathbf{i} + (\cos \phi_{ny})\mathbf{j} + (\cos \phi_{nz})\mathbf{k}.$$

The foregoing shows that the components of any unit vector are its direction cosines. (This is also shown in Art. 2.9.) The direction cosines, of course, must satisfy Eq. (2.25). To find the scalar component of a vector **A** in the direction of a line $L$ defined by a unit vector **n** (Fig. 2.17), note that

$$A_L = \mathbf{A} \cdot \mathbf{n}. \qquad (7.9)$$

Using Eq. (7.7),

$$A_L = A_x n_x + A_y n_y + A_z n_z. \qquad (7.10)$$

The components of **n** needed for Eq. (7.10) may be found from the direction angles of **n** by Eqs. (7.8).

EXAMPLE 7.1. Find the scalar component of the force

$$\mathbf{F} = -27\mathbf{i} + 18\mathbf{j} + 6\mathbf{k}\,\text{lb}$$

in the direction of a line defined by the unit vector

$$\mathbf{n} = \tfrac{2}{3}\mathbf{i} + \tfrac{1}{3}\mathbf{j} + \tfrac{2}{3}\mathbf{k}.$$

*Solution.* By Eq. (7.10),

$$F_L = (-27)(\tfrac{2}{3}) + (18)(\tfrac{1}{3}) + (6)(\tfrac{2}{3})$$
$$= -18 + 6 + 4 = -8\,\text{lb}.$$

Another application of the scalar product is the verification of certain theorems of geometry and trigonometry. To prove the three-dimensional Pythagorean theorem, for example, combine Eqs. (7.3) and (7.7) to obtain

$$A^2 = A_x^2 + A_y^2 + A_z^2.$$

To verify the cosine law of trigonometry, as another example, consider the triangle of Fig. 7.2(a). Taking vectors **a**, **b**, **c** along the sides of the triangle as in Fig. 7.2(b), we can see that the magnitude of **c** is equal to the difference between the scalar component of **a** along **c** and the scalar component of **b** along **c**, i.e.,

$$c = \mathbf{a} \cdot \frac{\mathbf{c}}{c} - \mathbf{b} \cdot \frac{\mathbf{c}}{c}.$$

Thus,

$$c^2 = \mathbf{a} \cdot (\mathbf{a} - \mathbf{b}) - \mathbf{b} \cdot (\mathbf{a} - \mathbf{b})$$
$$= \mathbf{a} \cdot \mathbf{a} + \mathbf{b} \cdot \mathbf{b} - 2\mathbf{a} \cdot \mathbf{b},$$

or

$$c^2 = a^2 + b^2 - 2ab \cos \gamma.$$

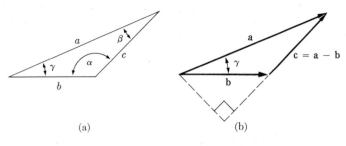

(a)          (b)

FIGURE 7.2

A third application of the scalar product is in finding the angle between two vectors. From Eq. (7.1),

$$\cos \phi = \frac{\mathbf{A} \cdot \mathbf{B}}{AB} = \mathbf{A}_0 \cdot \mathbf{B}_0.$$

If the vectors $\mathbf{A}$ and $\mathbf{B}$ have direction angles $\phi_{Ax}$, $\phi_{Ay}$, $\phi_{Az}$ and $\phi_{Bx}$, $\phi_{By}$, $\phi_{Bz}$, respectively, then, by Eqs. (7.7) and (7.8) and the last equation,

$$\cos \phi = \cos \phi_{Ax} \cos \phi_{Bx} + \cos \phi_{Ay} \cos \phi_{By} + \cos \phi_{Az} \cos \phi_{Bz}. \quad (7.11)$$

More generally, the angle $\phi$ between any two directed lines $L_1$ and $L_2$ is defined as the angle between their unit vectors $\mathbf{n}_1$ and $\mathbf{n}_2$ when these unit vectors are connected together tail-to-tail, so that

$$\cos \phi = \mathbf{n}_1 \cdot \mathbf{n}_2 = n_{1x}n_{2x} + n_{1y}n_{2y} + n_{1z}n_{2z}. \quad (7.12)$$

EXAMPLE 7.2. Show that the angle $\phi$ between a line $L_1$ directed from $(0, 0, 0)$ to $(7, -4, -4)$ and a line $L_2$ directed from $(6, 2, 5)$ to $(2, 3, -3)$, where all coordinates are in ft, is 90°.

*Solution.* To find the components of a unit vector when two points on its line of action are given, equations similar to Eqs. (3.8) are used. In the present example, the distance between the two known points on $L_1$ is

$$d_1 = \sqrt{(7)^2 + (-4)^2 + (-4)^2} = 9 \text{ ft},$$

so that

$$n_{1x} = \tfrac{7}{9}, \qquad n_{1y} = -\tfrac{4}{9}, \qquad n_{1z} = -\tfrac{4}{9},$$

and

$$\mathbf{n}_1 = \tfrac{7}{9}\mathbf{i} - \tfrac{4}{9}\mathbf{j} - \tfrac{4}{9}\mathbf{k}.$$

Similarly,

$$d_2 = \sqrt{(2 - 6)^2 + (3 - 2)^2 + (-3 - 5)^2}$$
$$= \sqrt{(-4)^2 + (1)^2 + (-8)^2} = 9 \text{ ft},$$

so that

$$n_{2x} = -\tfrac{4}{9}, \qquad n_{2y} = \tfrac{1}{9}, \qquad n_{2z} = -\tfrac{8}{9},$$

and

$$\mathbf{n}_2 = -\tfrac{4}{9}\mathbf{i} + \tfrac{1}{9}\mathbf{j} - \tfrac{8}{9}\mathbf{k}.$$

(Note that the components of $\mathbf{n}_1$ and $\mathbf{n}_2$ are dimensionless.)  By Eq. (7.12),

$$\cos \phi = (\tfrac{7}{9})(-\tfrac{4}{9}) + (-\tfrac{4}{9})(\tfrac{1}{9}) + (-\tfrac{4}{9})(-\tfrac{8}{9})$$
$$= \frac{-28 - 4 + 32}{81} = 0,$$

which means that

$$\phi = 90°.$$

**7.3 Vector product of two vectors.** By definition, the vector product $\mathbf{A} \times \mathbf{B}$ of two vectors $\mathbf{A}$ and $\mathbf{B}$ is a vector whose magnitude is the product of the magnitudes of $\mathbf{A}$ and $\mathbf{B}$ and the sine of the angle $\phi$ between them. The direction of the product is perpendicular to the plane defined by the two vectors when their tails are connected, and the sense of the product is determined by the thumb of the right hand when the fingers of the right hand are curled and point from $\mathbf{A}$ to $\mathbf{B}$ through the angle $\phi$. Figure 7.3 shows the vectors $\mathbf{A}$ and $\mathbf{B}$ with their tails together and shows a unit vector $\mathbf{p}$ with direction perpendicular to the plane of $\mathbf{A}$ and $\mathbf{B}$ and sense determined according to the foregoing right-hand rule. Expressed in symbols,

$$\mathbf{A} \times \mathbf{B} = (AB \sin \phi)\mathbf{p}. \quad (7.13)$$

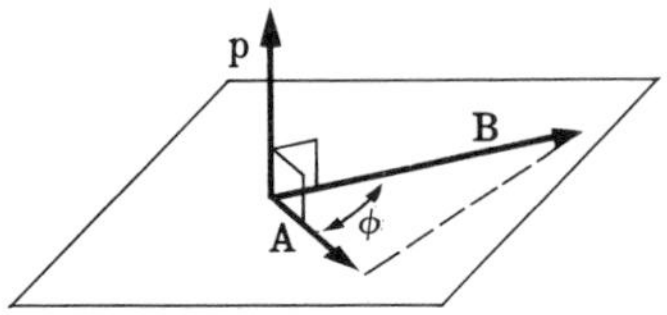

The angle $\phi$ is subjected to the same restrictions as for the scalar product discussed in Art. 7.2. Hence its sine is always positive (or zero), and

$$|\mathbf{A} \times \mathbf{B}| = AB \sin \phi. \quad (7.14)$$

FIGURE 7.3

The following properties of the vector product follow from the definition of Eq. (7.13):

(1) The vector product is not commutative, since, by the definition of the sense of the product,

$$\mathbf{A} \times \mathbf{B} = -\mathbf{B} \times \mathbf{A}. \quad (7.15)$$

(2) Since the sine of zero is zero, it follows that

$$\mathbf{A} \times \mathbf{A} = 0 \quad (7.16)$$

for any $\mathbf{A}$.

(3) If $\mathbf{A} \neq 0$ and $\mathbf{B} \neq 0$, then $\mathbf{A} \times \mathbf{B} = 0$ is a necessary and sufficient condition for parallelism between $\mathbf{A}$ and $\mathbf{B}$, since sin 0 and sin 180° are both zero and since 0 and 180° are the only angles (in the interval specified for $\phi$) with sine of zero.

(4) The vector product is distributive, i.e.,

$$\mathbf{A} \times (\mathbf{B} + \mathbf{C}) = \mathbf{A} \times \mathbf{B} + \mathbf{A} \times \mathbf{C}, \quad (7.17)$$

provided that the order of the vectors in each product is not changed. To verify this important property, consider the vectors $\mathbf{A}$, $\mathbf{B}$, and $\mathbf{C}$ in Fig. 7.4, and let the sum of $\mathbf{B}$ and $\mathbf{C}$ be temporarily called $\mathbf{S}$. Since the vectors $\mathbf{A} \times \mathbf{B}$, $\mathbf{A} \times \mathbf{C}$, and $\mathbf{A} \times \mathbf{S}$ are all perpendicular to $\mathbf{A}$, they may be drawn in a plane perpendicular to $\mathbf{A}$ as shown in Fig. 7.4. Projecting $\mathbf{B}$,

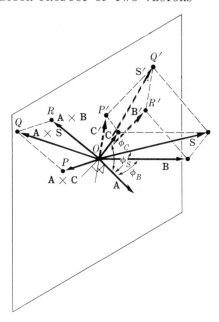

FIGURE 7.4

**C**, and **S** to that plane, we obtain the vectors **B′**, **C′**, and **S′**, where

$$B' = B \sin \phi_B, \qquad C' = C \sin \phi_C, \qquad S' = S \sin \phi_S.$$

By Eq. (7.14), then,

$$|\mathbf{A} \times \mathbf{B}| = AB \sin \phi_B = AB',$$

$$|\mathbf{A} \times \mathbf{C}| = AC \sin \phi_C = AC',$$

$$|\mathbf{A} \times \mathbf{S}| = AS \sin \phi_S = AS'.$$

Since $\mathbf{A} \times \mathbf{B}$ is perpendicular to the plane determined by **A** and **B**, and since **B′** lies in this plane, it follows that $\mathbf{A} \times \mathbf{B}$ is perpendicular to **B′**. Similarly, $\mathbf{A} \times \mathbf{C}$ is perpendicular to **C′**, and $\mathbf{A} \times \mathbf{S}$ is perpendicular to **S′**. Thus, figure $OPQR$ is similar to figure $OP'Q'R'$, inasmuch as two sides and the diagonal of the former are perpendicular to two sides and the diagonal of the latter and the lengths of the two sides and diagonal of the former are proportional to the corresponding lengths for the latter. But it is clear from the geometry of Fig. 7.4 that

$$\mathbf{S'} = \mathbf{B'} + \mathbf{C'}.$$

Hence,

$$\mathbf{A} \times \mathbf{S} = \mathbf{A} \times \mathbf{B} + \mathbf{A} \times \mathbf{C},$$

and Eq. (7.17) is verified.

(5) The vector product is associative, i.e.,

$$(M\mathbf{A}) \times (N\mathbf{B}) = MN(\mathbf{A} \times \mathbf{B}), \tag{7.18}$$

etc., provided again that the order of the vectors is preserved. This property follows directly from Eq. (7.13).

As with the scalar product, a useful equation for evaluating the vector product is derived by expressing $\mathbf{A}$ and $\mathbf{B}$ in terms of their scalar rectangular components, so that

$$\mathbf{A} \times \mathbf{B} = (A_x\mathbf{i} + A_y\mathbf{j} + A_z\mathbf{k}) \times (B_x\mathbf{i} + B_y\mathbf{j} + B_z\mathbf{k}).$$

Expanding the right-hand side by means of Eqs. (7.17) and (7.18),

$$\begin{aligned}
\mathbf{A} \times \mathbf{B} = \ &A_xB_x\mathbf{i} \times \mathbf{i} + A_xB_y\mathbf{i} \times \mathbf{j} + A_xB_z\mathbf{i} \times \mathbf{k} \\
&+ A_yB_x\mathbf{j} \times \mathbf{i} + A_yB_y\mathbf{j} \times \mathbf{j} + A_yB_z\mathbf{j} \times \mathbf{k} \\
&+ A_zB_x\mathbf{k} \times \mathbf{i} + A_zB_y\mathbf{k} \times \mathbf{j} + A_zB_z\mathbf{k} \times \mathbf{k}.
\end{aligned}$$

By property (2) of the vector product,

$$\mathbf{i} \times \mathbf{i} = \mathbf{j} \times \mathbf{j} = \mathbf{k} \times \mathbf{k} = 0, \tag{7.19}$$

and, by the definition of the vector product,

$$\begin{aligned}
\mathbf{i} \times \mathbf{j} = \mathbf{k}, \qquad \mathbf{j} \times \mathbf{k} = \mathbf{i}, \qquad \mathbf{k} \times \mathbf{i} = \mathbf{j}, \\
\mathbf{j} \times \mathbf{i} = -\mathbf{k}, \qquad \mathbf{k} \times \mathbf{j} = -\mathbf{i}, \qquad \mathbf{i} \times \mathbf{k} = -\mathbf{j}.
\end{aligned} \tag{7.20}$$

Hence,

$$\mathbf{A} \times \mathbf{B} = (A_yB_z - A_zB_y)\mathbf{i} + (A_zB_x - A_xB_z)\mathbf{j} + (A_xB_y - A_yB_x)\mathbf{k}. \tag{7.21}$$

Unlike all equations derived in the preceding portion of this book, Eqs. (7.20) and (7.21) require for their validity that the coordinate system used be right-handed. If a left-handed system were used, every term on the right-hand sides of Eqs. (7.20) and (7.21) would have its sign changed. To avoid that difficulty, only right-handed coordinate systems are used in the remainder of this book.

Only the $x$-component of $\mathbf{A} \times \mathbf{B}$ need be remembered; the $y$- and $z$- components can be derived from the $x$-component by a process known as *cyclical permutation*, which is a changing of subscripts in a cyclical order, $x$ to $y$, $y$ to $z$, $z$ to $x$. One permutation gives the $y$-component, a second gives the $z$-component, a third gives the $x$-component again, etc.

The vector product is extremely useful in mechanics. One of its most important applications, that of finding the "moment" of a force, is discussed in detail in the next chapter.

**7.4 Scalar triple product.** Since the vector product is itself a vector, it can be multiplied by other vectors with the use of either dot or cross multiplication. The dot product of a vector $\mathbf{A}$ and another vector $\mathbf{B} \times \mathbf{C}$ is a scalar called the *scalar triple product*. Temporarily designating the vector $\mathbf{B} \times \mathbf{C}$ by the symbol $\mathbf{D}$ and using Eq. (7.7), we have

$$\mathbf{A} \cdot (\mathbf{B} \times \mathbf{C}) = \mathbf{A} \cdot \mathbf{D} = A_x D_x + A_y D_y + A_z D_z.$$

Computing $D_x$, $D_y$, and $D_z$ from Eq. (7.21) and substituting,

$$\mathbf{A} \cdot (\mathbf{B} \times \mathbf{C}) = A_x(B_y C_z - B_z C_y) + A_y(B_z C_x - B_x C_z)$$
$$+ A_z(B_x C_y - B_y C_x),$$

and, regrouping terms,

$$\mathbf{A} \cdot (\mathbf{B} \times \mathbf{C}) = A_x B_y C_z + A_y B_z C_x + A_z B_x C_y$$
$$- A_x B_z C_y - A_y B_x C_z - A_z B_y C_x. \quad (7.22)$$

The right-hand side of Eq. (7.22) includes products of all combinations of different components of $\mathbf{A}$, $\mathbf{B}$, and $\mathbf{C}$, with a positive sign when the subscripts occur in cyclical order and a negative sign otherwise. Such a combination of six products is called a *third-order determinant* and is one of a general class of quantities which are determinants of various orders Equation (7.22) can be rewritten as follows:

$$\mathbf{A} \cdot (\mathbf{B} \times \mathbf{C}) = \begin{vmatrix} A_x & A_y & A_z \\ B_x & B_y & B_z \\ C_x & C_y & C_z \end{vmatrix}, \quad (7.23)$$

the symbol on the right-hand side representing the third-order determinant and hence being the same as the right-hand side of Eq. (7.22).

Inasmuch as the symbol $(\mathbf{A} \cdot \mathbf{B}) \times \mathbf{C}$ is meaningless, the parentheses in the symbol for the scalar triple product are superfluous, and the product may be written $\mathbf{A} \cdot \mathbf{B} \times \mathbf{C}$ without ambiguity, since the cross product must be taken first in every case.

The scalar triple product is significant as the product of $A$ and the scalar component of $\mathbf{B} \times \mathbf{C}$ in the direction of $\mathbf{A}$. Since $\mathbf{B}$ is perpendicular to $\mathbf{B} \times \mathbf{C}$, it follows that

$$\mathbf{B} \cdot \mathbf{B} \times \mathbf{C} = 0, \quad (7.24)$$

and, since $\mathbf{C}$ is perpendicular to $\mathbf{B} \times \mathbf{C}$,

$$\mathbf{C} \cdot \mathbf{B} \times \mathbf{C} = 0. \tag{7.25}$$

Furthermore, since $\mathbf{B} \times \mathbf{B} = \mathbf{0}$, it follows that

$$\mathbf{A} \cdot \mathbf{B} \times \mathbf{B} = 0. \tag{7.26}$$

Summarizing the last three equations, we can say that if any vector appears twice in a scalar triple product, the product is zero.

The following relation can be proved either by expanding the products in terms of components or by using certain properties of determinants:

$$\mathbf{A} \cdot \mathbf{B} \times \mathbf{C} = \mathbf{B} \cdot \mathbf{C} \times \mathbf{A} = \mathbf{C} \cdot \mathbf{A} \times \mathbf{B}. \tag{7.27}$$

Since the dot product is commutative, therefore,

$$\mathbf{A} \cdot \mathbf{B} \times \mathbf{C} = \mathbf{A} \times \mathbf{B} \cdot \mathbf{C}, \tag{7.28}$$

which means that the dot and cross may be interchanged in any scalar triple product. Finally, from Eq. (7.15),

$$\mathbf{A} \cdot \mathbf{B} \times \mathbf{C} = -\mathbf{A} \cdot \mathbf{C} \times \mathbf{B},$$

and thus

$$\mathbf{A} \cdot \mathbf{B} \times \mathbf{C} = -\mathbf{B} \cdot \mathbf{A} \times \mathbf{C}.$$

**7.5 Differentiation of products.** Using the $\Delta$-process, the following formulas for differentiating the products of two vector functions $\mathbf{V}_1(S)$ and $\mathbf{V}_2(S)$ can be derived:

$$\frac{d}{dS}(\mathbf{V}_1 \cdot \mathbf{V}_2) = \mathbf{V}_1 \cdot \frac{d\mathbf{V}_2}{dS} + \frac{d\mathbf{V}_1}{dS} \cdot \mathbf{V}_2 \tag{7.29}$$

and

$$\frac{d}{dS}(\mathbf{V}_1 \times \mathbf{V}_2) = \mathbf{V}_1 \times \frac{d\mathbf{V}_2}{dS} + \frac{d\mathbf{V}_1}{dS} \times \mathbf{V}_2. \tag{7.30}$$

The order of the vectors in each product on the right-hand side of Eq. (7.30) cannot be altered without appropriate changes in sign.

PROBLEMS

7.1 Find $\mathbf{A} \cdot \mathbf{B}$ and $\mathbf{A} \cdot \mathbf{A}$ if: (a) $\mathbf{A} = 3\mathbf{i} + 2\mathbf{j} + 5\mathbf{k}$ and $\mathbf{B} = 2\mathbf{i} + \mathbf{j}$, (b) $\mathbf{A} = 2\mathbf{i} - 3\mathbf{j} + \mathbf{k}$ and $\mathbf{B} = -\mathbf{i} + 3\mathbf{j} + 4\mathbf{k}$.

7.2 Find the scalar component of the force

$$\mathbf{F} = 26\mathbf{i} - 13\mathbf{j} - 52\mathbf{k}\ \text{lb}$$

along a line directed from $(0, 0, 0)$ to $(-3, -4, 12)$.

[*Ans.:* $-50$ lb.]

7.3 (a) Express in terms of $\mathbf{i}$, $\mathbf{j}$, $\mathbf{k}$ a unit vector $\mathbf{m}$ with three direction cosines that are positive and equal. (b) Express in terms of $\mathbf{i}$, $\mathbf{j}$, $\mathbf{k}$ a unit vector $\mathbf{n}$ which defines the positive direction of a line directed from $(1, 4, -7)$ to $(3, 0, -3)$. (c) Find the angle between $\mathbf{m}$ and $\mathbf{n}$.

7.4 (a) Using Eq. (7.14) and Fig. 7.3, show that the magnitude of $\mathbf{A} \times \mathbf{B}$ is equal to twice the area of the triangle having as two of its sides the arrows representing $\mathbf{A}$ and $\mathbf{B}$. (b) Using this fact and Eq. (7.21), find the area of the triangle having the following three vertices: $(0, 0, 0)$, $(2, 2, 2)$, $(-3, 4, 12)$, where all the coordinates are in inches.

[*Ans.:* (b) $18.38\ \text{in}^2$.]

7.5 Find $\mathbf{A} \times \mathbf{B}$ and $\mathbf{A} \times \mathbf{A}$ if: (a) $\mathbf{A} = 3\mathbf{i} + 2\mathbf{j} + 5\mathbf{k}$ and $\mathbf{B} = 2\mathbf{i} + \mathbf{j}$, (b) $\mathbf{A} = 2\mathbf{i} - 3\mathbf{j} + \mathbf{k}$ and $\mathbf{B} = -\mathbf{i} + 3\mathbf{j} + 4\mathbf{k}$.

7.6 Two vectors $\mathbf{A}$ and $\mathbf{B}$ are perpendicular. If

$$\mathbf{C} = \mathbf{A} \times \mathbf{B}, \quad |\mathbf{C}| = 45, \quad \mathbf{A} = -5\mathbf{i} + 14\mathbf{j} - 2\mathbf{k},$$

find $|\mathbf{B}|$.

[*Ans.:* 3.]

7.7 Two vectors $\mathbf{A}$ and $\mathbf{B}$ are perpendicular. If

$$\mathbf{A} = -5\mathbf{i} + 14\mathbf{j} - 2\mathbf{k}, \quad B_x = 10, \quad B_y = 3,$$

find $\mathbf{B}$.

7.8 Two vectors $\mathbf{A}$ and $\mathbf{B}$ are parallel but have opposite senses. If

$$M = \mathbf{A} \cdot \mathbf{B}, \quad |M| = 44, \quad \mathbf{A} = 2\mathbf{i} - 6\mathbf{j} + 9\mathbf{k},$$

find $|\mathbf{B}|$.

[*Ans.:* 4.]

7.9 Two vectors $\mathbf{A}$ and $\mathbf{B}$ are parallel but have opposite senses. If

$$\mathbf{A} = 2\mathbf{i} - 6\mathbf{j} + 9\mathbf{k}, \quad B_x = -4, \quad B_y = 12,$$

find $\mathbf{B}$.

7.10 Given:

$$\mathbf{A} = -3\mathbf{i} - 2\mathbf{j} + 4\mathbf{k}, \qquad \mathbf{B} = 2\mathbf{i} - \mathbf{j}, \qquad \mathbf{C} = \mathbf{i} + \mathbf{j} + \mathbf{k}.$$

Find $\mathbf{A} \cdot \mathbf{B} \times \mathbf{C}$.

[*Ans.:* 19.]

7.11 Use the Δ-process to verify the following formula:

$$\frac{d}{dS}(\mathbf{U} \cdot \mathbf{V} \times \mathbf{W}) = \mathbf{U} \cdot \mathbf{V} \times \frac{d\mathbf{W}}{dS} + \mathbf{U} \cdot \frac{d\mathbf{V}}{dS} \times \mathbf{W} + \frac{d\mathbf{U}}{dS} \cdot \mathbf{V} \times \mathbf{W}.$$

# CHAPTER 8

## NONCONCURRENT FORCE SYSTEMS

**8.1 Moment of a force.** The concept of *moment of a force about a point* can be introduced by considering the force **F** and the point $O$ shown in Fig. 8.1. If **r** is a position vector (i.e., $r$ has dimensions of length) from $O$ to any point $P$ on the line of action of **F**, then the moment **M** of **F** about $O$ is defined by

$$\mathbf{M} = \mathbf{r} \times \mathbf{F}. \tag{8.1}$$

The vector **M** is perpendicular to that plane through **F** which contains the point $O$. The magnitude of **M**, from Eq. (7.14), is given by

$$M = rF \sin \phi = eF, \tag{8.2}$$

where $e$ is the perpendicular distance from $O$ to the line of action of **F**. From these results it can be concluded that the moment **M** is influenced strongly by the line of action of the force as well as by its magnitude and direction. If the force were acting on a body constrained in such a way that point $O$ of the body always remained a fixed point in space, the tendency of the force to "rotate" the body about $O$ would be found by experiment to be influenced both by $F$, the magnitude of the force, and by $e$, its "lever arm." Hence, by Eq. (8.2), $M$ is a measure of the tendency of the force to produce rotation. The direction of **M** indicates the axis through $O$ about which **F** would tend to rotate the body (although any actual rotation might be about some other axis through $O$).

To demonstrate that the choice of the point $P$ on the line of action of **F** does not affect **M**, let us consider the use of any other point $P'$ and the corresponding position vector $\mathbf{r}'$, as shown in Fig. 8.2. A position vector

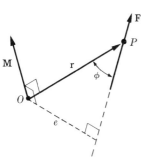

FIGURE 8.1

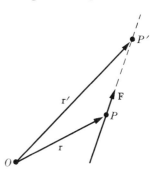

FIGURE 8.2

127

from $P$ to $P'$ can be expressed as the product of a scalar $k$ (with units of length/force) and the vector $\mathbf{F}$, so that

$$\mathbf{r}' = \mathbf{r} + k\mathbf{F}.$$

Hence,

$$\mathbf{r}' \times \mathbf{F} = (\mathbf{r} + k\mathbf{F}) \times \mathbf{F} = \mathbf{r} \times \mathbf{F} + k\mathbf{F} \times \mathbf{F}.$$

By Eq. (7.16), however,

$$\mathbf{F} \times \mathbf{F} = \mathbf{0},$$

so that

$$\mathbf{r}' \times \mathbf{F} = \mathbf{r} \times \mathbf{F}.$$

If the line of action of $\mathbf{F}$ intersects $O$, then any $\mathbf{r}$ from $O$ to a point on the line of action of $\mathbf{F}$ is parallel to $\mathbf{F}$, which means that $\mathbf{M} = \mathbf{0}$.

The concept of *moment of a force about a line* can be introduced by considering a line $L$ through $O$, as shown in Fig. 8.3. As usual, a unit vector $\mathbf{n}$ is used to identify the direction and sense of $L$. By definition, the moment of $\mathbf{F}$ about $L$ is the scalar component of the vector $\mathbf{M}$ in the $L$-direction, i.e.,

$$M_L = \mathbf{n} \cdot \mathbf{M} = \mathbf{n} \cdot \mathbf{r} \times \mathbf{F}. \tag{8.3}$$

If the force were acting on a body constrained in such a way that line $L$ in the body always remained a fixed line in space (i.e., a fixed axis of rotation), $M_L$ would be a measure of the tendency of the force to rotate the body about $L$.

The moment $M_L$ is independent of the choices of both $O$ and $P$; a position vector from any other point on $L$ to any other point on the line of action of $\mathbf{F}$ gives the same value as when $O$ and $P$ are used. To demonstrate this, consider points $O'$ and $P'$ in Fig. 8.4, and let $\mathbf{r}''$ be directed

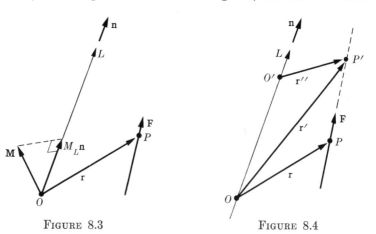

FIGURE 8.3                     FIGURE 8.4

from $O'$ to $P'$. In this case,

$$\mathbf{r}'' = \mathbf{r} + k_1\mathbf{F} - k_2\mathbf{n},$$

where $k_1$ has dimensions of length/force and $k_2$ has dimensions of length. Hence,

$$\mathbf{n} \cdot \mathbf{r}'' \times \mathbf{F} = \mathbf{n} \cdot (\mathbf{r} + k_1\mathbf{F} - k_2\mathbf{n}) \times \mathbf{F}$$
$$= \mathbf{n} \cdot \mathbf{r} \times \mathbf{F} + k_1\mathbf{n} \cdot \mathbf{F} \times \mathbf{F} - k_2\mathbf{n} \cdot \mathbf{n} \times \mathbf{F}.$$

By Eqs. (7.24) and (7.26), therefore,

$$\mathbf{n} \cdot \mathbf{r}'' \times \mathbf{F} = \mathbf{n} \cdot \mathbf{r} \times \mathbf{F}.$$

If the line of action of $\mathbf{F}$ intersects $L$ or if $\mathbf{F}$ is parallel to $L$, then $\mathbf{F}$ and $L$ define a plane in space, the moment $\mathbf{M}$ being perpendicular to this plane and the vector $\mathbf{n}$ lying in the plane. In that case, $\mathbf{n}$ and $\mathbf{M}$ are perpendicular, and, by Eq. (8.3), $M_L = 0$ (even though $\mathbf{M}$ is not necessarily a null vector).

Moments about $O$ and about lines through $O$ can be evaluated readily by employing a cartesian coordinate system with origin at $O$, as shown in Fig. 8.5. If $x$, $y$, $z$ are the coordinates of $P$ (i.e., the components of $\mathbf{r}$), then, by Eqs. (7.21) and (8.1),

$$\mathbf{M} = (yF_z - zF_y)\mathbf{i} + (zF_x - xF_z)\mathbf{j} + (xF_y - yF_x)\mathbf{k}. \tag{8.4}$$

By Eq. (8.3),

$$M_x = \mathbf{i} \cdot \mathbf{M} = yF_z - zF_y,$$
$$M_y = \mathbf{j} \cdot \mathbf{M} = zF_x - xF_z, \tag{8.5}$$
$$M_z = \mathbf{k} \cdot \mathbf{M} = xF_y - yF_x,$$

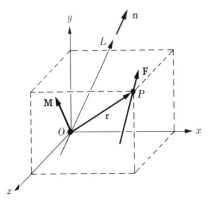

FIGURE 8.5

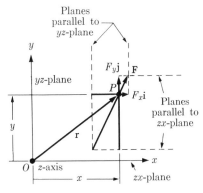

FIGURE 8.6

and, also by Eq. (8.3),

$$M_L = n_x M_x + n_y M_y + n_z M_z. \tag{8.6}$$

The units of $M_x$, $M_y$, $M_z$, and $M_L$ are length-force (e.g., ft-lb).

To investigate the significance of Eqs. (8.5), consider, for example, the last of the three equations. If a view is taken in the negative $z$-direction as in Fig. 8.6, the $yz$- and $zx$-planes appear edgewise and the $z$-axis appears as a point. (The point $P$, of course, is not in the plane of the paper in this figure.) It can now be seen that the moment $M_z$ about the $z$-axis is, by the third of Eqs. (8.5), composed of two parts: a *counterclockwise moment* equal to the product of $x$, the perpendicular distance from the $z$-axis to $F_y \mathbf{j}$, and $F_y$; and a *clockwise moment* equal to the product of $y$, the perpendicular distance from the $z$-axis to $F_x \mathbf{i}$, and $F_x$. The actual moment $M_z$ is computed by considering *counterclockwise moments positive and clockwise moments negative*, so that, when $x$, $y$, $F_x$, and $F_y$ are all positive quantities (as they are in Fig. 8.6), the moment $yF_x$ is subtracted from the moment $xF_y$. Similar statements apply to $M_x$ and $M_y$ when the view is taken in the negative $x$-direction and the negative $y$-direction, respectively.

Any of the six components on the right-hand sides of Eqs. (8.5) may be negative, and they must all be substituted into the equations with their correct signs, whereupon the equations automatically indicate whether the two parts must be added or subtracted and automatically give the correct sign to the moment components.

---

EXAMPLE 8.1. Find the moments of the force shown in Fig. 8.7: (a) about $O$, and (b) about a line through $O$ making equal angles with all three axes.

*Solution.* The force $\mathbf{F}$ may be expressed in terms of its rectangular components by the methods of Art. 3.4 to obtain

$$\mathbf{F} = -6\mathbf{i} + 18\mathbf{j} + 9\mathbf{k} \text{ lb.}$$

The arbitrariness of the point $P$ is advantageous in the actual computation of moments, since the point may be chosen for maximum convenience. In this example, choosing as $P$ the point where the line of action of $\mathbf{F}$ intersects the $x$-axis gives a very simple $\mathbf{r}$, namely,

$$\mathbf{r} = 4\mathbf{i} \text{ in.}$$

(a) Using the foregoing results and Eq. (8.4),

$$
\begin{aligned}
\mathbf{M} &= [(0)(9) - (0)(18)]\mathbf{i} + [(0)(-6) - (4)(9)]\mathbf{j} + [(4)(18) - (0)(-6)]\mathbf{k} \\
&= -36\mathbf{j} + 72\mathbf{k} \text{ in-lb.}
\end{aligned}
$$

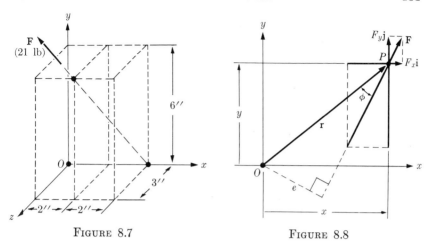

FIGURE 8.7                            FIGURE 8.8

(b) Since the components of a unit vector are its direction cosines, the unit vector **n** lying along a line which makes equal angles with all three axes is, by Eq. (2.25),

$$\mathbf{n} = \frac{1}{\sqrt{3}}\mathbf{i} + \frac{1}{\sqrt{3}}\mathbf{j} + \frac{1}{\sqrt{3}}\mathbf{k}.$$

Thus, by Eq. (8.6),

$$M_L = \left(\frac{1}{\sqrt{3}}\right)(-36) + \left(\frac{1}{\sqrt{3}}\right)(72) = 20.8 \text{ in-lb}.$$

If the force **F** lies in the $xy$-plane, as shown in Fig. 8.8, both $F_z$ and the $z$-coordinate of any point on the line of action of **F** are zero, and, by Eqs. (8.5),

$$M_x = 0, \qquad M_y = 0, \qquad M_z = xF_y - yF_x.$$

In this case, therefore,

$$M = |M_z| = eF.$$

The last equation gives the absolute value of $M_z$ but does not determine the proper sign for $M_z$. Hence, to find $M_z$ by this equation, the quantity $eF$ must be given a plus sign if the moment is counterclockwise when viewed in the negative $z$-direction and a minus sign if it is clockwise. The equation

$$M_z = xF_y - yF_x$$

automatically gives the correct sign to $M_z$.

It is obvious from the way in which moments are defined that the position of the force along its line of action affects neither its moment about a point nor its moment about a line.

**8.2 Moments of several forces.** For a group of $N$ nonconcurrent forces $F_1$, $F_2$, ..., $F_N$, let $F_i$ be any one of the group (that is, $i$ may be any integer from 1 to $N$). If $M_i$ is the moment of this force about $O$, then

$$M_i = r_i \times F_i, \tag{8.7}$$

where $r_i$ is a position vector from $O$ to any point on the line of action of $F_i$. For a line $L$ through $O$ with a unit vector $n$, the moment $M_{iL}$ of $F_i$ about $L$ is given by

$$M_{iL} = n \cdot M_i. \tag{8.8}$$

If a cartesian coordinate system with origin at $O$ is used, and if $x_i$, $y_i$, $z_i$ are the coordinates of the point $P_i$ chosen on the line of action of $F_i$, then

$$M_{ix} = y_i F_{iz} - z_i F_{iy},$$

$$M_{iy} = z_i F_{ix} - x_i F_{iz}, \tag{8.9}$$

$$M_{iz} = x_i F_{iy} - y_i F_{ix}.$$

The *total moment* $T$ of all the forces about the point $O$ is by definition the vector sum of the moments of the individual forces about $O$, that is,

$$T = M_1 + M_2 + \cdots + M_N. \tag{8.10}$$

By Eqs. (2.26),

$$T_x = \sum_{i=1}^{N} M_{ix}, \qquad T_y = \sum_{i=1}^{N} M_{iy}, \qquad T_z = \sum_{i=1}^{N} M_{iz}, \tag{8.11}$$

these equations being similar to Eqs. (3.9). The component of $T$ along the line $L$ through $O$ is called the total moment about $L$ and is found, using Eqs. (8.8) and (8.10), as follows:

$$T_L = n \cdot T = n \cdot (M_1 + M_2 + \cdots + M_N) = \sum_{i=1}^{N} n \cdot M_i = \sum_{i=1}^{N} M_{iL}. \tag{8.12}$$

In the special case where all the forces in the group are concurrent, a single position vector $r$ from $O$ to the point of concurrency may be used in finding all the moments. A group of three concurrent forces is shown in Fig. 8.9. As mentioned in Art. 3.4, the resultant $R$ is assigned a line of action through the point of concurrency. By Eq. (8.10),

$$T = r \times F_1 + r \times F_2 + r \times F_3,$$

and from this it follows, since the cross product is distributive, that

$$T = r \times (F_1 + F_2 + F_3) = r \times R.$$

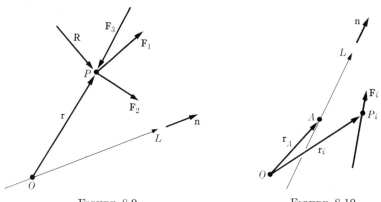

FIGURE 8.9                              FIGURE 8.10

Since **r** is the position vector of a point on the line of action of **R**, the vector **r** × **R** is the moment of **R** about $O$, and the last equation states that the total moment of the group of concurrent forces about the point $O$ is equal to the moment of their resultant about $O$. This result is known as *Varignon's theorem*. It applies for any number of concurrent forces and any point in space, but it is true only if **R** is assigned a line of action through the point of concurrency.

A similar theorem holds for any line $L$ through $O$; that is, the total moment of a group of concurrent forces about a line $L$ is equal to the moment of their resultant about $L$. The proof of this for three forces comes from Eq. (8.12) as follows:

$$T_L = \mathbf{n} \cdot \mathbf{r} \times \mathbf{F}_1 + \mathbf{n} \cdot \mathbf{r} \times \mathbf{F}_2 + \mathbf{n} \cdot \mathbf{r} \times \mathbf{F}_3$$
$$= \mathbf{n} \cdot \mathbf{r} \times (\mathbf{F}_1 + \mathbf{F}_2 + \mathbf{F}_3) = \mathbf{n} \cdot \mathbf{r} \times \mathbf{R}.$$

It is often necessary to compute moments about some reference point other than the origin or about some line that does not go through the origin. If $A$ is such a point and $L$ is such a line, as shown in Fig. 8.10, the moment of a force $\mathbf{F}_i$ about $A$ can be distinguished from that about $O$ by a superscript, so that

$$\mathbf{M}_i^A = (\mathbf{r}_i - \mathbf{r}_A) \times \mathbf{F}_i. \tag{8.13}$$

Similarly,

$$M_{iL}^A = \mathbf{n} \cdot \mathbf{M}_i^A, \tag{8.14}$$

and

$$M_{ix}^A = (y_i - y_A)F_{iz} - (z_i - z_A)F_{iy},$$
$$M_{iy}^A = (z_i - z_A)F_{ix} - (x_i - x_A)F_{iz}, \tag{8.15}$$
$$M_{iz}^A = (x_i - x_A)F_{iy} - (y_i - y_A)F_{ix},$$

where $M_{ix}^A$, $M_{iy}^A$, $M_{iz}^A$ are the moments about lines through $A$ parallel to the $x$-, $y$-, and $z$-axes, respectively.

Several moments about the same point or about the same line may be added, so that

$$\mathbf{T}^A = \mathbf{M}_1^A + \mathbf{M}_2^A + \cdots + \mathbf{M}_N^A, \tag{8.16}$$

and

$$T_x^A = \sum_{i=1}^{N} M_{ix}^A, \qquad T_y^A = \sum_{i=1}^{N} M_{iy}^A, \qquad T_z^A = \sum_{i=1}^{N} M_{iz}^A. \tag{8.17}$$

Likewise,

$$T_L^A = \mathbf{n} \cdot \mathbf{T}^A = \sum_{i=1}^{N} \mathbf{n} \cdot \mathbf{M}_i^A = \sum_{i=1}^{N} M_{iL}^A. \tag{8.18}$$

Using Eqs. (8.7), (8.10), (8.13), and (8.16) and the properties of the cross product, we can show that the total moment $\mathbf{T}^A$ of a group of nonconcurrent forces about a point $A$ is given in terms of its moment $\mathbf{T}$ about the origin by

$$\mathbf{T}^A = \mathbf{T} - \mathbf{r}_A \times \mathbf{R}, \tag{8.19}$$

where $\mathbf{r}_A$ is the position vector of $A$ and $\mathbf{R}$ is the resultant of the forces.

**8.3 Couples.** A *couple* is a set of two forces with equal magnitudes, opposite directions, and different lines of action. Two such forces $\mathbf{F}_1$ and $\mathbf{F}_2$ are shown in Fig. 8.11. As indicated in the figure, if $\mathbf{F}_1 = \mathbf{F}$, then $\mathbf{F}_2 = -\mathbf{F}$. The total moment of the two forces about $O$, called a *couple vector* and designated by the symbol $\mathbf{C}$, is, by Eqs. (8.7) and (8.10),

$$\mathbf{C} = \mathbf{M}_1 + \mathbf{M}_2 = \mathbf{r}_1 \times \mathbf{F}_1 + \mathbf{r}_2 \times \mathbf{F}_2.$$

Substituting for $\mathbf{F}_1$ and $\mathbf{F}_2$, we have

$$\mathbf{C} = \mathbf{r}_1 \times \mathbf{F} + \mathbf{r}_2 \times (-\mathbf{F}) = (\mathbf{r}_1 - \mathbf{r}_2) \times \mathbf{F},$$

and, letting

$$\mathbf{b} = \mathbf{r}_1 - \mathbf{r}_2,$$

we find that

$$\mathbf{C} = \mathbf{b} \times \mathbf{F}. \tag{8.20}$$

Since points $P_1$ and $P_2$ are arbitrary, $\mathbf{b}$ is a vector from any point on the line of action of $-\mathbf{F}$ to any point on the line of action of $\mathbf{F}$. It is clear from Eq. (8.20) that the vector $\mathbf{C}$ does not depend on the location of point $O$, which means that the total moment of the two forces forming a couple is the same about every point in space.

The magnitude of $\mathbf{C}$ is given by

$$C = fF, \tag{8.21}$$

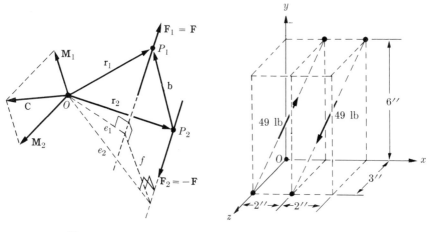

FIGURE 8.11                                    FIGURE 8.12

where $f$ is the perpendicular distance between the two lines of action (Fig. 8.11); the direction of $C$ is perpendicular to the plane determined by the two lines of action; and the sense of $C$ is indicated by the thumb of the right hand when the fingers of the right hand show the kind of rotation which the couple tends to produce.

If the force $F$ and the vector $b$ are expressed in terms of cartesian components, then, by Eqs. (7.21) and (8.20),

$$C = (b_y F_z - b_z F_y)i + (b_z F_x - b_x F_z)j + (b_x F_y - b_y F_x)k. \quad (8.22)$$

A couple vector $C$ differs from a moment in that $C$ is the sum of two moments.

EXAMPLE 8.2. Find the moment of the couple in Fig. 8.12 about any point in space.

Solution. Let the force intersecting the $z$-axis be $F$, and, for simplicity, let $b$ be parallel to the $x$-axis, so that

$$b = -2i \text{ in.}$$

and

$$F = 14i + 42j - 21k \text{ lb.}$$

By Eq. (8.22), since $b_y = b_z = 0$,

$$C = -(-2)(-21)j + (-2)(42)k = -42j - 84k \text{ in-lb.}$$

The total moment about a line $L$ of the two forces constituting a couple is, by Eq. (8.12), the $L$-component of $\mathbf{C}$, which is given by

$$C_L = \mathbf{n} \cdot \mathbf{C} = \mathbf{n} \cdot \mathbf{b} \times \mathbf{F}. \qquad (8.23)$$

This moment depends upon the direction of $L$ but not upon the actual location of $L$ in space.

Two couple vectors are equal if they have the same magnitude and direction. This means that the quantity $fF$ is the same for both couples (even though the factors $f$ and $F$ may be different for each couple) and that the two pairs of forces are in parallel planes (even though one pair of forces may not be parallel to the other). An example of two couples with equal couple vectors is shown in Fig. 8.13.

Addition of $N$ couple vectors is accomplished in the usual way, i.e.,

$$\mathbf{T} = \mathbf{C}_1 + \mathbf{C}_2 + \cdots + \mathbf{C}_N,$$

and

$$(8.24)$$

$$T_x = \sum_{i=1}^{N} C_{ix},$$

$$T_y = \sum_{i=1}^{N} C_{iy}, \qquad (8.25)$$

$$T_z = \sum_{i=1}^{N} C_{iz}.$$

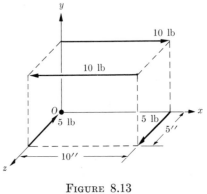

FIGURE 8.13

The total moment obtained in this way is, of course, the total moment about any point of all the $2N$ forces which make up the couples.

If all the forces making up a group of couples lie in the same plane, say the $xy$-plane, then all the couple vectors are parallel to the $z$-axis and may be replaced by the algebraic quantities $C_{iz}$. These quantities have units of length-force and are positive if the couples they represent produce counterclockwise rotation. They are often represented on drawings of the $xy$-plane by circular arrows labeled with the magnitudes of the couple vectors. Figure 8.14(a) shows a couple in the $xy$-plane, and Fig. 8.14(b) shows the way in which such a couple is represented. This method displays on the drawing all those aspects of the couple which are essential in determining its effect on a mechanical system, just as the couple-vector representation does in three dimensions.

Couples occur very frequently in mechanics, although they do not always consist of two distinct concentrated forces such as the couples considered so far. For example, the twisting effect or "torque" exerted on a driven wheel by its axle is essentially a couple and may be repre-

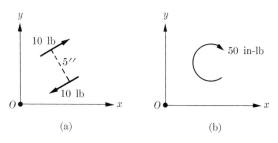

FIGURE 8.14

sented by a couple vector or by a curved arrow of the type shown in Fig. 8.14(b).

**8.4 Mechanical equivalence.** Two force systems are said to be *mechanically equivalent* or *equipollent* if they have equal resultants and equal total moments about any point in space. (The resultant of any group of forces, concurrent or nonconcurrent, is defined and discussed in Art. 3.2.) If single primes are used to denote one of the systems and double primes the other, the relationship of mechanical equivalence can be expressed by the following two equations:

$$\mathbf{R'} = \mathbf{R''}, \qquad \mathbf{T'} = \mathbf{T''}. \tag{8.26}$$

The second equation must hold for any other reference point as well as for the origin. It follows from Eq. (8.19), however, that, if two force systems have the same resultant, i.e., satisfy the first of Eqs. (8.26), then the second of Eqs. (8.26) is a necessary and sufficient condition for equal total moments about any point. This makes it necessary in establishing mechanical equivalence to use only one reference point for moments.

Either of the two force systems may contain some couples; these contribute nothing to the first of Eqs. (8.26) but give rise to couple vectors which must be included in the second of Eqs. (8.26). (Couple vectors may be added to moments about any point.)

The two vector conditions for mechanical equivalence may be restated as six scalar conditions, i.e.,

$$R'_x = R''_x, \qquad R'_y = R''_y, \qquad R'_z = R''_z,$$
$$T'_x = T''_x, \qquad T'_y = T''_y, \qquad T'_z = T''_z. \tag{8.27}$$

Substituting Eqs. (3.9) and (8.11) into Eqs. (8.27) leads to the following six equations (in which the summations are written in abbreviated form):

$$\sum F'_x = \sum F''_x, \qquad \sum F'_y = \sum F''_y, \qquad \sum F'_z = \sum F''_z,$$
$$\sum M'_x = \sum M''_x, \qquad \sum M'_y = \sum M''_y, \qquad \sum M'_z = \sum M''_z. \tag{8.28}$$

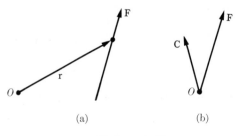

(a)                           (b)

FIGURE 8.15

The appropriate components of any couple vectors present must be included in the last three of Eqs. (8.28); this can be accomplished without
actually finding the couple vectors by including the moment components
of all the individual forces which make up the couples.

Two important force systems which are mechanically equivalent are a
concurrent force system and its resultant. (These two systems have the
same total moment about any point by Varignon's theorem.) For more
general force systems also, the resultant is given, whenever possible, a
line of action such that the resultant alone is mechanically equivalent to
the system from which it is derived. Finding this line of action is one of a
general class of problems in which one force system is replaced by another
that is mechanically equivalent to it.

It is often necessary, for example, to replace a given system by one consisting of a single force through a given point and a couple, the latter system being called a *force-couple system*. In such a system, the two forces of
which the couple is composed are unimportant; only the magnitude and
direction of the couple vector need be considered to ensure the mechanical
equivalence of the two systems. As the simplest problem of this type, consider the replacement of the single force $\mathbf{F}$ in Fig. 8.15(a) by a force-couple
system at $O$, as shown in Fig. 8.15(b). The first of Eqs. (8.26) is satisfied
if the force in the force-couple system is $\mathbf{F}$. The second of Eqs. (8.26) requires that

$$\mathbf{C} = \mathbf{r} \times \mathbf{F}.$$

The same result can be achieved by using the intermediate step depicted
in Fig. 8.16, i.e., by adding to the original system forces $\mathbf{F}$ and $-\mathbf{F}$ with
lines of action through $O$. (The added forces change neither $\mathbf{R}$ nor $\mathbf{T}$.) It
is now possible to discern a couple in Fig. 8.16 with a couple vector $\mathbf{r} \times \mathbf{F}$,
so that the previous result follows immediately. As mentioned earlier,
however, the forces which make up the couple need not be $\mathbf{F}$ and $-\mathbf{F}$.
Any other pair of forces $\mathbf{F}'$ and $-\mathbf{F}'$ (with vector $\mathbf{b}'$ from $-\mathbf{F}'$ to $\mathbf{F}'$) is
acceptable provided that

$$\mathbf{b}' \times \mathbf{F}' = \mathbf{r} \times \mathbf{F}.$$

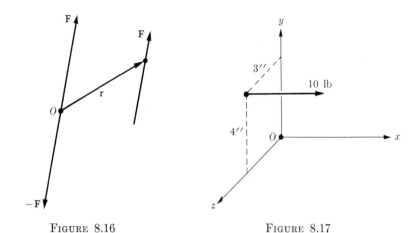

FIGURE 8.16　　　　　　　　　　　　FIGURE 8.17

EXAMPLE 8.3. Replace the single force in Fig. 8.17 by a force-couple system at $O$.

*Solution.* Referring to Fig. 8.15(b) for the unknown system, we find that Eqs. (8.28) require that

$$F_x = 10 \text{ lb}, \qquad F_y = 0, \qquad F_z = 0,$$

and

$$C_x = 0, \qquad C_y = 30 \text{ in-lb}, \qquad C_z = -40 \text{ in-lb}.$$

Hence the required force-couple system is

$$\mathbf{F} = 10\mathbf{i} \text{ lb}, \qquad \mathbf{C} = 30\mathbf{j} - 40\mathbf{k} \text{ in-lb}.$$

The same result can be obtained by adding to the original system forces $10\mathbf{i}$ lb and $-10\mathbf{i}$ lb at the origin.

---

The problem of replacing a force-couple system by a single force cannot usually be solved, since it can be shown that, when $\mathbf{F}$ and $\mathbf{C}$ are given vectors, the equation

$$\mathbf{r} \times \mathbf{F} = \mathbf{C}$$

is solvable for $\mathbf{r}$ only when $\mathbf{F}$ is perpendicular to $\mathbf{C}$. The finding of the single force in cases where the perpendicularity condition is fulfilled is discussed in the next article.

Replacing a complicated force system by a force-couple system is called *reduction* of the given system to a force-couple system. By the first of Eqs. (8.26), the force in the force-couple system must be $\mathbf{R}$, the resultant of the original system. Calling the couple vector **C**, the force-couple system is shown in Fig. 8.18, and Eqs. (8.28) require that

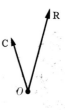

$$R_x = \Sigma F_x, \qquad R_y = \Sigma F_y, \qquad R_z = \Sigma F_z,$$
$$C_x = \Sigma M_x, \qquad C_y = \Sigma M_y, \qquad C_z = \Sigma M_z,$$
$$(8.29)$$

FIGURE 8.18

where the right-hand sides refer to the original system. The first three of Eqs. (8.29) are the same as Eqs. (3.9).

---

EXAMPLE 8.4. Reduce the plane force system shown in Fig. 8.19 to a force-couple system at $O$.

*Solution.* Referring to Fig. 8.18 for the unknown system, we find that Eqs. (8.29) give

$$R_x = 300 - 300 + \tfrac{4}{5}(500) = 400 \text{ lb},$$

$$R_y = -\tfrac{3}{5}(500) = -300 \text{ lb},$$

$$R_z = 0,$$

and, taking **r** for the 500-lb force along the $x$-axis,

$$C_x = 0, \qquad C_y = 0, \qquad C_z = 9(300) + 12(-300) = -900 \text{ ft-lb}.$$

Hence,

$$\mathbf{R} = 400\mathbf{i} - 300\mathbf{j} \text{ lb}, \qquad \mathbf{C} = -900\mathbf{k} \text{ ft-lb}.$$

The result is pictured in Fig. 8.20.

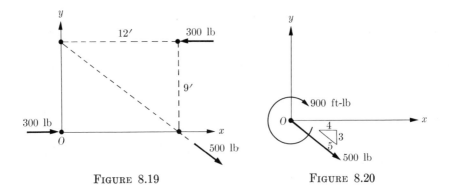

FIGURE 8.19            FIGURE 8.20

The following example demonstrates the reduction of a three-dimensional force system to a force-couple system.

---

EXAMPLE 8.5.   Reduce the force system shown in Fig. 8.21 to a force-couple system at $O$.

*Solution.* By Eqs. (8.29),

$$R_x = \tfrac{4}{5}(500) = 400 \text{ lb}, \quad R_y = -400 \text{ lb}, \quad R_z = 300 - \tfrac{3}{5}(500) = 0,$$

and

$$C_x = 9(300) + 9(400) - 9(300) = 3600 \text{ ft-lb},$$

$$C_y = -12(300) + 12(300) = 0,$$

$$C_z = -9(400) = -3600 \text{ ft-lb}.$$

Hence,

$$\mathbf{R} = 400\mathbf{i} - 400\mathbf{j} \text{ lb}, \quad \mathbf{C} = 3600\mathbf{i} - 3600\mathbf{k} \text{ ft-lb}.$$

**8.5 The resultant of a nonconcurrent force system.** Any force system can be reduced to a force-couple system in which the force is $\mathbf{R}$. In the event that $\mathbf{R} = \mathbf{0}$, the system is reducible to a single couple. In the event that both $\mathbf{R}$ and $\mathbf{C}$ are null vectors, the force system is a special type considered in Chapter 11.

If, in the force-couple system to which the given system is reduced, $\mathbf{R}$ is perpendicular to $\mathbf{C}$, the system can be reduced further to a single force, and the line of action required for this force is the line of action assigned to the resultant. Two cases where this is possible are the system in a plane ($\mathbf{R}$ being in the plane and $\mathbf{C}$ being perpendicular to it) and the parallel system ($\mathbf{R}$ being parallel to the given forces and $\mathbf{C}$ having no component in the direction of the given forces). Thus, any force system of these two types (for which $\mathbf{R}$ and $\mathbf{C}$ are not both null vectors) can be reduced either to a single force $\mathbf{R}$ or to a single couple $\mathbf{C}$ (if $\mathbf{R}$ is a null vector).

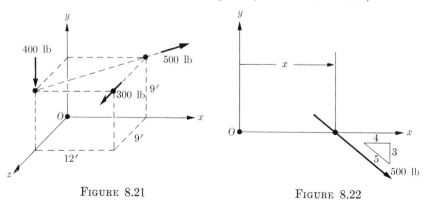

FIGURE 8.21                    FIGURE 8.22

EXAMPLE 8.6.   Locate the line of action of **R** for the nonconcurrent force system of Example 8.4.

*Solution.* The line of action of a force with known direction can be specified completely by stating the coordinates of one point on the line, and a convenient point to choose for the plane system is the point where the line intersects the $x$-axis. Figure 8.22 shows the single force to which the system of Fig. 8.20 must be reduced. By the last of Eqs. (8.28),

$$-300x = -900,$$

from which

$$x = 3 \text{ ft},$$

and the resultant intersects the $x$-axis 3 ft to the right of $O$.

––––––––––––––––––––

If **R** is not perpendicular to **C**, as is the case in Example 8.5, it is impossible to assign a line of action to **R**.

## PROBLEMS

8.1   Verify Eq. (8.19).

8.2   Find the moment about $O$ of a 600-lb force directed from $(6, 2, -1)$ to $(7, 4, -3)$, all coordinates in ft.

[*Ans.:* $-400\mathbf{i} + 2200\mathbf{j} + 2000\mathbf{k}$ ft-lb.]

8.3   The force **F** in Fig. 8.23 is horizontal (i.e., is parallel to the $zx$-plane) and is perpendicular to **r**. If $r = 17.32$ in. and $F_x = -40$ lb, find the moment of **F** about $O$.

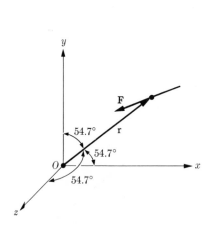

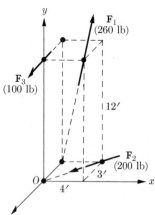

FIGURE 8.23                          FIGURE 8.24

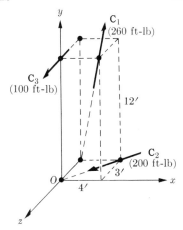

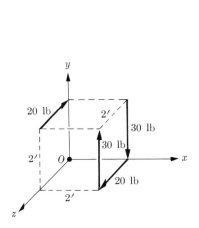

FIGURE 8.25        FIGURE 8.26

8.4 (a) In Fig. 8.24, find the moment of each of the forces shown about $O$. (b) Find the total moment about $O$. (c) Using the result of part (b), find the total moment about a line $L$ through $O$ defined by

$$n = \frac{1}{2}i - \frac{1}{2}j - \frac{1}{\sqrt{2}}k.$$

(d) Find the angle between $F_1$ and $F_2$.

[*Ans.:* (b) $1920i - 240j$ ft-lb; (c) $1080$ ft-lb; (d) $96.2°$.]

8.5 Using Varignon's theorem, find the total moment about $O$ of the three concurrent forces of Example 3.2.

8.6 Find the moment of each of the two couples shown in Fig. 8.25 about any point. What is the total moment of the two couples?

[*Ans.:* $T = -100i - 40j$ ft-lb.]

8.7 Find the total moment about any point of the three couples represented by the couple vectors in Fig. 8.26.

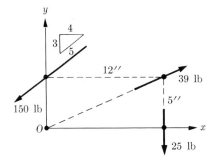

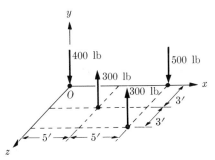

FIGURE 8.27        FIGURE 8.28

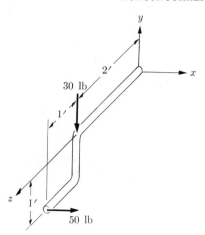

FIGURE 8.29

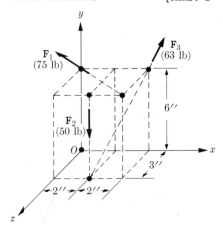

FIGURE 8.30

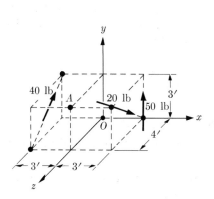

FIGURE 8.31

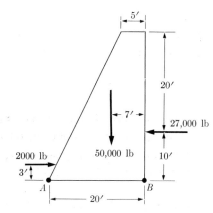

FIGURE 8.32

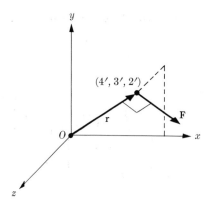

FIGURE 8.33

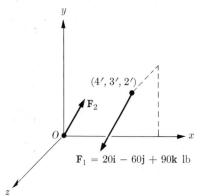

FIGURE 8.34

8.8 Reduce the force system shown in Fig. 8.27 to a force-couple system at $O$.

[*Ans.:* $R = -84i - 100j$ lb, $C = 300k$ in-lb.]

8.9 Reduce the parallel force system shown in Fig. 8.28 to a force-couple system at $O$.

8.10 The crank in Fig. 8.29 carries two forces, a 50-lb force parallel to the $x$-axis and a 30-lb force parallel to the $y$-axis. Reduce the system of two forces to a force-couple system at the origin.

[*Ans.:* $R = 50i - 30j$ lb, $C = 60i + 150j + 50k$ ft-lb.]

8.11 Reduce the force system in Fig. 8.30 to a force-couple system at $O$.

8.12 (a) Reduce the force system in Fig. 8.31 to a force-couple system at $A$. (b) Using the results of part (a), verify Eq. (8.19) for this particular force system.

[*Ans.:* (a) $R = 62j - 48k$ lb, $C = 296i - 48j + 42k$ ft-lb.]

8.13 (a) Reduce the system of three forces in Fig. 8.32 to a force-couple system at point $A$. (b) Find the resultant force and the point where its line of action intersects $AB$.

8.14 If the position vector $r$ in Fig. 8.33 is perpendicular to the force $F$, and if

$$F_x = 30 \text{ lb}, \qquad F_y = -20 \text{ lb},$$

replace the force by a force-couple system at $O$.

[*Ans.:* $F = 30i - 20j - 30k$ lb, $C = -50i + 180j - 170k$ ft-lb.]

8.15 The force $F_2$ in Fig. 8.34 is parallel to $F_1$ but has opposite sense and different magnitude. If

$$|F_1 \cdot F_2| = 6050 \text{ lb}^2,$$

reduce the system to a force-couple system at $O$.

8.16 Find the point where the resultant of Problem 8.8 intersects the $x$-axis.

[*Ans.:* $(-3 \text{ in.}, 0)$.]

8.17 Locate the line of action of the resultant of the parallel force system of Problem 8.9.

# CHAPTER 9

## CENTER OF MASS,
## CENTER OF GRAVITY, AND CENTROID

**9.1 Systems of particles.** For a system of $n$ particles with masses $m_1$, $m_2, \ldots, m_n$, the *center of mass* $G$ (an important point in mechanics) is defined by locating the particles relative to an origin $O$, as shown in Fig. 9.1. If $\mathbf{r}_1, \mathbf{r}_2, \ldots, \mathbf{r}_n$ are the position vectors of the particles, then, by definition, the position vector $\mathbf{r}_G$ of the center of mass is given by

$$\mathbf{r}_G = \frac{m_1\mathbf{r}_1 + m_2\mathbf{r}_2 + \cdots + m_n\mathbf{r}_n}{m_1 + m_2 + \cdots + m_n}. \tag{9.1}$$

The numerator of this equation is called the *first moment of the mass* with respect to $O$ (not to be confused with the moment of a force); the denominator, of course, is the total mass. If we use $G$ as a reference point instead of $O$, the first moment of the mass becomes

$$m_1(\mathbf{r}_1 - \mathbf{r}_G) + m_2(\mathbf{r}_2 - \mathbf{r}_G) + \cdots + m_n(\mathbf{r}_n - \mathbf{r}_G),$$

which can be rewritten as

$$m_1\mathbf{r}_1 + m_2\mathbf{r}_2 + \cdots + m_n\mathbf{r}_n - (m_1 + m_2 + \cdots + m_n)\mathbf{r}_G.$$

Substituting for $\mathbf{r}_G$ from Eq. (9.1), we can see that $G$ is the point with respect to which the first moment of the mass vanishes. Thus, the location of $G$ does not depend upon the coordinates selected; it depends only upon the relative positions of the particles. If the particles are moving as a group, $G$ is moving also. It does not change its position relative to the particles unless they change their positions relative to each other. (The first moment of the mass, on the other hand, does depend on the coordinate system and changes when the particles move as a group.)

If $W_1, W_2, \ldots, W_n$ are the weights of the particles in Fig. 9.1, the *center of gravity* of the system, also called $G$, is defined as the point with position vector $\mathbf{r}_G$ given by

$$\mathbf{r}_G = \frac{W_1\mathbf{r}_1 + W_2\mathbf{r}_2 + \cdots + W_n\mathbf{r}_n}{W_1 + W_2 + \cdots + W_n}. \tag{9.2}$$

If all the particles are approximately the same distance from the center of the earth,

$$W_i = m_i g$$

146

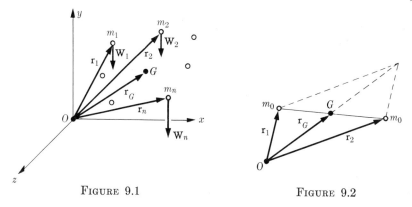

FIGURE 9.1                              FIGURE 9.2

for all $i$, where $g$ is the constant magnitude of the acceleration due to gravity. Hence, substituting into the right-hand side of Eq. (9.2), we see that the factor $g$ appears in every term of the numerator and every term of the denominator. When we divide both numerator and denominator by $g$, Eq. (9.2) reduces to Eq. (9.1). This means that the center of gravity coincides with the center of mass for systems of particles near the surface of the earth. It must be emphasized, however, that the two points are defined in different ways. The center of gravity depends upon the existence of a gravitational field for its definition, while the center of mass does not. If, for example, the system of particles is the group of planets in the solar system, the center of mass is an important point, whereas the concept of center of gravity is virtually meaningless.

If all $n$ particles in a system have the same mass $m_0$ (or the same weight $W_0$), the location of $G$ does not depend on the masses, since, by Eq. (9.1),

$$\mathbf{r}_G = \frac{m_0\mathbf{r}_1 + m_0\mathbf{r}_2 + \cdots + m_0\mathbf{r}_n}{nm_0} = \frac{1}{n}(\mathbf{r}_1 + \mathbf{r}_2 + \cdots + \mathbf{r}_n).$$

For example, the center of mass of the two identical particles in Fig. 9.2 is at the midpoint of the line joining the two particles, since

$$\mathbf{r}_G = \tfrac{1}{2}(\mathbf{r}_1 + \mathbf{r}_2).$$

The total weight force $\mathbf{W}$ for all the particles in Fig. 9.1 is the vector sum of the individual weight forces $\mathbf{W}_i$, that is,

$$\mathbf{W} = \mathbf{W}_1 + \mathbf{W}_2 + \cdots + \mathbf{W}_n. \tag{9.3}$$

If all the $\mathbf{W}_i$ are parallel, then

$$W = W_1 + W_2 + \cdots + W_n, \tag{9.4}$$

and the denominator in Eq. (9.2) is the magnitude of the total weight force. Suppose that all the individual weight forces are in the negative $y$-direction. Then

$$\mathbf{W}_i = -W_i \mathbf{j}$$

for all $i$, and

$$\mathbf{W} = -W \mathbf{j}.$$

Hence,

$$\frac{\mathbf{W}_i}{W_i} = \frac{\mathbf{W}}{W} \tag{9.5}$$

for all $i$. Consider now a single force $\mathbf{W}$ acting at $G$. The moment of this force about $O$, $\mathbf{r}_G \times \mathbf{W}$, is, by Eqs. (9.2) and (9.4),

$$\mathbf{r}_G \times \mathbf{W} = \frac{W_1 \mathbf{r}_1 + W_2 \mathbf{r}_2 + \cdots + W_n \mathbf{r}_n}{W} \times \mathbf{W}.$$

Therefore,

$$\mathbf{r}_G \times \mathbf{W} = \mathbf{r}_1 \times \frac{W_1}{W} \mathbf{W} + \mathbf{r}_2 \times \frac{W_2}{W} \mathbf{W} + \cdots + \mathbf{r}_n \times \frac{W_n}{W} \mathbf{W}.$$

Using Eq. (9.5),

$$\mathbf{r}_G \times \mathbf{W} = \mathbf{r}_1 \times \mathbf{W}_1 + \mathbf{r}_2 \times \mathbf{W}_2 + \cdots + \mathbf{r}_n \times \mathbf{W}_n. \tag{9.6}$$

Equations (9.3) and (9.6) show that the single force $\mathbf{W}$ acting at $G$ is mechanically equivalent to the actual system of weight forces, since the two conditions of Eqs. (8.26) are fulfilled. For a system of parallel weight forces due to a gravitational field in any other direction (as well as the negative $y$-direction), it can be proved in a manner similar to the foregoing that the same point $G$ can be used as a point of application for the total weight force. Thus, in many situations in mechanics, $G$ is the point where the total weight (and the total mass) can be considered concentrated.

Equations (9.1) and (9.2) can be written as three scalar equations each by letting $x_i$, $y_i$, $z_i$ be the coordinates of the point $P_i$ where the particle with mass $m_i$ is located. If $x_G$, $y_G$, $z_G$ are the coordinates of the center of mass,

$$x_G = \frac{\sum_{i=1}^{n} m_i x_i}{\sum_{i=1}^{n} m_i}, \qquad y_G = \frac{\sum_{i=1}^{n} m_i y_i}{\sum_{i=1}^{n} m_i}, \qquad z_G = \frac{\sum_{i=1}^{n} m_i z_i}{\sum_{i=1}^{n} m_i}. \tag{9.7}$$

The three numerators on the right-hand sides of these equations are called the *first moments of the mass* with respect to the $yz$-plane, $zx$-plane, and $xy$-plane, respectively. If $x_G$, $y_G$, $z_G$ are the coordinates of the center of gravity,

$$x_G = \frac{\sum_{i=1}^{n} W_i x_i}{\sum_{i=1}^{n} W_i}, \qquad y_G = \frac{\sum_{i=1}^{n} W_i y_i}{\sum_{i=1}^{n} W_i}, \qquad z_G = \frac{\sum_{i=1}^{n} W_i z_i}{\sum_{i=1}^{n} W_i}. \tag{9.8}$$

**9.2 Centroids of geometrical shapes.** As preparation for the extension of the concepts of center of mass and center of gravity to continuous bodies, it is useful to define, for various shapes, the purely geometric concept of *centroid*.

For an area $A$ in the $xy$-plane, such as that shown in Fig. 9.3, the coordinates $\bar{x}$, $\bar{y}$ of the centroid $C$ are defined by

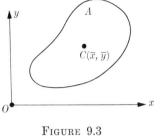

FIGURE 9.3

$$\bar{x} = \frac{\iint\limits_A x\, dA}{\iint\limits_A dA}, \qquad \bar{y} = \frac{\iint\limits_A y\, dA}{\iint\limits_A dA}. \qquad (9.9)$$

The two numerators are called the *first moments of the area* with respect to the $y$-axis and $x$-axis, respectively. The denominator in the two equations is called the *area* (a quantity having units of length$^2$) and is symbolized by $A$, so that

$$A = \iint\limits_A dA. \qquad (9.10)$$

For a volume $V$ in a cartesian coordinate system, such as that shown in Fig. 9.4, the coordinates $\bar{x}$, $\bar{y}$, $\bar{z}$ of the centroid $C$ are defined by

$$\bar{x} = \frac{\iiint\limits_V x\, dV}{\iiint\limits_V dV}, \qquad \bar{y} = \frac{\iiint\limits_V y\, dV}{\iiint\limits_V dV}, \qquad \bar{z} = \frac{\iiint\limits_V z\, dV}{\iiint\limits_V dV}. \qquad (9.11)$$

The three numerators are called the *first moments of the volume* with respect to the $yz$-plane, $zx$-plane, and $xy$-plane, respectively. The denomi-

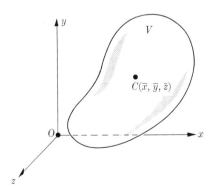

FIGURE 9.4

nator in the three equations is called the *volume* (a quantity having units of length$^3$) and is symbolized by $V$, so that

$$V = \iiint\limits_V dV. \tag{9.12}$$

For a curved line $L$ in space, such as that shown in Fig. 9.5, the coordinates $\bar{x}$, $\bar{y}$, $\bar{z}$ of the centroid $C$ are defined by

$$\bar{x} = \frac{\int\limits_L x\, dL}{\int\limits_L dL}, \qquad \bar{y} = \frac{\int\limits_L y\, dL}{\int\limits_L dL}, \qquad \bar{z} = \frac{\int\limits_L z\, dL}{\int\limits_L dL}. \tag{9.13}$$

The numerators are called the *first moments of the line*, and the denominator is called the *length L* of the line (units of length), so that

$$L = \int\limits_L dL. \tag{9.14}$$

For a curved line in the $xy$-plane, $\bar{z} = 0$, and the first two of Eqs. (9.13) locate the centroid. For a straight line along the $x$-axis (from $x_1$ to $x_2$), $\bar{y} = \bar{z} = 0$, and

$$\int\limits_L x\, dL = \int_{x_1}^{x_2} x\, dx = \frac{x^2}{2}\bigg|_{x_1}^{x_2} = \frac{x_2^2 - x_1^2}{2},$$

$$\int\limits_L dL = \int_{x_1}^{x_2} dx = x \bigg|_{x_1}^{x_2} = x_2 - x_1.$$

Hence,

$$\bar{x} = \frac{x_1 + x_2}{2},$$

and $C$ is at the midpoint of the line.

For a surface $S$ in space, such as that shown in Fig. 9.6, the coordinates $\bar{x}$, $\bar{y}$, $\bar{z}$ of the centroid $C$ are defined by

$$\bar{x} = \frac{\iint\limits_S x\, dS}{\iint\limits_S dS}, \qquad \bar{y} = \frac{\iint\limits_S y\, dS}{\iint\limits_S dS}, \qquad \bar{z} = \frac{\iint\limits_S z\, dS}{\iint\limits_S dS}. \tag{9.15}$$

In this case the *surface area S* (units of length$^2$) is defined by

$$S = \iint\limits_S dS. \tag{9.16}$$

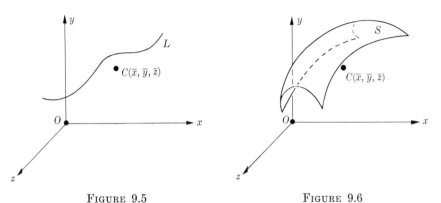

FIGURE 9.5                              FIGURE 9.6

For a plane surface in the $xy$-plane, $\bar{z} = 0$, and Eqs. (9.15) reduce to Eqs. (9.9).

The denominators in Eqs. (9.9), (9.11), (9.13), and (9.15) are always positive, while the numerators and the coordinates of $C$ may be either positive or negative. Also, the numerators and the coordinates of $C$ depend on the position of the coordinate system selected, whereas the denominators and the actual location of $C$ do not.

Plane areas and volumes are more important in elementary mechanics than lines and surfaces. Hence this book emphasizes methods of finding the centroids of areas and volumes, considering problems in which the double integrals of Eqs. (9.9) and the triple integrals of Eqs. (9.11) can be set up simply as ordinary definite integrals. Centroid problems involving the more complicated line integrals of Eqs. (9.13) and surface integrals of Eqs. (9.15) are not discussed.

**9.3 Centroid of an area.** To understand more fully the significance of the centroid of an area, consider the area $A$ in Fig. 9.7. If a set of $u$- and $v$-axes with origin at $C$ are taken parallel to the $x$- and $y$-axes, respectively, a typical elemental area $\Delta_i A$ has coordinates $u_i, v_i$ with respect to the $uv$-system and $x_i, y_i$ with respect to the $xy$-system. The first moment of $A$ with respect to the $y$-axis is given by

$$\iint_A x \, dA = \lim_{n \to \infty} \sum_{i=1}^{n} x_i \, \Delta_i A,$$

where the summation is taken over

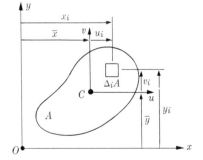

FIGURE 9.7

all the complete rectangles into which $A$ is subdivided.  But

$$x_i = \bar{x} + u_i,$$

and, substituting this into the preceding equation,

$$\iint_A x \, dA = \lim_{n \to \infty} \left( \sum_{i=1}^n \bar{x} \, \Delta_i A + \sum_{i=1}^n u_i \, \Delta_i A \right)$$

$$= \bar{x} \lim_{n \to \infty} \sum_{i=1}^n \Delta_i A + \lim_{n \to \infty} \sum_{i=1}^n u_i \, \Delta_i A.$$

Hence,

$$\iint_A x \, dA = \bar{x} \iint_A dA + \iint_A u \, dA.$$

This last equation can be derived by a shorter but less rigorous method which is very useful in mechanics although it is justified only by the fact that it gives the same results as the more rigorous method it replaces. The shorter method consists of designating the elemental area by the symbol $dA$ and its distance from the $y$-axis by $x$ and considering the integral

$$\iint_A x \, dA$$

to be the product of $x$ and $dA$ summed over the entire area $A$.  Figure 9.7 is replaced by Fig. 9.8, and it is noted that

$$x = \bar{x} + u.$$

Hence,

$$\iint_A x \, dA = \iint_A (\bar{x} + u) \, dA = \bar{x} \iint_A dA + \iint_A u \, dA,$$

which is the same equation as derived previously.  Solving for the first moment with respect to the $v$-axis,

$$\iint_A u \, dA = \iint_A x \, dA - \bar{x} \iint_A dA,$$

and, substituting for $\bar{x}$ from the first of Eqs. (9.9),

$$\iint_A u \, dA = 0. \qquad\qquad (9.17)$$

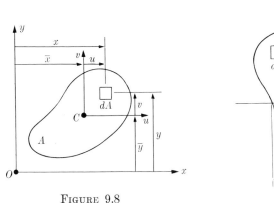

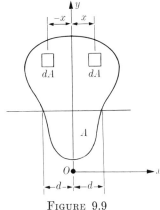

FIGURE 9.8                              FIGURE 9.9

Equation (9.17) is therefore a necessary and sufficient condition that the $v$-axis is through $C$. In a similar way it can be verified that the equation

$$\iint_A v \, dA = 0 \tag{9.18}$$

is a necessary and sufficient condition that the $u$-axis is through $C$. Thus, $C$ is the origin of those coordinate axes with respect to which the first moments of the area vanish. It can also be shown that the first moment of the area with respect to any line through $C$ is zero.

The centroids of some areas can be partially or completely located by symmetry considerations. If the $y$-axis is an axis of symmetry (i.e., if any line perpendicular to the $y$-axis intersects the boundary of the area at equal distances from the $y$-axis), as shown in Fig. 9.9, then, for every elemental area $dA$ a distance $x$ to the right of the $y$-axis, there is an identical area $dA$ a distance $-x$ to the left. Therefore the total first moment of $A$ with respect to the axis of symmetry is zero, and $C$ is on that axis. Figures 9.10(a) and (b) show two areas that have one axis of symmetry; for these shapes, $C$ is known to be somewhere on the line of symmetry. Figure 9.10(c) shows a rectangular area, which has two axes of

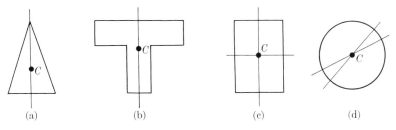

(a)            (b)            (c)            (d)

FIGURE 9.10

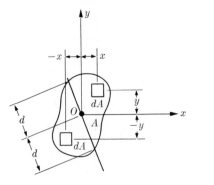

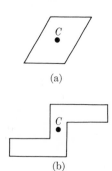

FIGURE 9.11                    FIGURE 9.12

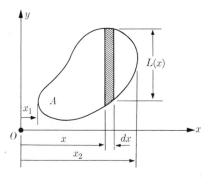

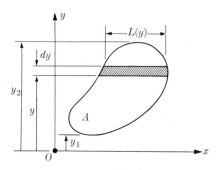

FIGURE 9.13                    FIGURE 9.14

symmetry; for this shape, the exact location of $C$ is known. For the circular area in Fig. 9.10(d), every diameter of the circle is an axis of symmetry; for this shape, $C$ is at the center of the circle.

If $O$ is a point of symmetry of an area (i.e., if any line through $O$ intersects the boundary of the area at equal distances from $O$), as shown in Fig. 9.11, then, for every $dA$ with coordinates $x$, $y$, there is an identical area $dA$ with coordinates $-x$, $-y$. Therefore both first moments are zero, and $C$ coincides with the point of symmetry $O$. Figures 9.12(a) and (b) show two areas in which $C$ is at a point of symmetry. Note that the shapes in Figs. 9.10(c) and (d) both have a point of symmetry.

To locate the centroid of any area $A$ such as that in Fig. 9.13, the double integrals in Eqs. (9.9) must be evaluated. This can be accomplished using only single integrations if, when finding $\bar{x}$, we take a strip parallel to the $y$-axis as an elemental area. (See crosshatched area in Fig. 9.13.) Let $dx$ be the thickness of the strip and $x$ the directed distance from the $y$-axis to the strip. Find the length of the strip as a function of $x$ and call this function $L(x)$. Then

$$dA = L(x)\,dx,$$

and
$$\bar{x} = \frac{\int_{x_1}^{x_2} xL(x)\,dx}{\int_{x_1}^{x_2} L(x)\,dx}.$$

To find $\bar{y}$, we can take a strip parallel to the $x$-axis, as shown in Fig. 9.14. In this case,
$$dA = L(y)\,dy,$$
and
$$\bar{y} = \frac{\int_{y_1}^{y_2} yL(y)\,dy}{\int_{y_1}^{y_2} L(y)\,dy}.$$

EXAMPLE 9.1. Find $\bar{y}$ for the triangular area shown in Fig. 9.15.

*Solution.* The elemental area is shown crosshatched in Fig. 9.15. The length $L$ of the strip can be found by similar triangles in this case, i.e.,

$$\frac{L(y)}{h - y} = \frac{b}{h},$$

so that

$$L(y) = b - \frac{b}{h}\,y.$$

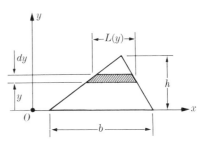

FIGURE 9.15

Hence,

$$\bar{y} = \frac{\int_0^h [by - (b/h)y^2]\,dy}{\int_0^h [b - (b/h)y]\,dy} = \frac{[(b/2)y^2 - (b/3h)y^3]\big|_0^h}{[by - (b/2h)y^2]\big|_0^h} = \frac{(1/6)bh^2}{(1/2)bh} = \frac{1}{3}\,h.$$

Figure 9.16 gives the area and location of centroid for some commonly encountered shapes.

For a composite area $A$ made up of several parts $A_1, A_2, \ldots, A_n$, as shown in Fig. 9.17, the location of the centroid can be determined without integration if the location of the centroid of each part is known. By definition,

$$\bar{x} = \frac{\iint_{A_1} x\,dA + \iint_{A_2} x\,dA + \cdots + \iint_{A_n} x\,dA}{\iint_{A_1} dA + \iint_{A_2} dA + \cdots + \iint_{A_n} dA}.$$

| | Shape | Area | $\bar{x}$ | $\bar{y}$ |
|---|---|---|---|---|
| (a) | 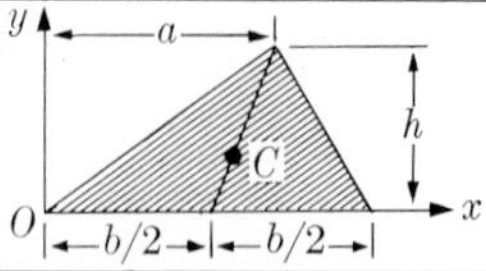 $y = \dfrac{h}{b}x$ shape with base $b$, height $h$, offset $a$, centroid $C$, $b/2$, $b/2$ | $\frac{1}{2}bh$ | $\frac{1}{3}(a+b)$ | $\frac{1}{3}h$ |
| (b) | 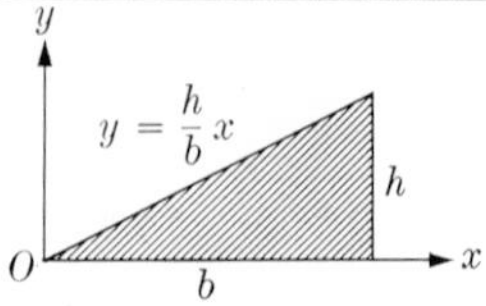 $y = \dfrac{h}{b}x$ | $\frac{1}{2}bh$ | $\frac{2}{3}b$ | $\frac{1}{3}h$ |
| (c) | 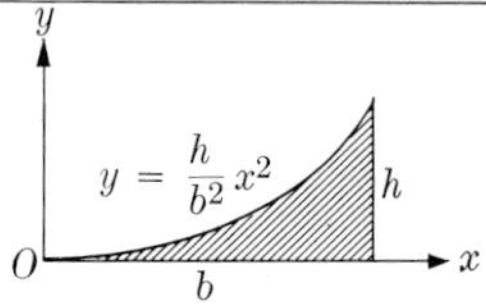 $y = \dfrac{h}{b^2}x^2$ | $\frac{1}{3}bh$ | $\frac{3}{4}b$ | $\frac{3}{10}h$ |
| (d) | 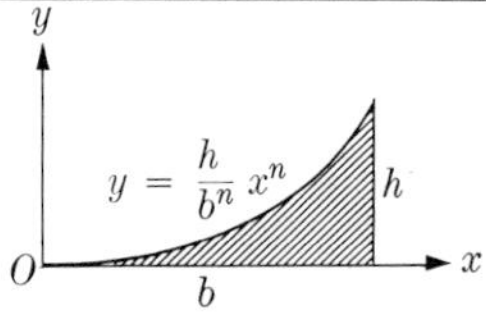 $y = \dfrac{h}{b^n}x^n$ | $\dfrac{1}{n+1}bh$ | $\dfrac{n+1}{n+2}b$ | $\dfrac{n+1}{2(2n+1)}h$ |
| (e) | 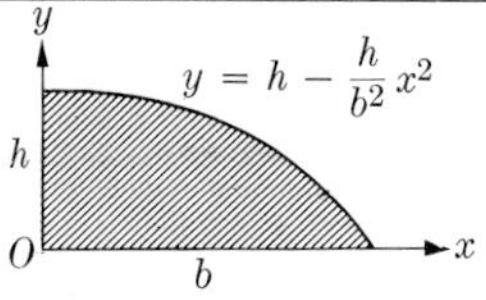 $y = h - \dfrac{h}{b^2}x^2$ | $\frac{2}{3}bh$ | $\frac{3}{8}b$ | $\frac{2}{5}h$ |
| (f) | 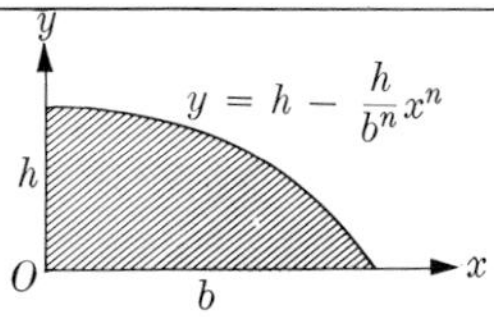 $y = h - \dfrac{h}{b^n}x^n$ | $\dfrac{n}{n+1}bh$ | $\dfrac{n+1}{2(n+2)}b$ | $\dfrac{n}{2n+1}h$ |
| (g) | 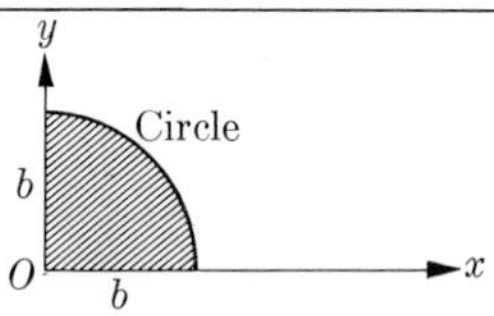 Circle | $\dfrac{\pi}{4}b^2$ | $\dfrac{4}{3\pi}b$ | $\dfrac{4}{3\pi}b$ |
| (h) | 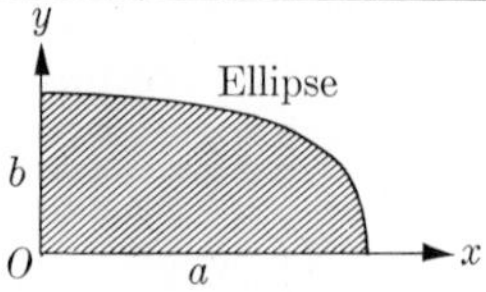 Ellipse | $\dfrac{\pi}{4}ab$ | $\dfrac{4}{3\pi}a$ | $\dfrac{4}{3\pi}b$ |

FIGURE 9.16

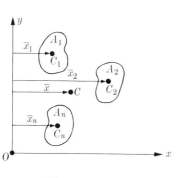

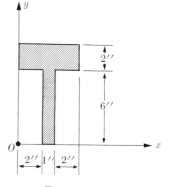

FIGURE 9.17           FIGURE 9.18

But

$$\bar{x}_i = \frac{\displaystyle\iint_{A_i} x \, dA}{\displaystyle\iint_{A_i} dA}$$

for each $i$, so that

$$\iint_{A_i} x \, dA \;=\; \bar{x}_i \iint_{A_i} dA \;=\; \bar{x}_i A_i.$$

Hence,

$$\bar{x} = \frac{\bar{x}_1 A_1 + \bar{x}_2 A_2 + \cdots + \bar{x}_n A_n}{A_1 + A_2 + \cdots + A_n}. \tag{9.19}$$

Similarly,

$$\bar{y} = \frac{\bar{y}_1 A_1 + \bar{y}_2 A_2 + \cdots + \bar{y}_n A_n}{A_1 + A_2 + \cdots + A_n}. \tag{9.20}$$

EXAMPLE 9.2. Locate the centroid of the area shown in Fig. 9.18.

*Solution.* By symmetry,

$$\bar{x} = 2.50 \text{ in.}$$

Dividing the area into two rectangles and using Eq. (9.20),

$$\bar{y} = \frac{7(10) + 3(6)}{10 + 6} = \frac{88}{16} = 5.50 \text{ in.}$$

To locate the centroid of an area $A$ resulting from the removal of a portion of area $A_2$ from a total area $A_1$, as shown in Fig. 9.19, the area $A_1$ can be regarded as the composite area, so that, by Eq. (9.19),

$$\bar{x}_1 = \frac{\bar{x}A + \bar{x}_2 A_2}{A + A_2}.$$

Solving this equation for $\bar{x}$ and noting that

$$A = A_1 - A_2,$$

we find that

$$\bar{x} = \frac{\bar{x}_1 A_1 - \bar{x}_2 A_2}{A_1 - A_2}.$$

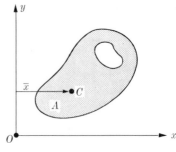

FIGURE 9.19

A similar equation holds for $\bar{y}$. More generally, it can be shown that, if an area $A$ is made up by adding together several parts $A_1, A_2, \ldots, A_n$ and removing several parts $A_{n+1}, A_{n+2}, \ldots, A_{n+m}$, then

$$\bar{x} = \frac{\bar{x}_1 A_1 + \cdots + \bar{x}_n A_n - \bar{x}_{n+1} A_{n+1} - \cdots - \bar{x}_{n+m} A_{n+m}}{A_1 + \cdots + A_n - A_{n+1} - \cdots - A_{n+m}},$$

and a similar equation holds for $\bar{y}$.

**9.4 Centroid of a volume.** The concept of centroid of a volume is expanded in a manner that closely parallels the foregoing treatment of the centroid of an area. Using a set of $u$-, $v$-, and $w$-axes parallel, respectively, to the $x$-, $y$-, and $z$-axes, it can be proved that the equation

$$\iiint_V u \, dV = 0$$

is a necessary and sufficient condition that the $vw$-plane contains the centroid, and similarly for the other two first moments. Thus $C$ is the

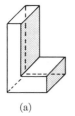
(a)

(b)

(c)

(d)

FIGURE 9.20

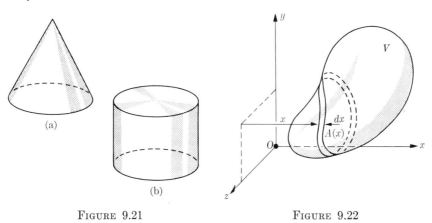

FIGURE 9.21                              FIGURE 9.22

origin of those coordinates with respect to which the first moments of the volume vanish. It can also be shown that the first moment of the volume with respect to any plane through $C$ is zero.

The centroids of some volumes can be partially or completely located by symmetry considerations. If the $yz$-plane is a plane of symmetry (i.e., if any line perpendicular to the plane intersects the boundary of the volume at equal distances from the plane), then, for every elemental volume $dV$ a distance $x$ to the right of the $yz$-plane, there is an identical volume $dV$ a distance $-x$ to the left. Therefore the total first moment of the volume with respect to the plane of symmetry is zero, and $C$ is in that plane. Figures 9.20(a), (b), (c), and (d) show volumes with one, two, three, and an infinite number of planes of symmetry, respectively. In the last two cases, the location of $C$ is completely known.

If the $z$-axis is an axis of symmetry of a volume (i.e., if any line intersecting the $z$-axis and perpendicular to it intersects the boundary of the volume at equal distances from the $z$-axis), then the first moments with respect to the $yz$- and $zx$-planes are both zero, and $C$ is on the $z$-axis. Figure 9.21(a) shows a volume with one line of symmetry. The right circular cylinder of Fig. 9.21(b) has one line of symmetry through the centers of its end faces and a plane of symmetry perpendicular to the line of symmetry; for this volume, the location of $C$ is completely known. Note that the volumes of Figs. 9.20(b), (c), and (d) have one or more lines of symmetry, while the volumes of Figs. 9.21(a) and (b) each have an infinite number of planes of symmetry.

If $O$ is a point of symmetry of a volume (i.e., if any line through $O$ intersects the boundary of the volume at equal distances from $O$), then the centroid is located at $O$. The volumes in Figs. 9.20(c), 9.20(d), and 9.21(b) each have a point of symmetry.

To locate the centroid of any volume $V$ such as that in Fig. 9.22, the triple integrals in Eqs. (9.11) must be evaluated. Interpreting these triple integrals as limits of summations, the volume may be subdivided into elemental portions in any convenient way that accounts for all the volume. To find $\bar{x}$, for example, take a slice parallel to the $yz$-plane as an elemental volume (as shown in Fig. 9.22). Let $dx$ be the thickness of the slice and $x$ the directed distance from the $yz$-plane to the slice. If the area $A(x)$ of the slice can be found readily, the triple integrals of Eqs. (9.11) may be replaced by ordinary definite integrals, since $dV = A(x)\, dx$ and hence

$$\bar{x} = \frac{\displaystyle\int_{x_1}^{x_2} x A(x)\, dx}{\displaystyle\int_{x_1}^{x_2} A(x)\, dx}.$$

The other coordinates of $C$ are found by taking slices parallel to the other coordinate planes.

EXAMPLE 9.3.  Find $\bar{y}$ for the right circular cone shown in Fig. 9.23.

*Solution.*  The radius $r$ of the slice can be found by simple proportion, i.e.,

$$\frac{r(y)}{h - y} = \frac{b}{h},$$

so that

$$r(y) = b - \frac{b}{h}\, y$$

and

$$A(y) = \pi \left( b^2 - \frac{2b^2}{h}\, y + \frac{b^2}{h^2}\, y^2 \right).$$

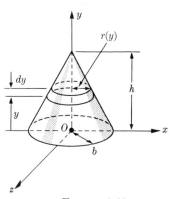

FIGURE 9.23

Hence,

$$\bar{y} = \frac{\displaystyle\int_0^h \pi[b^2 y - (2b^2/h)y^2 + (b^2/h^2)y^3]\, dy}{\displaystyle\int_0^h \pi[b^2 - (2b^2/h)y + (b^2/h^2)y^2]\, dy}$$

$$= \frac{\pi[(b^2/2)y^2 - (2b^2/3h)y^3 + (b^2/4h^2)y^4]\big|_0^h}{\pi[b^2 y - (b^2/h)y^2 + (b^2/3h^2)y^3]\big|_0^h}$$

$$= \frac{(\pi/12)b^2 h^2}{(\pi/3)b^2 h} = \frac{1}{4}\, h.$$

Figure 9.24 gives the volume and height of centroid for several shapes which can be analyzed by the procedure of Example 9.3.

| | Shape | Volume | $\bar{y}$ |
|---|---|---|---|
| (a) | 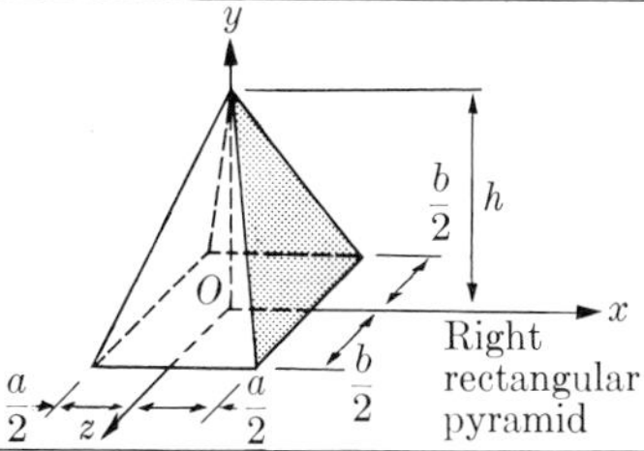 y h x O b/2 a/2 z a/2 b/2 Right rectangular pyramid | $\frac{1}{3}abh$ | $\frac{1}{4}h$ |
| (b) | 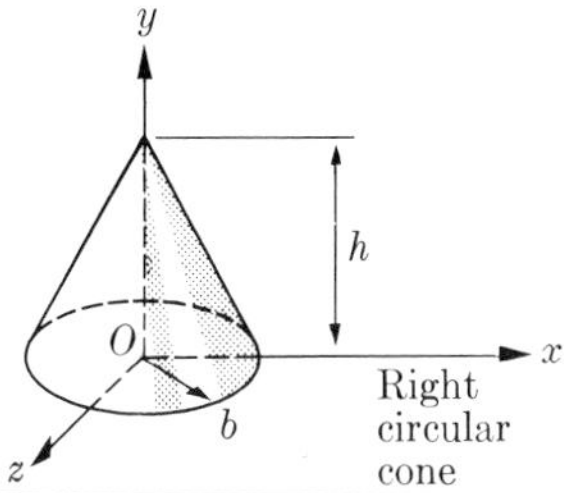 y h O x b z Right circular cone | $\frac{1}{3}\pi b^2 h$ | $\frac{1}{4}h$ |
| (c) | 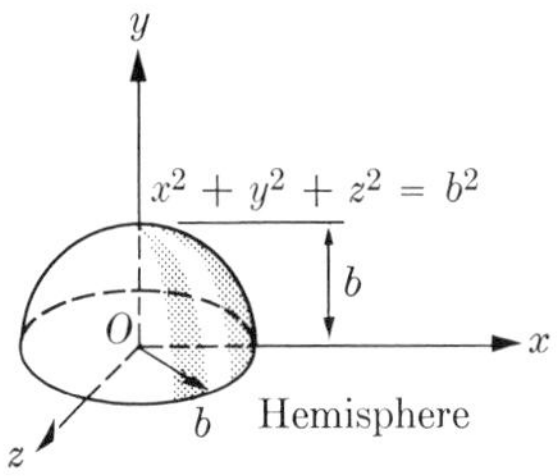 y x² + y² + z² = b² b O x z b Hemisphere | $\frac{2}{3}\pi b^3$ | $\frac{3}{8}b$ |
| (d) | 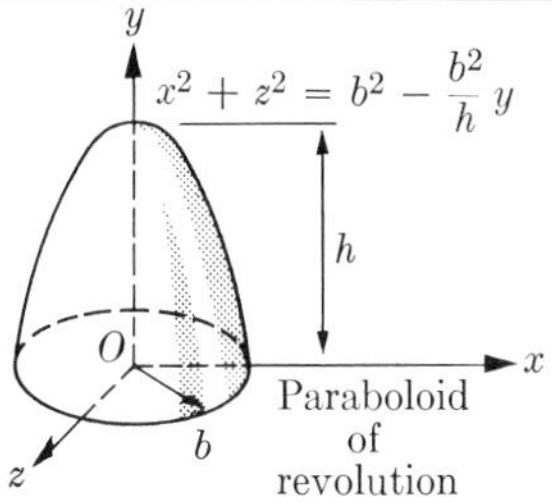 y x² + z² = b² − (b²/h) y h O x z b Paraboloid of revolution | $\frac{1}{2}\pi b^2 h$ | $\frac{1}{3}h$ |
| (e) | 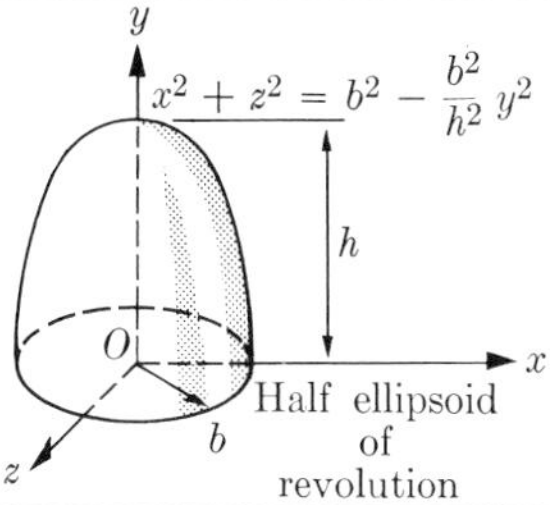 y x² + z² = b² − (b²/h²) y² h O x z b Half ellipsoid of revolution | $\frac{2}{3}\pi b^2 h$ | $\frac{3}{8}h$ |

FIGURE 9.24

For a composite volume $V$ made up of several parts $V_1, V_2, \ldots, V_n$, it can be shown by a procedure similar to that used for areas that

$$\bar{x} = \frac{\bar{x}_1 V_1 + \bar{x}_2 V_2 + \cdots + \bar{x}_n V_n}{V_1 + V_2 + \cdots + V_n},$$

$$\bar{y} = \frac{\bar{y}_1 V_1 + \bar{y}_2 V_2 + \cdots + \bar{y}_n V_n}{V_1 + V_2 + \cdots + V_n}, \qquad (9.21)$$

$$\bar{z} = \frac{\bar{z}_1 V_1 + \bar{z}_2 V_2 + \cdots + \bar{z}_n V_n}{V_1 + V_2 + \cdots + V_n}.$$

If some portions of volume are removed to make $V$, these are dealt with, as in the case of areas, by subtracting terms from the numerators and denominators in Eqs. (9.21).

---

EXAMPLE 9.4. Locate the centroid of the volume shown in Fig. 9.25.

*Solution.* By symmetry,

$$\bar{z} = 2 \text{ in.}$$

Dividing the volume into two rectangular parallelepipeds as indicated by the dashed line in Fig. 9.25 and using the first two of Eqs. (9.21),

$$\bar{x} = \frac{1(80) + 5(48)}{80 + 48} = \frac{320}{128} = 2.50 \text{ in.,}$$

$$\bar{y} = \frac{5(80) + 1(48)}{80 + 48} = \frac{448}{128} = 3.50 \text{ in.}$$

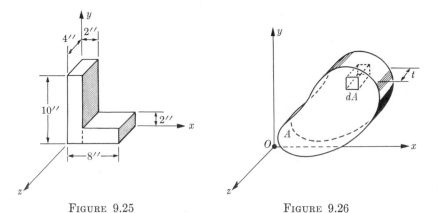

FIGURE 9.25                    FIGURE 9.26

The volume in Fig. 9.25 is one example of a class of volumes bounded by two parallel planes and a surface, where the surface is generated by a line which is always perpendicular to the two planes and which moves in such a way that it traces out an area in the two planes. Figure 9.26 shows a general volume of this type. Taking as an elemental volume a prism extending through the entire volume as shown, the integrals in the first two of Eqs. (9.11) are reduced to double integrals by replacing $dV$ with $t\,dA$, that is,

$$\bar{x} = \frac{\iint\limits_A xt\,dA}{\iint\limits_A t\,dA}, \qquad \bar{y} = \frac{\iint\limits_A yt\,dA}{\iint\limits_A t\,dA}.$$

Since $t$ is constant, it factors out of all four integrals and cancels from the equations, leaving

$$\bar{x} = \frac{\iint\limits_A x\,dA}{\iint\limits_A dA}, \qquad \bar{y} = \frac{\iint\limits_A y\,dA}{\iint\limits_A dA}.$$

These results indicate that the centroid of a volume of the type under consideration has the same $x$- and $y$-coordinates as does the centroid of the area $A$ of the plane face of the volume. (The $z$-coordinates of the two centroids, of course, are different.) The foregoing relationship can be seen to hold for the volume of Example 9.4 by noting that the expressions for $\bar{x}$ and $\bar{y}$ are unchanged when the numerators and denominators are divided by a constant $t$ of 4 in.

**9.5 Continuous bodies.** Before defining center of mass and center of gravity for a continuous body, it is necessary to establish the concepts of *density* and *specific weight*. Consider a body (or any portion of matter) occupying a region $V$ of space, as shown in Fig. 9.27. Let $m$ be the total mass of the body and $W$ the magnitude of the total weight force $\mathbf{W}$ exerted on the body by the earth. (This force is distributed over the volume of the body.) Let $P$ be any point in the body, and consider a portion of the body (of volume $\Delta V$) which encloses $P$. Let $\Delta m$ be the mass of the element $\Delta V$ and $\Delta W$ the magnitude of the weight force $\Delta\mathbf{W}$ exerted on $\Delta V$ by the earth. By definition, the density $\mu$ at the point is given by

$$\mu = \lim_{\Delta V \to 0} \frac{\Delta m}{\Delta V}, \tag{9.22}$$

where the limiting process is taken in such a way that $\Delta V$ always encloses $P$. The density $\mu$ is significant as the mass per unit volume at a point,

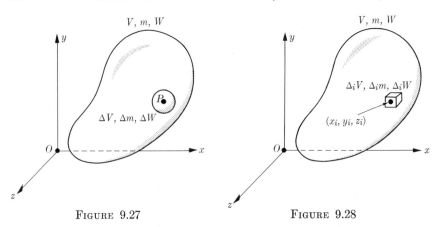

FIGURE 9.27                     FIGURE 9.28

and it may be a function of the coordinates $x$, $y$, $z$ of the point (through its dependence, for example, on other variables, such as the temperature at the point, etc.). The specific weight $\gamma$ at the point is defined in a similar way, i.e.,

$$\gamma = \lim_{\Delta V \to 0} \frac{\Delta W}{\Delta V}, \qquad (9.23)$$

and $\gamma$ is the weight per unit volume at $P$.

As $\Delta V$ approaches zero, the element assumes all the properties of a particle, so that, by Eq. (6.4),

$$\Delta W = g \, \Delta m,$$

where $g$ is the magnitude of the acceleration of gravity at $P$. Hence, by Eqs. (9.22) and (9.23),

$$\gamma(x, y, z) = g(x, y, z)\mu(x, y, z). \qquad (9.24)$$

As an example, consider a body which is made of copper and which is in the vicinity of the earth's surface. The specific weight at a point in such a body would be about 550 lb/ft$^3$. Taking $g$ as 32.2 ft/sec$^2$,

$$\mu = \frac{550}{32.2} = 17.1 \text{ slugs/ft}^3.$$

The center of mass of a continuous body is defined by successive subdivisions of the volume occupied by the body into $n$ elemental rectangular parallelepipeds by means of three sets of planes parallel to the three coordinate planes. (For each subdivision, only the complete parallelepipeds are retained.) Figure 9.28 shows a typical element $\Delta_i V$ of such a body.

Selecting an arbitrary point with coordinates $x_i$, $y_i$, $z_i$ in $\Delta_i V$, the density $\mu(x_i, y_i, z_i)$ and the specific weight $\gamma(x_i, y_i, z_i)$ are evaluated at the point. By definition, the center of mass $G$ is the point with coordinates $x_G$, $y_G$, $z_G$ given by the following equations:

$$x_G = \frac{\lim_{n \to \infty} \sum_{i=1}^{n} x_i \,\Delta_i m}{\lim_{n \to \infty} \sum_{i=1}^{n} \Delta_i m}, \qquad y_G = \frac{\lim_{n \to \infty} \sum_{i=1}^{n} y_i \,\Delta_i m}{\lim_{n \to \infty} \sum_{i=1}^{n} \Delta_i m},$$

$$z_G = \frac{\lim_{n \to \infty} \sum_{i=1}^{n} z_i \,\Delta_i m}{\lim_{n \to \infty} \sum_{i=1}^{n} \Delta_i m}. \tag{9.25}$$

Note the similarity between these equations and Eqs. (9.7). Because the volume $\Delta_i V$ of each element approaches zero as $n$ approaches infinity, and because the point $(x_i, y_i, z_i)$ is always inside $\Delta_i V$, it follows from Eq. (9.22) that, as the limit is approached,

$$\Delta_i m = \mu(x_i, y_i, z_i)\,\Delta_i V.$$

Substituting this into the first of Eqs. (9.25),

$$x_G = \frac{\lim_{n \to \infty} \sum_{i=1}^{n} x_i \mu(x_i, y_i, z_i)\,\Delta_i V}{\lim_{n \to \infty} \sum_{i=1}^{n} \mu(x_i, y_i, z_i)\,\Delta_i V},$$

and similarly for $y_G$ and $z_G$. Hence,

$$x_G = \frac{\iiint\limits_{V} x\mu(x, y, z)\,dV}{\iiint\limits_{V} \mu(x, y, z)\,dV}, \qquad y_G = \frac{\iiint\limits_{V} y\mu(x, y, z)\,dV}{\iiint\limits_{V} \mu(x, y, z)\,dV},$$

$$z_G = \frac{\iiint\limits_{V} z\mu(x, y, z)\,dV}{\iiint\limits_{V} \mu(x, y, z)\,dV}. \tag{9.26}$$

The center of mass of a continuous body may be defined in a more general way by an equation similar to Eq. (9.1). Letting $\mathbf{r}_i$ be the position vector of the point selected in $\Delta_i V$, $G$ is defined as the point having a position vector $\mathbf{r}_G$ given by

$$\mathbf{r}_G = \frac{\lim_{n \to \infty} (\Delta_1 m \mathbf{r}_1 + \Delta_2 m \mathbf{r}_2 + \cdots + \Delta_n m \mathbf{r}_n)}{\lim_{n \to \infty} (\Delta_1 m + \Delta_2 m + \cdots + \Delta_n m)}.$$

Substituting for $\Delta_i m$ as previously, the last equation can be rewritten in terms of triple integrals, i.e.,

$$\mathbf{r}_G = \frac{\iiint_V \mathbf{r}\mu \, dV}{\iiint_V \mu \, dV} \tag{9.27}$$

The numerator in this equation is the triple integral of a vector function, which is itself a vector, and the equation can be restated, for any coordinate system, as three scalar equations on the components of the vectors. Using a cartesian system, for example,

$$\mathbf{r} = x\mathbf{i} + y\mathbf{j} + z\mathbf{k},$$

so that the numerator of Eq. (9.27) becomes

$$\mathbf{i}\iiint_V x\mu(x, y, z) \, dV + \mathbf{j}\iiint_V y\mu(x, y, z) \, dV + \mathbf{k}\iiint_V z\mu(x, y, z) \, dV.$$

Equations (9.26), therefore, follow from Eq. (9.27).

The numerators in Eqs. (9.26) are called the first moments of the mass with respect to the $yz$-, $zx$-, and $xy$-planes, respectively, while the denominator in the three equations is the total mass $m$ of the body. It can be shown that the first moment of the mass with respect to a plane is zero if and only if the plane contains $G$.

The center of gravity of a continuous body, also called $G$, is defined by equations similar to Eqs. (9.25), using $\Delta_i W$ in each expression instead of $\Delta_i m$. Since

$$\Delta_i W = \gamma(x_i, y_i, z_i) \, \Delta_i V,$$

the equations become

$$x_G = \frac{\iiint_V x\gamma(x, y, z) \, dV}{\iiint_V \gamma(x, y, z) \, dV}, \tag{9.28}$$

etc. Substituting from Eq. (9.24),

$$x_G = \frac{\iiint_V xg(x, y, z)\mu(x, y, z) \, dV}{\iiint_V g(x, y, z)\mu(x, y, z) \, dV},$$

etc. If the body is of such a size that $g$ is constant throughout, $g$ factors out of both integrals and cancels from numerator and denominator, making the equations reduce to Eqs. (9.26). Hence, for most bodies encountered in engineering, the center of mass and center of gravity coincide. The total weight force $\mathbf{W}$ for the body is given by

$$\mathbf{W} = \lim_{n \to \infty} (\Delta_1 \mathbf{W} + \Delta_2 \mathbf{W} + \cdots + \Delta_n \mathbf{W}).$$

If the body is of such a size that the gravitational field is parallel, then

$$W = \lim_{n \to \infty} \sum_{i=1}^{n} \Delta_i W = \lim_{n \to \infty} \sum_{i=1}^{n} \gamma(x_i, y_i, z_i) \, \Delta_i V,$$

and the denominator of Eq. (9.28) is the total weight of the body. Suppose that the gravitational field is in the negative $y$-direction. Then, since

$$x_G W = \lim_{n \to \infty} \sum_{i=1}^{n} x_i \, \Delta_i W, \qquad z_G W = \lim_{n \to \infty} \sum_{i=1}^{n} z_i \, \Delta_i W$$

(by the definition of the center of gravity), both conditions for mechanical equivalence are fulfilled, and a single force $\mathbf{W}$ acting at $G$ is equivalent to the actual distributed weight force. The same is true for a parallel field in any direction.

If a body has uniform density, i.e.,

$$\mu(x, y, z) = k$$

(where $k$ is a constant), as can be assumed in many cases, then $\mu$ factors out of both integrals in each of Eqs. (9.26), and

$$x_G = \frac{\iiint\limits_V x \, dV}{\iiint\limits_V dV} = \bar{x},$$

etc., so that the center of mass coincides with the centroid of the volume occupied by the body. The values of $\bar{y}$ in Fig. 9.24 can therefore be used for $y_G$ if the shapes shown there represent solid bodies of uniform density.

The center of mass of a body with varying density can ordinarily be located by one or a combination of the three methods used for finding centroids, namely (1) symmetry, (2) integration, and (3) composition. To find $G$ by the first method, the body must have symmetry of shape and density distribution. For example, if the $yz$-plane is a plane of symmetry of shape, then the equation

$$\mu(x, y, z) = \mu(-x, y, z)$$

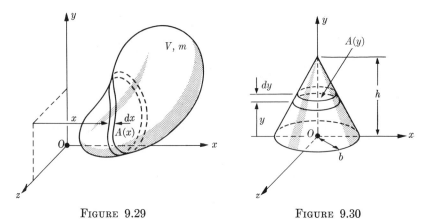

FIGURE 9.29    FIGURE 9.30

is a sufficient condition that the first moment of the mass with respect to the $yz$-plane is zero and therefore that the plane contains $G$. Similar statements hold for the other coordinate planes. Likewise, if the $z$-axis is an axis of symmetry of shape, then the equation

$$\mu(x, y, z) = \mu(-x, -y, z)$$

is a sufficient condition that $G$ is on the $z$-axis. Finally, if $O$ is a point of symmetry of shape, then the equation

$$\mu(x, y, z) = \mu(-x, -y, -z)$$

is a sufficient condition that $G$ coincides with $O$.

In many problems, integration must be used to locate $G$. To find $x_G$ for a body such as that shown in Fig. 9.29 without multiple integration, it is necessary that $\mu$ be a function of $x$ only, so that, upon substituting $A(x)\,dx$ for $dV$ in the first of Eqs. (9.26), the integrands contain functions of $x$ only, i.e.,

$$x_G = \frac{\int_{x_1}^{x_2} x\mu(x)\,A(x)\,dx}{\int_{x_1}^{x_2} \mu(x)\,A(x)\,dx}.$$

---

EXAMPLE 9.5. For the body shown in Fig. 9.30,

$$\mu(x, y, z) = \mu_0\left(1 + \frac{2}{h}\,y\right).$$

Locate $G$.

*Solution.* The given density distribution indicates that $\mu$ varies linearly from $\mu_0$ at the base to $3\mu_0$ at the apex. In this case, since $\mu$ is a function of $y$ only,

$$\mu(x, y, z) = \mu(-x, y, -z),$$

and this means that the $y$-axis is an axis of symmetry of shape and density distribution. Hence,

$$x_G = z_G = 0.$$

To find $y_G$, take a slice parallel to the $zx$-plane as in Example 9.3. From the solution of that example,

$$A(y) = \pi \left( b^2 - \frac{2b^2}{h} y + \frac{b^2}{h^2} y^2 \right).$$

Therefore,

$$y_G = \frac{\displaystyle\int_{y_1}^{y_2} y\mu(y) A(y)\, dy}{\displaystyle\int_{y_1}^{y_2} \mu(y) A(y)\, dy} = \frac{\displaystyle\int_0^h \pi\mu_0[b^2 y - (3b^2/h^2)y^3 + (2b^2/h^3)y^4]\, dy}{\displaystyle\int_0^h \pi\mu_0[b^2 - (3b^2/h^2)y^2 + (2b^2/h^3)y^3]\, dy}$$

$$= \frac{(3/20)\pi\mu_0 b^2 h^2}{(1/2)\pi\mu_0 b^2 h} = \frac{3}{10} h.$$

Note that the mass $m$ of the body is given by

$$m = \tfrac{1}{2}\pi\mu_0 b^2 h.$$

---

The type of density variation most commonly encountered in practical problems occurs when a body is made up by connecting parts composed of different materials. Though the density is constant in each part, it changes abruptly at the surfaces where the parts are connected. For this kind of body, and for any body which can be subdivided into components having known masses and centers of mass, $G$ may be located by treating the body as a composite body. By Eqs. (9.26),

$$x_G = \frac{\displaystyle\iiint_{V_1} x\mu\, dV + \iiint_{V_2} x\mu\, dV + \cdots + \iiint_{V_n} x\mu\, dV}{\displaystyle\iiint_{V_1} \mu\, dV + \iiint_{V_2} \mu\, dV + \cdots + \iiint_{V_n} \mu\, dV},$$

etc. But, for all $i$,

$$x_{Gi} = \frac{\displaystyle\iiint_{V_i} x\mu\, dV}{\displaystyle\iiint_{V_i} \mu\, dV} = \frac{\displaystyle\iiint_{V_i} x\mu\, dV}{m_i}.$$

Hence,

$$x_G = \frac{x_{G1}m_1 + x_{G2}m_2 + \cdots + x_{Gn}m_n}{m_1 + m_2 + \cdots + m_n},$$

$$y_G = \frac{y_{G1}m_1 + y_{G2}m_2 + \cdots + y_{Gn}m_n}{m_1 + m_2 + \cdots + m_n}, \qquad (9.29)$$

$$z_G = \frac{z_{G1}m_1 + z_{G2}m_2 + \cdots + z_{Gn}m_n}{m_1 + m_2 + \cdots + m_n}.$$

Similarly,

$$x_G = \frac{x_{G1}W_1 + x_{G2}W_2 + \cdots + x_{Gn}W_n}{W_1 + W_2 + \cdots + W_n}, \qquad \text{etc.}$$

---

EXAMPLE 9.6. Assuming that the density of steel is three times that of aluminum, locate $G$ for the composite body shown in Fig. 9.31.

*Solution.* By symmetry,

$$x_G = z_G = 0,$$

and, by the second of Eqs. (9.29),

$$y_G = \frac{y_{GS}\mu_S V_S + y_{GA}\mu_A V_A}{\mu_S V_S + \mu_A V_A},$$

where the subscript $S$ refers to the steel portion and the subscript $A$ to the aluminum portion. Using Fig. 9.24(b) for the steel portion,

$$y_G = \frac{7\mu_S(\tfrac{1}{3}\pi b^2)(4) + 3\mu_A(\pi b^2)(6)}{\mu_S(\tfrac{1}{3}\pi b^2)(4) + \mu_A(\pi b^2)(6)}.$$

Since $\mu_S = 3\mu_A$, therefore,

$$y_G = \frac{28 + 18}{4 + 6} = 4.60 \text{ in.}$$

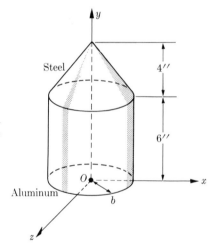

FIGURE 9.31

**9.6 Distributed forces.** The gravitational force on a continuous body, considered in the foregoing article, is an example of a force distributed over a volume. Forces distributed over plane areas (or surfaces) and along straight lines (or curved lines) also occur in mechanics, and such forces are often replaced by mechanically equivalent concentrated forces.

Consider a plane area $A$ in the $xy$-plane, and suppose that there is a normal force distributed over the area. The *pressure* $p(x, y)$ at a point in the area with coordinates $x$, $y$ is defined by selecting an element $\Delta A$

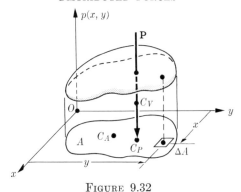

FIGURE 9.32

⸱ shown in Fig. 9.32 and calling the normal force
·h magnitude $\Delta P$). By definition,

$$p(x, y) = \lim_{\Delta A \to 0} \frac{\Delta P}{\Delta A},$$

/length². A three-dimensional graph of the
⸱ined plotted (to some scale) as a surface above
⸱g. 9.32. Since the distributed force is perpen-

ʊɪᴄᴜɪᴀɪ ʊʊ ─    ⸱             ⸱le force **P** is mechanically equivalent to the
distributed force if

$$P = \iint\limits_{A} p(x, y)\, dA \tag{9.30}$$

and

$$x_P P = \iint\limits_{A} x p(x, y)\, dA, \qquad y_P P = \iint\limits_{A} y p(x, y)\, dA,$$

where $x_P$ and $y_P$ are the coordinates of the point $C_P$ (called the *center of pressure*) where the force must be applied. Hence,

$$x_P = \frac{\iint\limits_{A} x p(x, y)\, dA}{\iint\limits_{A} p(x, y)\, dA}, \qquad y_P = \frac{\iint\limits_{A} y p(x, y)\, dA}{\iint\limits_{A} p(x, y)\, dA}. \tag{9.31}$$

It is often useful in mechanics to consider a double integral of the type appearing in Eq. (9.30) as a volume under a surface (in this case the surface of Fig. 9.32), even though the volume is not the purely geometric type of volume discussed in Arts. 9.2 and 9.4. In this case, for example, the volume has units of force (the product of force/length² and length²) rather than length³. The usual formulas, however, are used to determine the volume, the scale to which the function is plotted being immaterial. Interpreting the integral in Eq. (9.30) as the volume under a surface, it is seen that Eqs. (9.31) define the $x$- and $y$-coordinates of the centroid $C_V$ of the volume, so that $C_P$ is the point where a line perpendicular to the $xy$-plane and through $C_V$ pierces the $xy$-plane. (Note that, in general, $C_P$ does not coincide with the centroid $C_A$ of the area $A$.) Summarizing, it can be stated that the concentrated force **P** has a magnitude equal to the volume under the pressure surface and a line of action through the centroid of the volume.

One important application of the foregoing results is to a plane area submerged in a stationary, ideal fluid. If the fluid is incompressible, its specific weight $\gamma$ is constant, and the pressure (which is normal to the area) at any depth $D$ is given by

$$p = \gamma D.$$

Taking the $xy$-plane in such a way that it contains the area, with the $x$-axis in the surface of the fluid (Fig. 9.33), the pressure $p$ is given by

$$p(x, y) = \gamma y \sin \phi,$$

a function which is independent of $x$ and linear in $y$. The pressure surface is thus a plane through the $x$-axis, as shown in Fig. 9.33. For a complicated area $A$, formulas for the volume under the plane and the coordinates of the centroid of the volume may not be readily available, in which case it is advantageous to use a method, presented in Chapter 10, in which $P$ is evaluated and $C_P$ located by considering the properties of $A$ only. For a simple area $A$, on the other hand, the required properties of the volume may be known. Considering, for example, the rectangular area shown in Fig. 9.34, we see that the volume under the pressure surface is of the

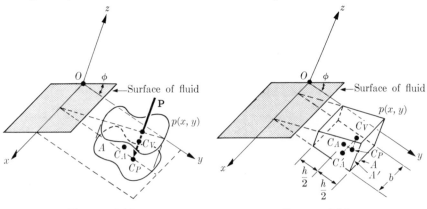

FIGURE 9.33                    FIGURE 9.34

type (discussed in Art. 9.4) for which the $y$- and $z$-coordinates of $C_V$ are the same as those of the centroid $C'_A$ of the area designated in Fig. 9.34 as $A'$.

EXAMPLE 9.7. The tank shown in Fig. 9.35 is filled to the top with water, for which $\gamma = 62.4 \text{ lb/ft}^3$. Find the magnitude and location of the equivalent concentrated normal force on the sloping end plate.

*Solution.* Figure 9.36, an edgewise view of the plate, shows (crosshatched) the graph of $p$, which has a maximum value of $624 \text{ lb/ft}^2$. Hence, computing the crosshatched area and multiplying by the width of the tank,

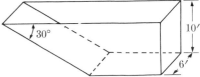

$$P = \tfrac{1}{2}(624)(20)(6) = 37{,}440 \text{ lb},$$

and, locating the centroid of the cross-hatched area,

$$y_P = \tfrac{2}{3}(20) = 13.33 \text{ ft}.$$

FIGURE 9.35

For a normal force distributed along a straight line $L$, let the $x$-axis coincide with the line, as shown in Fig. 9.37. The *intensity $q(x)$ of the force* at a point on the line is defined by letting the magnitude of the normal force on an element $\Delta x$ be $\Delta Q$. By definition,

$$q(x) = \lim_{\Delta x \to 0} \frac{\Delta Q}{\Delta x},$$

the units of $q$ being force/length. A graph of $q(x)$ can be imagined plotted

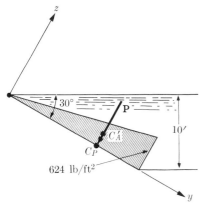

FIGURE 9.36

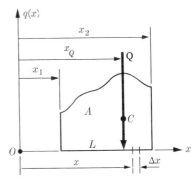

FIGURE 9.37

(to some scale) as the curve in Fig. 9.37. A single force $\mathbf{Q}$ is mechanically equivalent to the distributed force if

$$Q = \int_{x_1}^{x_2} q(x)\, dx \qquad (9.32)$$

and

$$x_Q Q = \int_{x_1}^{x_2} x q(x)\, dx,$$

where $x_Q$ is the directed distance from the origin to $\mathbf{Q}$. Hence,

$$x_Q = \frac{\displaystyle\int_{x_1}^{x_2} x q(x)\, dx}{\displaystyle\int_{x_1}^{x_2} q(x)\, dx}. \qquad (9.33)$$

The integral of Eq. (9.32) is the area $A$ under the curve between $x_1$ and $x_2$. This area has units of force (the product of force/length and length), but it can be found by the usual formulas for areas. Likewise, Eq. (9.33) defines the $x$-coordinate of the centroid $C$ of the area, and $C$ can often be located readily. Summarizing, the concentrated force $\mathbf{Q}$ has a magnitude equal to the area under the intensity curve and a line of action through the centroid of the area.

## Problems

9.1 Locate the center of mass of four particles with masses $m_0$, $2m_0$, $3m_0$, and $4m_0$ placed as shown in Fig. 9.38 at the corners of a square of side $L_0$.

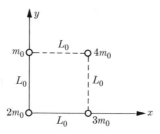

Figure 9.38

9.2 Using integration, verify the formulas of Fig. 9.16(c).

9.3 For the area shown in Fig. 9.39, find $\bar{y}$: (a) by integration, and (b) by dividing the area into a rectangular portion and a parabolic portion and using Fig. 9.16 for the latter portion.

9.4 Locate the centroid of the area in Fig. 9.40.

[Ans.: $\bar{x} = 2.56$ in., $\bar{y} = 4.11$ in.]

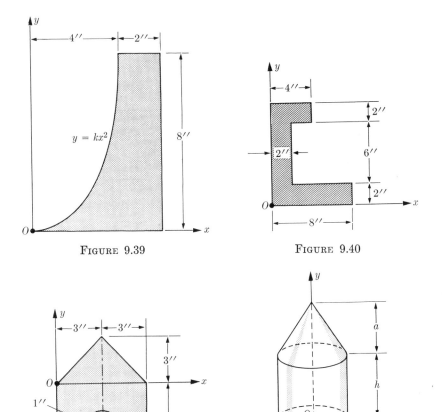

FIGURE 9.39

FIGURE 9.40

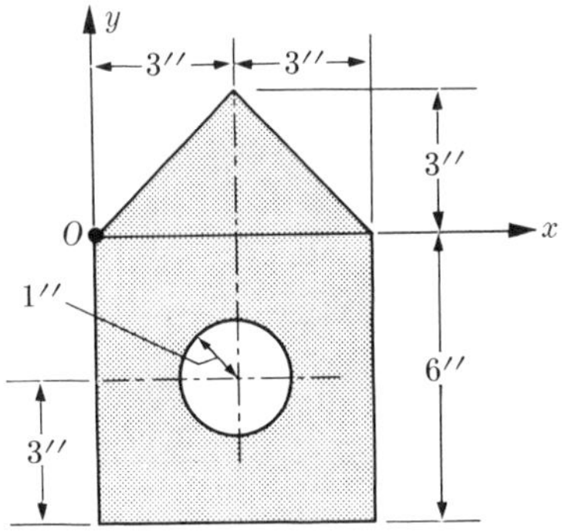

FIGURE 9.41

FIGURE 9.42

9.5 Without using integration, derive the formulas of Fig. 9.16(e) from those of Fig. 9.16(c).

9.6 Locate the centroid of the area shown in Fig. 9.41.

[*Ans.:* $\bar{x} = 3.00$ in., $\bar{y} = -2.14$ in.]

9.7 Using integration, verify the formulas of Fig. 9.24(a).

9.8 Using Fig. 9.24 when necessary, find an expression for the $y$-coordinate of the centroid of the composite volume shown in Fig. 9.42.

$$\left[ Ans.:\ \bar{y} = h\ \frac{6 + 4(a/h) + (a/h)^2}{12 + 4(a/h)}. \right]$$

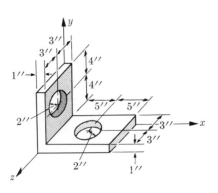

FIGURE 9.43

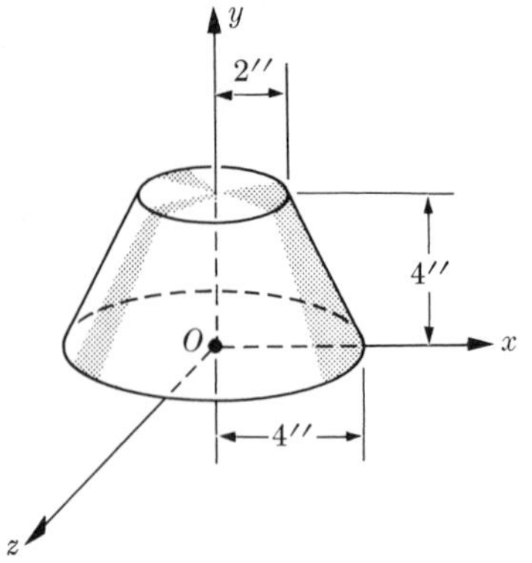

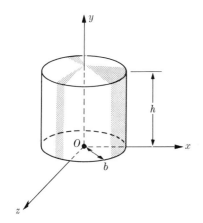

FIGURE 9.44

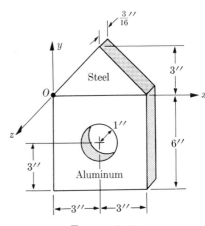

FIGURE 9.45

FIGURE 9.46

9.9 Locate the centroid of the volume shown in Fig. 9.43.

9.10 The body shown in Fig. 9.44 is a truncated, right circular cone which is solid and homogeneous. Determine the $y$-coordinate of its center of gravity.

[*Ans.:* 1.571 in.]

9.11 For the solid cylinder in Fig. 9.45,

$$\mu = \mu_0 e^{1-(y/h)},$$

where $\mu$ is the density. Locate the center of gravity. Given:

$$\int xe^{ax}\,dx = \frac{xe^{ax}}{a} - \frac{e^{ax}}{a^2} + C.$$

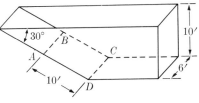

FIGURE 9.47

9.12 Locate the center of gravity of the composite plate in Fig. 9.46. Specific weights: aluminum, 163 lb/ft³; steel, 489 lb/ft³.

[*Ans.:* (3.00 in., −1.20 in., −0.094 in.)]

9.13 The tank in Fig. 9.47 is equipped with a gate *ABCD* in the sloping end plate. If the tank is filled to the top with water ($\gamma = 62.4$ lb/ft³), find the magnitude and location of the resultant normal force on the gate *ABCD*.

# CHAPTER 10

# SECOND MOMENTS OF MASSES AND AREAS

**10.1 Systems of particles.** In Art. 9.1 the first moment of the mass of a system of particles with respect to the origin is defined as the vector which is the numerator of Eq. (9.1), while the first moments with respect to the coordinate planes are defined as the scalar numerators in Eqs. (9.7). It is now possible to define the *second moment of the mass* of a system of particles with respect to the origin as

$$m_1 \mathbf{r}_1 \cdot \mathbf{r}_1 + m_2 \mathbf{r}_2 \cdot \mathbf{r}_2 + \cdots + m_n \mathbf{r}_n \cdot \mathbf{r}_n,$$

this being a quantity which is a scalar but which places more emphasis on the locations of the particles than does the first moment. Employing Eq. (7.7), the second moment can be rewritten as

$$\sum_{i=1}^{n} m_i x_i^2 + \sum_{i=1}^{n} m_i y_i^2 + \sum_{i=1}^{n} m_i z_i^2,$$

and the three sums in this expression are called the second moments of the mass with respect to the $yz$-, $zx$-, and $xy$-planes, respectively.

Second moments corresponding to the foregoing can also be defined for a continuous body, but these have little significance in mechanics, for the extension of Newton's laws to a rigid body reveals that the second moment of the mass with respect to a line is of much more importance than its second moments with respect to points and planes. It is desirable, therefore, to define the second moment of the mass of a system of particles with respect to a line. Figure 10.1 shows a system of $n$ particles with masses $m_1, m_2, \ldots, m_n$. If the perpendicular distance of the $i$th particle from a line $L$ is $\rho_i$, then, by definition, the second moment $I_L$ of the mass with respect to $L$ is given by

$$I_L = \sum_{i=1}^{n} m_i \rho_i^2. \tag{10.1}$$

The quantity $I_L$ is shown in Chapter 13 to be a measure of the tendency of the system to resist rotational motion about $L$, and hence $I_L$ is called the *moment of inertia* of the system about $L$. If the line $L$ is the $z$-axis, the moment of inertia is given by

$$I_z = \sum_{i=1}^{n} m_i(x_i^2 + y_i^2),$$

178

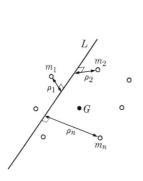

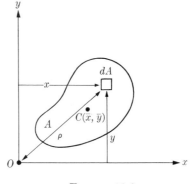

FIGURE 10.1                              FIGURE 10.2

from which it follows that

$$I_z = \sum_{i=1}^{n} m_i x_i^2 + \sum_{i=1}^{n} m_i y_i^2. \qquad (10.2)$$

**10.2 Second moments of areas.** Before amplifying the concept of second moment of mass to include continuous bodies, it is convenient to introduce, for areas, certain purely geometric second moments. (Second moments could also be defined for volumes, lines, and surfaces, but they would not be very useful in mechanics, whereas second moments of areas are important in the study of deformable bodies.)

For an area $A$ in the $xy$-plane, as shown in Fig. 10.2, the second moments with respect to the $y$- and $x$-axes, symbolized by $I_y$ and $I_x$, respectively, are defined by

$$I_y = \iint_A x^2 \, dA, \qquad I_x = \iint_A y^2 \, dA, \qquad (10.3)$$

and these quantities are always positive, since the two integrands are everywhere positive. Because of their resemblance to the moments of inertia of masses, the quantities $I_y$ and $I_x$ are often called the "moments of inertia" of the area about the $y$- and $x$-axes, respectively.

To find $I_x$ or $I_y$ by single integrations, take as an elemental area $dA$ a strip parallel to the axis with respect to which the second moment is being found. The elemental area for finding $I_y$ is shown crosshatched in Fig. 10.3. If the length of the strip is $L(x)$, then

$$dA = L(x) \, dx,$$

and

$$I_y = \int_{x_1}^{x_2} x^2 L(x) \, dx.$$

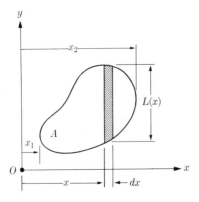

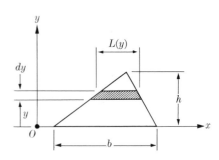

FIGURE 10.3                          FIGURE 10.4

EXAMPLE 10.1. Find $I_x$ for the triangular area shown in Fig. 10.4.

*Solution.* By similar triangles,

$$\frac{L(y)}{h - y} = \frac{b}{h},$$

so that

$$L(y) = b - \frac{b}{h} y.$$

Hence,

$$I_x = \int_{y_1}^{y_2} y^2 L(y)\, dy = \int_0^h \left( by^2 - \frac{b}{h} y^3 \right) dy = \left( \frac{b}{3} y^3 - \frac{b}{4h} y^4 \right) \bigg|_0^h$$

$$= \frac{1}{12} bh^3.$$

The polar coordinate $\rho$ of the element $dA$ in Fig. 10.2 is used to define another second moment of the area. By definition,

$$J_O = \iint_A \rho^2\, dA, \tag{10.4}$$

where $J_O$ is called the *polar moment of inertia* of the area about $O$. Hence,

$$J_O = \iint_A (x^2 + y^2)\, dA,$$

from which it follows that

$$J_O = I_x + I_y. \tag{10.5}$$

Equation (10.5) eliminates the need for using integration to evaluate $J_O$.

By definition,

$$k_x = \sqrt{I_x/A}, \qquad k_y = \sqrt{I_y/A}, \qquad k_O = \sqrt{J_O/A}, \qquad (10.6)$$

and $k_x$, $k_y$, and $k_O$ are called the *radii of gyration* of $A$ about, respectively, the $x$-axis, the $y$-axis, and $O$. (The radii of gyration are positive numbers with units of length.) Hence,

$$I_x = k_x^2 A, \qquad I_y = k_y^2 A, \qquad J_O = k_O^2 A,$$

and, by Eq. (10.5),

$$k_O^2 = k_x^2 + k_y^2.$$

There is a similarity between $k_x$ and $\bar{y}$ (or between $k_y$ and $\bar{x}$) for an area. Since the first moment of the area with respect to the $x$-axis, from Chapter 9, is $\bar{y}A$, $\bar{y}$ can be regarded as an "average" $y$-coordinate of the area that can be used for computing the first moment. Similarly, since the second moment of the area with respect to the $x$-axis is $k_x^2 A$, $k_x$ can be regarded as a different kind of "average" $y$-coordinate, one that can be used in computing the second moment. In general, of course, $\bar{y}$ is not equal to $k_x$, not even in absolute value.

---

EXAMPLE 10.2.  Find $k_x$ for the triangular area of Fig. 10.4.

*Solution.*  By the first of Eqs. (10.6),

$$k_x = \sqrt{\tfrac{1}{12}bh^3 / \tfrac{1}{2}bh} = \frac{1}{\sqrt{6}}\, h = 0.408h.$$

Note that this length is different from $\bar{y}$, which, from Example 9.1, is $\tfrac{1}{3}h$.

---

Another important second moment of an area such as that in Fig. 10.2 is called the *product of inertia*, symbolized by $I_{xy}$. By definition,

$$I_{xy} = \iint\limits_A xy\, dA. \qquad (10.7)$$

If either axis is an axis of symmetry, then $I_{xy} = 0$. To verify this, consider an area for which the $y$-axis is an axis of symmetry, as shown in Fig. 10.5. (Note that $C$ is on the $y$-axis.) For every elemental area $dA$ with coordinates $x$, $y$, there is an identical area $dA$ with coordinates $-x$, $y$. Upon summing over the area, then, the total product of inertia is zero, and a similar argument is used when the $x$-axis is an axis of symmetry. Unlike the other second moments introduced above, the product

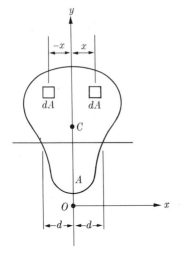

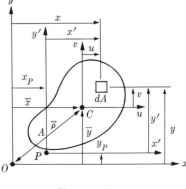

FIGURE 10.5                         FIGURE 10.6

of inertia may be either positive or negative. Because of the presence of both $x$ and $y$ in the integrand of Eq. (10.7), the evaluation of $I_{xy}$ ordinarily entails double integration.

As the coordinate axes are moved in the plane, the second moments $I_x$, $I_y$, $J_O$, and $I_{xy}$ vary, and it is important to understand the way in which they are affected by various changes in the position of the axes. Consider first a set of $x'$- and $y'$-axes (with origin $P$) which are parallel to the $x$- and $y$-axes, respectively, but which can be moved anywhere in the $xy$-plane. (This is called *translation* of axes and differs from *rotation* of axes, which is studied separately in Art. 10.3.) Figure 10.6 shows such a set of axes, as well as a set of $u$- and $v$-axes (called *centroidal* axes) with origin at $C$. Since

$$y = y_P + y',$$

it follows from the second of Eqs. (10.3) that

$$I_x = \iint_A y^2 \, dA = \iint_A (y_P + y')^2 \, dA = \iint_A (y_P^2 + 2y_P y' + y'^2) \, dA.$$

Expressing the integral of the sum as the sum of three integrals and factoring out all constant terms,

$$I_x = y_P^2 \iint_A dA + 2y_P \iint_A y' \, dA + \iint_A y'^2 \, dA.$$

Hence, rearranging the terms on the right-hand side,

$$I_x = I_{x'} + Ay_P^2 + 2y_P \iint_A y' \, dA, \qquad (10.8)$$

and, by a similar derivation,

$$I_y = I_{y'} + Ax_P^2 + 2x_P \iint_A x' \, dA. \qquad (10.9)$$

Substituting

$$x' = x - x_P, \qquad y' = y - y_P$$

into Eqs. (10.8) and (10.9) and solving for $I_{x'}$ and $I_{y'}$, we obtain

$$I_{x'} = I_x + Ay_P^2 - 2y_P \iint_A y \, dA,$$

$$I_{y'} = I_y + Ax_P^2 - 2x_P \iint_A x \, dA. \qquad (10.10)$$

For the special case where the $x'y'$-system coincides with the $uv$-system, Eqs. (10.8) and (10.9) become

$$I_x = I_u + A\bar{y}^2, \qquad I_y = I_v + A\bar{x}^2. \qquad (10.11)$$

Since $A$ is positive, Eqs. (10.11) show that

$$I_x \geq I_u$$

for any $x$-axis parallel to the $u$-axis and

$$I_y \geq I_v$$

for any $y$-axis parallel to the $v$-axis. For any centroidal axis and a non-centroidal axis parallel to it, the moment of inertia about the latter equals the sum of (1) the moment of inertia about the former and (2) the product of the area and the square of the distance between the axes. This statement is called the *parallel-axis theorem*.

By Eqs. (10.5) and (10.11),

$$J_O = I_u + I_v + A(\bar{x}^2 + \bar{y}^2),$$

from which it follows that

$$J_O = J_C + A\bar{\rho}^2. \qquad (10.12)$$

Since

$$x = x_P + x', \qquad y = y_P + y',$$

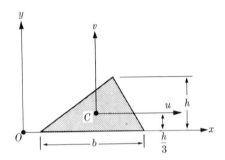

FIGURE 10.7

it follows from Eq. (10.7) that

$$I_{xy} = \iint_A (x_P + x')(y_P + y') \, dA$$

$$= \iint_A x_P y_P \, dA + \iint_A x_P y' \, dA + \iint_A y_P x' \, dA + \iint_A x' y' \, dA.$$

Hence,

$$I_{xy} = I_{x'y'} + A x_P y_P + x_P \iint_A y' \, dA + y_P \iint_A x' \, dA,$$

or, expressing $I_{x'y'}$ in terms of $I_{xy}$,

$$I_{x'y'} = I_{xy} + A x_P y_P - x_P \iint_A y \, dA - y_P \iint_A x \, dA. \qquad (10.13)$$

If the $x'y'$-system coincides with the $uv$-system,

$$I_{xy} = I_{uv} + A \bar{x} \bar{y}. \qquad (10.14)$$

---

EXAMPLE 10.3. Find $I_u$ for the triangular area shown in Fig. 10.7.

*Solution.* From Example 10.1,

$$I_x = \tfrac{1}{12} b h^3.$$

By the first of Eqs. (10.11), therefore,

$$I_u = I_x - A \bar{y}^2 = \tfrac{1}{12} b h^3 - \tfrac{1}{2} b h (\tfrac{1}{9} h^2) = \tfrac{1}{36} b h^3.$$

---

Figure 10.8 gives moments and products of inertia for some common areas.

| | Shape | $I_x$ | $I_u$ | $I_{xy}$ | $I_{uv}$ |
|---|---|---|---|---|---|
| (a) | 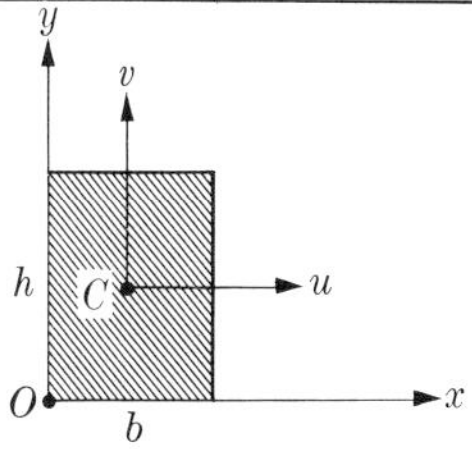 | $\frac{1}{3}bh^3$ | $\frac{1}{12}bh^3$ | $\frac{1}{4}b^2h^2$ | $0$ |
| (b) | 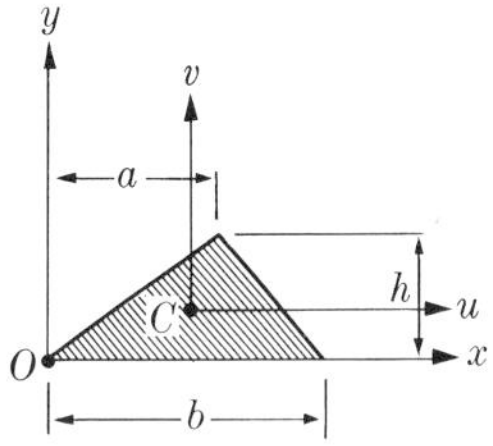 | $\frac{1}{12}bh^3$ | $\frac{1}{36}bh^3$ | $\frac{bh^2}{24}(2a+b)$ | $\frac{bh^2}{72}(2a-b)$ |
| (c) | 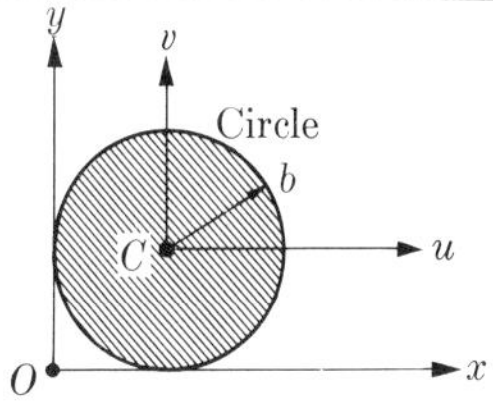 | $\frac{5\pi}{4}b^4$ | $\frac{\pi}{4}b^4$ | $\pi b^4$ | $0$ |
| (d) | 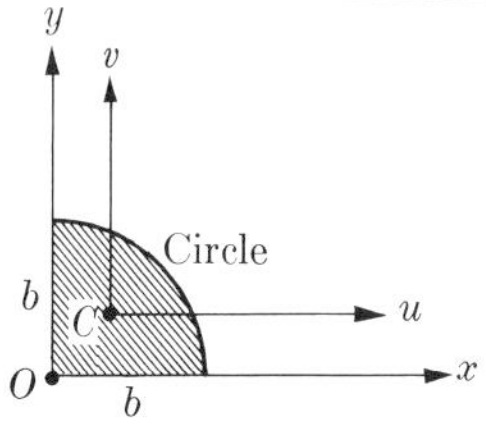 | $\frac{\pi}{16}b^4$ | $\frac{9\pi^2-64}{144\pi}b^4$ | $\frac{1}{8}b^4$ | $\frac{9\pi-32}{72\pi}b^4$ |
| (e) | 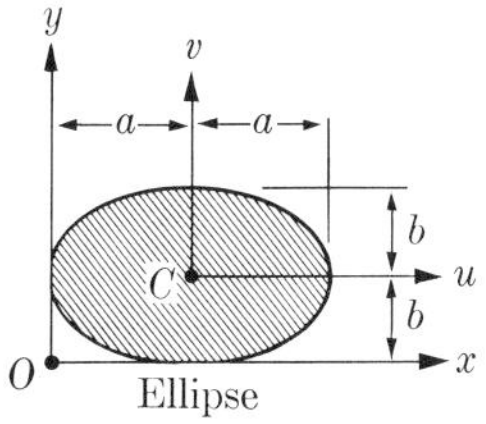 | $\frac{5\pi}{4}ab^3$ | $\frac{\pi}{4}ab^3$ | $\pi a^2b^2$ | $0$ |

FIGURE 10.8

For a composite area $A$ made up of several parts $A_1$, $A_2$, ..., $A_n$, as shown in Fig. 10.9, the moment of inertia of the entire area about the $x$-axis is the sum of the moments of inertia of the parts, i.e.,

$$I_x = (I_1)_x + (I_2)_x + \cdots + (I_n)_x,$$

where $(I_i)_x$ is the moment of inertia of $A_i$ about the $x$-axis. Using the first of Eqs. (10.11),

$$I_x = (I_{u1} + A_1\bar{y}_1^2) + (I_{u2} + A_2\bar{y}_2^2) + \cdots + (I_{un} + A_n\bar{y}_n^2), \qquad (10.15)$$

where $I_{ui}$ is the moment of inertia of $A_i$ about an axis (e.g., the $u_1$-axis in Fig. 10.9) which is through $C_i$ and parallel to the $x$-axis. For many simple shapes, the quantities $I_{ui}$ can be found from a table such as that of Fig. 10.8.

If $I_u$ also is required for the composite area (Fig. 10.9), the first of Eqs. (10.11) can be used to transfer from the $x$-axis to the $u$-axis, i.e.,

$$I_u = I_x - A\bar{y}^2,$$

where

$$A = A_1 + A_2 + \cdots + A_n.$$

If $I_u$ only is required, it is usually simpler to transfer from the centroidal axis of each area directly to the $u$-axis, since

$$I_u = (I_1)_u + (I_2)_u + \cdots + (I_n)_u.$$

Hence,

$$I_u = (I_{u1} + A_1\bar{v}_1^2) + (I_{u2} + A_2\bar{v}_2^2) + \cdots + (I_{un} + A_n\bar{v}_n^2). \qquad (10.16)$$

Equations similar to Eqs. (10.15) and (10.16) hold also for $I_y$ and $I_v$.

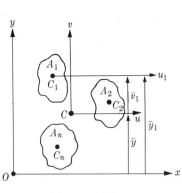

FIGURE 10.9

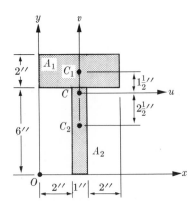

FIGURE 10.10

EXAMPLE 10.4. Find the moments of inertia of the area shown in Fig. 10.10 about its centroidal axes and the polar moment of inertia about its centroid. (This is the same area as in Example 9.2.)

*Solution.* The centroidal axes are shown in Fig. 10.10. By Eq. (10.16) and Fig. 10.8(a),

$$I_u = [\tfrac{1}{12}(5)(2)^3 + 10(\tfrac{3}{2})^2] + [\tfrac{1}{12}(1)(6)^3 + 6(\tfrac{5}{2})^2]$$

$$= \tfrac{10}{3} + \tfrac{45}{2} + 18 + \tfrac{75}{2} = \tfrac{244}{3} = 81.3 \text{ in}^4.$$

Similarly,

$$I_v = \tfrac{1}{12}(2)(5)^3 + \tfrac{1}{12}(6)(1)^3 = \tfrac{125}{6} + \tfrac{1}{2} = \tfrac{64}{3} = 21.3 \text{ in}^4.$$

By Eq. (10.5),

$$J_C = I_u + I_v = 102.6 \text{ in}^4.$$

_____

To find the product of inertia of a composite area with respect to the $u$- and $v$-axes,

$$I_{uv} = (I_{uv1} + A_1\overline{u}_1\overline{v}_1) + (I_{uv2} + A_2\overline{u}_2\overline{v}_2) + \cdots + (I_{uvn} + A_n\overline{u}_n\overline{v}_n),$$

where $I_{uvi}$ is the product of inertia of $A_i$ with respect to its own centroidal axes.

**10.3 Rotation of axes.** The question of how the second moments of an area with respect to the coordinate axes vary when the axes are rotated in the plane is an important problem in its own right and is typical of a class of problems involving transformation of quantities under a rotation of axes.

Consider a set of $\xi$- and $\eta$-axes with origin at $O$ but with an angle of rotation $\theta$ measured counterclockwise from the $x$-axis to the $\xi$-axis, as shown in Fig. 10.11. From that figure,

$$\eta = y \cos \theta - x \sin \theta,$$

$$\xi = x \cos \theta + y \sin \theta.$$

Hence,

$$I_\xi = \iint_A \eta^2 \, dA = \iint_A (y^2 \cos^2 \theta - 2xy \sin \theta \cos \theta + x^2 \sin^2 \theta) \, dA,$$

$$I_\eta = \iint_A \xi^2 \, dA = \iint_A (x^2 \cos^2 \theta + 2xy \sin \theta \cos \theta + y^2 \sin^2 \theta) \, dA.$$

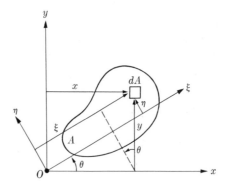

FIGURE 10.11

Arranging the right-hand sides of these equations as separate integrals and factoring out quantities which remain constant during integration,

$$I_\xi = \cos^2\theta \iint_A y^2\, dA - 2\sin\theta\cos\theta \iint_A xy\, dA + \sin^2\theta \iint_A x^2\, dA,$$

$$I_\eta = \cos^2\theta \iint_A x^2\, dA + 2\sin\theta\cos\theta \iint_A xy\, dA + \sin^2\theta \iint_A y^2\, dA.$$

Hence,

$$I_\xi = I_x \cos^2\theta + I_y \sin^2\theta - 2I_{xy}\sin\theta\cos\theta,$$

$$I_\eta = I_y \cos^2\theta + I_x \sin^2\theta + 2I_{xy}\sin\theta\cos\theta,$$

and, expressing all the trigonometric functions in terms of $2\theta$, these equations become

$$I_\xi = \tfrac{1}{2}(I_x + I_y) + \tfrac{1}{2}(I_x - I_y)\cos 2\theta - I_{xy}\sin 2\theta,$$

$$I_\eta = \tfrac{1}{2}(I_x + I_y) - \tfrac{1}{2}(I_x - I_y)\cos 2\theta + I_{xy}\sin 2\theta. \tag{10.17}$$

Equations (10.17) give the moments of inertia of $A$ about the rotated axes in terms of the angle $\theta$ and moments and products of inertia about the original axes. Similarly,

$$I_{\xi\eta} = \iint_A \xi\eta\, dA$$

$$= \iint_A (y^2 \sin\theta\cos\theta - x^2 \sin\theta\cos\theta + xy\cos^2\theta - xy\sin^2\theta)\, dA$$

$$= I_x \sin\theta\cos\theta - I_y \sin\theta\cos\theta + I_{xy}(\cos^2\theta - \sin^2\theta),$$

and hence

$$I_{\xi\eta} = \tfrac{1}{2}(I_x - I_y) \sin 2\theta + I_{xy} \cos 2\theta. \qquad (10.18)$$

As $\theta$ varies from 0 to 180°, the $\xi$-axis covers all possible directions through $O$, and the quantity $I_\xi$ varies with $\theta$ in accordance with the first of Eqs. (10.17), which shows that $I_\xi = I_x$ when $\theta = 0$ and that $I_\xi = I_x$ again when $\theta = 180°$. Thus, during the variation, $I_\xi$ must either remain constant (as it does in the special case when $I_x = I_y$ and $I_{xy} = 0$) or reach maximum and minimum values (as it does in general). To find the values of $\theta$ which yield these extreme values of $I_\xi$, apply the necessary condition for maximum or minimum, i.e.,

$$\frac{dI_\xi}{d\theta} = 0,$$

from which, by the first of Eqs. (10.17), it follows that

$$-(I_x - I_y) \sin 2\theta - 2I_{xy} \cos 2\theta = 0. \qquad (10.19)$$

Solving Eq. (10.19) for $\tan 2\theta$,

$$\tan 2\theta = -\frac{2I_{xy}}{I_x - I_y}. \qquad (10.20)$$

The values of $\tan 2\theta$ computed by Eq. (10.20) may be either positive or negative, but, in either case, the equation defines two values of $2\theta$ which differ by 180°. Let these be $2\theta_1$ and $2\theta_2$, so that

$$\theta_2 = \theta_1 + 90°. \qquad (10.21)$$

Further, let $\theta_1$ be such that, upon finding its sine and cosine from Eq. (10.20), we obtain the following equations:

$$\sin 2\theta_1 = \frac{-2I_{xy}}{\sqrt{(I_x - I_y)^2 + 4I_{xy}^2}}, \quad \cos 2\theta_1 = \frac{I_x - I_y}{\sqrt{(I_x - I_y)^2 + 4I_{xy}^2}}, \quad (10.22)$$

in which case, for $\theta_2$,

$$\sin 2\theta_2 = \frac{2I_{xy}}{\sqrt{(I_x - I_y)^2 + 4I_{xy}^2}}, \quad \cos 2\theta_2 = \frac{-(I_x - I_y)}{\sqrt{(I_x - I_y)^2 + 4I_{xy}^2}}. \quad (10.23)$$

The following are four possible combinations of circumstances for a given area, origin, and coordinate system and, in each case, the properties of $2\theta_1$ as determined by Eq. (10.20) and the first of Eqs. (10.22):

|    | *If* | *then* | *and* |
|----|------|--------|-------|
| (1) | $I_{xy} < 0,$ <br> $I_x > I_y;$ | $\tan 2\theta_1 > 0,$ <br> $\sin 2\theta_1 > 0,$ | $0 < 2\theta_1 < 90°.$ |
| (2) | $I_{xy} < 0,$ <br> $I_x < I_y;$ | $\tan 2\theta_1 < 0,$ <br> $\sin 2\theta_1 > 0,$ | $90° < 2\theta_1 < 180°.$ |
| (3) | $I_{xy} > 0,$ <br> $I_x < I_y;$ | $\tan 2\theta_1 > 0,$ <br> $\sin 2\theta_1 < 0,$ | $180° < 2\theta_1 < 270°.$ |
| (4) | $I_{xy} > 0,$ <br> $I_x > I_y;$ | $\tan 2\theta_1 < 0,$ <br> $\sin 2\theta_1 < 0,$ | $270° < 2\theta_1 < 360°.$ |

Let $I_1$ be the value of $I_\xi$ associated with $\theta_1$ and $I_2$ the value associated with $\theta_2$. Substituting Eqs. (10.22) and (10.23) into the first of Eqs. (10.17),

$$I_1 = \tfrac{1}{2}(I_x + I_y) + \tfrac{1}{2}\sqrt{(I_x - I_y)^2 + 4I_{xy}^2},$$
$$I_2 = \tfrac{1}{2}(I_x + I_y) - \tfrac{1}{2}\sqrt{(I_x - I_y)^2 + 4I_{xy}^2}. \tag{10.24}$$

From these equations it is obvious that $I_1$ is the maximum value which $I_\xi$ can attain and $I_2$ is the minimum value. The quantities $I_1$ and $I_2$ are called the *principal moments of inertia* of the area for axes through $O$. By Eq. (10.21), the maximum principal moment of inertia and the minimum one occur about axes that are perpendicular, and these axes are called the *principal axes of inertia* of the area at $O$. Thus, if the $\xi$-axis is one principal axis, then the $\eta$-axis is the other.

Comparing Eqs. (10.18) and (10.19), we see that

$$I_{\xi\eta} = 0 \tag{10.25}$$

is a necessary condition that the $\xi\eta$-system constitutes the principal axes. It can also be shown that the condition is sufficient, so that finding the principal axes is equivalent to finding those axes for which Eq. (10.25) is satisfied. If, therefore, there is an axis through $O$ which is an axis of symmetry of the area, that axis is a principal axis. The centroid is the point for which principal axes and principal moments of inertia are usually required, and, if the area has an axis of symmetry, it is known from Chapter 9 that $C$ lies on that axis. Hence, an axis of symmetry is always a principal axis at the centroid (as well as at any other point on the axis).

---

EXAMPLE 10.5. Locate the principal axes and find the principal moments of inertia at the centroid of the right-triangular area in Fig. 10.12 if: (a) $h = \tfrac{1}{2}b$, and (b) $h = b$.

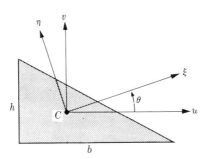

FIGURE 10.12

*Solution.* For any ratio of $h$ to $b$, from Fig. 10.8(b),

$$I_u = \tfrac{1}{36}bh^3, \qquad I_v = \tfrac{1}{36}b^3h, \qquad I_{uv} = -\tfrac{1}{72}b^2h^2.$$

By Eq. (10.20),

$$\tan 2\theta_1 = \tan 2\theta_2 = -\frac{-\tfrac{1}{36}b^2h^2}{\tfrac{1}{36}bh(h^2 - b^2)} = \frac{bh}{h^2 - b^2}.$$

and, by Eqs. (10.24),

$$I_1 = \tfrac{1}{2}(\tfrac{1}{36}bh^3 + \tfrac{1}{36}b^3h) + \tfrac{1}{2}\sqrt{(\tfrac{1}{36}bh^3 - \tfrac{1}{36}b^3h)^2 + 4(-\tfrac{1}{72}b^2h^2)^2}$$

$$= \tfrac{1}{72}bh(b^2 + h^2) + \tfrac{1}{2}\sqrt{\tfrac{1}{1296}b^2h^2(h^2 - b^2)^2 + \tfrac{1}{1296}b^4h^4}$$

$$= \tfrac{1}{72}\left[bh(b^2 + h^2) + \sqrt{b^2h^2(b^4 - b^2h^2 + h^4)}\right],$$

$$I_2 = \tfrac{1}{72}\left[bh(b^2 + h^2) - \sqrt{b^2h^2(b^4 - b^2h^2 + h^4)}\right].$$

(a) If $h = \tfrac{1}{2}b$,

$$\tan 2\theta_1 = \tan 2\theta_2 = \frac{\tfrac{1}{2}b^2}{\tfrac{1}{4}b^2 - b^2} = -\frac{2}{3}.$$

Since $I_{uv} < 0$,

$$90° < 2\theta_1 < 180°,$$

i.e.,

$$2\theta_1 = 146.3°, \qquad \theta_1 = 73.2°, \qquad \theta_2 = 163.2°.$$

The principal moments of inertia are

$$I_1 = \tfrac{1}{72}\left[\tfrac{1}{2}b^2(b^2 + \tfrac{1}{4}b^2) + \sqrt{\tfrac{1}{4}b^4(b^4 - \tfrac{1}{4}b^4 + \tfrac{1}{16}b^4)}\right] = \frac{5 + \sqrt{13}}{576}b^4,$$

$$I_2 = \frac{5 - \sqrt{13}}{576}b^4.$$

(b) If $h = b$ (in which case the triangle is an isosceles right triangle),

$$\tan 2\theta_1 = \tan 2\theta_2 = \infty,$$

and hence

$$2\theta_1 = 90°, \qquad \theta_1 = 45°, \qquad \theta_2 = 135°.$$

(These angles also follow from symmetry considerations.) The principal moments of inertia in this case are

$$I_1 = \tfrac{1}{72}[b^2(2b^2) + \sqrt{b^4(b^4 - b^4 + b^4)}] = \frac{2 + 1}{72} b^4 = \frac{1}{24} b^4,$$

$$I_2 = \frac{2 - 1}{72} b^4 = \frac{1}{72} b^4.$$

---

Since $I_2$ at the centroid is the smallest moment of inertia of all those about axes through the centroid, and since the moment of inertia about any axis through the centroid is the smallest of all those about parallel axes not through the centroid, it can be concluded that $I_2$ at the centroid is the smallest moment of inertia possible for an area.

For axes which are both translated and rotated (i.e., an $\xi\eta$-system with origin at $P$ in Fig. 10.6 and with an angle $\theta$ measured from the $x'$-axis to the $\xi$-axis), general transformation equations can be obtained for $I_\xi$, $I_\eta$, and $I_{\xi\eta}$ in terms of $I_x$, $I_y$, and $I_{xy}$. To accomplish this, replace $x$ and $y$ in Eqs. (10.17) and (10.18) by $x'$ and $y'$, respectively, and substitute the parallel-axis equations, Eqs. (10.10) and (10.13), into the resulting expressions.

**10.4 Pressure on submerged areas.** One application of second moments of areas is to the problem (discussed in Art. 9.6) of a plane area submerged in an ideal, incompressible fluid. Referring to Fig. 9.33, we recall that the pressure $p$ on the area is given by

$$p(x, y) = \gamma y \sin \phi,$$

where $\gamma$ is the specific weight of the fluid. By Eq. (9.30),

$$P = \iint_A \gamma y \sin \phi \, dA = \gamma \sin \phi \iint_A y \, dA,$$

and, if $\bar{y}_A$ is the $y$-coordinate of $C_A$ (the centroid of $A$),

$$P = \gamma \sin \phi \bar{y}_A A. \tag{10.26}$$

Equation (10.26) states that $P$ is the product of the pressure at $C_A$ and $A$.

If $x_P$ and $y_P$ are the coordinates of $C_P$ (the center of pressure), then, by Eqs. (9.31),

$$y_P = \frac{\iint_A \gamma y^2 \sin \phi \, dA}{\gamma \sin \phi \bar{y}_A A}, \qquad x_P = \frac{\iint_A \gamma xy \sin \phi \, dA}{\gamma \sin \phi \bar{y}_A A}.$$

Hence,

$$y_P = \frac{I_{xA}}{\bar{y}_A A}, \qquad x_P = \frac{I_{xyA}}{\bar{y}_A A}, \qquad (10.27)$$

where $I_{xA}$ and $I_{xyA}$ are the moment of inertia about the $x$-axis and the product of inertia, respectively, of the area $A$.

The quantity $y_P$ given by the first of Eqs. (10.27) is another kind of "average" $y$-coordinate (in addition to the two mentioned in Art. 10.2), in this case the quotient of the second moment and the first moment.

Note that the $x$-axis must be taken in the surface of the fluid to make Eqs. (10.26) and (10.27) valid.

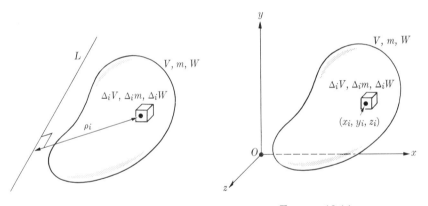

FIGURE 10.13                    FIGURE 10.14

**10.5 Continuous bodies.** The moment of inertia of the solid body shown in Fig. 10.13 about the line $L$ is defined by an equation similar to Eq. (10.1), namely,

$$I_L = \lim_{n \to \infty} \sum_{i=1}^{n} \rho_i^2 \, \Delta_i m, \qquad (10.28)$$

where $\rho_i$ is the perpendicular distance from the line $L$ to the element. If the line $L$ is the $z$-axis (Fig. 10.14), the moment of inertia is given by

$$I_z = \lim_{n \to \infty} \sum_{i=1}^{n} (x_i^2 + y_i^2) \, \Delta_i m,$$

which can be rewritten as

$$I_z = \lim_{n \to \infty} \sum_{i=1}^{n} (x_i^2 + y_i^2)\mu(x_i, y_i, z_i)\,\Delta_i V.$$

Moments of inertia $I_x$ and $I_y$ are defined in a similar manner, and hence

$$I_x = \iiint\limits_{V} (y^2 + z^2)\mu(x, y, z)\,dV,$$

$$I_y = \iiint\limits_{V} (z^2 + x^2)\mu(x, y, z)\,dV, \qquad (10.29)$$

$$I_z = \iiint\limits_{V} (x^2 + y^2)\mu(x, y, z)\,dV.$$

The products of inertia of the body with respect to the $x$-, $y$-, and $z$-axes, respectively, are defined by the following equations:

$$I_{yz} = \iiint\limits_{V} yz\mu(x, y, z)\,dV,$$

$$I_{zx} = \iiint\limits_{V} zx\mu(x, y, z)\,dV, \qquad (10.30)$$

$$I_{xy} = \iiint\limits_{V} xy\mu(x, y, z)\,dV.$$

The radii of gyration of the body about the three axes are defined by

$$k_x = \sqrt{I_x/m}, \qquad k_y = \sqrt{I_y/m}, \qquad k_z = \sqrt{I_z/m}, \qquad (10.31)$$

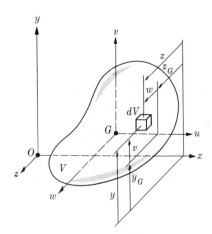

FIGURE 10.15

so that

$$I_x = k_x^2 m,$$

etc. If mass is measured in units of slugs, the moments and products of inertia are in slug-in$^2$ or slug-ft$^2$.

To develop the parallel-axis theorem for a body, consider a $uvw$-system of axes with origin at the center of mass $G$, as shown in Fig. 10.15. (A more general translated system with origin at any point $A$ could also be considered.) Since,

$$y = y_G + v, \qquad z = z_G + w,$$

it follows from the first of Eqs. (10.29) that

$$I_x = \iiint_V [(y_G^2 + 2y_G v + v^2) + (z_G^2 + 2z_G w + w^2)]\mu(u, v, w)\, dV$$

$$= (y_G^2 + z_G^2)\iiint_V \mu\, dV + \iiint_V (v^2 + w^2)\mu\, dV$$

$$+ 2y_G \iiint_V v\mu\, dV + 2z_G \iiint_V w\mu\, dV.$$

Since the last two integrals in this equation are zero,

$$I_x = I_u + m(y_G^2 + z_G^2). \tag{10.32}$$

Similar equations hold for $I_y$ and $I_z$, and, in general, the parallel-axis theorem states that, for any axis through $G$ and another axis parallel to it, the moment of inertia about the latter equals the sum of (1) the moment of inertia about the former and (2) the product of the mass and the square of the distance between the axes. A corollary to this theorem is that, for any family of parallel lines in space, the one through $G$ gives the smallest moment of inertia.

For the product of inertia,

$$I_{yz} = \iiint_V (y_G + v)(z_G + w)\mu(u, v, w)\, dV$$

$$= y_G z_G \iiint_V \mu\, dV + \iiint_V vw\mu\, dV + y_G \iiint_V w\mu\, dV + z_G \iiint_V v\mu\, dV,$$

and thus

$$I_{yz} = I_{vw} + m y_G z_G. \tag{10.33}$$

It is sometimes convenient to use the symbol $I_x^G$ instead of $I_u$ for the moment of inertia about an axis through $G$ parallel to the $x$-axis (with similar symbols for $I_v$ and $I_w$) and the symbol $I_{yz}^G$ instead of $I_{vw}$ for the

| | Body | $I_x$ | $I_u$ | $I_z$ |
|---|---|---|---|---|
| (a) | 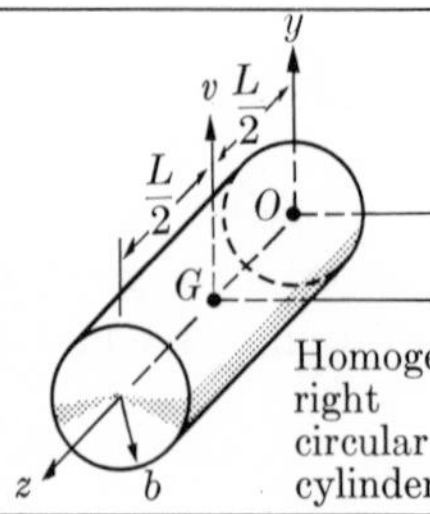 Homogeneous, right circular cylinder | $\frac{1}{12}m(4L^2 + 3b^2)$ | $\frac{1}{12}m(L^2 + 3b^2)$ | $\frac{1}{2}mb^2$ |
| (b) | 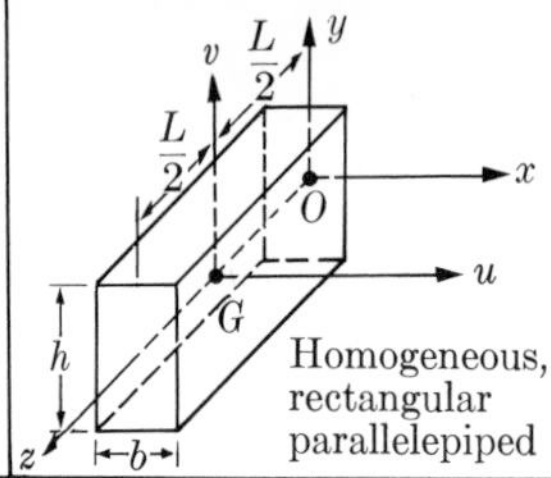 Homogeneous, rectangular parallelepiped | $\frac{1}{12}m(4L^2 + h^2)$ | $\frac{1}{12}m(L^2 + h^2)$ | $\frac{1}{12}m(b^2 + h^2)$ |
| (c) | 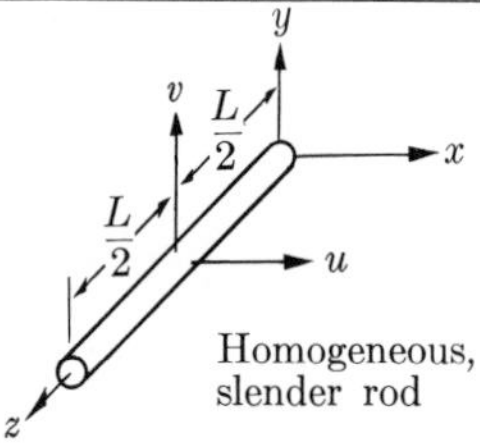 Homogeneous, slender rod | $\frac{1}{3}mL^2$ | $\frac{1}{12}mL^2$ | |
| (d) | 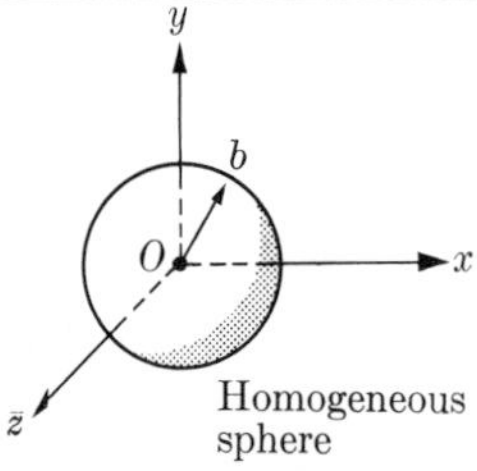 Homogeneous sphere | $\frac{2}{5}mb^2$ | | $\frac{2}{5}mb^2$ |
| (e) | 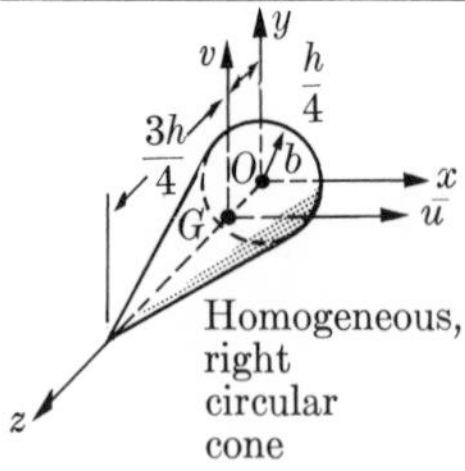 Homogeneous, right circular cone | $\frac{1}{20}m(3b^2 + 2h^2)$ | $\frac{3}{80}m(4b^2 + h^2)$ | $\frac{3}{10}mb^2$ |

FIGURE 10.16

product of inertia about an axis through $G$ parallel to the $x$-axis (with similar symbols for $I_{wu}$ and $I_{uv}$). Then, for any other reference point $A$, the superscript $A$ is used instead of $G$.

Figure 10.16 gives various moments of inertia for solid, homogeneous (i.e., constant-density) bodies in terms of the total mass $m$ of each body. The formulas for $I_x$ and $I_z$ in this figure can be obtained by triple integration. The formulas for $I_u$ can be obtained from those for $I_x$ by Eq. (10.32). For the cone of Fig. 10.16(e), for example,

$$I_u = I_x - mz_G^2 = \tfrac{1}{20} m(3b^2 + 2h^2) - m\left(\tfrac{1}{16}h^2\right)$$
$$= m\left(\tfrac{3}{20}b^2 + \tfrac{3}{80}h^2\right) = \tfrac{3}{80}m(4b^2 + h^2).$$

For a composite body,

$$I_L = (I_1)_L + (I_2)_L + \cdots + (I_n)_L, \tag{10.34}$$

provided that the moment of inertia of each part is computed about the same line $L$. This additive property of moments of inertia makes possible the finding of moments of inertia of bodies obtained by subdividing the bodies in Fig. 10.16 into identical parts (as long as all the parts have the same orientation with respect to the axis being used). For example, to find $I_x$ and $I_z$ for the homogeneous semicylinder in Fig. 10.17, let $m$ be the mass of the semicylinder and note that $I_x$ and $I_z$ are one-half the corresponding moments of inertia of the full cylinder in Fig. 10.16(a). Hence,

$$I_x = \tfrac{1}{2}[\tfrac{1}{12}(2m)(4L^2 + 3b^2)] = \tfrac{1}{12}m(4L^2 + 3b^2),$$

$$I_z = \tfrac{1}{2}[\tfrac{1}{2}(2m)b^2] = \tfrac{1}{2}mb^2.$$

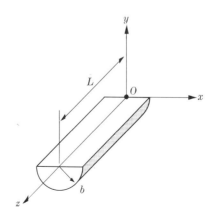

FIGURE 10.17

Moments of inertia (about various axes) of composite bodies made up by attaching together the simple shapes of Fig. 10.16 can be computed by using Eq. (10.34) in conjunction with the parallel-axis theorem.

---

EXAMPLE 10.6. Find $I_u$ for the body in Fig. 10.18. For specific weights, use 489 lb/ft$^3$ for steel and 163 lb/ft$^3$ for aluminum.

*Solution.* Letting $m_S$ and $m_A$ be the masses of the steel and aluminum portions, respectively, and using Eq. (10.32) and Fig. 10.16,

$$I_u = \tfrac{3}{80}m_S[4(4)^2 + (4)^2] + m_S(2.40)^2$$
$$+ \tfrac{1}{12}m_A[(6)^2 + 3(4)^2] + m_A(1.60)^2$$
$$= 8.76m_S + 9.56m_A.$$

But

$$m_S = \mu_S[\tfrac{1}{3}\pi(4)^2][4] = \frac{64\pi}{3}\mu_S,$$

$$m_A = \mu_A[\pi(4)^2][6] = 96\pi\mu_A,$$

and

$$\mu_A = \frac{163}{32.2} = 5.06 \text{ slugs/ft}^3,$$

$$\mu_S = 3\mu_A = 15.18 \text{ slugs/ft}^3.$$

Hence,

$$m_S = \frac{64\pi}{3}\left(\frac{15.18}{1728}\right) = 0.589 \text{ slugs},$$

$$m_A = 96\pi\left(\frac{5.06}{1728}\right) = 0.883 \text{ slugs},$$

and

$$I_u = 8.76(0.589) + 9.56(0.883) = 5.16 + 8.44 = 13.60 \text{ slug-in}^2.$$

---

The thin plate of uniform thickness and constant density is a type of body for which the moments of inertia are easily found. Letting the $xy$-plane be the plane of symmetry as shown in Fig. 10.19, a prism extending through the thickness is taken as an elemental volume, so that

$$dV = t\, dA.$$

Substituting this into Eqs. (10.29) and noting, since the plate is thin, that $z^2$ may be neglected in comparison with $x^2$ and $y^2$ in the first two

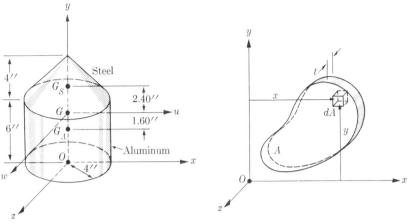

FIGURE 10.18                                    FIGURE 10.19

of Eqs. (10.29), the triple integrals reduce to double integrals, i.e.,

$$I_x = \iint_A y^2 \mu_0 t \, dA = \mu_0 t \iint_A y^2 \, dA,$$

$$I_y = \iint_A x^2 \mu_0 t \, dA = \mu_0 t \iint_A x^2 \, dA,$$

$$I_z = \iint_A (x^2 + y^2) \mu_0 t \, dA = \mu_0 t \iint_A (x^2 + y^2) \, dA.$$

By Eqs. (10.3) and (10.5),

$$I_x = \mu_0 t I_{xA}, \qquad I_y = \mu_0 t I_{yA},$$
$$I_z = \mu_0 t (I_{xA} + I_{yA}) = \mu_0 t J_{OA},$$

$$(10.35)$$

where the second subscript, $A$, indicates that the moments of inertia are of the area $A$ which is the face of the plate. Equations (10.35) show that, for a thin, homogeneous plate with the $z$-axis perpendicular to the plate,

$$I_z = I_x + I_y.$$

The formulas in Fig. 10.8 can now be used for finding moments of inertia of thin plates.

EXAMPLE 10.7. Find $I_x$, $I_y$, $I_z$ for the thin, homogeneous, circular plate shown in Fig. 10.20.

*Solution.* By Fig. 10.8(c) and Eqs. (10.35),

$$I_x = \mu_0 t \left( \frac{\pi}{4} b^4 \right), \qquad I_y = \mu_0 t \left( \frac{\pi}{4} b^4 \right), \qquad I_z = \mu_0 t \left( \frac{\pi}{2} b^4 \right).$$

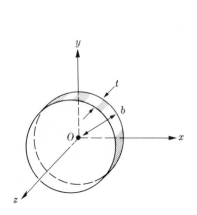

FIGURE 10.20                    FIGURE 10.21

Since

$$m = \pi b^2 t \mu_0,$$

it follows that

$$\mu_0 = \frac{m}{\pi b^2 t},$$

and therefore

$$I_x = I_y = \tfrac{1}{4}mb^2, \qquad I_z = \tfrac{1}{2}mb^2.$$

(These equations can also be obtained from Fig. 10.16(a) by letting $L$ approach zero.)

---

When we know the moments of inertia of thin plates, it is sometimes possible to find certain moments of inertia of other bodies by single integrations. This requires choosing as an elemental volume a thin slice perpendicular to the axis about which the moment of inertia is being computed, as illustrated in the following example.

---

EXAMPLE 10.8. Derive the formula for $I_z$ in Fig. 10.16(e).

Solution. The elemental slice is shown in Fig. 10.21. Let $dI_z$ be the moment of inertia of the slice about the $z$-axis. From Example 10.7,

$$dI_z = \frac{\pi}{2} [r(z)]^4 \mu(z) \, dz,$$

provided that $\mu$ varies only with $z$ (so that it is constant for the slice). But

$$r(z) = b - \frac{b}{h} z,$$

and therefore

$$I_z = \int_0^h \frac{\pi}{2} \left( b - \frac{b}{h} z \right)^4 \mu(z) \, dz.$$

If $\mu(z) = \mu_0$, where $\mu_0$ is a constant,

$$I_z = \frac{\pi}{2} \mu_0 \int_0^h \left( b - \frac{b}{h} z \right)^4 dz = \frac{\pi}{2} \mu_0 \left( - \frac{h}{5b} \right) \left( b - \frac{b}{h} z \right)^5 \bigg|_0^h = \frac{\pi}{10} \mu_0 b^4 h.$$

Since

$$m = \tfrac{1}{3} \pi b^2 h \mu_0,$$

it follows that

$$I_z = \tfrac{3}{10} m b^2.$$

Another special method for finding moments of inertia applies to thin shells of uniform density. If, for example, the radius $b$ of the solid, homogeneous sphere of Fig. 10.16(d) is increased by a small increment $db$, the change in $I_x$ is the moment of inertia of a thin spherical shell surrounding the solid sphere. This change can be determined approximately by finding the differential $dI_x$. Since

$$m = \frac{4\pi}{3} b^3 \mu_0,$$

it follows that

$$I_x = \frac{8\pi}{15} \mu_0 b^5.$$

Hence,

$$dI_x = \frac{8\pi}{3} \mu_0 b^4 \, db, \qquad dm = 4\pi \mu_0 b^2 \, db.$$

Thus,

$$dI_x = \tfrac{2}{3} b^2 \, dm.$$

An exact formula for the moment of inertia of a shell can be obtained by use of Eq. (10.34), i.e., by subtracting the moment of inertia of a removed portion from that of the corresponding solid body.

For a given body and a given origin $O$, the orientation of the $xyz$-system of coordinate axes can be altered, with the result that the moments and products of inertia defined by Eqs. (10.29) and (10.30) vary. The following statements can be verified by mathematical methods which are too complex to be included in this introduction to mechanics:

(1) There is one set of axes with origin at $O$ for which all three products of inertia are zero. (These are called the *principal axes of inertia* at $O$.)

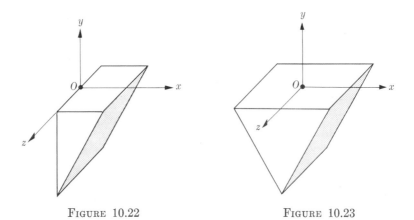

FIGURE 10.22                    FIGURE 10.23

(2) For these axes, one moment of inertia is the greatest for any axis through $O$, one is the smallest, and the remaining one has an intermediate value. (These are called the *principal moments of inertia* at $O$.)

(3) An axis of symmetry of shape and density distribution is a principal axis at any point of itself. (For example, the $z$-axis in each body of Fig. 10.16 is such an axis.)

(4) If the $xy$-plane is a plane of symmetry of shape and density distribution, then $I_{yz} = I_{zx} = 0$ and the $z$-axis is a principal axis at $O$. (Figure 10.22 shows a homogeneous body and a set of axes for which this is the case.) This statement holds also after cyclical permutation of the letters $x$, $y$, $z$.

(5) If both the $xy$-plane and the $yz$-plane are planes of symmetry, then the coordinate axes are principal axes. (Figure 10.23 shows an example of this situation.) This statement holds for any pair of coordinate planes.

It can be easily verified by symmetry considerations that all axes shown in Fig. 10.16 are principal axes at points $O$ and $G$. Except for the rectangular parallelepiped, all the bodies in Fig. 10.16 are degenerate cases in which two (and, for the sphere, all three) of the principal moments of inertia are equal, which means that, for those bodies, there is not a unique set of principal axes at points on the axis of symmetry.

203

PROBLEMS

10.1 For the area shown in Fig. 10.24, find: (a) $I_y$ (by integration), (b) $k_y$, (c) $I_v$ (by the parallel-axis theorem).

10.2 Find the moments of inertia of the area shown in Fig. 10.25 about the $x$-axis and about the $u$-axis.

[*Ans.:* $I_x = 439$ in$^4$, $I_u = 138$ in$^4$.]

10.3 Find $I_u$ and $I_v$ for the doubly symmetrical area in Fig. 10.26.

10.4 Find $I_u$, $I_v$, and $I_{uv}$ for the area shown in Fig. 10.27.

[*Ans.:* $I_u = 1329$ in$^4$, $I_v = 465$ in$^4$, $I_{uv} = -576$ in$^4$.]

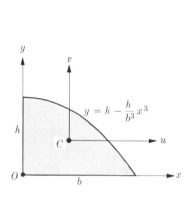

FIGURE 10.24

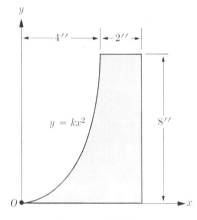

FIGURE 10.25

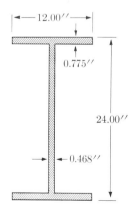

FIGURE 10.26

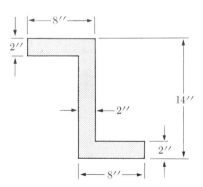

FIGURE 10.27

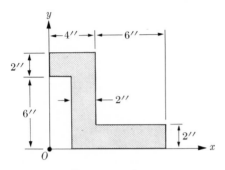

FIGURE 10.28

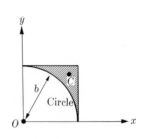

FIGURE 10.29

**10.5** Find $I_u$, $I_v$, $J_C$, and $I_{uv}$ for the area shown in Fig. 10.28.

**10.6** Using Figs. 9.16 and 10.8 whenever necessary, find $I_x$, $I_u$, and $J_C$ for the area shown in Fig. 10.29.

[*Ans.:* $I_x = 0.1370b^4$, $I_u = 0.0075b^4$, $J_C = 0.0150b^4$.]

**10.7** Locate the principal axes and find the principal moments of inertia at the centroid of the quarter circle of Fig. 10.8(d).

**10.8** Locate the principal axes and find the principal moments of inertia at the centroid of the area shown in Fig. 10.30.

[*Ans.:* $\theta_1 = 163.2°$, $\theta_2 = 253.2°$, $I_1 = 154.7 \text{ in}^4$, $I_2 = 50.5 \text{ in}^4$.]

**10.9** For the rectangular area $A$ of Fig. 9.34, show that Eqs. (10.26) and (10.27) give the same $P$, $x_P$, and $y_P$ as are obtained by using the volume under the pressure surface.

**10.10** Find the magnitude and location of the equivalent concentrated normal force for the plate shown in Fig. 10.31.

[*Ans.:* $P = 3744$ lb, $x_P = 2.40$ ft, $y_P = 6.13$ ft.]

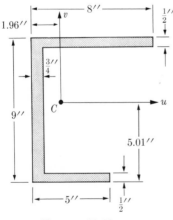

FIGURE 10.30

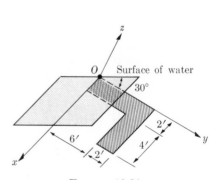

FIGURE 10.31

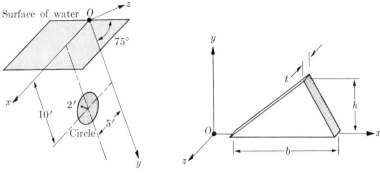

| FIGURE 10.32 | FIGURE 10.33 |

10.11 Find the magnitude and location of the equivalent concentrated normal force for the circular plate shown in Fig. 10.32.

10.12 Using the results of Example 10.6 and the parallel-axis theorem, find $I_x$ for the body of Fig. 10.18.

[*Ans.:* 44.7 slug-in$^2$.]

10.13 Find $I_y$ for the body of Fig. 10.18.

10.14 Find $I_x$ for the thin, homogeneous, triangular plate shown in Fig. 10.33.

[*Ans.:* $\frac{1}{6}mh^2$.]

10.15 Find $I_x$, $I_y$, $I_z$, $I_u$, $I_v$, $I_w$ for the thin plate shown in Fig. 10.34.

10.16 The thin, homogeneous plate in Fig. 10.35 has a total mass $m$. Derive a formula for the moment of inertia of the plate about the $x$-axis in terms of $m$, $b$, $h$, and $a$.

$$\left[ Ans.: \ I_x = m\,\frac{4bh^3 - 3\pi a^2(a^2 + h^2)}{12(bh - \pi a^2)}. \right]$$

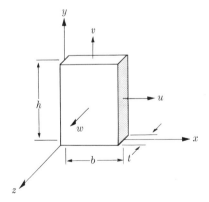

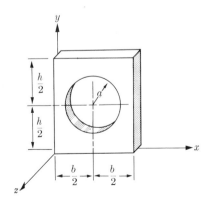

| FIGURE 10.34 | FIGURE 10.35 |

10.17  Using the results of Example 10.7 and the method of Example 10.8, show that the moment of inertia of a right circular cylinder about its axis is

$$\tfrac{1}{2}mb^2,$$

where $m$ is the total mass and $b$ is the radius. Assume that the density is uniform.

10.18  Show by the use of the differential that the moment of inertia of a thin, circular cylindrical shell about its axis is given approximately by

$$mb^2,$$

where $m$ is the total mass and $b$ is the radius.

# CHAPTER 11

## EQUILIBRIUM OF RIGID BODIES

**11.1 Introduction.** To say that a system of particles is in equilibrium means, by definition, that each particle of the system is in equilibrium (i.e., is either at rest or moving in a straight line with constant speed). A continuous body may be treated as a system of particles by arbitrarily subdividing it into a large number of elemental parts, and, if the body is rigid, these parts maintain fixed relative positions. Hence, for a rigid body not at rest to be in equilibrium, all points in the body must be moving on parallel straight lines (a type of motion called *rectilinear translation*) with the same constant speed. It is clear from the definition that, if a system of particles is in equilibrium, any portion of it is also in equilibrium.

Due to the factors discussed for a single particle in Art. 4.1, a system of particles can never be in equilibrium in an absolute sense, although, for most engineering purposes, assuming a body which is fixed on the surface of the earth to be in equilibrium is a sufficiently accurate approximation.

The laws of mechanics, when adapted to a system of particles, distinguish between *internal forces*, which are forces exerted on particles of the system by other particles of the same system, and *external forces*, which are any other forces exerted on particles of the system.

**11.2 Newton's Third Law.** Consider a system of $n$ particles such as that shown in Fig. 11.1. The double-subscript symbol $F_{ij}$ represents the internal force exerted on the $i$th particle by the $j$th particle, and the

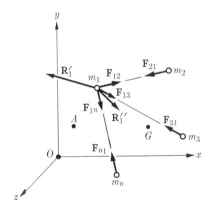

FIGURE 11.1

207

resultant $R_i$ of all the forces acting on the $i$th particle is divided into two parts, $R_i'$ and $R_i''$, the former being the resultant of all the external forces acting on $m_i$ (including its weight force and forces exerted on it by any particles outside the group of $n$ particles comprising the mechanical system), the latter being the resultant of all the internal forces acting on $m_i$. Hence, for the first particle,

$$R_1'' = F_{12} + F_{13} + \cdots + F_{1n}, \qquad (11.1)$$

and

$$R_1 = R_1' + R_1'', \qquad (11.2)$$

and similarly for all the other particles. If $R$ is the resultant of all the forces on all the particles, then

$$R = R_1 + R_2 + \cdots + R_n. \qquad (11.3)$$

Thus,

$$R = (R_1' + R_2' + \cdots + R_n') + (R_1'' + R_2'' + \cdots + R_n''). \qquad (11.4)$$

Using the notation of the present chapter, Newton's Third Law (Art. 1.5) may be stated as follows:

NEWTON'S THIRD LAW: *For all i and j, the forces $F_{ij}$ and $F_{ji}$ have the same line of action, and*

$$F_{ij} = -F_{ji}. \qquad (11.5)$$

This is a universal law of nature which is assumed to hold for all types of internal forces, including forces due to direct contact, gravitational attraction, etc.

Since all the internal forces occur in pairs having equal magnitudes and opposite directions, it follows that

$$R_1'' + R_2'' + \cdots + R_n'' = 0, \qquad (11.6)$$

and therefore, from Eq. (11.4),

$$R = R_1' + R_2' + \cdots + R_n'. \qquad (11.7)$$

Equation (11.7) shows that, whether or not the system is in equilibrium, the resultant of all the forces on all the particles is equal to the resultant of all the external forces. Henceforth, $R$ may be interpreted as the resultant of all the external forces.

By employing Newton's Third Law, the type of equilibrium problem involving a statically determinate mechanical system composed of several particles (or several bodies the dimensions of which are irrelevant) can be solved. (Some very simple examples of this type of problem are included in Chapter 4.)

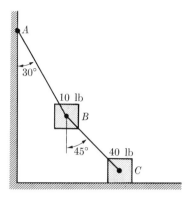

FIGURE 11.2

EXAMPLE 11.1. The blocks $B$ and $C$ in Fig. 11.2 are connected together and to the wall at $A$ by ideal strings. Find the minimum coefficient of static friction between block $C$ and the floor for equilibrium of the system in the position shown.

*Solution.* Free-body diagrams of blocks $B$ and $C$ are shown in Figs. 11.3(a) and 11.3(b), respectively. By Newton's Third Law, the forces exerted on the two blocks by string $BC$ are equal in magnitude and opposite in direction; this is shown on the free-body diagram by labeling the forces $\mathbf{T}_2$ and $-\mathbf{T}_2$. Hence there is a total of five unknowns in the problem, $T_1$, $T_2$, $N$, $F$, and $\mu_s$. Two equations of equilibrium for each block plus the equation of impending motion constitute the five equations required to make the problem statically determinate. Since there are three forces with unknown magnitude acting on block $C$, it is impossible to analyze that block until the magnitude $T_2$ is found from an analysis of block $B$. Applying the equations of equilibrium to block $B$,

$$\Sigma F_x = -0.500T_1 + 0.707T_2 = 0,$$
$$\Sigma F_y = 0.866T_1 - 0.707T_2 - 10 = 0.$$

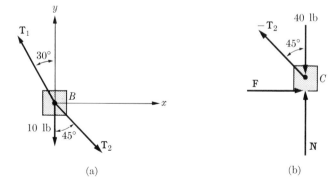

(a)                                        (b)

FIGURE 11.3

Solving simultaneously,
$$T_2 = 19.32 \text{ lb.}$$

Proceeding now to block $C$,

$$\sum F_x = F - 0.707(19.32) = 0,$$

$$\sum F_y = N + 0.707(19.32) - 40 = 0,$$

so that
$$F = 13.66 \text{ lb}, \qquad N = 26.34 \text{ lb.}$$

Finally, therefore,

$$\mu_s = \frac{13.66}{26.34} = 0.519.$$

---

If a system contains a very large number of particles, it may not be feasible to write the equations of equilibrium for each particle separately. Article 11.3 is concerned with the establishment of equations of equilibrium which apply to a system of particles as a whole.

**11.3 Equations of equilibrium.** If the system of Fig. 11.1 is in equilibrium, then, by Newton's First Law (Art. 4.2),

$$\mathbf{R}_i = \mathbf{0}$$

for all $i$. Thus,

$$\mathbf{R}_1 + \mathbf{R}_2 + \cdots + \mathbf{R}_n = \mathbf{0},$$

and, by Eq. (11.3),

$$\mathbf{R} = \mathbf{0}. \tag{11.8}$$

Equation (11.8) is a necessary condition for equilibrium of any system of particles. It is not a sufficient condition; even though it ensures that

$$\mathbf{R}_1 + \mathbf{R}_2 + \cdots + \mathbf{R}_n = \mathbf{0},$$

it does not guarantee that each $\mathbf{R}_i$ is a null vector separately. Consider, for example, the system of two particles shown in Fig. 11.4. Suppose that the particles repel each other with forces $\mathbf{Q}$ and $-\mathbf{Q}$. If forces $\mathbf{P}$ and $-\mathbf{P}$ are applied as shown, and if $\mathbf{P} \neq \mathbf{Q}$, the particles are not in equilibrium even though the external forces satisfy Eq. (11.8).

From Eq. (11.8), which is the same as Eq. (4.1), it can be concluded that Newton's First Law, originally stated for a single particle, holds also for a

FIGURE 11.4

system of particles. The law is modified, however, in that: (1) the equation is now only a necessary condition for equilibrium, and (2) only the external forces (which usually form a nonconcurrent system of forces) need be included in the equation. As usual, Eq. (11.8) may be written as three scalar equations, i.e.,

$$R_x = 0, \qquad R_y = 0, \qquad R_z = 0. \tag{11.9}$$

Another set of necessary conditions for equilibrium of the system of particles in Fig. 11.1 is obtained by taking moments about $O$ (or, in fact, about any reference point $A$). Let $\mathbf{T}_i$ be the total moment about $O$ of all the forces acting on the $i$th particle (this moment being, by Varignon's theorem, equal to $\mathbf{r}_i \times \mathbf{R}_i$). Further, let $\mathbf{T}_i'$ and $\mathbf{T}_i''$ be the total moments about $O$ of all the external forces and all the internal forces, respectively, on the $i$th particle. (These moments, by Varignon's theorem, are equal to $\mathbf{r}_i \times \mathbf{R}_i'$ and $\mathbf{r}_i \times \mathbf{R}_i''$, respectively.) Then,

$$\mathbf{T}_1 = \mathbf{T}_1' + \mathbf{T}_1'', \tag{11.10}$$

etc., and, if $\mathbf{T}$ is the total moment of all the forces on all the particles, then

$$\mathbf{T} = \mathbf{T}_1 + \mathbf{T}_2 + \cdots + \mathbf{T}_n. \tag{11.11}$$

Thus,

$$\mathbf{T} = (\mathbf{T}_1' + \mathbf{T}_2' + \cdots + \mathbf{T}_n') + (\mathbf{T}_1'' + \mathbf{T}_2'' + \cdots + \mathbf{T}_n''). \tag{11.12}$$

By Newton's Third Law, the internal forces occur in pairs having equal magnitudes, opposite directions, and the same line of action, so that

$$\mathbf{T}_1'' + \mathbf{T}_2'' + \cdots + \mathbf{T}_n'' = \mathbf{0}, \tag{11.13}$$

and therefore, from Eq. (11.12),

$$\mathbf{T} = \mathbf{T}_1' + \mathbf{T}_2' + \cdots + \mathbf{T}_n'. \tag{11.14}$$

Equation (11.14) shows that, whether or not the system is in equilibrium, the total moment of all the forces is equal to the total moment of the external forces. Henceforth, $\mathbf{T}$ may be interpreted as the total moment of the external forces about $O$.

If the system of particles is in equilibrium, $\mathbf{R}_i$ and hence $\mathbf{r}_i \times \mathbf{R}_i$ are null vectors for all $i$, so that

$$\mathbf{T}_i = \mathbf{0}$$

for all $i$. Thus,

$$\mathbf{T}_1 + \mathbf{T}_2 + \cdots + \mathbf{T}_n = \mathbf{0},$$

and, by Eq. (11.11),

$$\mathbf{T} = \mathbf{0}. \tag{11.15}$$

Equation (11.15) is another necessary condition for equilibrium of any system of particles. Note that the external forces in Fig. 11.4 satisfy Eq. (11.15) as well as Eq. (11.8), and yet the system of particles is not in equilibrium.

Equation (11.15) may be replaced by three scalar equations, i.e.,

$$T_x = 0, \qquad T_y = 0, \qquad T_z = 0. \tag{11.16}$$

For a rigid body such as that shown in Fig. 11.5, any distributed force acting on the body is replaced by a mechanically equivalent concentrated force. The weight force, for example, is a vertical concentrated force $\mathbf{W}$ acting at the center of gravity $G$. For this mechanical system,

$$\mathbf{R} = \mathbf{F}_1 + \mathbf{F}_2 + \cdots + \mathbf{F}_N, \qquad \mathbf{T} = \mathbf{M}_1 + \mathbf{M}_2 + \cdots + \mathbf{M}_N,$$

where the subscripts now refer to the forces instead of the particles ($\mathbf{M}_i$ being the moment of $\mathbf{F}_i$ about $O$), and the $N$ forces include $\mathbf{W}$ and any other equivalent concentrated forces. If the body is in equilibrium, then, by Eqs. (11.8) and (11.15),

$$\mathbf{R} = \mathbf{0}, \qquad \mathbf{T} = \mathbf{0},$$

so that Eqs. (11.9) and (11.16) apply. Hence, a set of necessary conditions for equilibrium of a rigid body is the following:

$$\begin{aligned} \sum F_x &= 0, & \sum F_y &= 0, & \sum F_z &= 0, \\ \sum M_x &= 0, & \sum M_y &= 0, & \sum M_z &= 0. \end{aligned} \tag{11.17}$$

Equations (11.17) are called the *equations of equilibrium of a rigid body.* They are equations on the external forces, and they are shown later to be, under certain circumstances, sufficient as well as necessary conditions for equilibrium if the mechanical system is a single rigid body.

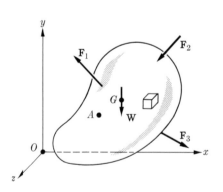

FIGURE 11.5

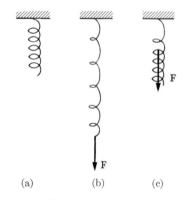

(a)          (b)          (c)

FIGURE 11.6

Comparing Eqs. (11.17) with Eqs. (8.29), we see that the equations of equilibrium are a statement of the fact that the external force system reduces to a force-couple system at $O$ for which both **R** and **C** are null vectors. (This is the special type of force system mentioned in the first paragraph of Art. 8.5.) Since, from Eq. (8.19), two force systems having the same resultant and equal total moments about $O$ have equal total moments about any point $A$, it follows that a force system which reduces to a null force-couple system at $O$ also reduces to a null force-couple system at any point $A$.

If the external forces on a rigid body are a concurrent system, the couple at the point of concurrency is null whether or not the body is in equilibrium, so that only the first three of Eqs. (11.17) are needed to express the existence of a state of equilibrium. This means that, for a concurrent force system, Eqs. (11.17), the general equations of equilibrium, reduce to Eqs. (4.4), the three equations of equilibrium for a single particle.

A force with given magnitude, direction, and line of action has the same effect on a rigid body regardless of its point of application. This statement, known as the *principle of transmissibility*, is verified for the case in which the body is in equilibrium by noting that the contribution of a force to Eqs. (11.17) is independent of its point of application. (The principle is verified for a rigid body in motion in Chapter 13.) This principle does not hold for a deformable body because the deformations are affected by the point of application of a force. Consider, for example, the spring shown in Fig. 11.6(a). If a force **F** is applied at the lower end of the spring, the spring is found to deform as in Fig. 11.6(b). If, on the other hand, the same force is applied near the top of the spring, the deformation is as in Fig. 11.6(c).

**11.4 Equilibrium of rigid bodies in a plane.** If all the external forces acting on a rigid body lie in the $xy$-plane, as in Fig. 11.7, the third, fourth, and fifth of Eqs. (11.17) are identically satisfied, so that Eqs. (11.17) re-

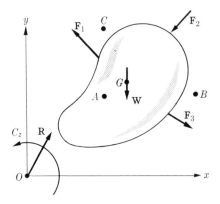

FIGURE 11.7

| Support | | | $A_x$ | $A_y$ | $C_{Az}$ | No. of unknowns |
|---|---|---|---|---|---|---|
|  (a) Roller, Rocker, Smooth contact | | | 0 | + | 0 | |
|  (b) Cable | | | 0 | − | 0 | 1 |
| 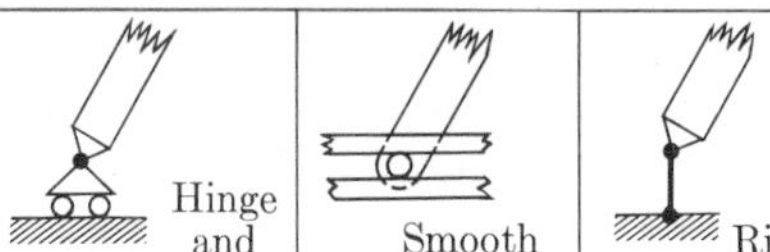 (c) Hinge and rollers*, Smooth slider, Rigid link | | | 0 | ± | 0 | |
| 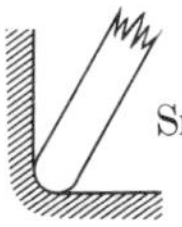 (d) Smooth contact | | | + | + | 0 | |
| 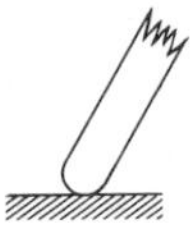 (e) Rough contact | | | ± (Limited absolute value) | + | 0 | 2 |
| 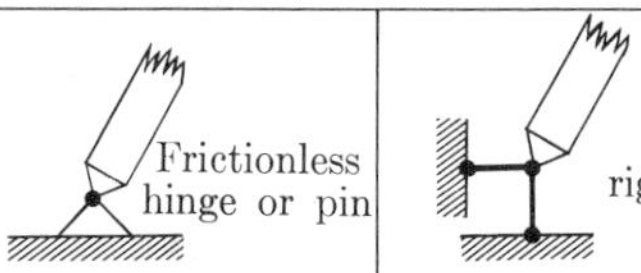 (f) Frictionless hinge or pin, Two rigid links | | | ± | ± | 0 | |
| 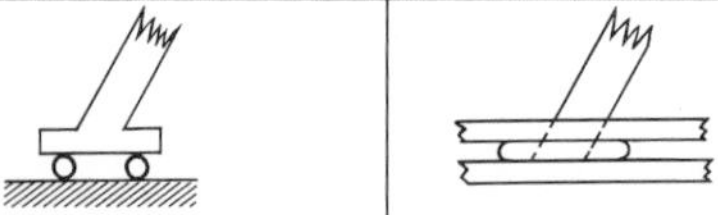 (g) Hingeless rollers*, Smooth slider | | | 0 | ± | ± | 2 |
| 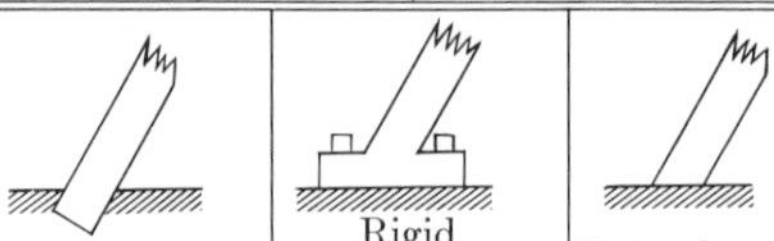 (h) Embedment, Rigid connection, General symbol | | | ± | ± | ± | 3 |

*Such rollers are assumed to be doubly constrained, i.e., restricted from moving upward as well as downward.

FIGURE 11.8

duce to the following three equations of equilibrium for a rigid body in two dimensions:

$$\sum F_x = 0, \quad \sum F_y = 0, \quad \sum M_z = 0. \tag{11.18}$$

These equations can be used to find three unknowns for a rigid body known to be in equilibrium. (If, on the other hand, all the external forces are known, then satisfaction of the three equations ensures equilibrium under certain circumstances.) More equations can be written (e.g., by summing force components in other directions or by summing moments about lines parallel to the $z$-axis but through points other than the origin), but it takes only three equations to specify that the force-couple system at $O$ (Fig. 11.7) to which the external forces reduce has null $\mathbf{R}$ and zero $C_z$. Hence, any additional equations written are not independent of the original three and therefore cannot yield values for additional unknowns.

The three equations used to specify that $\mathbf{R}$ is null and $C_z$ is zero need not be in the form of Eqs. (11.18). For example, three other suitable equations are the following:

$$\sum M_z^A = 0, \quad \sum M_z^B = 0, \quad \sum F_L = 0,$$

where $A$ and $B$ are any two points in the plane (Fig. 11.7) and $L$ is any line in the plane not perpendicular to the line $AB$. The first equation in the last group specifies that the force system reduces to a force-couple system at $A$ for which the couple is zero. The second equation in the group eliminates the component of $\mathbf{R}$ perpendicular to the line $AB$, and the third eliminates the component of $\mathbf{R}$ parallel to $AB$. Similarly, the three equations

$$\sum M_z^A = 0, \quad \sum M_z^B = 0, \quad \sum M_z^C = 0,$$

(where $C$ is any point not on the line $AB$) are suitable.

A free-body diagram of a mechanical system is a sketch which shows the system isolated from its surroundings and which shows all the *external* forces acting on the system and no other forces. In solving an equilibrium problem for a rigid body, it is always advisable, as in the case of a particle, to draw a free-body diagram for the purpose of showing what forces must be included in the equations of equilibrium. The external forces on a rigid body may be classified as: *active forces* or *loads*, which are those forces tending to set the body into motion (e.g., the weight force); and *reactive forces* or *reactions*, which are those forces set up by the surroundings to prevent motion (e.g., a friction force). The latter forces come into play only to the extent that is required for equilibrium, and they are frequently the unknowns in an equilibrium problem. Figure 11.8 shows various ways in which a rigid body may be supported or connected at a point $A$. Calling the unknown reactive force $\mathbf{A}$ (with $x$-component to the right and $y$-

component upward) and the unknown reactive couple (if any) $C_{Az}$, we see that Fig. 11.8 shows the number of scalar unknowns associated with each type of support. Supports (a) through (c) give a reaction force with known direction but unknown magnitude, while supports (d) through (f) give a reaction force with unknown magnitude and unknown direction.

The solution of problems can be simplified by writing equations each of which contains as few of the three unknowns as possible. If, for example, two of the unknowns are the magnitudes of two forces having known lines of action, taking moments about the point of intersection of the two lines of action yields the value of the third unknown immediately.

---

EXAMPLE 11.2. For the crane shown in Fig. 11.9, the boom $AB$ weighs 250 lb and the block $E$ weighs 1000 lb. Find all the reactions.

*Solution.* The free-body diagram of the boom $AB$ appears in Fig. 11.10. The tension **T** in the cable is shown on the diagram with its known sense. Taking $A$ as the reference point for moments,

$$\sum M_z^A = 15T - 20(1000) - 10(250) = 0,$$

from which

$$T = 1500 \text{ lb}.$$

Knowing $T$, we can find the components of **A** by summing force components in the $x$- and $y$-directions as follows:

$$\sum F_x = A_x - 1500 = 0,$$
$$\sum F_y = A_y - 1000 - 250 = 0.$$

Hence,

$$A_x = 1500 \text{ lb}, \qquad A_y = 1250 \text{ lb},$$

and

$$\mathbf{A} = 1500\mathbf{i} + 1250\mathbf{j} \text{ lb}.$$

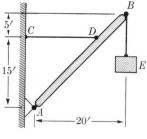

FIGURE 11.9

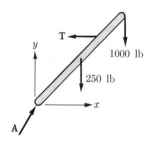

FIGURE 11.10

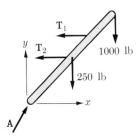

FIGURE 11.11

Any additional equations written for this body must be satisfied by the fore-going results and therefore can serve as a check on the computations. They can-not, however, be used to find additional unknowns. Suppose, for example, that a second horizontal cable were attached at the midpoint of the boom and at the vertical wall. The free-body diagram would then be as in Fig. 11.11, and, using $B$ as another reference point for moments, the following four equations in four unknowns could be written:

$$\sum M_z^A = 15T_1 + 10T_2 - 20(1000) - 10(250) = 0,$$

$$\sum M_z^B = 5T_1 + 10T_2 + 20A_y - 20A_x - 10(250) = 0,$$

$$\sum F_x = A_x - T_1 - T_2 = 0,$$

$$\sum F_y = A_y - 1000 - 250 = 0.$$

From the last two equations,

$$A_x = T_1 + T_2, \qquad A_y = 1250 \text{ lb},$$

and, substituting into the second equation,

$$5T_1 + 10T_2 + 20(1250) - 20(T_1 + T_2) - 10(250) = 0,$$

from which

$$-15T_1 - 10T_2 + 22{,}500 = 0.$$

It is obvious that this equation is not independent of the first of the original four equations, so that $T_1$ and $T_2$ and hence $A_x$ cannot be found. The problem, therefore, is statically indeterminate.

---

Some equilibrium problems contain unknown friction forces which must be included in the equations of equilibrium. If the body is known to be at impending motion, Eq. (4.9) can be used to write additional equations, and this permits solving for more than three unknowns.

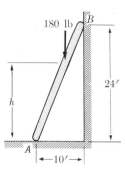

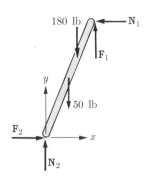

FIGURE 11.12                    FIGURE 11.13

EXAMPLE 11.3. Find the maximum height $h$ to which a man weighing 180 lb can climb on the 50-lb ladder shown in Fig. 11.12 before the ladder slips down. The coefficient of static friction is 0.3 between ladder and wall and between ladder and floor.

*Solution.* The free-body diagram is shown in Fig. 11.13. There are five unknowns, but since the ladder is at impending motion, there are also the following five independent equations:

$$\sum M_z^A = \tfrac{5}{12} h(180) + 5(50) - 24N_1 - 10F_1 = 0,$$
$$\sum F_x = F_2 - N_1 = 0,$$
$$\sum F_y = N_2 + F_1 - 180 - 50 = 0,$$
$$F_1 = 0.3N_1,$$
$$F_2 = 0.3N_2.$$

Hence, eliminating $F_1$ and $F_2$,

$$75h = 27N_1 - 250,$$
$$N_1 = 0.3N_2,$$
$$N_2 = 230 - 0.3N_1.$$

Solving the last two of these three equations for $N_1$,

$$N_1 = 0.3(230 - 0.3N_1),$$
$$1.09N_1 = 69,$$
$$N_1 = 63.3 \text{ lb},$$

so that

$$h = \frac{27(63.3) - 250}{75} = 19.45 \text{ ft}.$$

If the position of the man were given in this problem, e.g., at the midpoint of the ladder, the height $h$ would no longer be unknown. Since the ladder would then not be at impending motion, however, there would be four unknowns and only three equations, and this would make the problem statically indeterminate.

---

Some equilibrium problems involve several rigid bodies connected together or in contact with each other. In such a case the equations of equilibrium are not sufficient conditions for equilibrium, but, if the entire system is known to be in equilibrium, three equations of equilibrium can be written for each body to find, in general, a total number of unknowns equal to three times the number of bodies. (Three equations can also be written for the system as a whole, but these are not independent of the other equations.)

---

EXAMPLE 11.4. A rigid bar weighing 50 lb rests on a smooth cylinder weighing 100 lb, as shown in Fig. 11.14. Write enough equations to solve for all the reactions.

*Solution.* If both bodies are selected as the mechanical system, the three equations of equilibrium apply, but there are four unknowns (two at $A$, one at $D$,

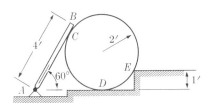

FIGURE 11.14

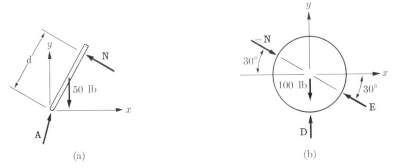

(a)                                           (b)

FIGURE 11.15

one at $E$). It is necessary in this type of problem, therefore, to isolate each body separately, drawing the two free-body diagrams of Fig. 11.15. The weight force for each body is concentrated at its own center of gravity, and the normal force **N** exerted on the bar by the cylinder is shown as an external force with unknown magnitude in Fig. 11.15(a), while an opposite force —**N** is shown in Fig. 11.15(b).

Since the force system in Fig. 11.15(b) is concurrent, there are only two usable equations, which makes it impossible to analyze the cylinder until $N$ is found. For the bar, $d$ is found from the geometry of the system by noting that the height of point $C$ above point $D$ is

$$2 + 2(0.500)$$

or 3 ft, so that

$$d = \frac{3}{\sin 60°} = \frac{6}{\sqrt{3}} \text{ ft.}$$

This leaves, for the bar, three unknowns and three equations, so that this body may be analyzed first as follows:

$$\sum M_z^A = \frac{6}{\sqrt{3}} N - 2(\tfrac{1}{2})(50) = 0,$$

$$\sum F_x = A_x - \frac{\sqrt{3}}{2} N = 0,$$

$$\sum F_y = A_y + \tfrac{1}{2}N - 50 = 0.$$

After $N$ is known, the following two equations can be written for the cylinder:

$$\sum F_x = \frac{\sqrt{3}}{2} N - \frac{\sqrt{3}}{2} E = 0,$$

$$\sum F_y = D - 100 - \tfrac{1}{2}N + \tfrac{1}{2}E = 0.$$

**11.5 Classification of rigid bodies.** If a rigid body is expected to remain in equilibrium regardless of the loads applied to it, the body must be supported in such a way that the equations of equilibrium can be satisfied for all possible systems of loads. A body for which this is the case is classified as *fully fixed* or *stable*. Consider only the reactive force system, and let $r$ be the number of unknown reaction elements (as determined from Fig. 11.8). Figure 11.16 then gives the criteria for classifying rigid bodies under general systems of loads and shows examples of the various classes. It is clear from this figure that, to have full fixity, there must be available at least three reaction elements (unlimited in absolute value and reversible) and all the reactions can be neither parallel nor concurrent.

| Case | Examples | Classification |
|---|---|---|
| 1. $r < 3$ | 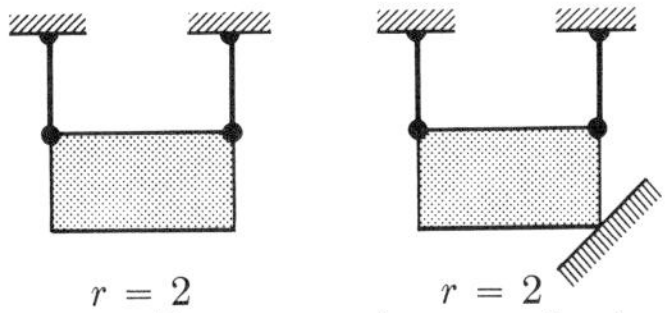 $r = 2$ regardless of loads   $r = 2$ for some loads (since sloping plane can resist motion to right only) | 1. Not fully fixed |
| 2. $r \geq 3$, but reactive force system | | 2. Geometrically lacking in fixity |
| (a) parallel ($\Sigma F_x = 0$ not satisfied) | 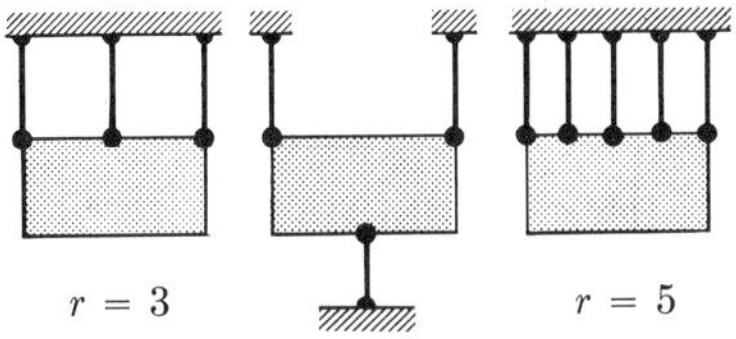 $r = 3$   $r = 3$ (can move slightly)   $r = 5$ | |
| (b) concurrent ($\Sigma M_z^A = 0$ not satisfied) | 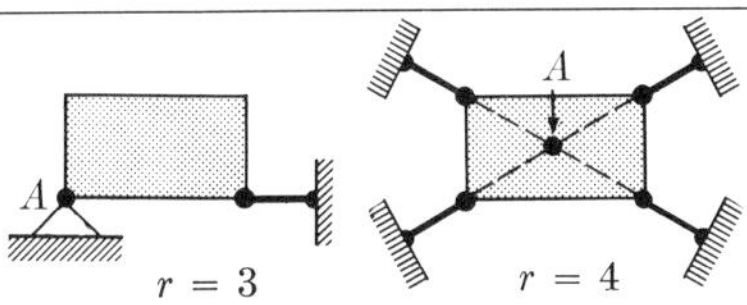 $r = 3$ (can move slightly)   $r = 4$ (can move slightly) | |
| 3. Neither 1 nor 2 and | | 3. Fully fixed and |
| (a) $r = 3$ | 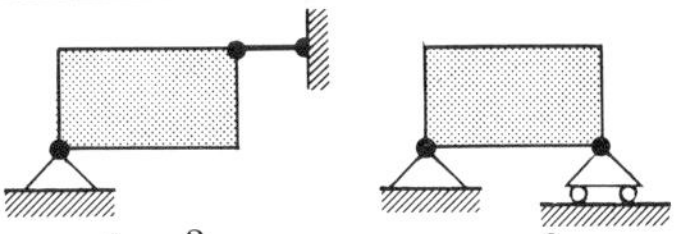 $r = 3$   $r = 3$ | (a) determinate |
| (b) $r > 3$ | 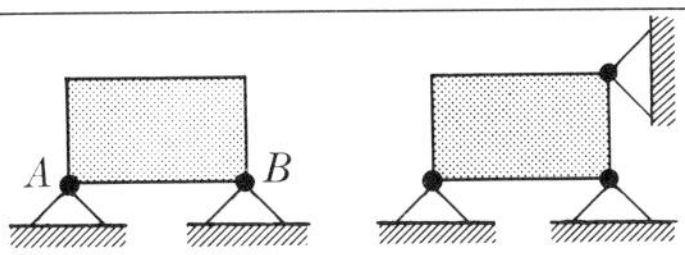 $r = 4$   $r = 6$ (can find $A_y$ and $B_y$ by taking moments about $B$ and $A$) | (b) indeterminate |

FIGURE 11.16

| Case | Examples | Classification |
|------|----------|----------------|
| 1. Fully fixed and determinate, i.e., 3(a) in Fig. 11.16 | 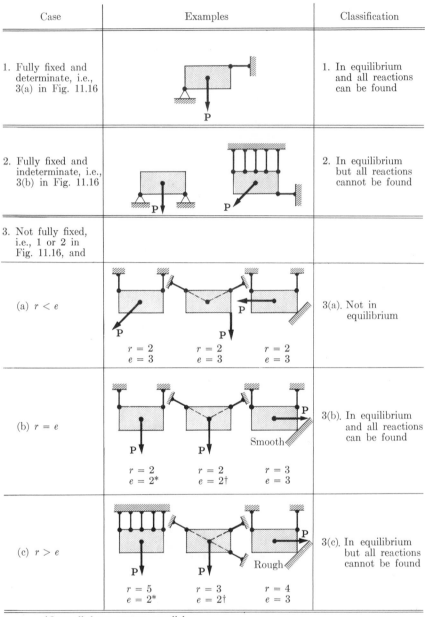 | 1. In equilibrium and all reactions can be found |
| 2. Fully fixed and indeterminate, i.e., 3(b) in Fig. 11.16 | | 2. In equilibrium but all reactions cannot be found |
| 3. Not fully fixed, i.e., 1 or 2 in Fig. 11.16, and | | |
| (a) $r < e$ | $r = 2$ $e = 3$     $r = 2$ $e = 3$     $r = 2$ $e = 3$ | 3(a). Not in equilibrium |
| (b) $r = e$ | $r = 2$ $e = 2^*$     $r = 2$ $e = 2\dagger$     $r = 3$ $e = 3$ | 3(b). In equilibrium and all reactions can be found |
| (c) $r > e$ | $r = 5$ $e = 2^*$     $r = 3$ $e = 2\dagger$     $r = 4$ $e = 3$ | 3(c). In equilibrium but all reactions cannot be found |

*Over-all force system parallel
†Over-all force system concurrent

FIGURE 11.17

In many applications a rigid body is expected to remain in equilibrium only for a particular set of loads. This may be the case even when the body is not fully fixed (as in Example 11.2). Figure 11.17 gives the criteria for classifying rigid bodies under given systems of loads and shows examples of the various classes. If the body is fully fixed, then it remains in equilibrium for any given set of loads. If not, it becomes necessary to compare, for the given loads, the number of reaction elements $r$ (as determined by the reactive force system) with the number of *usable* equations $e$ (as determined by the over-all force system). When friction forces are required for equilibrium, it is usually necessary to compute these forces to determine if they satisfy the law of static friction.

**11.6 Equilibrium of rigid bodies in space.** For a rigid body acted upon by a three-dimensional force system, all six of the equations of equilibrium, Eqs. (11.17), are applicable, and these equations can be used, in general, to find six unknowns. As in two dimensions, the equations may take any form which adequately expresses the fact that the external force system reduces to a null force-couple system at any point, but the number of independent equations which can be written cannot exceed six.

In certain special cases, some of Eqs. (11.17) are satisfied identically, which means that the number of usable equations (and the number of unknowns which can be found) may be less than six. If all the external forces are parallel to the $xy$-plane, for example, the third equation is useless, so that a force system parallel to any plane gives only five independent equations. If all the forces are parallel to the $y$-axis, as another example, the first, third, and fifth equations are useless, so that a force system parallel to any line gives only three independent equations. If the external forces are concurrent, as mentioned previously, there are only three independent equations, and, if all the forces intersect the same line, there are only five independent equations.

In solving problems in three dimensions, it is again advisable to draw a free-body diagram. Figure 11.18 shows some of the ways of supporting or connecting a body at a point $A$, with the number of unknown reaction elements indicated for each type of support. (The same orientation of axes, shown for the ball support, is used throughout the figure.) Figure 11.18 must be regarded as a small group of representative examples; since each of the six reaction elements may be zero, positive, negative, or reversible, there are, theoretically, $4^6$ or 4096 different ways to support a body at a point $A$. (There are only $4^3$ or 64 different ways for the plane case.) Nevertheless, the figure does contain several of the supports most commonly encountered in practical problems.

| Support | | $A_x$ | $A_y$ | $A_z$ | $C_{Ax}$ | $C_{Ay}$ | $C_{Az}$ | No. of unknowns |
|---|---|---|---|---|---|---|---|---|
| (a) | 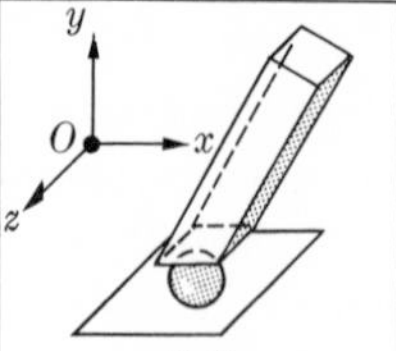 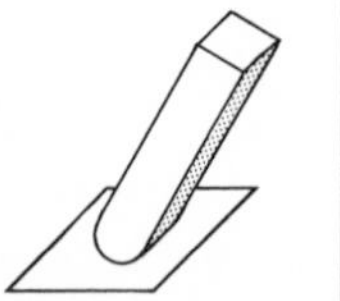 Ball · Smooth contact | 0 | + | 0 | 0 | 0 | 0 | |
| (b) | 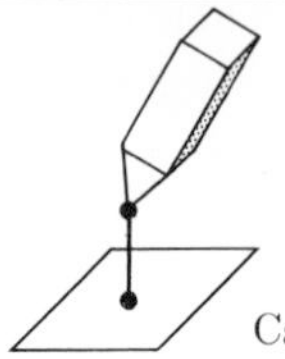 Cable | 0 | − | 0 | 0 | 0 | 0 | 1 |
| (c) | 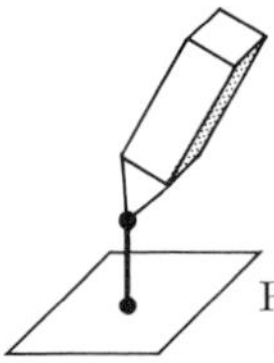 Rigid link | 0 | ± | 0 | 0 | 0 | 0 | |
| (d) | 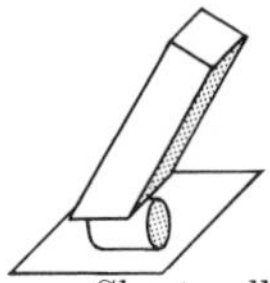 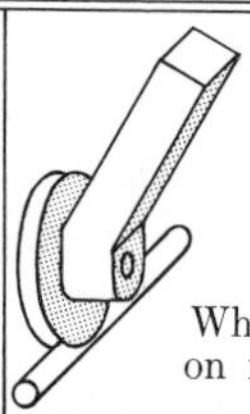 Short roller on rough surface · Wheel on rail | ± | + | 0 | 0 | 0 | 0 | |
| (e) | 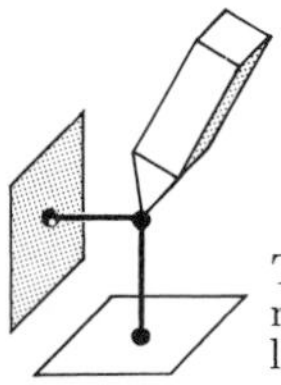 Two rigid links · Frictionless short hinge 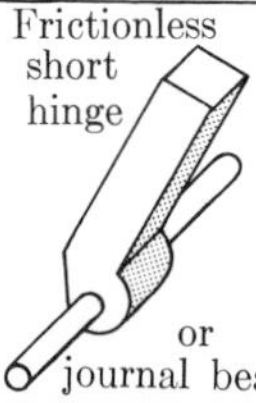 or journal bearing | ± | ± | 0 | 0 | 0 | 0 | 2 |
| (f) | Frictionless short hinge or thrust bearing 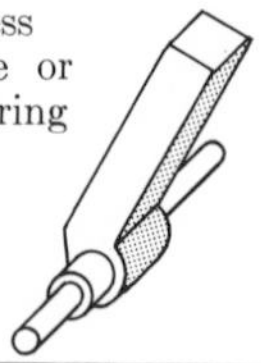 | ± | ± | − | 0 | 0 | 0 | |

FIGURE 11.18

| Support | $A_x$ | $A_y$ | $A_z$ | $C_{Ax}$ | $C_{Ay}$ | $C_{Az}$ | No. of unknowns |
|---|---|---|---|---|---|---|---|
| 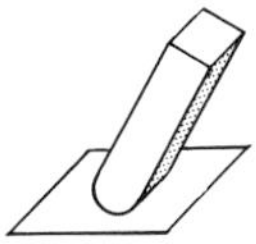 (g) Rough contact | ± | + | ± | 0 | 0 | 0 | ⎫ ⎬ 3 |
| 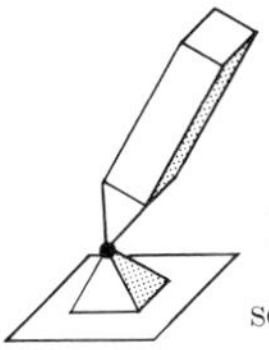 (h) Ball and socket 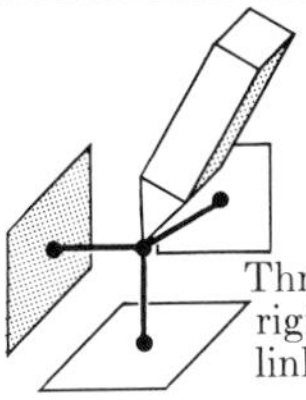    Three rigid links | ± | ± | ± | 0 | 0 | 0 | ⎭ |
| 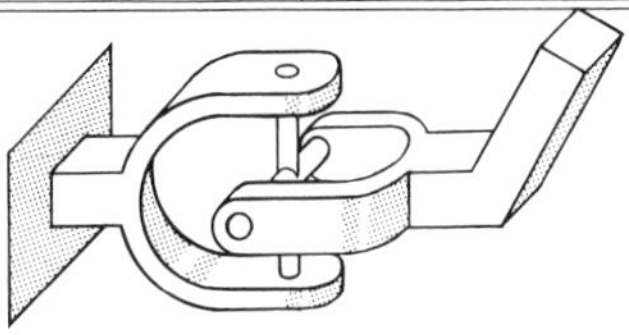 (i) Universal joint | ± | ± | ± | ± | 0 | 0 | 4 |
| 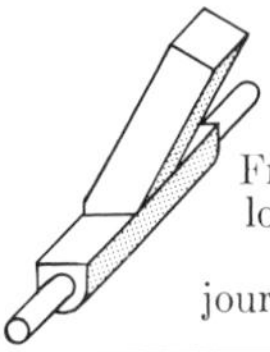 (j) Frictionless long hinge or journal bearing | ± | ± | 0 | ± | ± | 0 | 4 |
|  (k) Frictionless long hinge or thrust bearing | ± | ± | − | ± | ± | 0 | 5 |
| 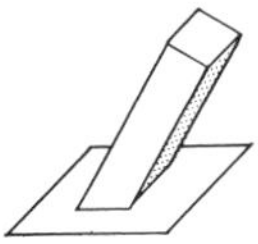 (l) Full fixity | ± | ± | ± | ± | ± | ± | 6 |

FIGURE 11.18 Continued

EXAMPLE 11.5. The plate in Fig. 11.19 is supported by short hinges at $A$ and $B$ and by a cable $DE$. If the plate weighs 10,000 lb, find all the reactions.

*Solution.* The free-body diagram is superimposed on the drawing of Fig. 11.19. Since all the forces are parallel to the $xy$-plane, the equation

$$\sum F_z = 0$$

is satisfied identically, and there are exactly five equations available for finding the five unknowns. Taking moments about the $z$-axis,

$$\sum M_z = 4(10,000) - 8(\tfrac{3}{5}T) = 0, \qquad T = 8330 \text{ lb.}$$

Similarly,

$$\sum M_x = 16B_y - 8(10,000) = 0, \qquad B_y = 5000 \text{ lb,}$$

and

$$\sum M_y = 16B_x = 0, \qquad B_x = 0.$$

Adding force components in the $x$-direction,

$$\sum F_x = A_x - \tfrac{4}{5}(8330) = 0, \qquad A_x = 6670 \text{ lb.}$$

Similarly,

$$\sum F_y = A_y + 5000 + \tfrac{3}{5}(8330) - 10,000 = 0, \qquad A_y = 0.$$

Hence,

$$\mathbf{A} = 6670\mathbf{i} \text{ lb}, \qquad \mathbf{B} = 5000\mathbf{j} \text{ lb}, \qquad T = 8330 \text{ lb.}$$

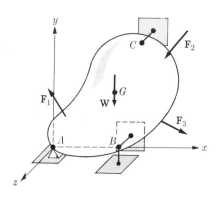

FIGURE 11.19

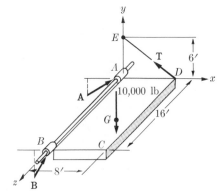

FIGURE 11.20

**11.7 Sufficiency of equations of equilibrium.** Suppose that a single rigid body, originally stationary, is subjected to a system of known external forces which satisfy all six equations of equilibrium. Assume that the body is no longer in equilibrium, and imagine the three supports shown in Fig. 11.20 to be introduced for the purpose of holding the body in equilibrium. The ball-and-socket support at $A$ prohibits any motion of the body except motion with point $A$ fixed. Adding the two rigid links at $B$ prohibits any motion of the body except rotation about the line $AB$ (since the body is rigid). Adding the link at $C$ then prohibits all motion and puts the body in equilibrium.

Since the body is now in equilibrium, the equations of equilibrium must be satisfied by the actual external forces plus the six added reaction elements. But, by hypothesis, the actual external forces alone satisfy the six equations, and therefore they cancel out when the equations are written. Hence,

$$\sum M_x = y_C C_z = 0,$$

and thus

$$C_z = 0.$$

Similarly,

$$\sum M_y = -x_B B_z = 0, \qquad B_z = 0,$$

and

$$\sum M_z = x_B B_y = 0, \qquad B_y = 0.$$

Finally,

$$\sum F_x = A_x = 0, \qquad \sum F_y = A_y = 0, \qquad \sum F_z = A_z = 0.$$

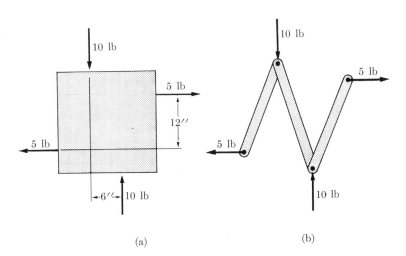

(a)                    (b)

FIGURE 11.21

Since all the reactions are zero, the supports are not needed, and satisfaction of the six equations of equilibrium is a sufficient condition for equilibrium when the body is originally stationary. Figure 11.21(a) shows a rigid body which must remain in equilibrium; Fig. 11.21(b) shows a system of three bodies which is subjected to the same external force system but which does not remain in equilibrium.

It is shown in Chapter 13 that certain types of motion of a rigid body initially in motion are possible even when the force system satisfies all the equations of equilibrium, as in Fig. 11.21(a). Among these types are rectilinear translation at constant speed (a state of equilibrium) and rotational motion about a fixed $z$-axis through $G$ with a constant number of revolutions per unit of time (not a state of equilibrium).

## PROBLEMS

11.1 The coefficient of static friction between block $A$ and the inclined plane in Fig. 11.22 is 0.3. Treating the cords and pulley as ideal, find the magnitude of the normal force and the magnitude and sense of the friction force on block $A$.

11.2 The coefficient of static friction between block $A$ and the plane on which it rests in Fig. 11.23 is 0.25. Find the minimum weight of $A$ for equilibrium. [Ans.: 2964 lb.]

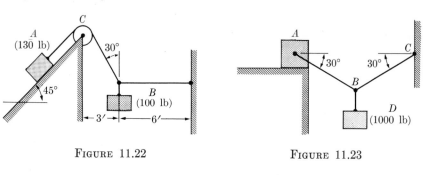

FIGURE 11.22          FIGURE 11.23

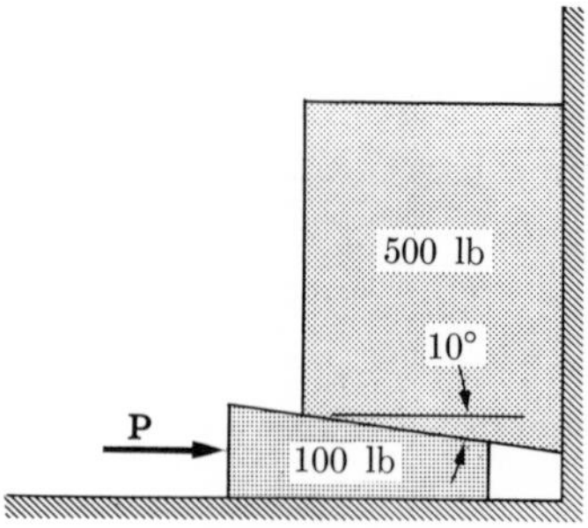

FIGURE 11.24

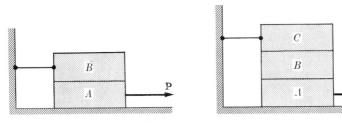

FIGURE 11.25          FIGURE 11.26

11.3  A 100-lb wedge is being used to raise a 500-lb block, as shown in Fig. 11.24. (a) If $\mu_s$ is 0.3 at all pairs of surfaces in contact, find $P$ for upward impending motion of the 500-lb block. (b) Find $P$ for equilibrium if all surfaces are smooth.

11.4  Blocks $A$ and $B$ in Fig. 11.25 weigh 10 lb each, and $\mu_s = 0.25$ at all surfaces. Find $P$ for impending motion of block $A$.

[*Ans.:* 7.5 lb.]

11.5  In Fig. 11.26 blocks $A$, $B$, and $C$ weigh 10 lb each, and $\mu_s = 0.25$ at all surfaces. Find $P$ for impending motion of block $A$.

11.6  (a) A square, homogeneous plate weighing 400 lb is supported as shown in Fig. 11.27. Find all the reactions. (b) If there is no restriction on the location of point $C$, show how the link at $B$ should be placed to make the force in the link as small as possible and to have the link in tension.

[*Ans.:* (a) $F_{BC} = 1000$ lb compression, $\mathbf{A} = 800\mathbf{i} + 1000\mathbf{j}$ lb.]

11.7  The weightless bar in Fig. 11.28 is in smooth contact with fixed pegs at $C$ and $D$ and a wall at $A$. Find all the reactions on the bar.

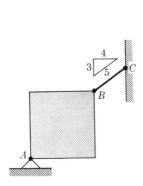

FIGURE 11.27

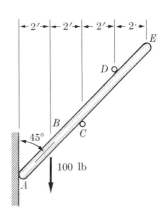

FIGURE 11.28

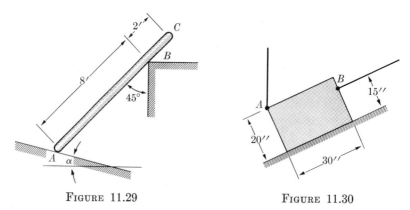

FIGURE 11.29                    FIGURE 11.30

11.8 The smooth, rigid bar $AC$ in Fig. 11.29 weighs 200 lb. It is supported by a smooth plane at $A$ and a smooth corner at $B$. Find the angle $\alpha$ required for equilibrium of the bar in the position shown.

[*Ans.*: 24.4°.]

11.9 The dimensions shown in Fig. 11.30 are for the block in Example 4.2. Assuming that the block is homogeneous, locate the line of action of the normal force **N**.

11.10 The slender, homogeneous bar in Fig. 11.31 is held in equilibrium by a rope $BC$ and by a rough floor at $A$. The coefficient of static friction between bar and floor is 0.4. Find the friction force acting on the bar at $A$.

[*Ans.*: $F = 50$ lb, **F** to right.]

11.11 A 1000-lb crate is being hoisted onto a platform by a force **P** applied as shown in Fig. 11.32. The coefficient of static friction between platform and crate is 0.45. If the crate is stationary in the position shown, find the normal and friction forces acting on it at $A$.

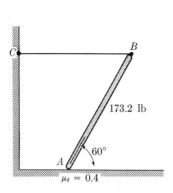

FIGURE 11.31

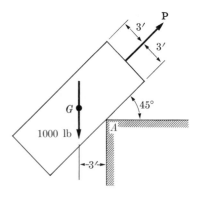

FIGURE 11.32

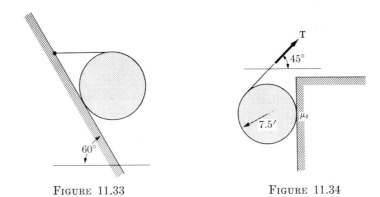

FIGURE 11.33                    FIGURE 11.34

11.12 A solid, homogeneous, circular cylinder is supported as shown in Fig. 11.33 by a horizontal cable wrapped around the cylinder. Find the minimum coefficient of static friction between cylinder and plane for equilibrium.

[*Ans.:* 0.577.]

11.13 A steel cylinder which weighs 230 tons is to be "rolled" to the top of a wharf by a cable wrapped around the cylinder. Determine the feasibility of this plan by finding the minimum coefficient of static friction for which the cylinder will remain in equilibrium in the position shown in Fig. 11.34.

11.14 Heavy blocks of stone are to be rested on a plane surface with inclination of 30° (Fig. 11.35). If the coefficient of static friction between blocks and plane is 0.6, determine the smallest permissible value of $b/h$ if the blocks are not to tip over upon being released. Show that the blocks will not slide when they are released.

[*Ans.:* 0.577.]

11.15 Determine whether the homogeneous block shown in Fig. 11.36 will slide first or tip over first as $P$ is increased. What is the maximum value of $P$ for equilibrium if the block weighs 100 lb?

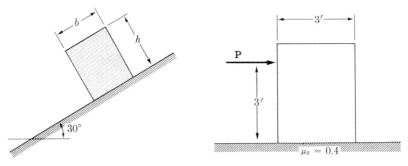

FIGURE 11.35                    FIGURE 11.36

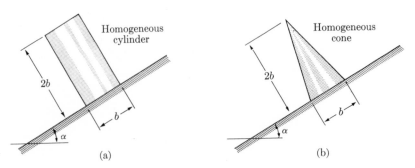

FIGURE 11.37

11.16  Find the maximum inclination $\alpha$ for equilibrium in the two cases shown in Fig. 11.37 if $\mu_s = 0.6$ in each case.

[*Ans.:* (a) 26.6°; (b) 31.0°.]

11.17  If $\mu_s = 0.25$ at $A$ and $D$, find the minimum angle $\alpha$ for which the homogeneous block shown in Fig. 11.38 will remain in equilibrium.

11.18  As shown in Fig. 11.39, a tank 20 ft deep is equipped with a gate $AB$, used for draining the tank, which is 20 ft long and which presses against a stop at $B$.  When the tank is filled to the top with water, find the tension $T$ required to open the gate, i.e., to reduce the stop reaction to zero.  (Specific weight of water: 62.4 lb/ft³.)

[*Ans.:* 120,100 lb.]

11.19  Neglecting the weights of the bars $AC$ and $DF$ in Fig. 11.40 and treating the cables as ideal, find the magnitude of the force **P** required to hold the 1000-lb weight in equilibrium in the position shown.

11.20  Neglecting the weights of the bars $AB$ and $BC$ in Fig. 11.41 and treating the cables as ideal, find the reactions at $A$.

[*Ans.:* **A** $= 1732\mathbf{i} + 1000\mathbf{j}$ lb, $C_{Az} = 10,000$ ft-lb.]

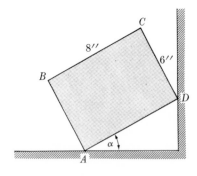

FIGURE 11.38

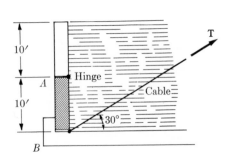

FIGURE 11.39

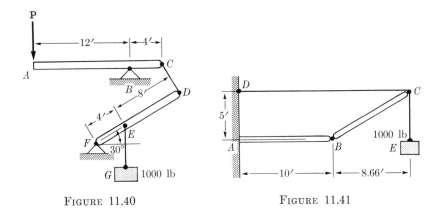

FIGURE 11.40                    FIGURE 11.41

11.21 Find the minimum value of the coefficient of static friction between block $A$ and the sloping plane if there is to be no motion of the system shown in Fig. 11.42.

11.22 A rigid, uniform beam weighing 200 lb is supported by a hinge at $A$ and by a cable at $C$ (Fig. 11.43). The cable runs over a pulley at $D$ and is attached to a 500-lb weight $B$ which rests on top of the beam when the beam is horizontal. Find the tension in the cable.

[*Ans.:* 300 lb.]

11.23 A boom $ABC$ in Fig. 11.44 is held in equilibrium by an ideal cable $BD$ and a 4-ft by 6-ft block $DEFG$. The coefficient of static friction between the block and the plane is $\frac{1}{4}$. Find the maximum weight $W$ in terms of $W_0$.

11.24 It is desired to hold a sloping, homogeneous rod $AB$ of weight $W_0$ in equilibrium in the position shown in Fig. 11.45 by means of a horizontal, homogeneous rod $BC$ pinned to $AB$ at $B$ and resting against a smooth plane at $C$. What is the required weight of the horizontal rod?

[*Ans.:* 0.866 $W_0$.]

11.25 The homogeneous triangular plate in Fig. 11.46 weighs 1200 lb and is supported by six ropes fixed at $A$, $B$, $C$, $D$, $E$, and $F$. Find the tension in each rope.

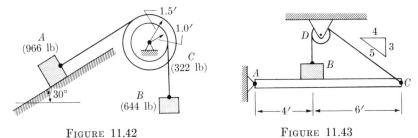

FIGURE 11.42                    FIGURE 11.43

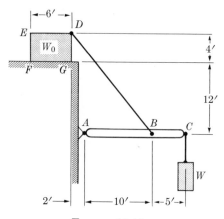

FIGURE 11.44

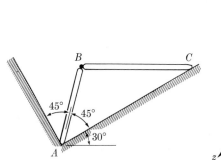

FIGURE 11.45

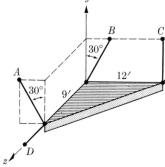

FIGURE 11.46

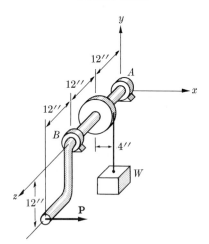

FIGURE 11.47

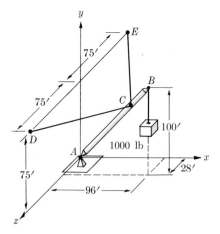

FIGURE 11.48

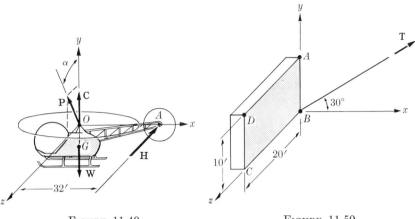

FIGURE 11.49                    FIGURE 11.50

11.26  The windlass in Fig. 11.47 is supported by short journal bearings at $A$ and $B$. When the crank is in the position shown, a horizontal force $\mathbf{P}$ applied at the end of the crank will hold the weight $W$ in equilibrium. Find $P$ and the reactions at $A$ and $B$ in terms of $W$.

$$\left[ Ans.:\ P = \frac{W}{3},\ \mathbf{A} = \frac{W}{6}\mathbf{i} + \frac{W}{2}\mathbf{j},\ \mathbf{B} = -\frac{W}{2}\mathbf{i} + \frac{W}{2}\mathbf{j}. \right]$$

11.27  In the crane shown in Fig. 11.48, cables $CD$ and $CE$ are horizontal. Find the tensions in these cables and the reaction at $A$. The boom $AB$ is homogeneous and weighs 250 lb.

11.28  The helicopter in Fig. 11.49 weighs 3000 lb and is hovering (i.e., is stationary in the air) in the position shown. A horizontal component of $\mathbf{P}$ is achieved by varying the pitch of the main rotor blades during each revolution. If the reactive couple $\mathbf{C}$ from the main rotor is $-5000\mathbf{j}$ ft-lb, find $\mathbf{H}$ and $\mathbf{P}$.

$[Ans.:\ \mathbf{H} = -156\mathbf{k}\ \text{lb},\ \mathbf{P} = 3000\mathbf{j} + 156\mathbf{k}\ \text{lb.}]$

11.29  If the gate in Problem 11.18 is attached by means of short hinges at $A$ and $D$ (Fig. 11.50), with the cable at corner $B$, find the tension $T$ required to open the gate and, for that $T$, the reactions at $A$ and $D$.

# CHAPTER 12

## KINEMATICS OF RIGID BODIES

**12.1 Introduction.** The basic kinematical concepts for a single particle are introduced in Chapter 5, and, as background for rigid-body kinematics, the discussion of particle kinematics is continued in the present chapter with a general treatment of relative motion of two particles.

Although kinematics of rigid bodies, as in the case of particles, deals only with the geometrical aspects of the motion of such bodies, a general and rigorous study of the motion requires mathematical methods of an advanced nature. To simplify the development, only the special case of *plane motion*, i.e., motion for which all points in the body move in planes parallel to the same fixed plane, is considered in this book, and, when necessary, an intuitive approach is used to establish the basic concepts.

**12.2 Relative motion of two particles.** Consider the two moving particles $A$ and $P$ shown in Fig. 12.1, and let the dashed lines represent the paths of the particles. The $xyz$-system of coordinates is a fixed cartesian system, and the $x'y'z'$-system is a *translating* system (i.e., the $x'$-axis is always parallel to the $x$-axis, etc.) with origin at the base particle $A$. (More general types of motion for the moving coordinate system can also be studied.) If the position vectors of particles $P$ and $A$ with respect to the fixed origin $O$ are, respectively, $\mathbf{r}$ and $\mathbf{R}$, then, by definition, the *relative position vector* $\mathbf{r}'$ of $P$ with respect to $A$ is given by

$$\mathbf{r}' = \mathbf{r} - \mathbf{R}, \tag{12.1}$$

and the vector $\mathbf{r}'$ is shown in Fig. 12.1. By definition, the *relative velocity* $\mathbf{v}'$ of $P$ with respect to $A$ is given by

$$\mathbf{v}' = \frac{d\mathbf{r}'}{dt}, \tag{12.2}$$

where $t$ is time, and the *relative acceleration* $\mathbf{a}'$ of $P$ with respect to $A$ is given by

$$\mathbf{a}' = \frac{d\mathbf{v}'}{dt}. \tag{12.3}$$

The quantities $\mathbf{v}'$ and $\mathbf{a}'$ describe the motion of $P$ as it would appear to an observer moving with $A$ but not rotating in any way about $A$. Substituting Eq. (12.1) into Eq. (12.2),

$$\mathbf{v}' = \frac{d\mathbf{r}}{dt} - \frac{d\mathbf{R}}{dt},$$

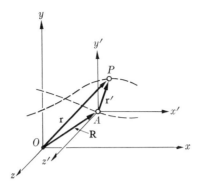

FIGURE 12.1

from which it follows that

$$\mathbf{v}' = \mathbf{v} - \frac{d\mathbf{R}}{dt}, \qquad (12.4)$$

and, substituting Eq. (12.4) into Eq. (12.3),

$$\mathbf{a}' = \frac{d\mathbf{v}}{dt} - \frac{d^2\mathbf{R}}{dt^2},$$

from which it follows that

$$\mathbf{a}' = \mathbf{a} - \frac{d^2\mathbf{R}}{dt^2}. \qquad (12.5)$$

Solving Eqs. (12.1), (12.4), and (12.5) for $\mathbf{r}$, $\mathbf{v}$, and $\mathbf{a}$, we have

$$\mathbf{r} = \mathbf{R} + \mathbf{r}', \qquad \mathbf{v} = \frac{d\mathbf{R}}{dt} + \mathbf{v}', \qquad \mathbf{a} = \frac{d^2\mathbf{R}}{dt^2} + \mathbf{a}'. \qquad (12.6)$$

Equations (12.6) show that any one of the three kinematical quantities for $P$ is equal to the corresponding quantity for $A$ plus the relative quantity for $P$ with respect to $A$. For example, the absolute acceleration of $P$ equals the absolute acceleration of $A$ plus the relative acceleration of $P$ with respect to $A$. This relation is often expressed in the following way:

$$\mathbf{a}_P = \mathbf{a}_A + \mathbf{a}_{P/A}.$$

In Fig. 12.2 the positions of the two particles at times $t_1$ and $t_2$ are shown. By the definition of Eq. (2.28), the displacement $\mathbf{u}$ of particle $P$ is given by

$$\mathbf{u} = \mathbf{r}_2 - \mathbf{r}_1.$$

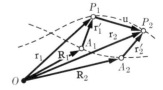

FIGURE 12.2

By the first of Eqs. (12.6), therefore,

$$\mathbf{u} = (\mathbf{R}_2 + \mathbf{r}_2') - (\mathbf{R}_1 + \mathbf{r}_1') = (\mathbf{R}_2 - \mathbf{R}_1) + (\mathbf{r}_2' - \mathbf{r}_1').$$

The vector $\mathbf{r}_2' - \mathbf{r}_1'$ is called the *relative displacement* of $P$ with respect to $A$ and is symbolized by $\mathbf{u}'$, so that

$$\mathbf{u} = (\mathbf{R}_2 - \mathbf{R}_1) + \mathbf{u}'. \tag{12.7}$$

Equation (12.7) states that the absolute displacement of $P$ equals the absolute displacement of $A$ plus the relative displacement of $P$ with respect to $A$.

Using any coordinate system, all the foregoing vector equations may be replaced by scalar equations. In particular, for the two cartesian systems shown in Fig. 12.1, Eqs. (12.6) and (12.7) are equivalent to three scalar equations each, the equations on the $x$-components being as follows:

$$x_P = x_A + x_P', \qquad \dot{x}_P = \dot{x}_A + \dot{x}_P',$$
$$\ddot{x}_P = \ddot{x}_A + \ddot{x}_P', \qquad \Delta x_P = \Delta x_A + \Delta x_P'. \tag{12.8}$$

---

EXAMPLE 12.1. A man on the passenger conveyor belt in Fig. 12.3 moves from a point $A$ on the belt to a point $B$ during an interval of time in which the belt moves 75 ft in the positive $y$-direction. Find the absolute displacement of the man.

*Solution.* In this problem,

$$\mathbf{R}_2 - \mathbf{R}_1 = 75\mathbf{j} \text{ ft}, \qquad \mathbf{u}' = 15\mathbf{i} - 10\mathbf{j} \text{ ft}.$$

Hence, by Eq. (12.7),

$$\mathbf{u} = 15\mathbf{i} + 65\mathbf{j} \text{ ft}.$$

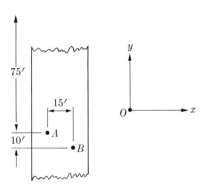

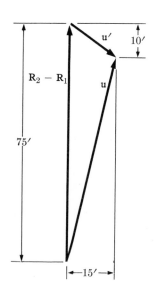

FIGURE 12.3                        FIGURE 12.4

A semigraphical solution to this problem involves sketching the known vectors $R_2 - R_1$ and $u'$ as in Fig. 12.4 and adding them to obtain $u$.

---

In the foregoing example, the absolute part of the motion is unknown. In many problems it is the relative part of the motion which is unknown.

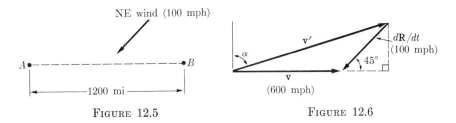

FIGURE 12.5                    FIGURE 12.6

EXAMPLE 12.2.  An airplane is to fly a straight-line path from an origin $A$ to a destination $B$ 1200 miles due east of $A$ (Fig. 12.5). If there is a steady northeast wind with a speed of 100 mph, find the bearing and air speed required for the airplane if the trip is to be made in two hours.

*Solution.* The absolute velocity must have an easterly direction and a magnitude (which is called the "ground speed") of 600 mph. When we sketch the known vectors $v$ and $dR/dt$ with their heads together as in Fig. 12.6, the relative velocity $v'$ is found by subtracting $dR/dt$ from $v$. Hence, referring to that right triangle in Fig. 12.6 which has $v'$ as a hypotenuse,

$$\tan(90° - \alpha) = \frac{70.7}{670.7} = 0.105,$$

$$90° - \alpha = 6°,$$

$$\alpha = 84°,$$

and the bearing is N84°E. The air speed $|v'|$ is found as follows:

$$|v'| = \frac{70.7}{\sin 6°} = \frac{70.7}{0.1045} = 676 \text{ mph}.$$

**12.3 Motion of a rigid body parallel to a plane.**  The mechanism in Fig. 12.7(a) contains rigid bodies which undergo various types of plane motion when the gear mounted at $A$ is turned as indicated by the curved arrow.

A diagrammatic sketch of the mechanism is shown in Fig. 12.7(b), with the dashed lines representing the positions of the components after a displacement.  The piston illustrates *rectilinear translation* of a body; all points in the body move on parallel straight lines.  The link $CD$ illustrates

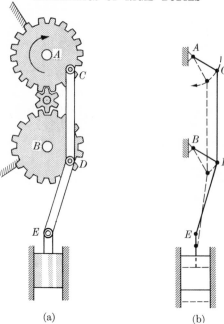

(a)                                        (b)

FIGURE 12.7

*curvilinear translation,* in which points in the body travel on curved paths but any line fixed in the body moves so as to remain parallel to itself. The three gears are in *rotation,* which means that there is an axis fixed in space (e.g., at $A$) such that lines in the body intersecting that axis (e.g., line $AC$) continue to intersect it. In this type of plane motion, all points in the body move on circular paths about the fixed axis. Finally, the link $DE$ is in *general plane motion.* This motion is characterized by changes in direction of lines in the body and different types of motion for different points in the body.

The motion of a rigid body in either type of translation is analyzed by selecting any point in the body and applying the techniques of Chapter 5 to that point, so that no further discussion of the kinematics of translation is required.

For pure rotation it is convenient to take the origin $O$ on the fixed axis of rotation as shown in Fig. 12.8. The $z$-axis can then be taken along the axis of rotation. An angle $\theta$ is measured counterclockwise from a line fixed in space to a line fixed in the body, both lines being parallel to the $xy$-plane and intersecting the $z$-axis at the same point but being otherwise arbitrary. Since the body is in motion, $\theta$ is a function of time. The distance $\rho$ is an independent variable used to locate an arbitrary point $P$ in the body. By definition, the *angular velocity* of the body is a vector $\boldsymbol{\omega}$ with magnitude

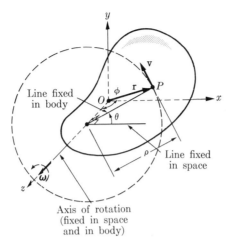

FIGURE 12.8

$|\dot{\theta}|$, direction parallel to the axis of rotation, and sense as given by the right-hand rule applied to the angular direction of the motion (shown by the curved arrow in Fig. 12.8). The angular velocity $\boldsymbol{\omega}$ is meaningful for the more general case of motion of a rigid body with one fixed point $O$, in which case $\boldsymbol{\omega}$ can change direction, but, for the rotation about a fixed $z$-axis presently under consideration, $\boldsymbol{\omega}$ is always parallel to the $z$-axis. Hence,

$$\boldsymbol{\omega} = \dot{\theta}\mathbf{k}, \tag{12.9}$$

where $\mathbf{k}$ is the unit vector in the positive $z$-direction. Since, for rotation about the $z$-axis, $\boldsymbol{\omega}$ is always in the $z$-direction, only its $z$-component need be considered, and, from Eq. (12.9),

$$\omega_z = \dot{\theta}. \tag{12.10}$$

It is clear that $\omega_z$ is positive when $\theta$ is increasing, i.e., when the motion is counterclockwise.

The velocity $\mathbf{v}$ of any point $P$ in a body in rotation can be found by noting that the path of the point is circular. Equations (5.46) therefore give the cylindrical components of $\mathbf{v}$, that is, using Eq. (12.10),

$$v_\rho = 0, \qquad v_\theta = \rho\omega_z, \qquad v_z = 0. \tag{12.11}$$

Therefore, referring to Fig. 12.8 and letting $\omega$ be the magnitude of $\boldsymbol{\omega}$,

$$v = \rho|\omega_z| = |\omega_z|r \sin \phi = \omega r \sin \phi.$$

Since $\mathbf{v}$ is perpendicular to the plane defined by $\boldsymbol{\omega}$ and $\mathbf{r}$, and since the sense of **v** is given by the right-hand rule applied to **ω** and **r**, it follows that

$$\mathbf{v} = \boldsymbol{\omega} \times \mathbf{r}. \qquad (12.12)$$

Equation (12.12) can also be shown to hold in the more general case of motion with one point fixed (when **ω** can have any direction), and it is therefore an important and powerful equation. For rotation about the $z$-axis only, Eq. (12.12) reduces to Eqs. (12.11).

The angular acceleration **α** of a body moving with one point fixed is defined as the time derivative of **ω**, that is,

$$\boldsymbol{\alpha} = \frac{d\boldsymbol{\omega}}{dt}, \qquad (12.13)$$

and **α** therefore measures the change in direction as well as the change in magnitude of **ω**. For the special case where **ω** is always in the $z$-direction, it follows from Eq. (12.13) that **α** is always in the $z$-direction (since the derivative of a vector with constant direction is parallel to the vector). This can also be seen by substituting Eq. (12.9) into Eq. (12.13) to obtain

$$\boldsymbol{\alpha} = \ddot{\theta}\mathbf{k}. \qquad (12.14)$$

From this equation it follows that

$$\alpha_z = \ddot{\theta}, \qquad (12.15)$$

which means that the sign of $\ddot{\theta}$ determines the sense of **α**. The sense of **α** is therefore the same as that of **ω** when $\theta$ and $\ddot{\theta}$ have the same sign and opposite otherwise.

The components of the acceleration **a** of any point $P$ in a body in rotation can be found from Eqs. (5.47) by substituting Eqs. (12.10) and (12.15), i.e.,

$$a_\rho = -\rho\omega_z^2, \qquad a_\theta = \rho\alpha_z, \qquad a_z = 0. \qquad (12.16)$$

There is an important similarity between the equations which govern pure rotation, Eqs. (12.10) and (12.15), and those which govern rectilinear motion of a particle, Eqs. (5.29) and (5.30). In fact, $\theta$, $\omega_z$, and $\alpha_z$ are related to each other in the same way as are $x$, $v_x$, and $a_x$ for rectilinear motion of a particle. Hence there is a class of rotation problems which are solved in a manner similar to the examples discussed in Art. 5.3.

---

EXAMPLE 12.3. The rotor of an electric motor is turning at 1200 rpm when the power is shut off. If $\alpha_z$ is $-2$ rad/sec$^2$, determine the number of revolutions executed by the rotor before it comes to rest.

*Solution.* By Eqs. (12.10) and (12.15),

$$d\omega_z = \alpha_z(t)\, dt,$$

and hence

$$\omega_z = \int \alpha_z(t)\, dt.$$

In this example,

$$\omega_z = \int -2\, dt = -2t + C_1.$$

Substituting $\omega_z(0) = 1200$ rpm $= 40\pi$ rad/sec,

$$\omega_z = -2t + 40\pi.$$

Hence, $\omega_z$ is zero when

$$t = 20\pi \text{ sec.}$$

Integrating again,

$$\theta = -t^2 + 40\pi t + C_2,$$

and, measuring $\theta$ from the instant that the power is shut off,

$$\theta = -t^2 + 40\pi t.$$

For $t = 20\pi$ sec,

$$\theta = -400\pi^2 + 800\pi^2 = 400\pi^2 \text{ rad}$$
$$= 200\pi \text{ rev} = 628 \text{ rev.}$$

---

In some problems it is necessary to derive an equation for $\theta$ as a function of $t$ and then differentiate to find $\omega_z$ and $\alpha_z$.

---

EXAMPLE 12.4.  Starting at $d = 0$ when $t = 0$, the block in Fig. 12.9 moves to the right with a constant speed $v_0$. Find $\omega_z$ and $\alpha_z$ for the bar as functions of time.

*Solution.* Since the speed of the block is constant,

$$d = v_0 t.$$

From Fig. 12.9,

$$\theta = \arctan \frac{h}{d},$$

and therefore

$$\theta = \arctan \frac{h}{v_0 t}.$$

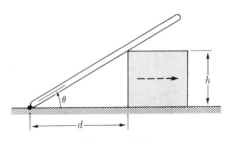

FIGURE 12.9

Differentiating,

$$\omega_z = -\frac{h v_0}{h^2 + v_0^2 t^2} \quad \text{and} \quad \alpha_z = \frac{2 h v_0^3 t}{(h^2 + v_0^2 t^2)^2}.$$

General plane motion of a rigid body parallel to the $xy$-plane can be studied by selecting an arbitrary reference point $A$ (called a *pole*) fixed in the body, as shown in Fig. 12.10. The dashed curve in this figure represents the path of the pole, a path which is parallel to the $xy$-plane. A translating coordinate system with origin at $A$ can be employed temporarily, and an angle $\theta$ measured counterclockwise from the positive $x$-direction to a line $AP$ fixed in the body can be used to describe the orientation of the body at any time. The angular velocity $\boldsymbol{\omega}$ of the body is defined in terms of $\theta$ in the same way as for pure rotation, $\boldsymbol{\omega}$ again being in the $z$-direction (for plane motion). Since only the time derivative of $\theta$ is involved, $\theta$ itself may be measured counterclockwise from any line fixed in space to any line fixed in the body, as long as both lines are parallel to the $xy$-plane. The angular acceleration $\boldsymbol{\alpha}$ is still defined by Eq. (12.13) and is still in the $z$-direction (for plane motion).

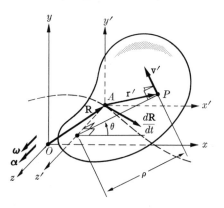

FIGURE 12.10

The equations of relative motion for any two particles, Eqs. (12.6) and (12.7), can be applied to points $A$ and $P$ in the rigid body of Fig. 12.10, the equations taking on a special form for the rigid body because of the condition that $A$ and $P$ must remain a fixed distance apart. For pure rotation, this condition leads to the conclusion that the path of $P$ is circular and the velocity of $P$ is given by Eq. (12.12). In general plane motion, the conclusion is that the relative velocity $\mathbf{v}'$ of $P$ with respect to $A$ is given by

$$\mathbf{v}' = \boldsymbol{\omega} \times \mathbf{r}'. \tag{12.17}$$

Hence, dealing first with velocities only, the second of Eqs. (12.6) becomes, for a rigid body,

$$\mathbf{v} = \frac{d\mathbf{R}}{dt} + \boldsymbol{\omega} \times \mathbf{r}'. \tag{12.18}$$

By Eq. (7.21), since $\omega_x = \omega_y = 0$,

$$\boldsymbol{\omega} \times \mathbf{r}' = -\omega_z y'_P \mathbf{i} + \omega_z x'_P \mathbf{j}.$$

Using Eq. (12.18) and expressing $x'_P$ and $y'_P$ in terms of coordinates measured from the fixed axes,

$$\dot{x}_P = \dot{x}_A - \omega_z(y_P - y_A), \qquad \dot{y}_P = \dot{y}_A + \omega_z(x_P - x_A). \quad (12.19)$$

The first of these two equations is the special form assumed by the second of Eqs. (12.8) when $A$ and $P$ are two points in a rigid body in plane motion.

Equations (12.19) can also be derived by resolving $\mathbf{v}'$ (Fig. 12.10) into $x$- and $y$-components. By Eqs. (12.11),

$$|\mathbf{v}'| = \rho|\omega_z|,$$

so that

$$\dot{x}'_P = -\rho\omega_z \sin \theta, \qquad \dot{y}'_P = \rho\omega_z \cos \theta.$$

Noting that

$$\rho \sin \theta = y_P - y_A, \qquad \rho \cos \theta = x_P - x_A,$$

we see that Eqs. (12.19) follow immediately.

There are many plane-motion problems which can be solved by means of Eqs. (12.19).

_____

EXAMPLE 12.5. The mechanism shown in Fig. 12.11 consists of a wheel rotating about a fixed axis at $A$ and two rigid bars $BC$ and $CD$. If the wheel rotates clockwise with a constant angular speed of 40 rad/sec, determine, for the position shown, the angular velocity of bar $BC$ and the velocity of point $C$.

_Solution._ All unknowns in this problem can be found by starting with a point having known velocity components (e.g., $A$ is known to be stationary) and working through all the bodies in the mechanism to a final point (such as $D$) also having known velocity components. For points $A$ and $B$ in the wheel,

$$\dot{x}_B = \dot{x}_A - \omega_{AB}(y_B - y_A), \qquad \dot{y}_B = \dot{y}_A + \omega_{AB}(x_B - x_A).$$

Since only differences in coordinates are required, the actual location of the coordinate axes need not be specified. Hence,

$$\dot{x}_B = -(-40)(4) = 160 \text{ in./sec},$$

$$\dot{y}_B = (-40)(3) = -120 \text{ in./sec}.$$

For points $B$ and $C$ in body $BC$,

$$\dot{x}_C = 160 - \omega_{BC}(-12) = 160 + 12\omega_{BC},$$

$$\dot{y}_C = -120 + \omega_{BC}(8) = -120 + 8\omega_{BC}.$$

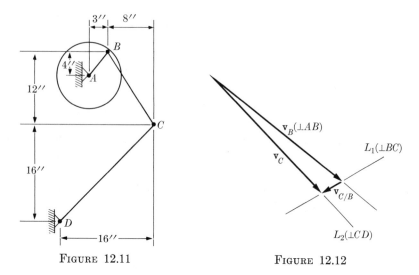

FIGURE 12.11                           FIGURE 12.12

Finally, for points $C$ and $D$ in body $CD$, since $D$ is stationary,

$$0 = 160 + 12\omega_{BC} + 16\omega_{CD},$$

$$0 = -120 + 8\omega_{BC} - 16\omega_{CD}.$$

Adding the last two equations,

$$\omega_{BC} = -2 \text{ rad/sec.}$$

Since this result is negative, bar $BC$ is rotating clockwise at the instant under consideration. Substituting into previous equations,

$$\dot{x}_C = 160 + 12(-2) = 136 \text{ in./sec,}$$

$$\dot{y}_C = -120 + 8(-2) = -136 \text{ in./sec,}$$

and hence

$$\mathbf{v}_C = 136\mathbf{i} - 136\mathbf{j} \text{ in./sec.}$$

Incidentally,

$$\omega_{CD} = \frac{-160 - 12(-2)}{16} = -\frac{136}{16} = -8.5 \text{ rad/sec.}$$

The foregoing results can be obtained graphically by the construction illustrated in Fig. 12.12. The arrow representing $\mathbf{v}_B$ is drawn first with a length representing 5(40) or 200 in./sec and with known direction and sense. Lines $L_1$ and $L_2$ are then drawn, as indicated, through the head and tail of $\mathbf{v}_B$, respectively. The absolute velocity $\mathbf{v}_C$ is found from the drawing, and

$$|\omega_{BC}| = \frac{|\mathbf{v}_{C/B}|}{L_{BC}},$$

where $L_{BC}$ is the length of bar $BC$ (14.42 in. in this mechanism).

After we know the velocity of one point in any one of the three bodies and the angular velocity of the body, it is possible to find the velocity of any other point in the body.

---

At any one instant of the general plane motion of a rigid body, there is a line (perpendicular to the $xy$-plane) in the body such that the velocity of all points on the line is a null vector. (The acceleration of the points is not necessarily null.) This line is called the *instantaneous axis of null velocity*, and the intersection point $C$ of the line with the $xy$-plane is called the *instantaneous center of null velocity*. To establish the existence of such a line, let $P$ in Eqs. (12.19) be $C$, so that

$$\dot{x}_A - \omega_z(y_C - y_A) = 0, \qquad \dot{y}_A + \omega_z(x_C - x_A) = 0.$$

Solving for the coordinates of $C$,

$$x_C = x_A - \frac{\dot{y}_A}{\omega_z}, \qquad y_C = y_A + \frac{\dot{x}_A}{\omega_z}. \tag{12.20}$$

These equations show under what conditions the axis exists. For example, if the body is in translation, $\omega_z = 0$, and $C$ does not exist, since division by zero is not defined. (As $\omega_z$ approaches zero, $x_C$ and $y_C$ approach infinity.) If the body is in pure rotation about the $z$-axis, select $O$ as the base point $A$; Eqs. (12.20) then give

$$x_C = 0, \qquad y_C = 0,$$

and the axis of rotation is the instantaneous axis at all times. For general plane motion, the coordinates of $C$ are shown by Eqs. (12.20) to be functions of time (all other quantities in the equations being functions of

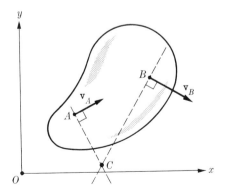

FIGURE 12.13

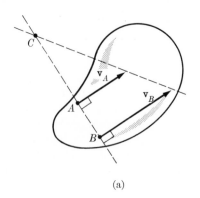

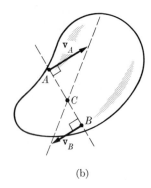

(a)　　　　　　　　　　　　　　　　　　　(b)

FIGURE 12.14

time), and the instantaneous center moves in the plane. It also moves relatively to the body.

The instantaneous axis of null velocity can be considered as an axis about which the rigid body is in pure rotation at any instant. The axis may be outside the limits of the body, but it must still be regarded as a line belonging to the body, since it is defined by the relative-velocity equations of a rigid body.

If the directions of the velocities of two points $A$ and $B$ in a rigid body are known at an instant, the instantaneous center $C$ can be located by taking planes through $A$ and $B$ perpendicular to the known directions, as shown in Fig. 12.13. The intersection line of the two planes is the instantaneous axis of null velocity, since, for pure rotation, all points have velocities perpendicular to planes radiating from the axis of rotation. If the two planes coincide, as shown in Figs. 12.14(a) and (b), the two velocities $\mathbf{v}_A$ and $\mathbf{v}_B$ must be completely known, so that $C$ may be located as shown.

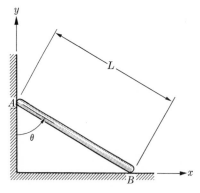

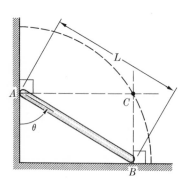

FIGURE 12.15　　　　　　　　　　　　FIGURE 12.16

EXAMPLE 12.6. A rod $AB$ moves as shown in Fig. 12.15 with its end points in contact with a vertical plane and a horizontal plane. Locate the instantaneous center and find $\dot{y}_A$ in terms of $\dot{x}_B$ and $\theta$.

*Solution.* The instantaneous center $C$ is shown in Fig. 12.16. Applying the first of Eqs. (12.19) to points $B$ and $C$,

$$\dot{x}_B = -\omega_z(-L\cos\theta),$$

and hence

$$\omega_z = \frac{\dot{x}_B}{L\cos\theta},$$

the angular motion being counterclockwise when $\dot{x}_B$ is positive. Applying the second of Eqs. (12.19) to points $A$ and $C$,

$$\dot{y}_A = \frac{\dot{x}_B}{L\cos\theta}(-L\sin\theta) = -\dot{x}_B\tan\theta.$$

This example illustrates the way in which $C$ can move in space and in the body. From Fig. 12.16,

$$x_C = L\sin\theta, \qquad y_C = L\cos\theta.$$

Eliminating the parameter $\theta$,

$$x_C^2 + y_C^2 = L^2,$$

and $C$ therefore moves on a circle of radius $L$ (shown dashed in Fig. 12.16). Since $C$ coincides with $A$ when the rod is vertical and with $B$ when the rod is horizontal, it is obvious that $C$ also moves relatively to the body.

---

Referring again to Fig. 12.10, we find that the acceleration of $P$ can be expressed in terms of the acceleration of $A$ by equations similar to those developed for the velocities of the two points, Eqs. (12.19). This can be accomplished by resolving the relative acceleration $\mathbf{a}'$ into cylindrical components by Eqs. (12.16) and then finding the $x$- and $y$-components of each of these components. A more direct way, however, is to simply differentiate Eq. (12.18), a process which gives

$$\mathbf{a} = \frac{d^2\mathbf{R}}{dt^2} + \boldsymbol{\omega} \times \frac{d\mathbf{r}'}{dt} + \frac{d\boldsymbol{\omega}}{dt} \times \mathbf{r}'.$$

By Eqs. (12.2) and (12.13), therefore,

$$\mathbf{a} = \frac{d^2\mathbf{R}}{dt^2} + \boldsymbol{\omega} \times \mathbf{v}' + \boldsymbol{\alpha} \times \mathbf{r}',$$

and, since $\omega_x = \omega_y = \alpha_x = \alpha_y = 0$,

$$\ddot{x}_P = \ddot{x}_A - \omega_z \dot{y}'_P - \alpha_z y'_P, \qquad \ddot{y}_P = \ddot{y}_A + \omega_z \dot{x}'_P + \alpha_z x'_P.$$

But, from Eqs. (12.19),

$$\dot{x}'_P = -\omega_z(y_P - y_A), \qquad \dot{y}'_P = \omega_z(x_P - x_A),$$

and therefore, expressing $x'_P$ and $y'_P$ in terms of coordinates measured from the fixed axes,

$$\ddot{x}_P = \ddot{x}_A - \omega_z^2(x_P - x_A) - \alpha_z(y_P - y_A),$$
$$\ddot{y}_P = \ddot{y}_A - \omega_z^2(y_P - y_A) + \alpha_z(x_P - x_A). \tag{12.21}$$

Equations (12.21) can be used in conjunction with Eqs. (12.19) to solve problems involving both velocities and accelerations.

---

EXAMPLE 12.7. Find $\alpha_{BC}$ and $\mathbf{a}_C$ for the mechanism of Example 12.5.

*Solution.* With all three angular velocities known from the previous solution, Eqs. (12.21) can be applied to the three bodies in succession to find the unknown accelerations and angular accelerations. For points $A$ and $B$ in body $AB$,

$$\ddot{x}_B = \ddot{x}_A - \omega_{AB}^2(x_B - x_A) - \alpha_{AB}(y_B - y_A),$$
$$\ddot{y}_B = \ddot{y}_A - \omega_{AB}^2(y_B - y_A) + \alpha_{AB}(x_B - x_A).$$

Substituting the known quantities,

$$\ddot{x}_B = -(-40)^2(3) = -4800 \text{ in./sec}^2,$$
$$\ddot{y}_B = -(-40)^2(4) = -6400 \text{ in./sec}^2.$$

For points $B$ and $C$ of bar $BC$,

$$\ddot{x}_C = -4800 - (-2)^2(8) - \alpha_{BC}(-12) = -4830 + 12\alpha_{BC},$$
$$\ddot{y}_C = -6400 - (-2)^2(-12) + \alpha_{BC}(8) = -6350 + 8\alpha_{BC}.$$

Finally, for $C$ and $D$ of bar $CD$,

$$0 = -4830 + 12\alpha_{BC} - (-8.5)^2(-16) - \alpha_{CD}(-16),$$
$$0 = -6350 + 8\alpha_{BC} - (-8.5)^2(-16) + \alpha_{CD}(-16).$$

Adding the last two equations, $\alpha_{BC} = 444$ rad/sec$^2$, and, substituting back,

$$\ddot{x}_C = 500 \text{ in./sec}^2, \qquad \ddot{y}_C = -2800 \text{ in./sec}^2,$$

so that                     $\mathbf{a}_C = 500\mathbf{i} - 2800\mathbf{j} \text{ in./sec}^2.$

Equations (12.21) can be used to locate an *instantaneous axis of null acceleration* by setting the left-hand sides equal to zero. In general, this axis does not coincide with the instantaneous axis of null velocity and is not as useful in solving problems as the latter.

**12.4 Rolling without slipping.** By definition, the rigid body shown in Fig. 12.17 is *rolling without slipping* on the fixed surface if a $z$-axis through the point of contact is the instantaneous axis of null velocity. In that case, the velocity of any point in the body has a direction perpendicular to the plane through the given point and the instantaneous axis and a magnitude proportional to the perpendicular distance from the given point to the instantaneous axis.

The special case of a circular wheel rolling on a plane is of considerable importance in engineering. To study this case in more detail, consider the wheel in Fig. 12.18. If the wheel rolls down the plane without slipping, a point $P$ on the rim of the wheel describes the path shown by the dashed curve, while the center $A$ is in rectilinear motion. Let $\theta$ be measured counterclockwise from the $x$-axis to the line $PQ$ fixed in the body. An alternative definition of rolling without slipping is the statement that the arc $CQ$ is equal in length to the line $CQ_0$. If this condition is fulfilled, then

$$x_A = b\left(\frac{\pi}{2} - \theta\right), \qquad y_A = 0,$$

and hence

$$x_P = b\left(\frac{\pi}{2} - \theta\right) + b\cos\theta, \qquad y_P = b\sin\theta. \tag{12.22}$$

Equations (12.22) are parametric equations of the path of $P$. One way to study the motion of $P$ is to apply the relative motion equations, Eqs. (12.19) and (12.21), to points $A$ and $P$. Another way is simply to differentiate Eqs. (12.22) with respect to time to obtain

$$\dot{x}_P = -b\omega_z - b\omega_z\sin\theta, \qquad \dot{y}_P = b\omega_z\cos\theta. \tag{12.23}$$

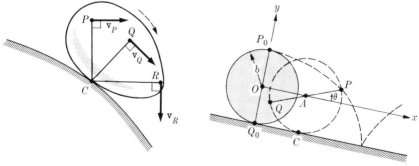

FIGURE 12.17                                  FIGURE 12.18

At $\theta = \pi/2$,
$$\dot{x}_P = -2b\omega_z, \qquad \dot{y}_P = 0,$$

and, at $\theta = -\pi/2$, when $P$ is in contact with the plane,

$$\dot{x}_P = 0, \qquad \dot{y}_P = 0,$$

the last two equations demonstrating that the two definitions of rolling without slipping are equivalent. Differentiating Eqs. (12.23) with respect to time,

$$\ddot{x}_P = -b\alpha_z - b\omega_z^2 \cos\theta - b\alpha_z \sin\theta,$$
$$\ddot{y}_P = -b\omega_z^2 \sin\theta + b\alpha_z \cos\theta. \tag{12.24}$$

At $\theta = \pi/2$,
$$\ddot{x}_P = -2b\alpha_z, \qquad \ddot{y}_P = -b\omega_z^2,$$

and, at $\theta = -\pi/2$,

$$\ddot{x}_P = 0, \qquad \ddot{y}_P = b\omega_z^2. \tag{12.25}$$

Equations (12.25) give the acceleration of the instantaneous center of null velocity of a circular wheel rolling without slipping on a plane.

It can be seen in Fig. 12.18 that $C$ moves along the plane in space and along the rim of the wheel in the body. (This motion of $C$ does not contradict the definition of $C$ as the point with null velocity because at each different time it is a different point in the body which is stationary.) Studying the path of $P$ shows how a typical point on the rim stops moving instantaneously when the point is in contact with the plane.

---

EXAMPLE 12.8. The flanged wheel shown in Fig. 12.19 has a string wrapped around the inner hub. If the string has a constant velocity $\mathbf{v}_0$ to the right and the wheel rolls without slipping, find the velocity and acceleration of point $P$ for the position shown.

*Solution.* Applying the first of Eqs. (12.19) and the first of Eqs. (12.21) to points $Q$ and $C$,

$$v_0 = -\omega_z(b_1 + b_2), \qquad 0 = -\alpha_z(b_1 + b_2),$$

from which

$$\omega_z = -\frac{v_0}{b_1 + b_2}, \qquad \alpha_z = 0.$$

Applying Eqs. (12.19) to $P$ and $C$,

$$\dot{x}_P = -\left(-\frac{v_0}{b_1 + b_2}\right)(b_2) = \frac{b_2}{b_1 + b_2} v_0,$$

$$\dot{y}_P = \left(-\frac{v_0}{b_1 + b_2}\right)(b_3) = -\frac{b_3}{b_1 + b_2} v_0,$$

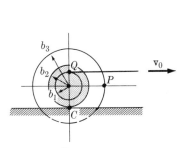

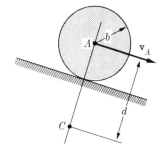

FIGURE 12.19                    FIGURE 12.20

so that

$$\mathbf{v}_P = \frac{b_2}{b_1 + b_2} v_0 \mathbf{i} - \frac{b_3}{b_1 + b_2} v_0 \mathbf{j}.$$

Applying Eqs. (12.21) to $P$ and $C$,

$$\ddot{x}_P = -\left(-\frac{v_0}{b_1 + b_2}\right)^2 (b_3) = -\frac{b_3}{(b_1 + b_2)^2} v_0^2,$$

$$\ddot{y}_P = b_2 \left(-\frac{v_0}{b_1 + b_2}\right)^2 - \left(-\frac{v_0}{b_1 + b_2}\right)^2 (b_2) = 0,$$

so that

$$\mathbf{a}_P = -\frac{b_3}{(b_1 + b_2)^2} v_0^2 \mathbf{i}.$$

---

Several cases of a circular wheel moving in contact with a plane can be distinguished according to the location of the instantaneous center $C$ in Fig. 12.20. Since

$$d = \frac{v_A}{|\omega_z|},$$

the following table gives the criteria for various cases:

| *If* | *then the wheel is* |
|---|---|
| (1) $d = 0$, | in pure rotation about $A$. |
| (2) $0 < d < b$, | rolling with slipping (velocity of contact point up the plane). |
| (3) $d = b$, | rolling without slipping. |
| (4) $b < d < \infty$ | rolling with slipping (velocity of contact point down the plane). |
| (5) $d = \infty$ | in pure translation. |

PROBLEMS

12.1 It is required that an object be projected from the top of an airplane flying horizontally at 600 mph so that the object travels up and falls to earth on a vertical straight line. The gun used imparts a speed to the object of 1000 ft/sec relative to the muzzle, and there is no wind. (a) In what direction must the gun be aimed? (b) What is the absolute speed of the object? (c) If the object must rise 6 ft to clear the tail assembly, how far forward of the tail assembly must the muzzle of the gun be located? Neglect air resistance and the acceleration due to gravity.

12.2 A gun with muzzle speed of 644 ft/sec and inclination of 30° is fired at a fixed target from a vehicle moving toward the target. What must be the speed of the vehicle if the target is 4000 yards away at the instant of firing?

[*Ans.:* 42 ft/sec.]

12.3 If the wheel in Fig. 12.21 moves to the right in such a way that the speed of point $A$ is a constant $v_0$, determine the angular acceleration of the bar as a function of $b$, $d$, and $v_0$.

12.4 The rod $AB$ in Fig. 12.22 moves in such a way that it remains in contact with the floor at $B$ and with the corner at $C$. If end $B$ moves to the right with a constant speed $v_0$, find $\alpha_z$ as a function of $d$.

$$\left[ Ans.:\ \alpha_z = -\frac{2hv_0^2 d}{(h^2 + d^2)^2} . \right]$$

12.5 The winch in Fig. 12.23 starts from rest and winds up cable so as to give the block an upward acceleration with magnitude of 10 ft/sec². How many revolutions are required before the block is traveling with a speed of 50 ft/sec?

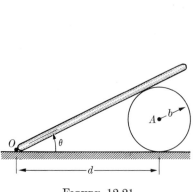

FIGURE 12.21

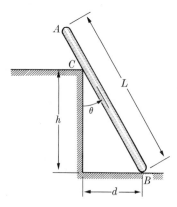

FIGURE 12.22

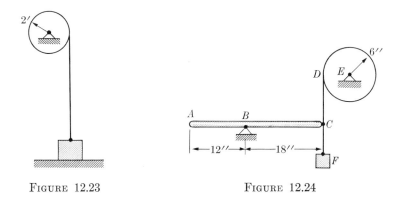

FIGURE 12.23                    FIGURE 12.24

12.6 For the position shown in Fig. 12.24, the drum $DE$ has an angular velocity of 10 rad/sec and an angular acceleration of 5 rad/sec², both counterclockwise. Find the angular velocity and angular acceleration of the beam $ABC$ for the position shown.

[*Ans.:* $\omega_{AC} = -3.33$ rad/sec, $\alpha_{AC} = -1.67$ rad/sec².]

12.7 The mechanism in Fig. 12.25 consists of a wheel rotating about a fixed axis at $D$ and two rigid bars $AB$ and $BC$. If the wheel rotates clockwise with a constant angular speed of 10 rad/sec, find the acceleration of point $B$ for the position shown.

12.8 A slender rod $AB$ of length $L$ (Fig. 12.26) moves in such a way that end $A$ remains in contact with a vertical wall and end $B$ remains in contact with a horizontal floor. Using the relative-motion equations, Eqs. (12.19) and (12.21), find $\ddot{y}_A$ in terms of $\ddot{x}_B$, $\dot{x}_B$, and $\theta$.

$$\left[ Ans.: \ddot{y}_A = -\ddot{x}_B \tan \theta - \frac{\dot{x}_B^2}{L \cos \theta} (1 + \tan^2 \theta). \right]$$

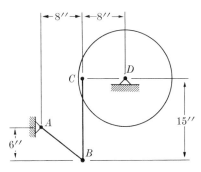

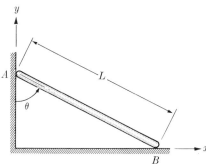

FIGURE 12.25                    FIGURE 12.26

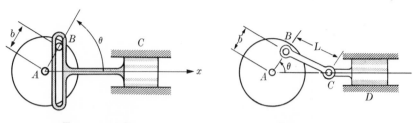

FIGURE 12.27                    FIGURE 12.28

12.9  The flywheel in the mechanism shown in Fig. 12.27 is on a fixed shaft and has a constant angular speed $\omega_0$ counterclockwise. Using the relative-motion equations, find the velocity and acceleration of the piston in terms of $\theta$ and the values of $\theta$ (between 0 and 180°) at which the speed of the piston is a maximum.

12.10  The flywheel in the mechanism in Fig. 12.28 has a constant angular speed $\omega_0$ counterclockwise. Find the velocity of the piston as a function of $\theta$.

$$\left[ Ans.: v_x = -\omega_0 b \sin\theta - \frac{\omega_0 b^2 \sin\theta \cos\theta}{\sqrt{L^2 - b^2 \sin^2\theta}} \cdot \right]$$

12.11  In Fig. 12.29, points $A$ and $C$ are originally together, and the mechanism is at rest.  Point $C$ then travels to the right with a constant acceleration of 8 in./sec². Find the angular velocity of bar $AB$ when the mechanism is in the position shown.

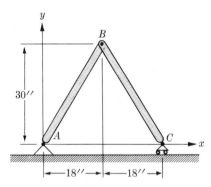

FIGURE 12.29

12.12  The cylinder in Fig. 12.30 rolls to the right without slipping at a constant angular speed $\omega_0$, and the block is pushed along the plane by a pin $B$ fixed on the cylinder.  (a) Find the velocity and acceleration of the block in terms of $\theta$.  (b) What are these quantities when $\theta = 0$ and when $\theta = 90°$?

$[Ans.:$ (a) $v_x = b\omega_0(1 + \sin\theta),\ a_x = -b\omega_0^2 \cos\theta;$
        (b) $v_x(0) = b\omega_0,\ a_x(0) = -b\omega_0^2,\ v_x(90°) = 2b\omega_0,\ a_x(90°) = 0.]$

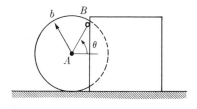

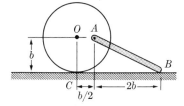

FIGURE 12.30                              FIGURE 12.31

12.13 In Fig. 12.31, the rod $AB$ is pinned to the wheel at $A$ and slides along the horizontal plane at $B$. If the wheel rolls without slipping, determine, for the position shown, $\omega_{AB}$ and $\alpha_{AB}$ in terms of $\omega_{OA}$ and $\alpha_{OA}$.

# CHAPTER 13

## KINETICS OF RIGID BODIES

**13.1 Motion of a system of particles.** The motion of a system of particles such as that in Fig. 11.1 is investigated by applying Newton's Second Law (Art. 6.2) to each particle, i.e., by noting that

$$\mathbf{R}_i = m_i \mathbf{a}_i \tag{13.1}$$

for all $i$, where $\mathbf{R}_i$ is the resultant of all the forces on the $i$th particle and $\mathbf{a}_i$ is the acceleration of the $i$th particle. By Eq. (11.3), therefore,

$$\mathbf{R} = m_1 \mathbf{a}_1 + m_2 \mathbf{a}_2 + \cdots + m_n \mathbf{a}_n, \tag{13.2}$$

and, by Eq. (11.7), $\mathbf{R}$ can be interpreted as the resultant of all the external forces on the system. The last equation shows that the condition

$$\mathbf{R} = 0$$

is a necessary but not a sufficient condition for equilibrium, since equilibrium means that

$$\mathbf{a}_i = 0$$

for all $i$. Rewriting Eq. (13.2),

$$\mathbf{R} = m_1 \frac{d^2 \mathbf{r}_1}{dt^2} + m_2 \frac{d^2 \mathbf{r}_2}{dt^2} + \cdots + m_n \frac{d^2 \mathbf{r}_n}{dt^2}$$

$$= \frac{d^2}{dt^2} (m_1 \mathbf{r}_1 + m_2 \mathbf{r}_2 + \cdots + m_n \mathbf{r}_n),$$

and hence, by Eq. (9.1),

$$\mathbf{R} = \frac{d^2}{dt^2} (m \mathbf{r}_G),$$

where $m$ is the total mass of all the particles. Finally, therefore,

$$\mathbf{R} = m \mathbf{a}_G, \tag{13.3}$$

and a comparison of this equation with Eq. (6.2) shows that the center of mass of the system of particles travels in the same way as a single particle of mass $m$ located at $G$ and subjected to the same forces as the external forces on the system (except with their lines of action altered to make them concur at $G$). Equation (13.3), of course, says nothing about the motion of any individual particle.

Writing Eq. (13.3) in terms of cartesian components,

$$R_x = m\ddot{x}_G, \qquad R_y = m\ddot{y}_G, \qquad R_z = m\ddot{z}_G. \qquad (13.4)$$

Equations (13.4) predict certain phenomena when applied to the motion of particular systems of particles. For example, if a shell is traveling on a parabolic trajectory under the action of its weight force only, as in Fig. 6.6, then, for this single particle,

$$R_x = 0, \qquad R_y = -W, \qquad R_z = 0.$$

If, at a point on the path, the shell explodes into a large number of fragments, and if there is no air resistance, then, for the entire group of particles,

$$R_x = 0, \qquad R_y = -W, \qquad R_z = 0.$$

Equations (13.4) therefore indicate that the center of mass of the fragments continues on the same parabolic trajectory as the original shell.

As another example, if a sphere and a particle such as those in Fig. 6.12 exert gravitational forces upon each other but there are no external forces on the system, then Eqs. (13.4) require that $G$ have no acceleration. Hence, if $G$ is stationary and the particle is in orbital motion, $G$ must remain stationary, and this means that the sphere must be moving as well as the particle, since $G$ is always on the line joining the particle and the center of the sphere. In fact, both bodies orbit about $G$, the one with the larger mass having the smaller orbit. (In cases where the mass of the sphere is much greater than that of the particle, the orbit of the sphere may be negligibly small; this is assumed in Fig. 6.14.)

To generalize the moment equations for a system of particles to the case where the particles are not in equilibrium in a manner similar to that used in the foregoing discussion of the force equations, note that, by Varignon's theorem,

$$\mathbf{T}_i = \mathbf{r}_i \times \mathbf{R}_i, \qquad (13.5)$$

where $\mathbf{T}_i$ is the total moment of all the forces on the $i$th particle and $\mathbf{r}_i$ is the position vector of the $i$th particle. By Eq. (13.1), therefore,

$$\mathbf{T}_i = m_i(\mathbf{r}_i \times \mathbf{a}_i), \qquad (13.6)$$

and, by Eq. (11.11),

$$\mathbf{T} = m_1(\mathbf{r}_1 \times \mathbf{a}_1) + m_2(\mathbf{r}_2 \times \mathbf{a}_2) + \cdots + m_n(\mathbf{r}_n \times \mathbf{a}_n). \qquad (13.7)$$

Finally, by Eq. (11.14), $\mathbf{T}$ need include only the moments of the external forces on the system. Because of the presence of the $\mathbf{r}_i$, which are functions of time, in Eq. (13.7), the equation cannot be further simplified by the method used for Eq. (13.2). The equation can, however, be written in terms of cartesian components as follows:

$$T_x = \sum_{i=1}^{n} m_i(y_i\ddot{z}_i - z_i\ddot{y}_i),$$

$$T_y = \sum_{i=1}^{n} m_i(z_i\ddot{x}_i - x_i\ddot{z}_i), \qquad (13.8)$$

$$T_z = \sum_{i=1}^{n} m_i(x_i\ddot{y}_i - y_i\ddot{x}_i).$$

**13.2 Equations of motion for a rigid body in plane motion.** For a rigid body such as that shown in Fig. 13.1, Eqs. (13.3) and (13.4) apply without any change, and Eqs. (13.4) may be restated in terms of the external forces $\mathbf{F}_i$ as follows:

$$\sum F_x = m\ddot{x}_G,$$

$$\sum F_y = m\ddot{y}_G, \qquad (13.9)$$

$$\sum F_z = m\ddot{z}_G.$$

If the body is in translation, the subscript $G$ in Eqs. (13.9) is superfluous and may be dropped, resulting in Eqs. (6.7). The moment equations, Eqs. (13.8), may be adapted to the rigid body of Fig. 13.1 by treating the elemental portion $dV$ of the body as a particle of mass $dm$, where, letting $\mu(x, y, z)$ be the density,

$$dm = \mu(x, y, z)\, dV.$$

The components of $\mathbf{T}$ are expressed in terms of the moments of the external forces $\mathbf{F}_i$, and the summations are replaced by integrals over the volume $V$. Then, using Eqs. (8.11), the moment equations become:

$$\sum M_x = \iiint\limits_{V} [y\ddot{z}(x, y, z) - z\ddot{y}(x, y, z)]\mu(x, y, z)\, dV,$$

$$\sum M_y = \iiint\limits_{V} [z\ddot{x}(x, y, z) - x\ddot{z}(x, y, z)]\mu(x, y, z)\, dV,$$

$$\sum M_z = \iiint\limits_{V} [x\ddot{y}(x, y, z) - y\ddot{x}(x, y, z)]\mu(x, y, z)\, dV.$$

More generality is achieved by writing similar equations for moments about translating axes with origin at an arbitrary reference point $A$ in the

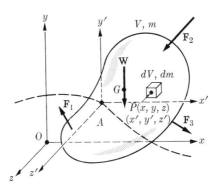

FIGURE 13.1

body, i.e., about the primed axes in Fig. 13.1, in which case the equations are:

$$\sum M_x^A = \iiint\limits_V [(y - y_A)\ddot{z} - (z - z_A)\ddot{y}]\mu\, dV,$$

$$\sum M_y^A = \iiint\limits_V [(z - z_A)\ddot{x} - (x - x_A)\ddot{z}]\mu\, dV,$$

$$\sum M_z^A = \iiint\limits_V [(x - x_A)\ddot{y} - (y - y_A)\ddot{x}]\mu\, dV.$$

Considering only the case of plane motion, Eqs. (13.9) become

$$\sum F_x = m\ddot{x}_G, \qquad \sum F_y = m\ddot{y}_G, \qquad \sum F_z = 0, \qquad (13.10)$$

and the three moment equations reduce to the following:

$$\sum M_x^A = \iiint\limits_V -(z - z_A)\ddot{y}\mu\, dV,$$

$$\sum M_y^A = \iiint\limits_V (z - z_A)\ddot{x}\mu\, dV, \qquad (13.11)$$

$$\sum M_z^A = \iiint\limits_V [(x - x_A)\ddot{y} - (y - y_A)\ddot{x}]\mu\, dV.$$

The way in which $\ddot{x}$ and $\ddot{y}$ vary throughout the body is known from Eqs. (12.21), i.e.,

$$\ddot{x} = \ddot{x}_A - \omega_z^2(x - x_A) - \alpha_z(y - y_A),$$

$$\ddot{y} = \ddot{y}_A - \omega_z^2(y - y_A) + \alpha_z(x - x_A).$$

Substituting these equations into Eqs. (13.11),

$$\sum M_x^A = -\ddot{y}_A \iiint_V (z - z_A)\mu\, dV + \omega_z^2 \iiint_V (y - y_A)(z - z_A)\mu\, dV$$
$$- \alpha_z \iiint_V (z - z_A)(x - x_A)\mu\, dV,$$

$$\sum M_y^A = \ddot{x}_A \iiint_V (z - z_A)\mu\, dV - \omega_z^2 \iiint_V (z - z_A)(x - x_A)\mu\, dV$$
$$- \alpha_z \iiint_V (y - y_A)(z - z_A)\mu\, dV,$$

$$\sum M_z^A = \ddot{y}_A \iiint_V (x - x_A)\mu\, dV - \ddot{x}_A \iiint_V (y - y_A)\mu\, dV$$
$$+ \alpha_z \iiint_V [(x - x_A)^2 + (y - y_A)^2]\mu\, dV.$$

The integrals in these equations are the first and second moments of the mass of the body, quantities discussed in Chapters 9 and 10, with respect to the coordinate planes and axes through $A$. For example,

$$\iiint_V (z - z_A)\mu\, dV$$

is the first moment of the mass with respect to the $x'y'$-plane and can be written as

$$(z_G - z_A)m.$$

Similarly,

$$\iiint_V (y - y_A)(z - z_A)\mu\, dV$$

is the product of inertia of the mass with respect to the $x'$-axis, a quantity which can be found when the shape and density distribution of the body and the location of $A$ are known. Using notation mentioned in Chapter 10, the moment equations become

$$\sum M_x^A = -m\ddot{y}_A(z_G - z_A) + I_{yz}^A \omega_z^2 - I_{zx}^A \alpha_z,$$
$$\sum M_y^A = m\ddot{x}_A(z_G - z_A) - I_{zx}^A \omega_z^2 - I_{yz}^A \alpha_z, \qquad (13.12)$$
$$\sum M_z^A = m\ddot{y}_A(x_G - x_A) - m\ddot{x}_A(y_G - y_A) + I_z^A \alpha_z.$$

Equations (13.10) and (13.12) are called the *equations of motion of a rigid body in plane motion*. As the body moves, the forces contributing to the left-hand sides of the equations of motion will be changing in various ways with time, making the left-hand sides, in general, functions of time. Con-

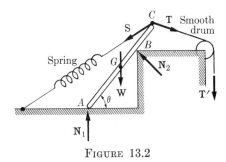

FIGURE 13.2

sider, for example, the forces on the slender rod of Fig. 13.2 as it moves so as to remain in contact with smooth supports at $A$ and $B$. Let $\mathbf{T}'$ be a force with constant magnitude, in which case $\mathbf{T}$ is also. As $\theta$ changes, $\mathbf{W}$ does not change in either magnitude or direction, $\mathbf{N}_1$ changes in magnitude but not in direction, $\mathbf{T}$ changes in direction but not in magnitude, and $\mathbf{N}_2$ and $\mathbf{S}$ change in both magnitude and direction. All five of the foregoing forces have changing lines of action, whereas, if the contact at $A$ were rough, the friction force $\mathbf{F}_1$ there would have a varying magnitude but constant direction and line of action. As for points of application, $\mathbf{N}_2$ has a fixed point of application in space, while $\mathbf{W}$, $\mathbf{N}_1$, $\mathbf{T}$, and $\mathbf{S}$ have fixed points of application in the body. Even though the equations of motion apply to a body such as $ABC$ at all times, they are written in many problems only for a particular configuration, i.e., at a particular instant.

Returning to the general body of Fig. 13.1, it is clear that at any instant the equations of motion are not affected by the actual position of the forces along their lines of action, and hence the principle of transmissibility holds even for a rigid body in motion.

If the $x'y'$-plane is a plane of symmetry of shape and density distribution, then, from Art. 9.5, it contains $G$, that is,

$$z_A = z_G,$$

and, from Art. 10.5,

$$I_{yz}^A = I_{zx}^A = 0.$$

This condition therefore gives the following simplified equations of motion:

$$\sum F_x = m\ddot{x}_G, \qquad \sum F_y = m\ddot{y}_G, \qquad \sum F_z = 0,$$

$$\sum M_x^A = 0, \qquad \sum M_y^A = 0, \qquad (13.13)$$

$$\sum M_z^A = m\ddot{y}_A(x_G - x_A) - m\ddot{x}_A(y_G - y_A) + I_z^A \alpha_z.$$

If, in addition, all the forces lie in the $x'y'$-plane, the third, fourth, and

fifth of Eqs. (13.13) are satisfied identically, leaving the following three
equations of motion which can be used to find unknowns:

$$\Sigma F_x = m\ddot{x}_G, \qquad \Sigma F_y = m\ddot{y}_G,$$

$$\Sigma M_z^A = m\ddot{y}_A(x_G - x_A) - m\ddot{x}_A(y_G - y_A) + I_z^A \alpha_z. \tag{13.14}$$

In many problems, it is convenient to take $G$ as the reference point $A$,
in which case the last of Eqs. (13.14) reduces to

$$\Sigma M_z^G = I_z^G \alpha_z. \tag{13.15}$$

If a body initially at rest is subjected to a force system which is mechanically equivalent to a null force-couple system at any point, it is shown in
Art. 11.7 that the body remains in equilibrium. This can also be shown,
for a plane force system, by Eqs. (13.14) and (13.15), which prove that the
conditions

$$\Sigma F_x = 0, \qquad \Sigma F_y = 0, \qquad \Sigma M_z^G = 0$$

are a set of sufficient conditions for

$$\ddot{x}_G = 0, \qquad \ddot{y}_G = 0, \qquad \alpha_z = 0.$$

Hence, if $\dot{x}_G$, $\dot{y}_G$, and $\omega_z$ are zero initially, then they must remain zero. If,
on the other hand, they have initial values $\dot{x}_{G0}$, $\dot{y}_{G0}$, $\omega_{z0}$, then, at all later
times,

$$\dot{x}_G = \dot{x}_{G0}, \qquad \dot{y}_G = \dot{y}_{G0}, \qquad \omega_z = \omega_{z0}. \tag{13.16}$$

Equations (13.16) represent a type of motion which is possible even when
the external force system reduces to a null force-couple system at any
point. When $\omega_{z0} = 0$, the motion is rectilinear translation with constant
speed, a state of equilibrium. When $\omega_{z0} \neq 0$, however, the motion is a
type which is not a state of equilibrium. An example of the latter is pure
rotation about a $z$-axis through $G$ (in which case $\dot{x}_{G0} = \dot{y}_{G0} = 0$) at constant angular speed.

**13.3 Translation.** For a rigid body in plane translation, the three equations of motion can be written in the following form:

$$\Sigma F_x = m\ddot{x}_G, \qquad \Sigma F_y = m\ddot{y}_G, \qquad \Sigma M_z^G = 0. \tag{13.17}$$

It must be emphasized that the right-hand side of the moment equation is
zero only if $G$ is used as the reference point.

If the translation is rectilinear, it is usually convenient to take the $x$-
axis parallel to the direction of motion. If the translation is curvilinear,
it is often desirable to express the force equations in terms of polar components instead of rectangular.

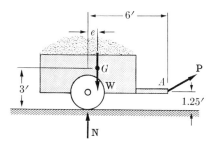

FIGURE 13.3

EXAMPLE 13.1. The trailer pictured in Fig. 13.3 is loaded so that the center of mass of the trailer and load is forward of the wheels. The trailer is towed by means of a hitch at $A$ which can exert a force with horizontal and vertical components on the trailer, and the mass of the wheels may be neglected. (a) Find $P_y$ in terms of $e$ and the weight $W$ and acceleration $a_x$ of the trailer and load. (b) If $a_x = 10$ ft/sec$^2$, determine the value of $e$ necessary to make $P_y = 0$. (c) With this value of $e$, what is $P_y$ when $a_x = -10$ ft/sec$^2$ and $W = 2000$ lb?

*Solution.* Figure 13.3 shows all the external forces acting on the trailer and hence can be used as a free-body diagram. The trailer is idealized as a rigid body.

(a) By Eqs. (13.17),

$$\sum F_x = P_x = \frac{W}{g} a_x,$$

$$\sum F_y = N + P_y - W = 0,$$

$$\sum M_z^G = eN - (6 - e)P_y - 1.75 P_x = 0.$$

Treating $e$, $W$, and $a_x$ as known quantities, we may regard these equations as three equations on the three unknowns $P_x$, $P_y$, and $N$. Substituting $P_x$ and $N$ (in terms of $P_y$) from the first two equations into the third, the required expression for $P_y$ is obtained, i.e.,

$$P_y = \frac{W}{6}\left(e - 1.75\frac{a_x}{g}\right).$$

(b) From the last equation, $P_y = 0$ when

$$e = 1.75\frac{a_x}{g}.$$

If $a_x = 10$ ft/sec$^2$,

$$e = 1.75\frac{10}{32.2} = 0.543 \text{ ft.}$$

(c) The equation for $P_y$ holds for either positive or negative $a_x$, so that, when $a_x = -10$ ft/sec$^2$ and $W = 2000$ lb,

$$P_y = \frac{2000}{6}\left(0.543 + 1.75\frac{10}{32.2}\right) = 362 \text{ lb.}$$

**13.4 Rotation.** Figure 13.4 shows a rigid body which is rotating about a fixed axis through $O$ (the $z$-axis). It is assumed that the $xy$-plane is a plane of symmetry and contains all the external forces. For this type of motion, Eq. (13.3) may be expressed in terms of cartesian components as in Eqs. (13.10) or, as is usually more convenient, in polar components parallel and perpendicular to the line $OG$. Using the latter representation, it follows from an application of Eqs. (12.16) to point $G$ that

$$\sum F_\rho = -m\rho_G\omega_z^2, \qquad \sum F_\theta = m\rho_G\alpha_z. \tag{13.18}$$

The simplified moment equation, Eq. (13.15), may be used as the third equation for this class of problems, but it is usually more convenient to take moments about the actual $z$-axis, in which case the third of Eqs. (13.14) reduces to the following:

$$\sum M_z = I_z\alpha_z. \tag{13.19}$$

Equation (13.19) shows that $I_z$ is a measure of the tendency of the body to resist changes in its angular velocity, i.e., is a measure of the rotational inertia. For example, a body with a large $I_z$ requires a large unbalanced moment about the $z$-axis to produce a given $\alpha_z$.

In many rotation problems, $G$ lies on the axis of rotation; in that event, the right-hand sides of Eqs. (13.18) are zero.

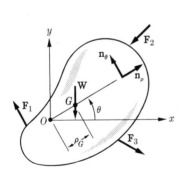

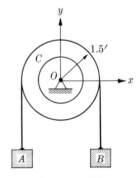

FIGURE 13.4                              FIGURE 13.5

EXAMPLE 13.2.   The blocks $A$ and $B$ shown in Fig. 13.5 weigh 966 lb and 644 lb, respectively, and they are connected together by an inextensible rope running over a symmetrical pulley $C$ which weighs 322 lb and has a radius of gyration $k_z$ of 1.25 ft. The friction between rope and pulley is sufficient to prevent any slipping of the rope on the pulley. (a) Find the angular acceleration of the pulley. (b) If the system is released from rest, how long does it take the lighter block to rise 10 ft?

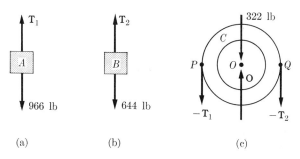

FIGURE 13.6

*Solution.* This example illustrates the analysis of a system containing several rigid bodies. (The two blocks are in rectilinear motion.) To avoid considering the complicated motion of the mass center of the system as a whole, it is necessary to isolate each body separately, using the free-body diagrams of Fig. 13.6.

(a) For body $A$,

$$\sum F_y = T_1 - 966 = \frac{966}{32.2} \ddot{y}_A;$$

for body $B$,

$$\sum F_y = T_2 - 644 = \frac{644}{32.2} \ddot{y}_B;$$

and, for body $C$,

$$\sum M_z = 1.5(T_1 - T_2) = \frac{322}{32.2} (1.25)^2 \alpha_z.$$

These three equations contain five unknowns, but there are kinematical relations between $\ddot{y}_A$, $\ddot{y}_B$, and $\alpha_z$. Utilizing points $P$ and $Q$ in Fig. 13.6(c),

$$\ddot{y}_A = -1.5\alpha_z, \qquad \ddot{y}_B = 1.5\alpha_z,$$

and, substituting these relations into the equations of motion,

$$T_1 - 966 = -45\alpha_z, \qquad T_2 - 644 = 30\alpha_z, \qquad 1.5(T_1 - T_2) = 15.62\alpha_z.$$

Solving for $\alpha_z$,

$$\alpha_z = 3.77 \text{ rad/sec}^2.$$

(b) From part (a),

$$\ddot{y}_B = 1.5\alpha_z = 1.5(3.77) = 5.65 \text{ ft/sec}^2.$$

Hence,

$$\dot{y}_B = 5.65t, \qquad y_B = 2.83t^2 + y_{B0}.$$

When $y_B - y_{B0} = 10$ ft,

$$t = \sqrt{10/2.83} = 1.88 \text{ sec}.$$

For a rigid body which rotates about a fixed axis through some point $O$ not coincident with $G$, a comparison of Eqs. (13.15) and (13.19) shows that the right-hand side of the moment equation changes as the reference point is changed. There is one point $P$ on the line $OG$ for which

$$\sum M_z^P = 0. \tag{13.20}$$

To locate $P$, consider Fig. 13.7, which shows the force-couple system at $O$ to which all the external forces (including any reactions at $O$) are mechanically equivalent. By Eq. (13.20),

$$C_z - \rho_P R_\theta = 0,$$

and, by Eqs. (13.18) and (13.19),

$$R_\theta = m\rho_G \alpha_z, \qquad C_z = I_z \alpha_z.$$

Substituting these two equations into the preceding equation,

$$I_z \alpha_z - \rho_P m\rho_G \alpha_z = 0,$$

and thus

$$\rho_P = \frac{I_z}{m\rho_G}. \tag{13.21}$$

By the parallel-axis theorem,

$$I_z = I_z^G + m\rho_G^2,$$

so that

$$\rho_P = \rho_G + \frac{I_z^G}{m\rho_G}. \tag{13.22}$$

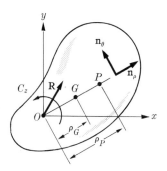

FIGURE 13.7

Equation (13.22) shows that $\rho_P$ is always greater than $\rho_G$.

An important property of the point $P$ is the following: If the body is supported on a smooth shaft at $O$ and if there is only one applied force and that force has a line of action through $P$, then the reactive force at $O$ is always along the line $OG$, regardless of the magnitude or direction of the applied force. This property follows from Eq. (13.20), and, because of it, $P$ is called the *center of percussion* of the body. Note that its location depends on the point of support $O$. As $O$ is moved toward $G$, so that $\rho_G$ approaches zero, Eq. (13.22) shows that $\rho_P$ approaches infinity. It can also be shown by Eq. (13.22) that, if $P$ is the center of percussion associated with a point of support $O$, then $O$ is the center of percussion associated with $P$.

**13.5 General plane motion.** A symmetrical body in general plane motion behaves in accordance with Eqs. (13.14). In solving problems, Eq. (13.15) is frequently used instead of the third of Eqs. (13.14).

If a body in plane motion is moving so as to remain in contact with a rough, fixed surface, as shown in Fig. 13.8, there are the following three possibilities:

(1) The body is rolling without slipping. This is a type of motion, defined in Art. 12.4, in which the particle at the point of contact is stationary. Hence, the law of static friction (Art. 4.5) applies, i.e.,

$$F \leq \mu_s N,$$

where $\mu_s$ is the coefficient of static friction.

(2) The body is at "impending slipping." In this case, the particle at the point of contact is still the instantaneous center of null velocity, but

$$F = \mu_s N.$$

(3) The body is slipping. The particle at the point of contact is in motion, $F$ is opposite the direction of motion of the particle, and

$$F = \mu_k N,$$

where $\mu_k$ is the coefficient of kinetic friction.

The friction in the first two of these three situations is generally referred to as *rolling friction*. But there is another phenomenon associated with a rolling body called *rolling resistance*. For an explanation of this, consider a wheel of weight $W$ rolling freely to the right (without slipping) on a rough, horizontal plane. The free-body diagram of Fig. 13.9 shows

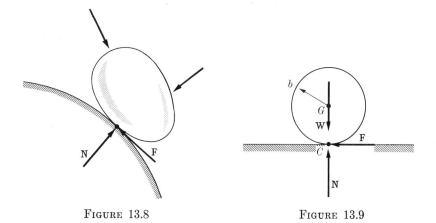

FIGURE 13.8                    FIGURE 13.9

all the external forces. The equations of motion in this case are the following:

$$\sum F_x = -F = \frac{W}{g}\ddot{x}_G, \quad \sum F_y = N - W = 0, \quad \sum M_z^G = -bF = I_z^G\alpha_z,$$

and, eliminating $F$ from the first and third equations,

$$\frac{bW}{g}\ddot{x}_G = I_z^G\alpha_z.$$

Applying the first of Eqs. (12.21) to $C$ and $G$, and noting by Eq. (12.25) that $\ddot{x}_C = 0$, it can be concluded that

$$\ddot{x}_G = -b\alpha_z.$$

Eliminating $\alpha_z$ from the two relations between $\ddot{x}_G$ and $\alpha_z$,

$$\ddot{x}_G\left(\frac{1}{b} + \frac{bW}{gI_z^G}\right) = 0.$$

Since the expression in parentheses cannot be zero, it follows that

$$\ddot{x}_G = 0$$

and therefore that $F = 0$ (by the first equation of motion) and $\dot{x}_G$ is constant (by integration). The theory therefore leads to the conclusions that there is no tendency for the wheel to slip and that, even though the plane is rough, the wheel continues to roll at a constant speed. In reality the wheel is observed to slow down, an occurrence which is due to the rolling resistance accompanying small deformations of the wheel and the plane surface at the point of contact. (The idealization of rigidity in the elementary theory of rolling excludes rolling resistance from the analysis.) Figure 13.10 shows on an exaggerated scale how deformations result in a surface of contact rather than a point. The distributed force transmitted across the surface is equivalent to a reaction $\mathbf{Q}$ capable of decreasing both the angular speed of the body and the linear speed of point $G$. Henceforth, rolling resistance is neglected in this book.

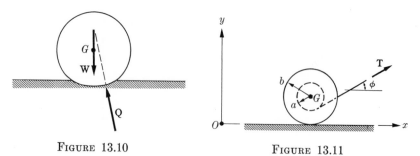

FIGURE 13.10                    FIGURE 13.11

EXAMPLE 13.3.  The spool in Fig. 13.11 moves on a plane under the action of a force **T** applied to a string wrapped around the inner cylinder, and the angle $\phi$ is kept constant during the motion.  Investigate the effect of $T$ and $\phi$ on the acceleration of point $G$ and the angular acceleration of the spool.

*Solution.*  Figure 13.12 shows a free-body diagram of the spool.  The equations of motion, which apply whether or not there is slipping, are the following:

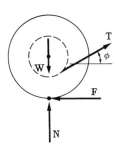

$$\sum F_x = T \cos \phi - F = \frac{W}{g} \ddot{x}_G,$$

$$\sum F_y = N + T \sin \phi - W = 0,$$

$$\sum M_z^G = aT - bF = I_z^G \alpha_z.$$

When we treat $W$, $T$, and $\phi$ as known quantities, these are three equations on the four unknowns $N$, $F$, $\ddot{x}_G$, and $\alpha_z$.

FIGURE 13.12

For any combination of circumstances which produces rolling without slipping, the fourth equation is a kinematical relation mentioned previously, namely,

$$\ddot{x}_G = -b\alpha_z.$$

Solving the four equations in four unknowns,

$$\ddot{x}_G = \frac{bT(b \cos \phi - a)}{(W/g)b^2 + I_z^G},$$

$$\alpha_z = - \frac{T(b \cos \phi - a)}{(W/g)b^2 + I_z^G},$$

$$N = W - T \sin \phi,$$

$$F = T \left[ \frac{(W/g)ab + I_z^G \cos \phi}{(W/g)b^2 + I_z^G} \right].$$

The criterion for rolling without slipping is

$$\frac{F}{N} = \frac{T}{W - T \sin \phi} \left[ \frac{(W/g)ab + I_z^G \cos \phi}{(W/g)b^2 + I_z^G} \right] \le \mu_s,$$

and, in numerical problems of this type, it is usually necessary to assume rolling without slipping and to check the assumption after $F$ and $N$ are found (unless there are constraints on the body which dictate that it is slipping).

The equations for $\ddot{x}_G$ and $\alpha_z$ resulting from the foregoing analysis indicate that the spool can sustain a force **T** and still remain stationary (or travel in such a way that $\dot{x}_G$ and $\omega_z$ are constant) only if

$$\cos \phi = a/b.$$

This is the case (illustrated in Fig. 13.13) where $\mathbf{T}$ intersects the point of contact. (The magnitude of $\mathbf{T}$ must be small enough so that the criterion for no slipping is satisfied.) If $\cos \phi > a/b$, then $\ddot{x}_G$ is positive and the spool accelerates to the right. If $\cos \phi < a/b$, the acceleration is to the left.

If the combination of $T$ and $\phi$ is such that the criterion for no slipping is violated, the results of the foregoing analysis are invalid. Instead of the kinematical equation, the fourth equation is the friction equation

$$F = \mu_k N.$$

Solving the set of equations composed of this one and the three equations of motion,

$$\ddot{x}_G = \frac{g}{W} [T \cos \phi - \mu_k(W - T \sin \phi)],$$

$$\alpha_z = \frac{aT - \mu_k b(W - T \sin \phi)}{I_z^G},$$

$$N = W - T \sin \phi,$$

$$F = \mu_k(W - T \sin \phi).$$

By the proper combinations of $T$ and $\phi$, either $\ddot{x}_G$ or $\alpha_z$ may be made zero. These situations include, respectively, pure rotation and pure translation.

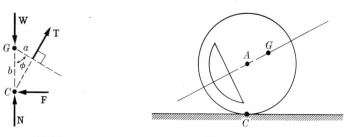

FIGURE 13.13                    FIGURE 13.14

In some plane-motion problems it is convenient to take moments about the instantaneous center $C$. If, for example, the body of Fig. 13.9 is rolling without slipping, then

$$x_G - x_C = 0 \quad \text{and} \quad \ddot{x}_C = 0,$$

so that the third of Eqs. (13.14) reduces to

$$\sum M_z^C = I_z^C \alpha_z. \tag{13.23}$$

If, on the other hand, the body of Fig. 13.14 is rolling without slipping, then

$$x_G - x_C \neq 0,$$

and Eq. (13.23) is not valid.

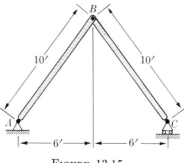

FIGURE 13.15

Multiple-body plane-motion problems are solved by writing the equations of motion for each body separately, as illustrated in the following example.

EXAMPLE 13.4. The system of Fig. 13.15 is released from rest in the position shown. If bars $AB$ and $BC$ are homogeneous and weigh 100 lb each, write enough equations to find the reactions at $A$ and $C$ immediately after release.

*Solution.* Figures 13.16(a) and (b) show the free-body diagrams of bars $AB$ and $BC$, respectively. For the former,

$$\sum F_x = A_x + B_x = \frac{100}{g}\ddot{x}_G,$$

$$\sum F_y = A_y + B_y - 100 = \frac{100}{g}\ddot{y}_G,$$

$$\sum M_z^G = 4A_x - 3A_y - 4B_x + 3B_y = \frac{1}{12}\frac{100}{g}(100)\alpha_{AB},$$

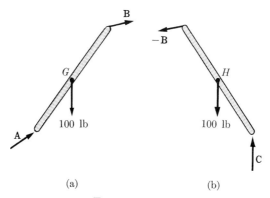

(a)                        (b)

FIGURE 13.16

and, for the latter,

$$\sum F_x = -B_x = \frac{100}{g}\ddot{x}_H,$$

$$\sum F_y = -B_y + C - 100 = \frac{100}{g}\ddot{y}_H,$$

$$\sum M_z^H = 3C + 3B_y + 4B_x = \frac{1}{12}\frac{100}{g}(100)\alpha_{BC}.$$

Thus, there are six equations of motion on the five unknown force components $A_x$, $A_y$, $B_x$, $B_y$, $C$ and the six kinematical unknowns $\ddot{x}_G$, $\ddot{y}_G$, $\alpha_{AB}$, $\ddot{x}_H$, $\ddot{y}_H$, $\alpha_{BC}$. In effect, then, five more equations relating the kinematical quantities are needed. Applying Eqs. (12.21) to points $A$ and $B$ and to points $B$ and $C$, we find that

$$\alpha_{BC} = -\alpha_{AB}.$$

Applying the same equations to $A$ and $G$,

$$\ddot{x}_G = -4\alpha_{AB}, \qquad \ddot{y}_G = 3\alpha_{AB},$$

and, to $B$ and $H$,

$$\ddot{x}_H = -12\alpha_{AB}, \qquad \ddot{y}_H = 3\alpha_{AB}.$$

The last five equations give five of the six kinematical quantities in terms of the remaining one, and substitution of these five equations into the six equations of motion leaves six equations in six unknowns.

## PROBLEMS

13.1 For a rigid body subjected to a plane, external force system such that

$$\sum F_x = 0, \qquad \sum F_y = 0, \qquad \sum M_z^G = 0,$$

it is shown in the text that the motion satisfies Eqs. (13.16). Applying Eqs. (12.21) to $G$ and any point $A$, show by the third of Eqs. (13.14) that, for this type of motion,

$$\sum M_z^A = 0.$$

13.2 The brakes of the automobile in Fig. 13.17 are arranged so that, during braking, the same friction force is exerted by the road on each of the four wheels as long as the wheels are rolling without slipping. If $\mu_s = 0.8$, $\mu_k = 0.5$, find the value of $k$ necessary to have all four wheels come to impending slipping simultaneously if the brakes are applied while the car is traveling forward. What is the acceleration of the car under these circumstances? Neglect the mass of the wheels and treat the car as a rigid body.

[*Ans.:* $k = 0.3$, $a_x = -25.8$ ft/sec².]

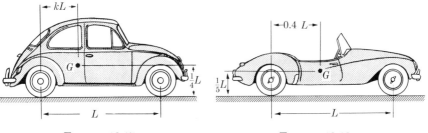

FIGURE 13.17           FIGURE 13.18

**13.3** The car in Fig. 13.18 is capable of bringing the driving wheels to impending slipping during forward motion. Assume that $\mu_s = 0.8$ and $\mu_k = 0.5$. Neglect the mass of the wheels and treat the car as a rigid body. (a) Find the maximum possible acceleration if the car has rear-wheel drive. (b) Find the maximum if the car has front-wheel drive. (c) Discuss the effect on these accelerations of lowering $G$ and of moving $G$ toward the front of the car.

**13.4** As shown in Fig. 13.19, a solid, homogeneous block of weight $W$ rests on a horizontal plane for which $\mu_s = \frac{3}{5}$, $\mu_k = \frac{2}{5}$. The magnitude of force **P** is increased gradually from zero. (a) Find the maximum $h$ for which slipping will precede overturning. (b) For this $h$, what is $P$ at impending motion? (c) For this $h$, what is the acceleration of the block immediately after slipping begins? (d) For this $h$, how great must $P$ become to cause overturning after slipping has begun?

[*Ans.:* (a) $\frac{5}{6}b$; (b) $\frac{3}{5}W$; (c) $\frac{1}{5}g$; (d) $\frac{9}{10}W$.]

**13.5** Blocks $A$ and $B$ in Fig. 13.20 weigh 50 lb and 30 lb, respectively, and they are connected together by an inextensible string running over an ideal pulley. If there is no friction, find the acceleration of block $B$.

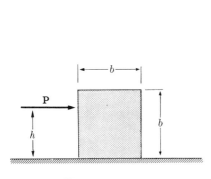

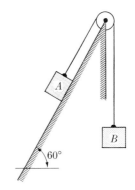

FIGURE 13.19           FIGURE 13.20

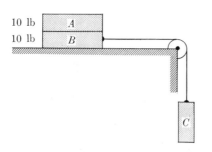

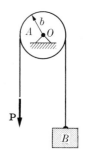

FIGURE 13.21                    FIGURE 13.22

13.6  For the system shown in Fig. 13.21, the pulley and string are ideal, while $\mu_s = 0.4$ and $\mu_k = 0.3$ at all contacts. Find the weight of $C$ necessary to cause impending slipping between blocks $A$ and $B$.

[Ans.: 23.3 lb.]

13.7  The 32.2-lb body $B$ in Fig. 13.22 is being raised by a force $P$ of 62.2-lb magnitude applied to a rope running over the solid, homogeneous cylinder $A$. The cylinder weighs 64.4 lb and rotates about a fixed axis through $O$. If there is no slipping between rope and cylinder, find the acceleration of $B$.

13.8  For each of the arrangements shown in Fig. 13.23, the pulley has a weight of 322 lb, a radius of gyration about its axis of rotation of 1.25 ft, and inner-hub and outer-hub radii of 1.00 ft and 1.50 ft, respectively. If block $B$ weighs 644 lb, find its acceleration in each case.

[Ans.: (a) 22.6 ft/sec$^2$ up; (b) 7.8 ft/sec$^2$ up; (c) 0.78 ft/sec$^2$ up.]

13.9  In Fig. 13.24, the drum $A$ is rotating freely about a fixed shaft in a clockwise direction and with an angular speed of 955 rpm. Brake $B$ is hinged to a plate $C$, which is fixed on the shaft. (a) If a force $P$ of 300-lb magnitude is applied to the brake as shown, find the number of revolutions executed by the drum before it comes to rest. (b) Solve the same problem with counterclockwise motion at 955 rpm. (c) Find the magnitude of $P$ required to stop the drum in 5 sec if it is rotating at 955 rpm clockwise.

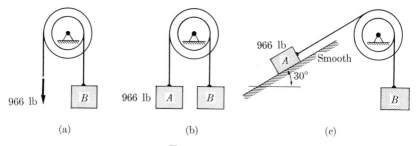

(a)                    (b)                    (c)

FIGURE 13.23

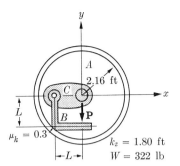

FIGURE 13.24

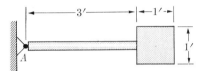

FIGURE 13.25

13.10 A symmetrical rigid body is composed of a 32.2-lb slender rod 3 ft long and a 96.6-lb solid cube with edges 1 ft long. (See Fig. 13.25.) If the body is released from rest in the position shown, determine the reaction at $A$ immediately after motion begins.

[*Ans.:* **A** = 13.6**j** lb.]

13.11 The small car shown in Fig. 13.26 is to be driven on the inside wall of a cylindrical tank of 32-ft radius. Find the minimum speed required if the coefficient of static friction is: (a) $\frac{3}{4}$, and (b) $\frac{5}{4}$. [*Hint:* From Eqs. (13.12), since the $xy$-plane is a plane of symmetry of the body,

$$\sum M_y^A = 0$$

for any point $A$ in the $xy$-plane. For each part of the problem, compute the minimum values of speed as controlled by both overturning and slipping, and specify the larger value.]

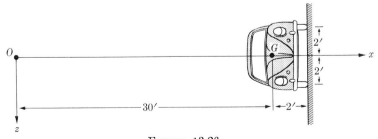

FIGURE 13.26

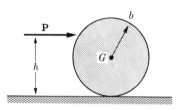

FIGURE 13.27            FIGURE 13.28

13.12 A solid, homogeneous cylinder (Fig. 13.27) rolls under the action of a horizontal force **P** on a plane for which $\mu_s = \frac{1}{4}$. (a) Assuming no slipping, find the magnitude $F$ of the friction force in terms of $h$, $b$, and $P$. (b) What value of $h$ is required to make $F = 0$?

$$\left[ Ans.: \text{ (a) } F = P \left| 1 - \frac{2h}{3b} \right| ; \text{ (b) } \tfrac{3}{2}b. \right]$$

13.13 A solid, homogeneous cylinder of weight $W$ and radius $b$ has a string wound around its middle. One end of the string is fixed as shown in Fig. 13.28. The cylinder is released from rest and falls vertically, unwinding the string. Find the tension in the string.

13.14 As in Fig. 13.29, a wheel of known weight $W$, known radius $b$, and known moment of inertia $I_z^G$ is released from rest on a rough plane having known inclination $\beta$. The coefficients of friction $\mu_s$ and $\mu_k$ are also known. Find the angular acceleration and the time it takes for $G$ to travel a distance $d$ down the plane if:

(a) $\dfrac{\tan \beta}{1 + (Wb^2/gI_z^G)} \leq \mu_s,$     (b) $\dfrac{\tan \beta}{1 + (Wb^2/gI_z^G)} > \mu_s.$

$$\left[ Ans.: \text{ (a) } \alpha_z = \frac{g}{b} \frac{\sin \beta}{1 + (gI_z^G/Wb^2)} ; \quad t = \sqrt{\frac{2d}{g} \left( \frac{1 + (gI_z^G/Wb^2)}{\sin \beta} \right)}. \right]$$

13.15 The solid, homogeneous cylinder $A$ in Fig. 13.30 weighs 644 lb and has a radius of 2 ft. The block $B$ weighs 322 lb, and the fixed pulley at $C$ is weightless and frictionless. Find the coefficient of static friction required such that the cylinder rolls without slipping.

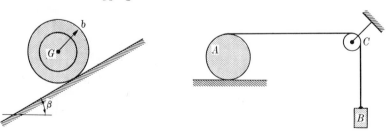

FIGURE 13.29            FIGURE 13.30

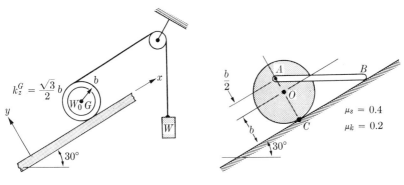

FIGURE 13.31             FIGURE 13.32

13.16 A wheel of weight $W_0$ rolls on an inclined track, as shown in Fig. 13.31. If

$$\ddot{x}_G = -\frac{g}{6},$$

find the weight $W$ of the block in terms of $W_0$. (Assume that $\mu_s$ is great enough to ensure rolling without slipping, and neglect the mass of the pulley.)

[*Ans.:* $W = \frac{5}{64}W_0$.]

13.17 For the system shown in Fig. 13.31,

$$W = \tfrac{1}{8}W_0.$$

Assuming that $\mu_s$ is great enough to ensure rolling without slipping and neglecting the mass of the pulley, find $\ddot{x}_G$.

13.18 The solid, homogeneous cylinder shown in Fig. 13.32 has a weight $W$. A horizontal rod with weight $W/2$ is pinned to each end of the cylinder and rests on the rough plane. If the system is released from rest, express in terms of $b$ and $g$ the angular acceleration of the cylinder immediately after motion begins.

$$\left[ Ans.:\ 0.301\,\frac{g}{b}\,. \right]$$

# Part 3
# MECHANICS OF
# DEFORMABLE BODIES

# CHAPTER 14

## STRESS AND STRAIN

**14.1 Introduction.** When a set of external forces which is mechanically equivalent to a null force-couple system at any point is slowly applied to a body at rest, the body is said to be a *deformable body* if it is unable to sustain the forces without some changes in size and shape. The branch of mechanics which deals with this type of body is called *mechanics of deformable bodies, mechanics of materials,* or *strength of materials.* The changes in size and shape are called the *deformations* of the body. The idealization of rigidity used in Part 2 of this book is permissible only when the deformations are small enough to be neglected. Unless the body ruptures when it is subjected to the loads, its "resistance" to them normally increases during the deformation until the body arrives at a state of equilibrium. This phenomenon is illustrated by the behavior of the spring in Fig. 11.6. If the same type of force system (often called an "equilibrium" system) is applied to the body suddenly, vibratory deformations occur, but these are found to diminish in amplitude until they become static deformations after a lapse of time. If the force system to which a deformable body is subjected is not an equilibrium system, the body undergoes accelerations as a whole which are accompanied by deformations.

As an aid in the study of deformable bodies, it is convenient to classify them according to the following scheme:

(1) One-dimensional or slender bodies
    (a) Straight bars
    (b) Curved bars
    (c) Completely flexible but not completely inextensible cables, a
        special case of (a) and (b)
(2) Two-dimensional or thin bodies
    (a) Plates
    (b) Shells
    (c) Completely flexible but not completely inextensible membranes,
        a special case of (a) and (b)
(3) Three-dimensional bodies

Generally speaking, the smaller the number of dimensions involved, the less complicated the analysis.

Many objects with which the engineer is concerned (e.g., ships, machines, bridges) either can be idealized as one-dimensional or two-dimensional bodies or can be imagined separated into parts for which the idealizations are suitable.

283

Being only an introduction to the subject of engineering mechanics, this book deals mainly with the simplest case, the straight bar. The further simplifying assumption that the bar is very "stiff" and hence that the forces cause only "small" changes in size and shape is also usually made.

An important part of the study of deformable bodies is the determination of *internal forces* in bodies, a subject introduced in the next article.

**14.2 Internal forces in a body.** Figure 14.1 shows a body in equilibrium in a deformed state under a set of $N$ external forces (some active and some reactive). The dashed outline represents the shape of the body in its undeformed state, i.e., before the loads are applied. Consider now an imaginary plane in the body which divides it into two parts, the plane being parallel to the $yz$ plane as in Fig. 14.1, and let each part be treated as a separate mechanical system. In the free-body diagram of Fig. 14.2(a), the left-hand portion of the body is shown, and the total surface-force system acting across the dividing plane from the right-hand portion to the left-hand portion is replaced by a mechanically equivalent force-couple system at the centroid of the area $A$. By applying Newton's Third Law

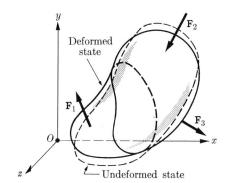

FIGURE 14.1

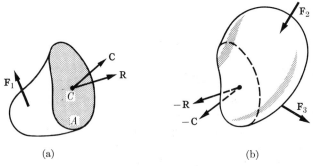

(a)                              (b)

FIGURE 14.2

to each pair of adjacent surface "particles" from the two portions of the body, we can show that the total surface-force system acting on the right-hand portion due to the left-hand portion is mechanically equivalent to a force-couple system composed of the negatives of the force and couple from the preceding system, as shown in Fig. 14.2(b). For a deformable body, it is impossible to replace a group of forces by their resultant (even if the forces are reducible to a single force) without altering their effect on the body. Thus, when we analyze such a body by separating it into parts as in Fig. 14.2, the forces acting on each part must be kept with that part. Similarly, distributed forces on the body cannot be replaced by equivalent forces and couples until *after* the body is subdivided, so that the weight force of each part of the body must be considered as acting at the center of gravity of that part.

Figure 14.3 shows the left-hand portion of the body with **R** and **C** resolved into components in the three coordinate directions. Since the force $R_x\mathbf{i}$ is perpendicular to the dividing plane, it is called the *normal force*, while $R_y\mathbf{j}$ and $R_z\mathbf{k}$ are called the *shear forces* or *shears*. The couple $C_x\mathbf{i}$ is called the *torsional couple* or *twisting moment* or *torque*, and $C_y\mathbf{j}$ and $C_z\mathbf{k}$ are called the *bending couples* or *bending moments* (the former name being more accurate, the latter more common).

Since the body as a whole is in equilibrium, any portion of it is also in equilibrium, and hence the portion of body of Fig. 14.3 is a system known to be in equilibrium. The six equations of equilibrium, being necessary conditions for equilibrium of any system, therefore hold, and they can be applied to the portion of body of Fig. 14.3 (or to the remaining part of the original body) to find the six "internal" force and couple components (provided that all the "external" forces on the portion being used are known). The procedure is demonstrated for various types of external force systems in subsequent chapters of this book.

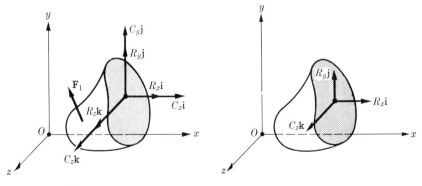

FIGURE 14.3                    FIGURE 14.4

Other kinds of dividing planes can be considered, e.g., planes perpendicular to the $y$- and $z$-axes or even planes with any orientation, in which case any one of the internal forces or couples (e.g., the normal force) has a different direction as well as a different magnitude.

In the special case where all the external forces lie in a plane parallel to the $xy$-plane (and any external couple vectors are perpendicular to the $xy$-plane), the internal force-couple system on a plane perpendicular to the $x$-axis reduces to the set of three elements shown in Fig. 14.4. In this case only three equations are used, namely the three equations of equilibrium in a plane.

By definition, a straight bar is a slender body for which a straight line exists in the body such that the line passes through the centroid of every dividing plane taken perpendicular to the line. The line is called the *centerline* and any one of the dividing planes is called a *cross section.* The bar may be tapered, but the taper cannot be so severe as to make the dimensions of the cross section become sizable in comparison with the length of the bar and thereby violate the assumption of slenderness.

Consider the case in which the bar has a longitudinal plane of symmetry and all the external forces are in this plane, and take the $xy$-plane as the plane of symmetry and the $x$-axis along the centerline as in Fig. 14.5. (This figure shows the bar separated into two parts by a typical cross section.) The $x$-axis is actually along the original centerline, the centerline no longer being straight after the deformations take place. Since the deformations are small, however, they are not shown in Fig. 14.5. If a bar is carrying loads with components perpendicular to the $x$-axis, as in Fig. 14.5, it is usually called a *beam.*

Instead of using $R_x$, $R_y$, and $C_z$ to describe the internal force system, it is desirable now to have three algebraic quantities whose signs depend not on whether the internal forces have same or opposite direction as the axes but rather on the physical effect of the internal forces on the bar. Therefore, let $N$ be a quantity with absolute value $|R_x|$ which is positive if tensile and negative if compressive. The scalar $N$ is commonly called the "normal force" or "axial force." Let $S$ be a quantity with absolute value $|R_y|$ which is positive if there is a force down on the left face of the

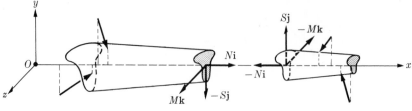

FIGURE 14.5

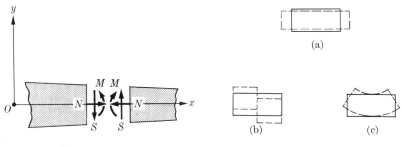

FIGURE 14.6          FIGURE 14.7

cut and up on the right, and negative otherwise. The scalar $S$ is called the "shear force" or "shear." Finally, let $M$ be a quantity with absolute value $|C_z|$ which is positive if associated with compression on the top and tension on the bottom, and negative otherwise. The scalar $M$ is called the "bending moment." The three quantities $N$, $S$, and $M$ are, in general, functions of $x$.

The internal system in Fig. 14.5 is one in which $N$, $S$, and $M$ are all positive. It is customary to show such a system as in Fig. 14.6. The dashed lines in Figs. 14.7(a), (b), and (c) show (greatly exaggerated) the kinds of deformation produced by positive $N$, $S$, and $M$, respectively, in a short piece of the bar.

If $\mathbf{R}$ and $\mathbf{C}$ are the force and couple on the surface of the left-hand portion of the body as previously, then the sign conventions established above for $N$, $S$, and $M$ lead to the following equations:

$$N = R_x, \qquad S = -R_y, \qquad M = C_z. \qquad (14.1)$$

The minus sign in the second equation follows an established custom on the definition of positive shear in a bar.

**14.3 Stress.** To define the *stresses* at a point $P$ in a body, select a plane through $P$ perpendicular to the $x$-axis as in Fig. 14.8 (which shows the left portion of the body isolated from the right portion). Consider a rectangular area $\Delta A$ enclosing $P$, and let that part of $\mathbf{R}$ which is transmitted across $\Delta A$ (from right to left) be called $\Delta \mathbf{R}$. By definition, the traction $\mathbf{T}$ across the plane $A$ at point $P$ is given by

$$\mathbf{T} = \lim_{\Delta A \to 0} \frac{\Delta \mathbf{R}}{\Delta A}. \qquad (14.2)$$

Since the portion of couple $\Delta \mathbf{C}$ acting on $\Delta A$ is due to variations of the distributed forces over $\Delta A$ while $\Delta \mathbf{R}$ is due to the distributed forces themselves, it is reasonable to assume that, as $\Delta A$ becomes smaller and the distributed forces over $\Delta A$ become more nearly uniform, $\Delta \mathbf{C}$ approaches

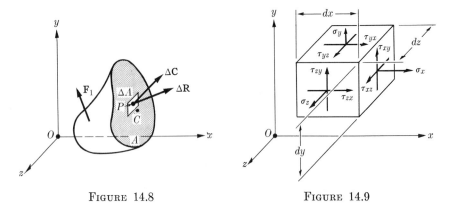

FIGURE 14.8                          FIGURE 14.9

a null vector more quickly than $\Delta\mathbf{R}$, and hence

$$\lim_{\Delta A \to 0} \frac{\Delta\mathbf{C}}{\Delta A} = \mathbf{0}. \qquad (14.3)$$

If the components of $\Delta\mathbf{R}$ are called $\Delta R_x$, $\Delta R_y$, $\Delta R_z$, then the components of $\mathbf{T}$, called the "stresses" on plane $A$ at point $P$ and designated by $\sigma_x$, $\tau_{xy}$, $\tau_{xz}$, are given by

$$\sigma_x = \lim_{\Delta A \to 0} \frac{\Delta R_x}{\Delta A}, \qquad \tau_{xy} = \lim_{\Delta A \to 0} \frac{\Delta R_y}{\Delta A}, \qquad \tau_{xz} = \lim_{\Delta A \to 0} \frac{\Delta R_z}{\Delta A}. \qquad (14.4)$$

These equations may be regarded as definitions of the stresses. The first stress, $\sigma_x$, is called the *normal stress* on plane $A$ at point $P$, while $\tau_{xy}$ and $\tau_{xz}$ are called the *shear stresses in the y- and z-directions*, respectively, on plane $A$ at point $P$. (The first subscript on these shear stresses identifies the plane through $P$ as a plane perpendicular to the $x$-axis, while the second identifies the "direction" of the particular stress. Similarly, the symbol $\sigma_{xx}$ is often used to designate the stress in the $x$-direction on the plane perpendicular to the $x$-axis, i.e., the normal stress. Thus, any stress depends on two selections, namely the orientation of the plane through $P$ and the direction of the stress once the plane is chosen.)

By convention, the three stresses defined by Eqs. (14.4) are positive if they are in the positive coordinate directions on the face of the cut shown in Fig. 14.8 (a face sometimes called a "positive" face because an outward unit vector normal to it is in the positive direction of an axis) and in the negative directions on the opposite face (called a "negative" face), and negative otherwise. An alternative way of stating this sign convention is to say that the stresses are positive when the components of $\Delta\mathbf{R}$ are positive, $\Delta\mathbf{R}$ being the force acting on the positive face as in Fig. 14.8. If $\sigma_x$ is positive, it is called a *tensile stress*, and, if negative, a *compressive stress*.

The units of $\sigma_x$, $\tau_{xy}$, and $\tau_{xz}$ are lb/in$^2$ (usually written psi). Since the values of the stresses in these units may be large numbers, it is sometimes convenient to employ a unit of force called a *kip* (for kilo-pound), which is 1000 lb, and to measure the stresses in kips/in$^2$ (or ksi).

Two other sets of three stresses similar to the set discussed above can be defined by taking planes through $P$ perpendicular to the $y$-axis (for $\sigma_y$, $\tau_{yz}$, $\tau_{yx}$) and perpendicular to the $z$-axis (for $\sigma_z$, $\tau_{zx}$, $\tau_{zy}$). In general, all nine stresses vary from point to point in the body (and are therefore functions of $x$, $y$, $z$) for a given set of external forces. Figure 14.9 shows a small rectangular parallelepiped obtained by taking three pairs of planes which are parallel to the coordinate planes and which enclose a point $P$. Since the element is small, the planes are very close to $P$, and it can be assumed that the stresses acting on the faces of the parallelepiped are essentially the stresses at point $P$. Also, the stresses may be assumed constant over the faces, so that it is necessary only to multiply each stress by the area on which it acts to find the corresponding force. More precisely, the nine stresses may be considered average values of the actual stresses over the faces of the element. In the limit as the dimensions of the element approach zero, the average stresses on the faces approach the exact stresses at point $P$. (This is not true if $P$ is a point on the surface of the body where there is a concentrated force, since the stresses then tend to approach infinity. In actuality, all surface forces must be applied over a finite region of the surface, so that the stresses are finite, but the elementary methods of finding stresses make no attempt to evaluate the stresses near a "concentrated" force.) All three visible faces in Fig. 14.9 are positive faces, and all nine of the stresses are shown as positive. (The arrows give the directions of the stresses, and there are three invisible faces with stresses having opposite directions from those shown.)

The weight force of the element of Fig. 14.9 has a negligible magnitude in comparison with any one of the surface forces transmitted through the faces, the former being of the order of a small length cubed and the latter of a small length squared, and hence the weight force may be omitted when studying the stresses at a point (although the weight force is important in a study of the *changes* in the stresses from point to point).

If the element of Fig. 14.9 is part of a body in equilibrium, then it too is in equilibrium. The three force equations of equilibrium are automatically satisfied because all forces cancel out in pairs. Calling the one invisible corner of the rectangular parallelepiped $A$, we write the three moment equations as follows:

$$\sum M_x^A = dz(\tau_{zy}\, dx\, dy) - dy(\tau_{yz}\, dz\, dx) = 0,$$

$$\sum M_y^A = dx(\tau_{xz}\, dy\, dz) - dz(\tau_{zx}\, dx\, dy) = 0,$$

$$\sum M_z^A = dy(\tau_{yx}\, dz\, dx) - dx(\tau_{xy}\, dy\, dz) = 0,$$

the moments due to all the other forces canceling out in pairs.  Hence,

$$\tau_{zy} = \tau_{yz}, \qquad \tau_{xz} = \tau_{zx}, \qquad \tau_{yx} = \tau_{xy}. \tag{14.5}$$

Equations (14.5) hold at every point in a body in equilibrium, and they can be established by a more rigorous procedure than that used in the foregoing discussion.  It is clear now that there are only six independent stresses at a point, namely, $\sigma_x, \sigma_y, \sigma_z, \tau_{yz}, \tau_{zx}, \tau_{xy}$.  If all six of these are not zero at a point, a *state of stress* is said to exist at the point.  It can be shown that, once the six stresses are given at a point, the stresses on any plane through the point can be found, and a set of values for the six stresses is therefore said to constitute a complete specification of the state of stress at the point.

**14.4 Strain.**  To define the *strains* at a point $P$ in a body, imagine a small element of the body having dimensions $\Delta x$, $\Delta y$, $\Delta z$ to enclose the point $P$ when the body is in its unstressed state.  (See Fig. 14.10.)  If, during the application of the loads, the dimension $\Delta x$ measured through point $P$ changes an amount $\Delta (\Delta x)$ (Fig. 14.11), then, by definition, the *normal strain* $\epsilon_x$ in the $x$-direction is given by

$$\epsilon_x = \lim_{\Delta x \to 0} \frac{\Delta (\Delta x)}{\Delta x}, \tag{14.6}$$

the strain being positive if the change in length is an increase and negative if a decrease.  If, during the application of the loads, that rectangular cross section (of the parallelepiped) parallel to the $xy$-plane and containing point $P$ is distorted as in Fig. 14.12, then, by definition, the *shear strain* parallel to the $xy$-plane is given by

$$\gamma_{xy} = \lim_{\substack{\Delta x \to 0 \\ \Delta y \to 0}} (\tan \alpha_1 + \tan \beta_1), \tag{14.7}$$

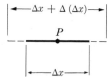

FIGURE 14.11

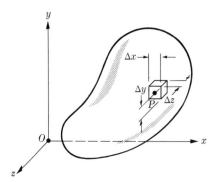

FIGURE 14.10

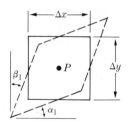

FIGURE 14.12

the strain being positive if the angle between the two positive faces of
the element decreases and negative otherwise. For small deformations,
the angles $\alpha_1$ and $\beta_1$ are small, in which case

$$\gamma_{xy} = \lim_{\substack{\Delta x \to 0 \\ \Delta y \to 0}} (\alpha_1 + \beta_1). \tag{14.8}$$

The shear strain $\gamma_{xy}$, which measures the distortion of the element, can
thus be expressed in terms of the sum $\alpha_1 + \beta_1$ as in Eq. (14.8). Another
quantity, $\zeta_{xy}$, which measures the "rotation" of the element, is defined
in terms of the difference $\alpha_1 - \beta_1$, that is,

$$\zeta_{xy} = \lim_{\substack{\Delta x \to 0 \\ \Delta y \to 0}} (\alpha_1 - \beta_1).$$

If $\alpha_1 = \beta_1$, then the element is said to be distorted without rotation.

Two other normal strains, $\epsilon_y$ and $\epsilon_z$, and two other shear strains, $\gamma_{yz}$
and $\gamma_{zx}$, are defined in a manner similar to the foregoing. The six strains
$\epsilon_x$, $\epsilon_y$, $\epsilon_z$, $\gamma_{yz}$, $\gamma_{zx}$, $\gamma_{xy}$ are in general functions of $x$, $y$, $z$, and the six functions constitute a quantitative measure of the deformation of the body.
(Note that the six strains are dimensionless.) At any point $P$, the six
strains are said to define the *state of strain* at the point.

It is important that the difference in meaning between the words
"stress" and "strain" in technical usage be clearly understood. Stress is
a measure of the intensity of force, while strain is a measure of deformation.
A state of stress may exist without a state of strain, as would be the case,
for example, at a point in a rigid body subjected to external forces, and a
state of strain may exist without a state of stress, as, for example, at a point
in a deformable body subjected to a uniform temperature change but no
external forces.

**14.5 Stress-strain relations.** When a real body is subjected to stresses,
it is usually found that the body undergoes some strains, and the material
of which the body is composed is classified according to the way in which
the stresses are related to the strains. For the purpose of this classification,
consider a prismatic rod subjected (at constant temperature) to a one-
dimensional state of stress as in Fig. 14.13. (The forces $\mathbf{P}$ and $-\mathbf{P}$ are
assumed to be applied in the form of uniformly distributed forces over the
ends of the rod, which means that the stress $\sigma_x$ is constant throughout
the rod.) The dashed lines show the body in its deformed state, with the
deformations greatly exaggerated. (The lateral contraction of the rod,
discussed later in this article, is assumed to be small enough so that the
cross-sectional area $A$ is not changed appreciably by the deformation.)
By the first of Eqs. (14.4), since the internal force system is a uniformly

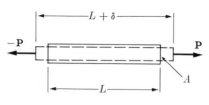

FIGURE 14.13

distributed normal force $N$ on any cross section,

$$\sigma_x = \frac{N}{A} \tag{14.9}$$

at any point in the rod, while all other stresses are everywhere zero. Applying one equation of equilibrium to any segment of the rod that includes an end,

$$N = P$$

at any cross section, so that

$$\sigma_x = \frac{P}{A} \tag{14.10}$$

at any point in the rod. Similarly, assuming that the strain is uniform throughout the rod, it follows from Eq. (14.6) that

$$\epsilon_x = \frac{\delta}{L} \tag{14.11}$$

at any point in the rod.

Rods of various materials can be put into a testing machine to determine stress-strain curves experimentally. The testing machine is essentially a device which grips the specimen at the ends and applies an

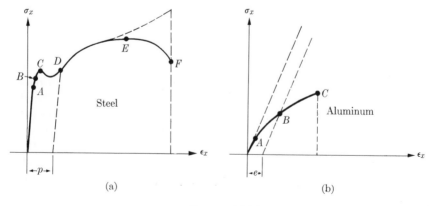

FIGURE 14.14

elongation $\delta$ by moving the two ends apart, measuring the magnitude of the force **P** at all times. Knowing $A$ and $L$, we compute $\sigma_x$ and $\epsilon_x$ by Eqs. (14.10) and (14.11), and it is customary to plot $\sigma_x$ against $\epsilon_x$. Figures 14.14(a) and (b) show typical stress-strain curves for common types of steel and aluminum, respectively.

For the steel, the curve follows a straight line to some point $A$ (the stress at which is called the *proportional limit*) and then begins to deviate slightly from linearity. If, at any point up to $B$, the machine is reversed and $\delta$ decreased, the stress-strain curve during "unloading" coincides with that obtained during "loading," and, when the stress is reduced to zero, there is complete recovery from strain. This phenomenon is called *elasticity*, and the stress at $B$ is called the *elastic limit*. At point $C$, the material "yields," i.e., the curve becomes horizontal, indicating that the strain can be increased without further increase in stress. (The actual drop in stress shown in the figure occurs because the yielding tends to relieve the load when the machine is applying deformations at a constant rate. If the test were being conducted by hanging "dead weights" on a specimen, there would be a horizontal portion of curve extending to the right from $C$.) The stress at $C$ is called the *yield point*. If, at some point $D$, the machine is reversed and $\delta$ decreased, the stress-strain curve follows the dashed straight line in the figure, a line which is found to be very nearly parallel to the initial straight portion of the curve. Hence, when the stress is reduced to zero, there is a residual strain $p$, called a "permanent set." Upon reloading, the dashed line is retraced to point $D$, after which the curve continues as if there had been no unloading. At point $E$, the magnitude of the force and $\sigma_x$ reach peak values and begin to drop off. For strains this large, however, the reduction in the cross-sectional area is appreciable, and the "true stress," computed using the current area, continues to increase (dashed curve). Only the "nominal stress," based on the original area, experiences a peak value. Finally, at $F$, the specimen fractures.

For the aluminum, the stress-strain curve has no straight portion, although the material may experience complete recovery from strain, i.e., it may be elastic, up to some point $A$ (at which the stress is the elastic limit). Since there is no definite yielding, it is common to locate a point $B$ by means of some arbitrary offset $e$ from the initial tangent and to call the stress at $B$ the *yield strength*. The specimen fractures at $C$.

If an increment of stress is applied, even slowly, to a real specimen, there is a time lag after the stress reaches its final value before the strain reaches its final value. Including time in the stress-strain relations leads to an advanced branch of the mechanics of deformable bodies. If the time lag is small, the material may be regarded as a "time-independent" material, i.e., the strain may be assumed to change in precise accord with the stress.

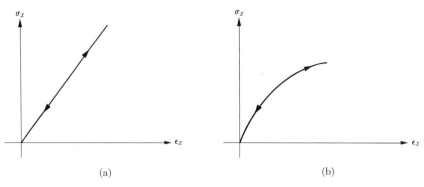

FIGURE 14.15

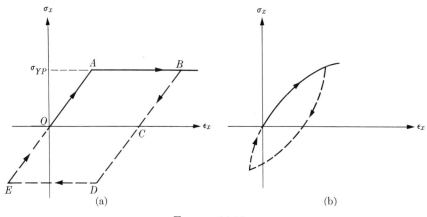

FIGURE 14.16

The stress-strain curves for ideal time-independent materials are modeled after those for real materials. Figures 14.15(a) and (b) show two elastic materials, called the *linearly elastic* and *nonlinearly elastic* materials, respectively. (The unloading curve coincides with the loading curve for these materials.) Figures 14.16(a) and (b) show two inelastic materials, called the *perfectly plastic* and the *generally inelastic* materials, respectively. In Fig. 14.16(a), the material has a definite yield point $\sigma_{YP}$, and the dashed line $BC$ shows a typical unloading curve. In order to remove all strain once yielding has occurred in tension for this material, it is necessary to make the stress compressive and to cause reverse yielding along line $DE$. If the lines $AE$ and $BD$ of Fig. 14.16(a) are vertical, the material is called *rigid-plastic*.

Most materials behave in compression in a manner similar to their behavior in tension, and the ideal materials are usually assumed to have

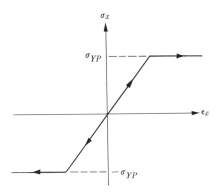

FIGURE 14.17

identically shaped curves in tension and compression. This is shown for
the perfectly plastic material in Fig. 14.17. (Note that this material is
linearly elastic as long as $-\sigma_{YP} < \sigma_x < \sigma_{YP}$.)

For the linearly elastic material in a one-dimensional state of stress,

$$\sigma_x = E\epsilon_x, \tag{14.12}$$

where $E$ is a constant called the *modulus of elasticity* or *Young's modulus*.
(The value of $E$ for most steels is about 30,000 ksi.) Substituting Eqs.
(14.10) and (14.11) into Eq. (14.12),

$$\frac{P}{A} = E\,\frac{\delta}{L},$$

or

$$P = \left(\frac{EA}{L}\right)\delta. \tag{14.13}$$

Equation (14.13) is the original law of elasticity stated by Hooke (Art. 1.5).
Because of this, the linearly elastic material is sometimes called the
"Hookean" material, and Eq. (14.12) is called "Hooke's Law." Solving
Eq. (14.13) for $\delta$,

$$\delta = \frac{PL}{EA}$$

for positive $N$. For either positive or negative $N$, by Eqs. (14.9), (14.11),
and (14.12),

$$\delta = \frac{NL}{EA}. \tag{14.14}$$

---

EXAMPLE 14.1. A steel elevator cable 400 ft long and 1 in. in diameter is
subjected to an added load of 3000 lb when the elevator is level with a floor.

If $E = 24{,}000$ ksi and the proportional limit of the material is not exceeded, how far down does the elevator move?

*Solution.* Calling the diameter of the cable $d$,

$$A = \frac{\pi}{4}\, d^2 = 0.7854(1)^2 = 0.7854 \text{ in}^2.$$

Thus, by Eq. (14.14),

$$\delta = \frac{3(400)(12)}{(24{,}000)(0.7854)} = 0.764 \text{ in}.$$

Equation (14.14) can be applied to each member of a system containing several members, as illustrated in the next example.

EXAMPLE 14.2.  When the rigid weight $W$ of Fig. 14.18 is connected to the two bars, it stretches them a total amount $\delta$. Find $L_1$ and $L_2$ in terms of $W$, $\delta$, $E_1$, $E_2$, $A_1$, $A_2$, and $L$.

*Solution.* In this case,

$$\delta = \frac{WL_1}{E_1 A_1} + \frac{WL_2}{E_2 A_2},$$

and

$$L = L_1 + L_2.$$

Thus, there are two equations on the two unknowns $L_1$ and $L_2$. Solving the second for $L_2$ in terms of $L_1$ and substituting into the first,

$$\frac{WL_1}{E_1 A_1} + \frac{W(L - L_1)}{E_2 A_2} = \delta,$$

from which

$$L_1 = \frac{\delta - (WL/E_2 A_2)}{(W/E_1 A_1) - (W/E_2 A_2)}.$$

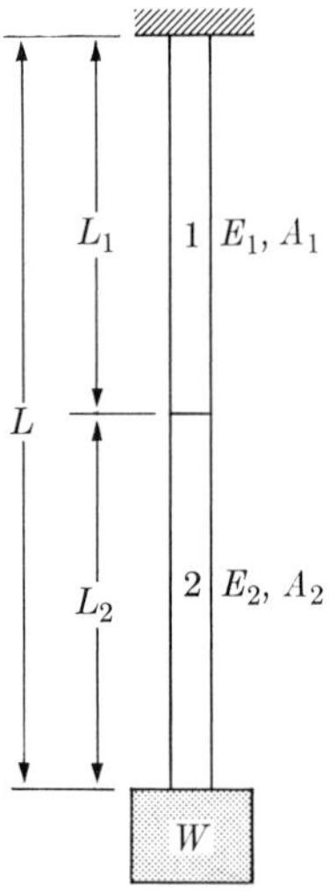

From the second of the two simultaneous equations,

$$L_2 = \frac{\delta - (WL/E_1 A_1)}{(W/E_2 A_2) - (W/E_1 A_1)}.$$

FIGURE 14.18

These results are valid, of course, only if they yield positive values for both $L_1$ and $L_2$.

In some cases the normal force $N$ in a bar may vary along the length of the bar. Taking an elemental length $dx$ of the bar over which $N$ may be assumed constant (Fig. 14.19), Eq. (14.14) gives that part of the total elongation $\delta$ of the bar contributed by the elemental length, i.e.,

$$d\delta = \frac{N}{EA}\, dx.$$

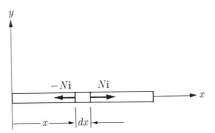

FIGURE 14.19

By integration, then,

$$\delta = \int_L \frac{N}{EA}\, dx, \qquad (14.15)$$

and

$$\delta = \frac{NL}{EA}$$

only if $N$, $E$, and $A$ are constant.

---

EXAMPLE 14.3. Figure 14.20 shows an elevator of weight $W$ and a cable having a weight per unit length of $w$. (a) Derive an equation for the total elongation $\delta$ of the cable in terms of $W$, $w$, $L$, $E$, $A$. (b) If $W = 20$ kips, $w = 0.222$ lb/in., $L = 400$ ft, $E = 24{,}000$ ksi, and $A = 0.7854$ in$^2$, evaluate the parts of $\delta$ due to the weight of the elevator and due to the weight of the cable.

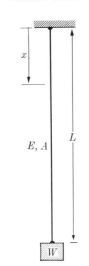

FIGURE 14.20

*Solution.* (a) The normal force $N$ at point $x$ in Fig. 14.20 is equal to $W$ plus the weight of the portion of cable below that point, i.e.,

$$N = W + (L - x)w.$$

Thus, by Eq. (14.15),

$$\delta = \frac{1}{EA} \int_0^L [W + (L - x)w]\, dx = \frac{WL}{EA} + \frac{wL^2}{2EA}.$$

(b) Due to the weight of the elevator alone,

$$\delta_E = \frac{WL}{EA} = \frac{(20)(400)(12)}{(24{,}000)(0.7854)} = 5.09 \text{ in.}$$

Due to the weight of the cable alone,

$$\delta_C = \frac{wL^2}{2EA} = \frac{(0.222)(160{,}000)(144)}{2(24{,}000{,}000)(0.7854)} = 0.136 \text{ in.}$$

When a bar is subjected to a one-dimensional stress $\sigma_x$, there normally occur strains $\epsilon_y$ and $\epsilon_z$ as well as $\epsilon_x$. These other strains are associated with the lateral contraction shown in Fig. 14.13. For the linearly elastic material,

$$\epsilon_y = \epsilon_z = -\nu\epsilon_x, \tag{14.16}$$

where $\nu$ is a constant called *Poisson's ratio*. (For steel, $\nu$ is about $\frac{1}{4}$.)

---

EXAMPLE 14.4. If $\nu = 0.25$ for the cable of Example 14.1, how much does its diameter decrease due to the added load?

*Solution.* From Example 14.1,

$$\epsilon_x = \frac{0.764}{(400)(12)} = 0.0001592.$$

Thus, by Eq. (14.16),

$$\epsilon_y = -0.25(0.0001592) = -0.0000398.$$

But

$$\epsilon_y = \frac{\Delta d}{d},$$

so that

$$\Delta d = (-0.0000398)(1) = -0.0000398 \text{ in.}$$

---

The element of Fig. 14.9 is said to be in a state of *two-dimensional pure shear* when it carries only the stresses in Fig. 14.21, which shows one face of the rectangular parallelepiped and takes account of the third of Eqs. (14.5). If the material is linearly elastic, then

$$\tau_{xy} = G\gamma_{xy}, \tag{14.17}$$

where $G$ is a constant called the *shear modulus* or the *modulus of rigidity* (the latter being a misnomer). (For steel, $G$ is about 12,000 ksi.) It is often desirable to compute an average shear stress in pure shear by dividing the force transmitted in shear by the appropriate area, i.e.,

$$\tau_{xy} = \frac{P}{A}. \tag{14.18}$$

This is illustrated in the following example.

---

EXAMPLE 14.5. A shaft delivers a torque of 2000 in-lb into a wheel through a key 1 in. long, as shown in Fig. 14.22. Find the average shear stress in the key.

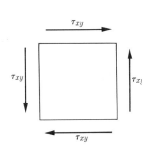

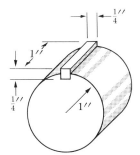

FIGURE 14.21                    FIGURE 14.22

*Solution.* Using a horizontal plane through the key for computing the area and taking the force as 2000 lb, it follows from Eq. (14.18) that

$$\tau_{xy} = \frac{2000}{(1)(\frac{1}{4})} = 8000 \text{ psi.}$$

A material is said to be *isotropic* if the stress-strain relations are the same regardless of the orientation of the axes at a point. If an isotropic, linearly elastic material is subjected to a three-dimensional state of stress and a temperature change, then, by a generalization of the foregoing equations, the strains are given by the following equations:

$$\epsilon_x = \frac{1}{E}\left[\sigma_x - \nu(\sigma_y + \sigma_z)\right] + \alpha(T - T_0),$$

$$\epsilon_y = \frac{1}{E}\left[\sigma_y - \nu(\sigma_z + \sigma_x)\right] + \alpha(T - T_0),$$

$$(14.19)$$

$$\epsilon_z = \frac{1}{E}\left[\sigma_z - \nu(\sigma_x + \sigma_y)\right] + \alpha(T - T_0),$$

$$\gamma_{yz} = \frac{1}{G}\tau_{yz}, \qquad \gamma_{zx} = \frac{1}{G}\tau_{zx}, \qquad \gamma_{xy} = \frac{1}{G}\tau_{xy},$$

where $E$, $G$, and $\nu$ are the previously mentioned elastic constants (which are the same for any orientation of axes) and where $\alpha$ is the coefficient of linear expansion, $T$ is the temperature, and $T_0$ is the original temperature (at which all stresses and strains are zero). Equations (14.19) are the stress-strain relations for any point of a linearly elastic, isotropic body, and they reduce to Eqs. (14.12), (14.16), and (14.17) for the special cases covered by those equations. If $E$, $G$, $\nu$, and $\alpha$ are the same at every point of the body, as is usually assumed, the material is said to be *homogeneous*.

It can be shown that $E$, $G$, and $\nu$ are related by the equation

$$G = \frac{E}{2(1 + \nu)} \tag{14.20}$$

and hence that all three of them are not independent.

Solving Eqs. (14.19) for the stresses in terms of the strains gives the following equations:

$$\sigma_x = \frac{E}{(1 + \nu)(1 - 2\nu)} [(1 - \nu)\epsilon_x + \nu(\epsilon_y + \epsilon_z)]$$

$$- \frac{E}{1 - 2\nu} \alpha(T - T_0),$$

$$\sigma_y = \frac{E}{(1 + \nu)(1 - 2\nu)} [(1 - \nu)\epsilon_y + \nu(\epsilon_z + \epsilon_x)]$$

$$- \frac{E}{1 - 2\nu} \alpha(T - T_0), \tag{14.21}$$

$$\sigma_z = \frac{E}{(1 + \nu)(1 - 2\nu)} [(1 - \nu)\epsilon_z + \nu(\epsilon_x + \epsilon_y)]$$

$$- \frac{E}{1 - 2\nu} \alpha(T - T_0),$$

$$\tau_{yz} = G\gamma_{yz}, \qquad \tau_{zx} = G\gamma_{zx}, \qquad \tau_{xy} = G\gamma_{xy}.$$

In addition to the properties of a material previously mentioned, such as elastic limit and yield point or yield strength, there are other properties, some qualitative and some quantitative, which may be included in a description of the material. One of these is *stiffness*, a property measured by the moduli $E$ and $G$. Another is *ductility*, the ability to deform in tension without fracture. The steel in Fig. 14.14(a) is ductile since the strain at fracture, i.e., at point $F$, is relatively large. A material such as cast iron that fractures at a small strain is called *brittle*. The *nominal ultimate tensile strength* of the steel in Fig. 14.14(a) is the stress at point $E$. Other important properties are *hardness, toughness, resilience*, etc.

When a specimen is subjected to a stress that fluctuates from compression to tension a large number of times, the specimen fractures even though the maximum stress is at a much lower value than the material is capable of withstanding statically. This phenomenon is called *fatigue*. The number of cycles required for fracture increases as the maximum stress decreases, and the stress that the specimen can endure for an infinite number of cycles without a fatigue fracture is called the *endurance limit*.

When a specimen is subjected to a high, sustained stress for a long period of time, the strain gradually increases from its original value, a phenomenon called *creep*. Creep is aggravated by high temperature.

**14.6 Plane stress.** Figure 14.23 shows the element of Fig. 14.9 in a state of *plane stress*, which means that

$$\sigma_z = \tau_{yz} = \tau_{zx} = 0.$$

The state of stress in this case is completely specified by three quantities, namely, $\sigma_x$, $\sigma_y$, $\tau_{xy}$. If these three stresses are known at a point, but it is desired to find the stresses on a plane through the point other than the $yz$- and $zx$-planes, an element of the shape shown in Fig. 14.24 may be selected at the point. The stresses $\sigma_\xi$ and $\tau_{\xi\eta}$ occur on a plane having a normal direction which makes an angle $\theta$ with the $x$-axis, and the problem of finding the unknown stresses in terms of the known ones is a problem on the transformation of the stresses under a rotation of axes. Calling the length of the oblique face $L$, we write an equation of equilibrium as follows:

$$\sum F_\xi = \sigma_\xi L \, dz - \sigma_x (L \cos \theta) \, (dz) \cos \theta$$
$$- \tau_{xy}(L \cos \theta) \, (dz) \sin \theta - \sigma_y(L \sin \theta) \, (dz) \sin \theta$$
$$- \tau_{xy}(L \sin \theta) \, (dz) \cos \theta = 0.$$

From this equation,

$$\sigma_\xi = \tfrac{1}{2}(\sigma_x + \sigma_y) + \tfrac{1}{2}(\sigma_x - \sigma_y) \cos 2\theta + \tau_{xy} \sin 2\theta. \qquad (14.22)$$

In a similar way, using

$$\sum F_\eta = 0,$$

we find that

$$\tau_{\xi\eta} = -\tfrac{1}{2}(\sigma_x - \sigma_y) \sin 2\theta + \tau_{xy} \cos 2\theta. \qquad (14.23)$$

Note that Eqs. (14.22) and (14.23) have the same form as the first of Eqs. (10.17) and Eq. (10.18). Thus, except for signs, the stresses in plane stress transform under a rotation of axes in the same way as the moment

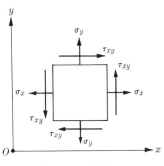

FIGURE 14.23

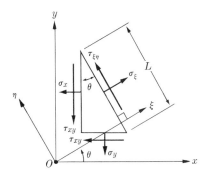

FIGURE 14.24

and product of inertia of a plane area. To find the maximum and minimum normal stresses, then, the equation

$$\frac{d\sigma_\xi}{d\theta} = 0$$

is used to obtain the following expression for the angle $\theta$:

$$\tan 2\theta = \frac{2\tau_{xy}}{\sigma_x - \sigma_y}. \tag{14.24}$$

Equation (14.24) defines two angles $\theta_1$, $\theta_2$ which locate the *principal axes of stress* at the point under consideration. As in the case of the area, the two directions differ by 90° and define planes on which $\tau_{xy}$ is zero. Substituting the angles $\theta_1$, $\theta_2$ into Eq. (14.22), the maximum and minimum normal stresses are found to be given, respectively, by

$$\sigma_1 = \tfrac{1}{2}(\sigma_x + \sigma_y) + \tfrac{1}{2}\sqrt{(\sigma_x - \sigma_y)^2 + 4\tau_{xy}^2},$$

$$\sigma_2 = \tfrac{1}{2}(\sigma_x + \sigma_y) - \tfrac{1}{2}\sqrt{(\sigma_x - \sigma_y)^2 + 4\tau_{xy}^2}. \tag{14.25}$$

These are called the *principal stresses* at the point.

If a linearly elastic, homogeneous, isotropic material is in a state of plane stress, and if $T - T_0 = 0$, then Eqs. (14.19) reduce to the following:

$$\epsilon_x = \frac{1}{E}(\sigma_x - \nu\sigma_y), \qquad \epsilon_y = \frac{1}{E}(\sigma_y - \nu\sigma_x), \qquad \gamma_{xy} = \frac{1}{G}\tau_{xy}. \tag{14.26}$$

Solving these equations for the stresses in terms of the strains,

$$\sigma_x = \frac{E}{1 - \nu^2}(\epsilon_x + \nu\epsilon_y),$$

$$\sigma_y = \frac{E}{1 - \nu^2}(\epsilon_y + \nu\epsilon_x), \tag{14.27}$$

$$\tau_{xy} = G\gamma_{xy}.$$

PROBLEMS

14.1 Verify Eqs. (14.21).

14.2 Find $\nu$ for an aluminum alloy for which $E = 10{,}500$ ksi and $G = 4000$ ksi.

[*Ans.:* 0.31.]

14.3 A bar with rectangular cross section 2 in. by 4 in. and length of 40 in. is subjected to a uniform tensile stress which produces an elongation of 0.036 in. If $\nu = 0.25$, (a) find the decrease in the cross-sectional area of the bar, and (b) find the increase in the volume of the bar.

14.4 A bar with rectangular cross section $b$ by $h$ and length $L$ is subjected to a uniform tensile stress which produces an elongation $\delta$. (a) Derive an equation for the increase $\Delta V$ in the volume of the bar in terms of $b$, $h$, $L$, $\delta$, and $\nu$. (b) Neglecting terms in this equation which contain squares and cubes of $\delta$, find the value of $\nu$ such that $\Delta V = 0$.

$$\left[ \textit{Ans.:} \ (a) \ \Delta V = bhL \left( \frac{\delta}{L} (1 - 2\nu) + \nu \frac{\delta^2}{L^2} (\nu - 2) + \nu^2 \frac{\delta^3}{L^3} \right) ; \ (b) \ \frac{1}{2}. \right]$$

14.5 A uniform steel measuring tape which is 0.32 in. wide and 0.01 in. thick is laid flat on the ground and pulled at each end with a force of 25-lb magnitude. Assume that $E = 30{,}000$ ksi. (a) What is the stress in the tape? (b) What is the strain? (c) If the tape is 100 ft long when unstretched, what is its elongation? (d) If the tape was graduated in an unstretched state and now indicates that a dimension is 80 ft, what is the true dimension?

14.6 An unknown weight is suspended from a steel wire 12 ft long and $\frac{1}{16}$ in. in diameter. The elongation that results is 0.0720 in. The same weight is then suspended from a copper wire 10 ft long and $\frac{1}{8}$ in. in diameter. The copper wire

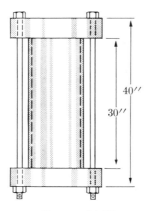

FIGURE 14.25

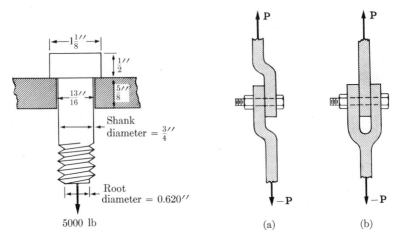

FIGURE 14.26                    FIGURE 14.27

lengthens 0.0310 in., and its diameter decreases 0.0000108 in. Knowing that $E$ = 30,000 ksi for the steel, find $E$ and $\nu$ for the copper.

[*Ans.:* $E$ = 14,500 ksi, $\nu$ = 0.334.]

14.7 Two steel bolts each 1 in. in diameter are used to cap a hollow cylinder with two rigid plates as shown in Fig. 14.25. The cross-sectional area of the cylinder is 5 in², and it is required that the plates exert a compressive stress of 4000 psi upon this area. To ensure that this stress is attained, the bolts are to be tightened until their measured elongation is equal to that calculated for the given stress. (a) If $E$ = 30,000 ksi for the bolts, determine the elongation in the 40-in. length. (b) If the cylinder is made of an aluminum alloy for which $E$ = 10,500 ksi, and if there are 8 threads per inch on the bolts (i.e., the nuts advance $\frac{1}{8}$ in. per turn), find the number of turns required for each nut after all the parts are in contact.

14.8 A 5000-lb force is transmitted to a $\frac{5}{8}$-in.-thick aluminum plate by a $\frac{3}{4}$-in.-diameter steel bolt having a square head. The dimensions of the head are shown in Fig. 14.26. The hole is circular and $\frac{13}{16}$ in. in diameter. Find: (a) the tensile stress on the root area of the bolt threads, (b) the tensile stress in the bolt shank, (c) the shear stress in the bolt head, considering shear on a circular cylindrical surface of the same diameter as the bolt shank, (d) the shear stress in the plate, considering shear on a square cylindrical surface of the same width as the bolt head.

[*Ans.:* (a) 16,560 psi; (b) 11,310 psi; (c) 4240 psi; (d) 1780 psi.]

14.9 The two connections shown in Fig. 14.27 are designed to transmit a force of 1000-lb magnitude. Each is equipped with a single bolt having a shank of $\frac{1}{2}$-in. diameter. Neglecting friction between the connected parts, find the average shear stress in the bolt in each case.

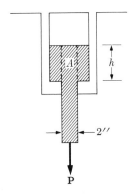

FIGURE 14.28

14.10 The wooden member $A$ in Fig. 14.28 has a uniform thickness $t$. If the tensile stress in the 2-in.-wide portion of the member is 1200 psi, find the height $h$ required to make the average shear stress on the dashed planes 200 psi.

[*Ans.:* 6 in.]

# CHAPTER 15

## AXIAL FORCES

**15.1 Analysis and design.** A *failure* is said to have occurred in a machine or structure when there is a fracture in some part, a separation of parts which were connected together, or some other mishap (such as excessively large deformations) which interferes with the functioning of the machine or structure. Many failures are associated with critical values of the tensile, compressive, or shear stresses, these values being called the *failure stresses* in tension, compression, and shear. The failure stresses depend on the material (e.g., the failure stress in either tension or compression is usually the yield point or yield strength for a ductile material and the fracture stress for a brittle material); the type of loading (e.g., the failure stress in tension if the stress is applied cyclically and there is a fatigue failure may be much smaller than if there is sustained loading); and other conditions (e.g., a high temperature may cause excessive creep to be the mode of failure).

The *allowable stresses* in tension, compression, and shear are the maximum values of each type of stress which it is arbitrarily decided, on the basis of all pertinent factors, to permit anywhere in the structure. Once these are specified, the two general types of problems which may arise are: (1) *analysis* problems, in which, for a given or assumed structure, either (a) the maximum stresses due to known loads are computed, or (b) the maximum permissible loads for the given allowable stresses are computed; and (2) *design* problems, in which the materials and proportions are prescribed for a structure to carry certain loads (or, more generally, to perform a specified function) without exceeding the allowable stresses (or, more properly, with some required degree of safety from failure). (There may also be other design requirements on weight, economy, appearance, etc.) The allowable stresses must be smaller than the failure stresses to provide a margin of safety, since there are uncertainties in the loads, inaccuracies in the formulas used to compute stresses, contingencies such as overloads, shocks, and defects in the materials, and other areas where the model differs from the real situation. In some cases the margin of safety must be quite large, as, for example, in the design of an elevator cable.

To put the concept of safety on a quantitative basis, a *factor of safety n* is defined. If the structure is to carry a single load **P**, then

$$n = P_f/P_a, \tag{15.1}$$

where $P_f$ is the magnitude $P$ of $\mathbf{P}$ at failure and $P_a$ is, in analysis problems of type (a) above, the actual value of $P$; in analysis problems of type (b) above, the allowable value of $P$; and, in design problems, the actual value of $P$ to be supported (called the "design" value of $P$). If the structure is loaded by several applied forces, this definition of $n$ breaks down unless all the magnitudes can be expressed in terms of a single parameter, in which case $n$ is the ratio of the parameter at failure to the design value of the parameter. An alternative definition of $n$ is the smallest ratio of failure stress to allowable stress computed for any part of the structure and based on the allowable stresses $\sigma_a^T, \sigma_a^C$, and $\tau_a$ in tension, compression, and shear, respectively. (In design problems, different factors of safety may be specified for different parts of the structure or for different types of stress, in which case the factor of safety for the structure as a whole is the smallest of these.) This definition is meaningful for any number of loads. For a single load, however, it gives a different value of $n$ from Eq. (15.1) in all but the simplest cases of uniform one-dimensional stress and pure shear. When the stresses are nonuniformly distributed in the body, it usually does not mean that the structure has failed as a whole simply because the stress at one point has reached its failure value. Also, for an indeterminate structure, an entire member may fail without causing the structure to collapse. Consider, for example, the system in Fig. 4.8. When one rope fails, the other two ropes may still be able to carry additional load. For these reasons, the alternative definition of $n$ is a less rational basis for design, although it is a simpler and more commonly used one.

**15.2 Bars and cables.** If the mechanical system under consideration is made up of bars and cables each of which is in a one-dimensional and uniform state of stress, each member of the system has a failure stress determined by its material and by whether it is in tension or compression.

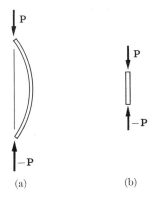

FIGURE 15.1

A long, slender member in compression (called a *column*) presents special problems in design because it fails by "buckling" as in Fig. 15.1(a) at a stress smaller in absolute value than the same member can carry in tension or than a short member of the same cross section can carry in compression as in Fig. 15.1(b). (This is easily demonstrated by a simple experiment with a yardstick.) In fact, the failure stress in compression depends on the shape of the cross section, the length of the column, and the type of end restraints as well as the material, while the failure stress in tension (or the failure stress in compression when the ratio of thickness to length is large enough to make yielding precede buckling) is independent of these other factors.

For any member in this type of structure, the factor of safety is given by

$$n = \frac{\sigma_f}{\sigma_a}, \tag{15.2}$$

where $\sigma_f$ is the appropriate one of the failure stresses $\sigma_f^T$ and $\sigma_f^C$, and $\sigma_a$ is the appropriate one of the actual stresses or allowable stresses $\sigma_a^T$ and $\sigma_a^C$. (Note that the subscript $x$ used for the stress in Chapter 14 is no longer needed.) For the entire structure, the safety factor is the smallest of those for all its members. In design, an attempt is usually made to have $n$ nearly the same for all members.

For a single member carrying an axial force of magnitude $P$, the two definitions of $n$, Eqs. (15.1) and (15.2), give the same design, as illustrated in the following example.

---

EXAMPLE 15.1. Design the cable of Example 11.5 to make $n = 4$ if the failure stress of the cable in tension is 100,000 psi.

*Solution.* From Eq. (15.2), the allowable stress is computed as follows:

$$\sigma_a = \frac{\sigma_f}{n} = \frac{100,000}{4} = 25,000 \text{ psi.}$$

Thus, by Eq. (14.10),

$$A = \frac{P_a}{\sigma_a} = \frac{8330}{25,000} = 0.333 \text{ in}^2.$$

This is the required cross-sectional area. To find the required diameter $d$, note that

$$A = \frac{\pi}{4} d^2 = 0.7854 \, d^2$$

and therefore that

$$d = 1.128\sqrt{A}.$$

In this problem,

$$d = 1.128(0.577) = 0.651 \text{ in.}$$

Using Eq. (14.10) again,

$$P_f = A\sigma_f = (0.333)(100,000) = 33,300 \text{ lb}$$
$$= 4(8330),$$

and thus the magnitude of the failure load is $n$ times that of the design load.

---

The next example illustrates the analysis of a two-member structure carrying known loads.

---

EXAMPLE 15.2.  The structure of Fig. 15.2 carries a weight $P$ of 1000 lb.  The steel cable $BC$ is $\frac{1}{4}$ in. in diameter and the wooden member $AB$ is 2 in. by 4 in., rectangular cross section, true dimensions.  If the failure stresses are 40,000 psi in tension for the steel and 400 psi in compression for the wood, find the stresses in the steel and wood and the safety factor of the structure.  (Neglect the weights of the members.)

*Solution.*  Figure 15.3 shows a free-body diagram of bar $AB$.  By the equations of equilibrium,

$$\sum M_z^A = L(\tfrac{3}{5}T) - L(1000) = 0, \qquad T = \tfrac{5}{3}(1000) = 1667 \text{ lb},$$

and

$$\sum F_x = A - \tfrac{4}{5}(1667) = 0, \qquad A = 1333 \text{ lb}.$$

(The equation $\sum F_y = 0$ merely verifies that **A** is horizontal.)  Hence,

$$N_{AB} = -1333 \text{ lb}, \qquad N_{BC} = 1667 \text{ lb},$$

so that

$$\sigma_{AB} = -\frac{1333}{8} = -167 \text{ psi},$$

$$\sigma_{BC} = \frac{1667}{0.7854(1/16)} = 34,000 \text{ psi}.$$

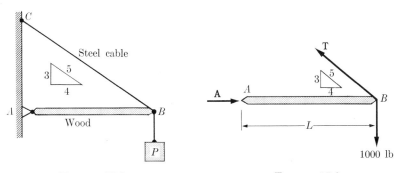

FIGURE 15.2                    FIGURE 15.3

Thus, by Eq. (15.2),

$$n_{AB} = \frac{-400}{-167} = 2.40, \qquad n_{BC} = \frac{40,000}{34,000} = 1.18,$$

and

$$n = 1.18.$$

---

The other type of analysis problem involves the determination of allowable loads.

---

EXAMPLE 15.3.   The rigid platform in Fig. 15.4 is supported on two 2-ft-long and two 6-ft-long hollow, steel posts with cross-sectional areas of 3 in² each. A single load **P** acts in the plane of symmetry of the structure. (a) If the allowable compressive stresses are 20 ksi in the shorter legs and 15 ksi in the longer, find the maximum permissible $P$. (b) For this $P$, find the vertical deflections at $A$ and $B$ due to shortening of the posts.

*Solution.* (a) By the equations of equilibrium,

$$N_A = -\tfrac{5}{8}P,$$

$$N_B = -\tfrac{3}{8}P,$$

and, by Eq. (14.9), the allowable values of $N$ for each pair of posts are given by

$$N_A = (-20)(2)(3) = -120 \text{ kips},$$
$$N_B = (-15)(2)(3) = -90 \text{ kips}.$$

Hence the allowable values of $P$ as controlled by each pair of posts are

$$P_A = -\tfrac{8}{5}(-120) = 192 \text{ kips},$$
$$P_B = -\tfrac{8}{3}(-90) = 240 \text{ kips},$$

and

$$P_a = 192 \text{ kips}.$$

(b) By Eq. (14.14), which is valid because $N$ and $A$ are constant over the length of each set of posts,

$$\delta_A = \frac{N_A L_A}{EA}, \qquad \delta_B = \frac{N_B L_B}{EA},$$

or

$$\delta_A = \frac{-(5/8)(192)(2)}{(30,000)(6)} = -0.00133 \text{ ft},$$

$$\delta_B = \frac{-(3/8)(192)(6)}{(30,000)(6)} = -0.00240 \text{ ft}.$$

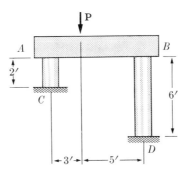

FIGURE 15.4

Since the results of part (b) indicate that the platform is no longer exactly level after the load is applied, the question arises as to where the load should be placed to make the platform stay level. This problem cannot be solved by statics alone, i.e., it is a case of statical indeterminateness. Such problems are discussed in Chapter 18.

The following example illustrates the design of a structure composed of several members.

EXAMPLE 15.4. Design the structure of Fig. 15.2 for a load $P$ of 1000 lb if $n$ is to be 3 and if the failure stresses are 40,000 psi in tension for the steel and 400 psi in compression for the wood. Let the wooden member have a square cross section and the cable a round cross section.

*Solution.* By Eq. (15.2), $\sigma_a^C$ is $-(400/3)$ or $-133$ psi for $AB$ and $\sigma_a^T$ is 40,000/3 or 13,330 psi for $BC$. Hence, using values of $N$ found in Example 15.2,

$$A_{AB} = \frac{-1333}{-133} = 10 \text{ in}^2, \qquad A_{BC} = \frac{1667}{13,330} = 0.125 \text{ in}^2.$$

This means that $AB$ must be at least $\sqrt{10}$ or 3.16 in. square and $BC$ must be at least $1.128\sqrt{0.125}$ or 0.399 in. in diameter.

The analysis and design of statically determinate pin-connected frames such as that shown in Fig. 15.5 are effected by separating the frame into bars as in Figs. 15.6(a), 15.6(b), and 15.6(c), which are free-body diagrams of the bars. There are a total of nine unknowns, $A_x$, $A_y$, $B_x$, $B_y$, $C_x$, $C_y$, $D_x$, $D_y$, and $E$, and there are three equations for each bar or nine equations.

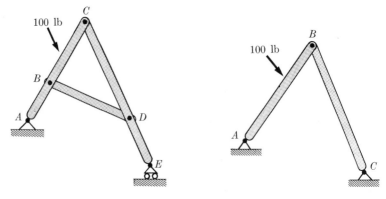

FIGURE 15.5                         FIGURE 15.7

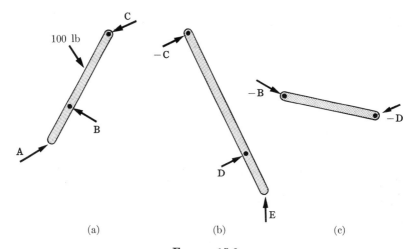

(a)                    (b)                    (c)

FIGURE 15.6

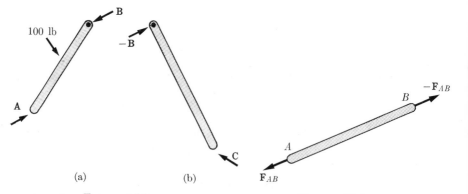

(a)                    (b)

FIGURE 15.8                         FIGURE 15.9

(The three equations for the frame as a whole are not independent of these nine.) Another type of frame, shown in Fig. 15.7, is not in itself rigid but is held fixed by its supports. This frame is also separated into bars as in Figs. 15.8(a) and 15.8(b), where there are six unknowns, $A_x$, $A_y$, $B_x$, $B_y$, $C_x$, and $C_y$, and six equations (three for each bar). Most of the bars in the frames of Figs. 15.5 and 15.7 carry shear and bending moment as well as axial force. But the bars of Figs. 15.6(c) and 15.8(b) are special cases in which there are only two forces on a bar, one at each end. For any such bar $AB$, as shown in Fig. 15.9, the equations of equilibrium require that the two forces be axial, which means that the bar may be treated as being in a one-dimensional and uniform state of stress. (The equations of equilibrium for the bar are completely used up in establishing that the forces are axial and therefore cannot give the magnitude of $\mathbf{F}_{AB}$.) Article 15.3 is concerned with frameworks (called *trusses*) which are composed exclusively of these so-called "two-force" members.

**15.3 Simple trusses.** Figure 15.10 shows a typical truss and gives some terminology. The idealizations usually made for a truss are the following:

(1) The members are straight, nearly rigid, and weightless.
(2) The joints are frictionless hinges or pins.
(3) The loads and reactions are applied only at the joints.

Under these assumptions, each member is carrying axial force only. A real truss departs from these idealizations in that the joints are usually riveted or welded, there are distributed forces along the members, the centerlines of all members framing into a joint are not concurrent, etc. For most trusses these departures from the ideal do not affect the stresses materially. The idealizations, which greatly simplify the analysis of trusses, are therefore usually justified.

To understand the manner in which a truss supports its loads, consider the problem of connecting three points $A$, $B$, $C$ (not lying on a straight line) together rigidly. As a first step, let $A$ and $B$ be connected by a rigid

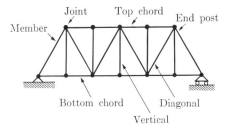

FIGURE 15.10

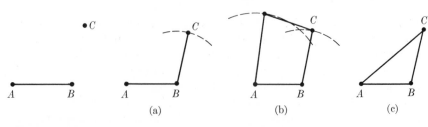

FIGURE 15.11                        FIGURE 15.12

bar $AB$ as in Fig. 15.11. Figures 15.12(a), 15.12(b), and 15.12(c) show three ways to then connect $C$, by adding one, three, and two bars, respectively. Only the third arrangement gives a rigid element. (Points in the others can move on the dashed circles.) Thus, the triangular element is the basic element from which trusses are built up. To connect a fourth point $D$ rigidly to the basic element $ABC$ requires two more bars, any of the schemes pictured in Fig. 15.13 being suitable. Figure 15.14 shows a truss built up in this manner from triangular elements. Such a truss is called a *simple truss*, while trusses made up of several simple trusses rigidly connected together are called *compound trusses*. If $m$ is the number of members and $j$ is the number of joints in a simple truss, then, from the foregoing discussion,

$$m = 3 + 2(j - 3),$$

since three members are contributed by the first triangle and two additional members are contributed by each joint in excess of the first three. Thus,

$$m = 2j - 3. \tag{15.3}$$

Equation (15.3) can be shown to be a necessary but not a sufficient con-

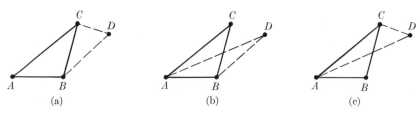

FIGURE 15.13

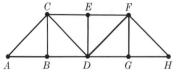

FIGURE 15.14

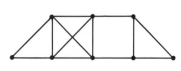

FIGURE 15.15

dition for "rigidity" of any truss. Compare, for example, the two trusses in Figs. 15.14 and 15.15. Each has eight joints and thirteen members and therefore satisfies Eq. (15.3), but the simple truss is rigid while the other is not (since the square panel without diagonals is collapsible).

To find the axial forces in all the members of a simple truss, the truss can first be treated as a rigid body. If it is supported in a statically determinate manner, the three external reactions can be found by the three equations of equilibrium. Each joint of the truss can then be analyzed as a particle, writing the two equations of equilibrium for each one. This kind of truss analysis is called the *method of joints*. There are $2j$ equations at the joints and there are three unknown reactions plus $m$ unknown axial forces in the members. Hence, by Eq. (15.3), the entire problem is determinate. (The three equations for the truss as a whole are not independent of the other $2j$ equations.) It is advisable to start by finding the reactions, then to proceed from joint to joint, at each step selecting a joint having no more than two remaining unknown bar forces. The three surplus equations serve as check equations at the end of the process, as illustrated in the following example.

---

EXAMPLE 15.5. Find the axial forces in all members of the truss of Fig. 15.16. Give the required cross-sectional area of each member if the failure stresses are 4 ksi in tension, 3 ksi for 12-ft compression members, and 2 ksi for 15-ft compression members and the desired factor of safety is 2.

*Solution.* For the truss as a whole,

$$\sum M_z^D = 3(12)A_y - 2(12)(20) - 12(5) = 0,$$

$$A_y = 15 \text{ kips,}$$

and

$$\sum M_z^A = 3(12)D_y - 2(12)(5) - 12(20) = 0,$$

$$D_y = 10 \text{ kips.}$$

As a check,

$$\sum F_y = 15 + 10 - 20 - 5 = 0.$$

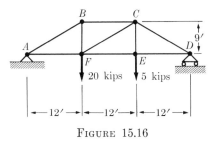

FIGURE 15.16          FIGURE 15.17

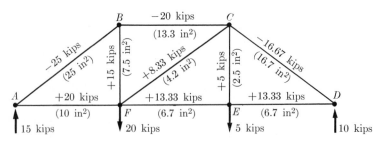

FIGURE 15.18

Beginning with joint $A$, the free-body diagram of Fig. 15.17 is drawn in such a way that the unknown axial forces are assumed positive (i.e., tensile). By the equations of equilibrium,

$$\sum F_x = N_{AF} + \tfrac{4}{5} N_{AB} = 0, \qquad \sum F_y = 15 + \tfrac{3}{5} N_{AB} = 0,$$

and thus

$$N_{AB} = -25 \text{ kips}, \qquad N_{AF} = 20 \text{ kips}.$$

This information is now stored on a drawing of the truss as in Fig. 15.18. Proceeding to joint $B$, the free-body diagram of Fig. 15.19 is drawn. (Note that the 25-kip force is shown with its known direction.) By the equations of equilibrium,

$$\sum F_x = N_{BC} + \tfrac{4}{5}(25) = 0, \qquad \sum F_y = -N_{BF} + \tfrac{3}{5}(25) = 0,$$

and thus

$$N_{BC} = -20 \text{ kips}, \qquad N_{BF} = 15 \text{ kips}.$$

The next two free-body diagrams, of joints $F$ and $C$, are shown in Figs. 15.20 and 15.21. These lead to all the rest of the axial forces in Fig. 15.18 except $N_{DE}$. At joint $E$, there is one equation for finding $N_{DE}$ ($\sum F_x = 0$) and one check equation ($\sum F_y = 0$). At joint $D$, there are two check equations.

Using Eqs. (14.9) and (15.2), the required cross-sectional areas are given by

$$A = \frac{|N|n}{|\sigma_f|},$$

where $n$ is 2 in this example. The values of $A$ computed by this formula are shown in parentheses in Fig. 15.18.

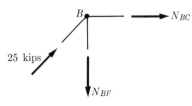

FIGURE 15.19

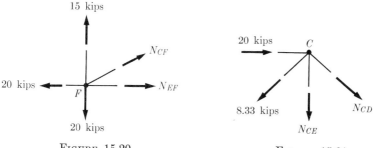

FIGURE 15.20                              FIGURE 15.21

To find the axial force in one or two members near the center of a truss, another method of analysis, called the *method of sections*, is more efficient than the method of joints. The method of sections consists of separating the truss into two parts by cutting across the member whose axial force is required (and no more than two other unknown members) and writing three equations of equilibrium for either portion of the truss. In some cases it is even unnecessary to find the reactions, as illustrated in the next example.

EXAMPLE 15.6.   The cross-sectional area of every member of the truss of Fig. 15.22 is 4 in². Find the stress in member $HI$.

*Solution.* The cutting section is shown in Fig. 15.22, and the free-body diagram of the upper portion of the truss is in Fig. 15.23. Taking moments about $B$,

$$\sum M_z^B = 10N_{HI} + 5(5) + 10(5) + 15(5) = 0,$$
$$N_{HI} = -15 \text{ kips.}$$

Hence,

$$\sigma_{HI} = -\tfrac{15}{4} = -3.75 \text{ ksi.}$$

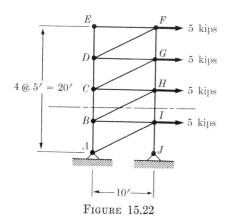

FIGURE 15.22

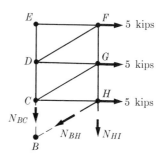

FIGURE 15.23

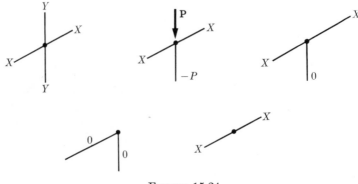

FIGURE 15.24

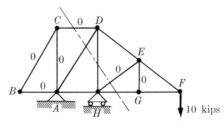

FIGURE 15.25

Figure 15.24 shows various special joints which occur in trusses. The equations of equilibrium give information about these joints which can be determined by inspection. For example, certain pairs of bars must have equal axial forces (labeled $X$ or $Y$ in Fig. 15.24), while other bars must have axial forces with known values (appropriately labeled in Fig. 15.24). Whenever possible, zero bars should be marked immediately after inspection, as in Fig. 15.25. This can simplify much of the later analysis. For example, the cutting section in Fig. 15.25 can be used to find the axial forces in members $AD$ and $DH$ immediately.

The most efficient truss analysis is often some combination of the method of joints and the method of sections.

## Problems

15.1 The homogeneous block in Fig. 15.26 weighs 8000 lb and is supported by three cables with cross-sectional areas of 0.5 in$^2$ each. Find the stress in each cable.

15.2 In the crane shown in Fig. 15.27, cables $BC$ and $BD$ have failure stresses in tension of 90 ksi, and the boom $AB$ has a failure stress in compression of 10 ksi. Neglecting the weights of the parts of the structure, find the permissible load which the crane can support at $D$ with a safety factor of 2.

[*Ans.:* 17.3 kips.]

15.3 A simplified representation of the human arm is shown in Fig. 15.28. Find the allowable weight $W$ as controlled by members $AD$ and $BE$ if the allowable stresses are 8000 psi in tension and 1000 psi in compression.

15.4 For the crane shown in Fig. 15.29, the allowable stresses are 20 ksi in tension and 10 ksi in compression. (a) If $W = 10$ kips and $A_{AB} = 2$ in$^2$, find the stress in $AB$. (b) If $A_{BD} = 1$ in$^2$, find the allowable weight $W_a$ as controlled by $BD$. (c) If $W = 10$ kips, find the required cross-sectional area of $AC$.

[*Ans.:* (a) $-3420$ psi; (b) 32.7 kips; (c) 0.866 in$^2$.]

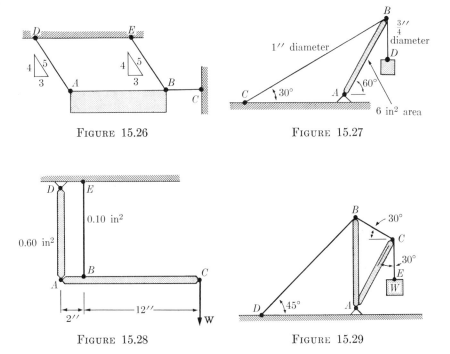

FIGURE 15.26

FIGURE 15.27

FIGURE 15.28

FIGURE 15.29

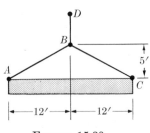

FIGURE 15.30

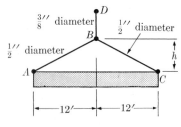

FIGURE 15.31

15.5 A sling for lifting a 3000-lb homogeneous beam is to be composed of three cables all having the same diameter (Fig. 15.30). If the allowable tensile stress in the cables is 40,000 psi, find the diameter required.

15.6 A sling for lifting a 3000-lb homogeneous beam is to be composed of three cables having the diameters shown in Fig. 15.31. Find the height $h$ required if the stress is to be the same in every cable. What is the stress?

[*Ans.:* $h = 3.51$ ft, $\sigma = 27{,}200$ psi.]

15.7 A 10-kip sign is supported as shown in Fig. 15.32 by two cables $AB$ and $CD$ and a bar $EF$. For the cables, $\sigma_f^T = 90{,}000$ psi and $n = 3$. For the bar, $\sigma_f^C = -15{,}000$ psi and $n = 2$. Determine the cross-sectional areas required for the cables and the bar.

15.8 A spider weighing 0.0010 lb wishes to spin a filament of web $ABC$ between two walls 16 ft apart in such a way that the weight of the spider can be supported at the midpoint $B$ as shown in Fig. 15.33 without exceeding a stress in the filament of 10,000 psi. If the web has a cross-sectional area of 0.00000013 in$^2$, what is the smallest total length $ABC$ that the spider can make the filament?

[*Ans.:* 17.3 ft.]

15.9 The plate in Fig. 15.34 is supported by a ball and socket at $A$ and by two 1-in.-diameter cables fixed at $E$. If the allowable tensile stress in the cables is 50 ksi, find the allowable weight of the plate.

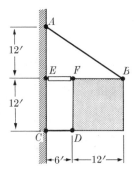

FIGURE 15.32

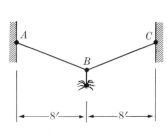

FIGURE 15.33

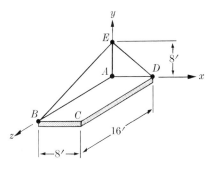

FIGURE 15.34

15.10 A 96.6-lb weight is to be raised 40 ft from rest in 4 sec by a rope. The acceleration is to be constant. What cross-sectional area should the rope have if the tensile stress is not to exceed 1150 psi?

[*Ans.*: 0.097 in².]

15.11 The cable for the elevator of Problem 6.2 is $\frac{1}{2}$ in. in diameter. (a) Find the maximum stress in the cable during the first two seconds of motion. (b) If the failure stress is 80 ksi, what is the safety factor?

15.12 If the particle $P$ of a conical pendulum such as that in Problem 6.16 weighs 1000 lb, find the cross-sectional area of cable required to limit the stress to 60,000 psi when $\alpha = 60°$.

[*Ans.*: 0.0333 in².]

15.13 Find the axial force in each member in terms of $P$, $L$, and $h$ for the two trusses shown in Fig. 15.35.

15.14 A chain hoist is supported at $C$ on the tubular steel truss shown in Fig. 15.36. Find the internal force in each member in terms of the weight $W$. If the

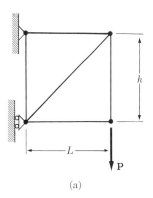

(a)

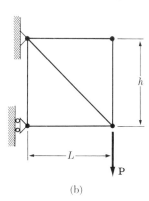

(b)

FIGURE 15.35

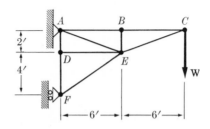

FIGURE 15.36

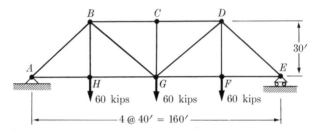

FIGURE 15.37

cross-sectional area of each member is 4 in², what is the maximum weight $W$ which the hoist can lift without exceeding a stress in any member of 15,000 psi in compression or 20,000 psi in tension?

[*Ans.:* $W_{max} = 19.0$ kips.]

15.15 Find the axial forces in all members of the truss shown in Fig. 15.37. Give the required cross-sectional area of each member if the failure stresses are 40 ksi in tension, 24 ksi for 40-ft compression members, and 16 ksi for 50-ft compression members and the desired factor of safety is 2.

15.16 If member $DG$ of the truss in Fig. 15.38 is a 2 in. by 6 in. timber (actual dimensions), find the stress in that member.

[*Ans.:* −344 psi.]

15.17 A 20-kip monorail car rounds a curve of 1000-ft radius at a speed of 150 ft/sec. Assuming that the entire reaction on the car is provided by the single

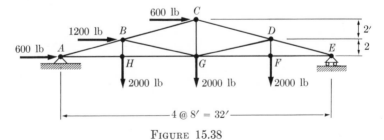

FIGURE 15.38

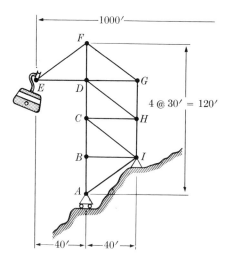

FIGURE 15.39

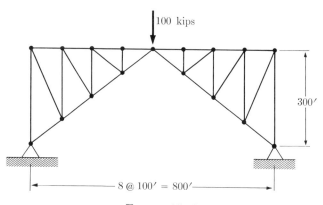

FIGURE 15.40

supporting truss shown in Fig. 15.39, design members $DE$ and $BC$ of the truss for allowable stresses of 20 ksi in tension and 10 ksi in compression. What will be the stress in member $DE$ if the car stops on the curve?

15.18 The truss of Fig. 15.25 has four equal panel lengths of 15 ft and an over-all height of 20 ft. If the cross-sectional areas of members $AD$ and $DH$ are 5 in² each, find the stresses in those members.

[$Ans.$: $\sigma_{AD} = 5.00$ ksi, $\sigma_{DH} = -6.00$ ksi.]

15.19 Find the axial force in each member of the trussed structure shown in Fig. 15.40.

# CHAPTER 16

## FLEXURE

**16.1 Introduction.** In a restricted sense, the word "beam" refers to a member which is stiff enough to carry transverse loads on an open span as in Figs. 16.1(a), 16.1(c), and 16.1(e). The *bending* or *flexure* which such a beam is subjected to in the performance of its function occurs also in other types of bodies such as those in Figs. 15.6(a), 15.6(b), and 15.8(a) and in a variety of levers, machine parts, posts, retaining walls, etc. The present chapter is concerned with the determination of stresses and deformations in flexural members.

The beam in Fig. 16.1(a) may be idealized as the *simply supported beam* of Fig. 16.1(b), which shows a concentrated load and a portion of distributed load as the system of applied forces on the body. The beam in Fig. 16.1(c), called a *cantilever beam,* is shown in its idealized form in Fig. 16.1(d). (Here the distributed load represents the weight of the beam itself.) The beam in Fig. 16.1(e) is a beam with *overhangs,* idealized in Fig. 16.1(f).

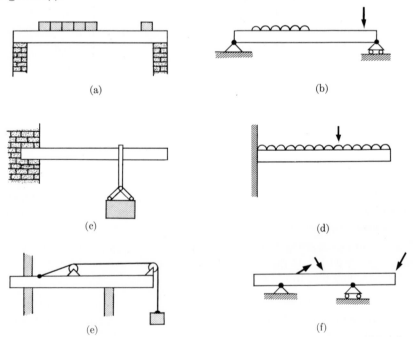

(a)

(b)

(c)

(d)

(e)

(f)

FIGURE 16.1

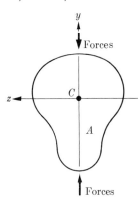

FIGURE 16.2

In this book only that case is considered in which the beam has a longitudinal plane of symmetry (the $xy$-plane) and all the forces, active and reactive, concentrated and distributed, are in this plane. (See Fig. 14.5.) The $x$-axis is taken along the centerline, so that a view of any cross section, such as Fig. 16.2, shows the centroid $C$ of the area $A$ as the intersection point of the $y$- and $z$-axes. With the force system idealized as two-dimensional, the beam is statically determinate when there are no more than three unknown reaction elements, as in Figs. 16.1(b), (d), and (f).

**16.2 Normal force, shear, and bending moment.** To find, at some cross section, the quantities $N$, $S$, and $M$ defined in Art. 14.2, it is necessary to apply the three equations of equilibrium to a portion of the beam which is cut off by that cross section and which has all its external forces already known. If the internal forces are assumed positive, as in Fig. 14.6, they will come out of the solution of the equations with their correct signs. The procedure is illustrated for a beam carrying no normal force in the following example.

EXAMPLE 16.1.   Find the shear and bending moment on cross section $C$ of the beam shown in Fig. 16.3.

*Solution.*   The reactions **A** and **B**, which must be found first, are shown in Fig. 16.3, giving a free-body diagram to which the equations of equilibrium are applied as follows:

$$\sum M_z^A = 20B_y - 6(2)(12) - 16(10) = 0,$$

$$\sum M_z^B = 20A_y - 14(2)(12) - 4(10) = 0.$$

Solving these equations,

$$A_y = 18.8 \text{ kips}, \qquad B_y = 15.2 \text{ kips},$$

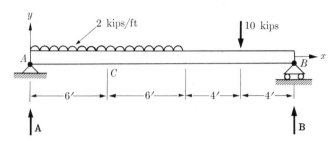

FIGURE 16.3

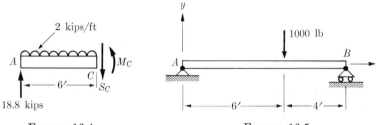

FIGURE 16.4

FIGURE 16.5

FIGURE 16.6

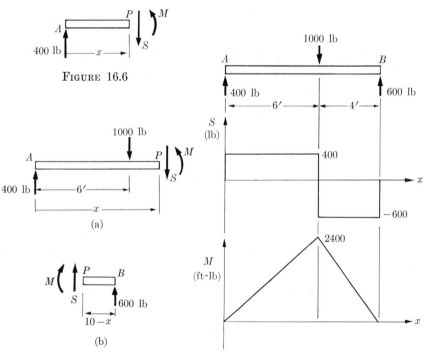

(a)

(b)

FIGURE 16.7

FIGURE 16.8

and, writing a check equation,

$$\sum F_y = 18.8 + 15.2 - 2(12) - 10 = 34 - 34 = 0.$$

Drawing next a free-body diagram of the portion of the beam to the left of $C$ as in Fig. 16.4 (the portion to the right of $C$ also being suitable), we find $M_C$ by taking moments about a $z$-axis through the centroid of the cross section, i.e.,

$$\sum M_z^C = M_C + 3(2)(6) - 6(18.8) = 0,$$
$$M_C = 76.8 \text{ ft-kips.}$$

We find $S_C$ by writing $\sum F_y = 0$, that is,

$$\sum F_y = -S_C - 2(6) + 18.8 = 0,$$
$$S_C = 6.8 \text{ kips.}$$

The shear and bending moment are functions of the position of the cross section, and graphs of $S(x)$ and $M(x)$ vs. $x$ for a particular beam are called the *shear diagram* and the *bending-moment diagram*, respectively. One way to construct these diagrams is to use a cross section at some general distance $x$ from the origin, repeating the procedure for each part of the beam in which a different mathematical expression results for either $S(x)$ or $M(x)$. Such a part is called a *segment* of the beam, and it is shown later that the beam is divided into segments by concentrated forces, concentrated couples, and changes in the distributed forces.

EXAMPLE 16.2.    Draw shear and bending-moment diagrams for the beam of Fig. 16.5.

*Solution.* Applying the equations of equilibrium to the beam as a whole, we find the reactions at $A$ and $B$ to be upward and to have magnitudes of 400 lb and 600 lb, respectively.

Figure 16.6 shows a free-body diagram of the portion of beam between $A$ and any cross section $P$ lying between $A$ and the load. The equations of equilibrium are

$$\sum M_z^P = M - 400x = 0, \qquad \sum F_y = 400 - S = 0,$$

from which

$$S = 400, \qquad M = 400x.$$

Figures 16.7(a) and (b) show two free-body diagrams, either of which is suitable for finding $S(x)$ and $M(x)$ at any cross section $P$ between the load and $B$. Applying the equations of equilibrium to either portion, we obtain

$$S = -600, \qquad M = -600x + 6000.$$

Plotting the functions $S(x)$ and $M(x)$ against $x$ gives the graphs of Fig. 16.8.

To find the mathematical relationships which connect the functions $S(x)$ and $M(x)$ with each other and with the loads applied to the beam, consider an elemental length of beam as in Fig. 16.9. Assume that the beam carries distributed loads of intensity $q_x(x)$ in the $x$-direction (called the *axial distributed load*) and $q_y(x)$ in the $y$-direction (called the *transverse distributed load*). Although these intensities are in general functions of $x$, they may be regarded as constant along the length of the element due to the shortness of the element (or, more precisely, they may be regarded as average values over a finite length $\Delta x$, the average values approaching the actual values at a point as $\Delta x$ approaches zero).

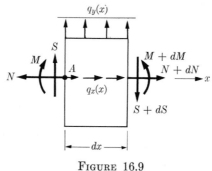

FIGURE 16.9

Applying the equations of equilibrium to the element,

$$\sum F_x = (N + dN) - N + q_x \, dx = 0,$$

$$\sum F_y = S - (S + dS) + q_y \, dx = 0,$$

$$\sum M_z^A = (M + dM) - M - dx(S + dS) + \frac{dx}{2}\,(q_y \, dx) = 0.$$

From the first of these equations,

$$q_x = -\frac{dN}{dx}, \tag{16.1}$$

and, from the second and third equations (neglecting products of differentials in the third),

$$q_y = \frac{dS}{dx}, \tag{16.2}$$

and

$$S = \frac{dM}{dx}. \tag{16.3}$$

Equations (16.1), (16.2), and (16.3) can be derived more rigorously by writing the equations of equilibrium for a finite length of beam $\Delta x$, using the average values of $q_x$ and $q_y$ mentioned above and taking the limit as $\Delta x$ approaches zero.

From Eqs. (16.1) and (16.2) it follows that, if $q_x = 0$ over some portion of the beam, then $N$ is constant for that portion, and, if $q_y = 0$ over some portion, then $S$ is constant for that portion.

As an example of the use of Eq. (16.1), consider the cable in Example 14.3. Since $q_x = w$, where $w$ is the weight per unit length of the cable,

$$\frac{dN}{dx} = -w,$$

and

$$N = -wx + C.$$

But

$$N(0) = W + wL = C.$$

Therefore,

$$N = W + (L - x)w,$$

which agrees with the expression for $N$ derived in the solution of Example 14.3.

Comparing Eqs. (16.2) and (16.3) with Eqs. (5.30) and (5.29), respectively, it is observed that an analogy exists between $M$, $S$, $q_y$, and $x$ in beam theory and $x$, $v_x$, $a_x$, and $t$ in kinematics of rectilinear motion. Thus, drawing the shear and bending-moment diagrams for a portion of beam in which $q_y(x)$ is known is accomplished in a manner similar to that used in drawing the $x$-$t$ and $v_x$-$t$ curves in rectilinear motion for an interval of time in which $a_x(t)$ is known. For example, knowing that the function $q_y(x)$ represents the slope of the shear diagram and that the shear diagram in turn represents the slope of the bending-moment diagram can facilitate plotting the graphs.

---

EXAMPLE 16.3. Draw shear and bending-moment diagrams for the beam of Fig. 16.10, which is carrying a full, uniformly distributed, downward load of intensity $q_0$.

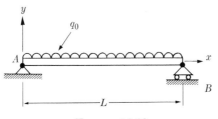

FIGURE 16.10

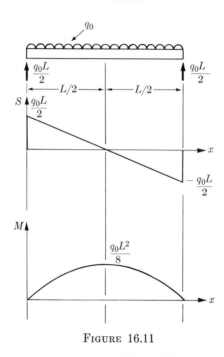

FIGURE 16.11

*Solution.* Figure 16.11 shows the required diagrams. In this case,

$$q_y = -q_0,$$

which means that the shear diagram has a constant, negative slope. (Note that the upward reaction at the left end causes the shear diagram to begin with a positive ordinate equal to the magnitude of the reaction, while the upward reaction at the right end causes the diagram to end with a negative ordinate of the same absolute value.)

The shear diagram indicates that the bending-moment diagram begins with a positive slope which then decreases to zero at the center of the beam. A further decrease in slope in the right half-span makes the $M$-diagram end with a negative slope. Using integration to obtain $S(x)$ and $M(x)$, we find the actual shape of the $M$-diagram to be a parabola with axis at the center of the span, i.e.,

$$M(x) = \frac{q_0}{2}(-x^2 + Lx).$$

The maximum ordinate of the bending-moment diagram is given by

$$M(L/2) = \frac{q_0 L^2}{8}.$$

Note that $M$ has its relative maximum where $S = 0$.

Points of discontinuity and nondifferentiability such as those in Fig. 16.8 are quite common in shear and bending-moment diagrams. It can be seen from Eqs. (16.2) and (16.3) and from the foregoing examples that changes in the mathematical expressions for $S(x)$ or $M(x)$ are caused by concentrated forces, concentrated couples, and changes in the mathematical expression for $q_y(x)$. Hence, these "irregularities" divide the beam into segments.

Another important aid in the construction of $S$- and $M$-diagrams is the definite integral. From Eqs. (16.2) and (16.3),

$$dS = q_y\, dx, \qquad dM = S\, dx,$$

so that, for two points $x_1$ and $x_2$ in a beam,

$$S_2 - S_1 = \int_{x_1}^{x_2} q_y\, dx, \tag{16.4}$$

and

$$M_2 - M_1 = \int_{x_1}^{x_2} S\, dx. \tag{16.5}$$

The right-hand side of Eq. (16.4) is the net area under the graph of $q_y(x)$ between the two points, while the right-hand side of Eq. (16.5) is the net area under the shear diagram between the two points. Because of the properties of the definite integral, Eq. (16.4) holds for any two points between which there are no concentrated loads, regardless of what changes may occur in $q_y(x)$ between the two points. Similarly, Eq. (16.5) holds for any two points between which there are no concentrated couples, regardless of the shape of the shear diagram. In most problems, however, the two equations are applied to each segment separately, as illustrated in the next example.

EXAMPLE 16.4.  Draw shear and bending-moment diagrams for the beam of Fig. 16.12.

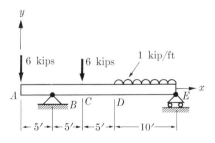

FIGURE 16.12

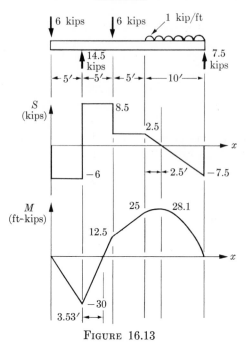

FIGURE 16.13

*Solution.* Figure 16.13 shows the required diagrams. The $S$-diagram is drawn for each segment by noting that the curve is horizontal in the three segments where $q_y = 0$ and has a constant negative slope where $q_y = -1$ kip/ft. The concentrated forces cause discontinuities in the form of abrupt "jumps" up or down which are equal in absolute value to the magnitudes of the forces.

The $M$-diagram is drawn by applying Eq. (16.5) to each segment (with the last segment divided into two parts as shown). Three important points on the bending-moment diagram are the maximum of 28.1 ft-kips, the minimum of $-30$ ft-kips, and the point where $M$ is zero (called a *point of contraflexure*).

---

Figure 16.14 shows shear and bending-moment diagrams for some simple but general cases. Results for more specialized cases can be obtained from the figure by assigning $\xi$ special values such as 0, $L/2$, etc. If the same beam, e.g., that in Figs. 16.14(e) and 16.14(f), carries several loads, e.g., both the concentrated force of Fig. 16.14(e) and the distributed force of Fig. 16.14(f), the complete $S$- and $M$-diagrams may be obtained by adding the two $S$-diagrams and the two $M$-diagrams of those figures. This is called the *principle of superposition of internal forces*. The procedure is valid in this case because $S$ and $M$ at a given point are linear functions of $P$ and $q_0$, but it is not usually valid for bodies which are both inelastic and indeterminate or which suffer large deformations under the loads.

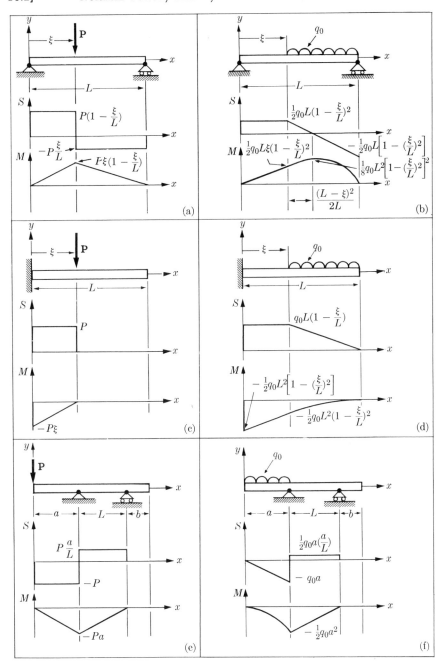

FIGURE 16.14

When a beam carries normal force as well as shear and bending moment, it may be required that a normal-force diagram be included in the analysis of internal forces. Equation (16.1) can assist with the drawing of the $N$-diagram in the same way that Eq. (16.2) does for the $S$-diagram.

EXAMPLE 16.5. Draw normal-force, shear, and bending-moment diagrams for the beam in Fig. 16.15.

*Solution.* Figure 16.16 shows the required diagrams. Note that $N$ is increased by the introduction of a concentrated axial force in the negative $x$-direction and is decreased by an axial force in the positive $x$-direction. Similar statements hold for distributed axial forces, and this behavior is due to the minus sign in Eq. (16.1).

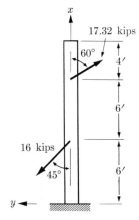

FIGURE 16.15

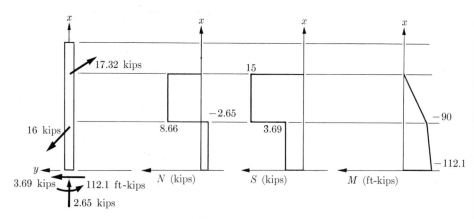

FIGURE 16.16

**16.3 Normal stresses in beams.** Figure 16.17 shows at the left a portion of beam loaded by a transverse distributed force $q_y(x)$, with a view of the cross section shown at the right. The $x$-axis is taken along the centerline of the undeformed beam as before. The normal strain $\epsilon_x$ at any point in the beam is found by considering the deformation of a portion of the beam of length $dx$. During the deformation, the centerline assumes some new position such as that shown in Fig. 16.17. The transverse displacement $u_y(x)$ of the centerline, called the *deflection* of the beam, is greatly exaggerated in the figure.

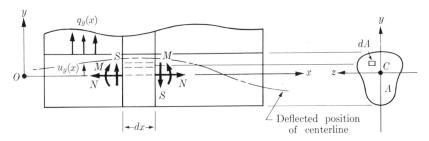

FIGURE 16.17

The basic assumption in elementary beam theory, called *Navier's hypothesis*, is that, during bending, plane cross sections remain plane and perpendicular to the centerline. This assumption leads to results which are in good agreement with experimental results for most beams. It is also assumed that cross sections remain perpendicular to the $xy$-plane, i.e., that the deflected centerline is in the $xy$-plane. (The latter assumption is violated by a beam not fulfilling the conditions of symmetry, etc., mentioned in Art. 16.1 or by a beam so narrow that it buckles laterally under load.)

The strain $\epsilon_x$ in the beam depends on the *curvature $K$* of the deflected centerline, where, from the mathematical theory of plane curves,

$$K = \frac{u_y''}{[1 + (u_y')^2]^{3/2}} . \tag{16.6}$$

Note that $K$ is an algebraic quantity having the same sign as $u_y''$. Figure 16.18(a) shows the portion of beam of length $dx$ before deformation, while Figs. 16.18(b) and 16.18(c) show the same portion after it is stretched by $N$ and bent by negative and positive $M$, respectively. The *radius of curvature $R$* shown in these figures is, by definition, given by

$$R = \frac{1}{|K|} . \tag{16.7}$$

Consider now the strain $\epsilon_x$ in an element of length $dx$ and cross-sectional

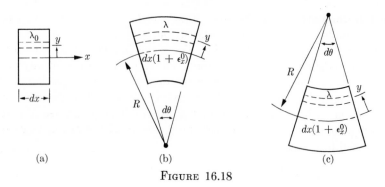

FIGURE 16.18

area $dA$. (See Fig. 16.17.) If $\lambda$ is the final length of the element, then

$$\epsilon_x = \frac{\lambda - \lambda_0}{\lambda_0},\qquad(16.8)$$

where

$$\lambda_0 = dx.$$

If $\epsilon_x^0$ denotes the strain at the centerline, then, from Figs. 16.18(b) and (c),

$$dx(1 + \epsilon_x^0) = R\, d\theta,$$

or

$$d\theta = \frac{dx}{R}(1 + \epsilon_x^0).\qquad(16.9)$$

For the case shown in Fig. 16.18(b), the length $\lambda$ is computed using Eq. (16.9) as follows:

$$\lambda = (R + y)\, d\theta = dx(1 + \epsilon_x^0)\left(1 + \frac{y}{R}\right)$$
$$= dx\left(1 + \epsilon_x^0 + \frac{y}{R} + \epsilon_x^0 \frac{y}{R}\right).$$

Two more assumptions are now made. One, the assumption of *small strains*, is that $\epsilon_x^0 \ll 1$. The other, the assumption of a *slender beam*, is that $y/R \ll 1$. The product of $\epsilon_x^0$ and $y/R$ is thus negligible in comparison with the quantities themselves, so that

$$\lambda = dx\left(1 + \epsilon_x^0 + \frac{y}{R}\right).$$

Substituting this into Eq. (16.8),

$$\epsilon_x = \epsilon_x^0 + \frac{y}{R}.\qquad(16.10)$$

By a similar treatment of the case in Fig. 16.18(c),

$$\epsilon_x = \epsilon_x^0 - \frac{y}{R}. \tag{16.11}$$

In either case,

$$\epsilon_x = \epsilon_x^0 - Ky, \tag{16.12}$$

since the negative moment produces a negative $u_y''$ and the positive moment a positive $u_y''$. Equation (16.12), valid for positive or negative values of $\epsilon_x^0$, $K$, and $y$, shows the dependence of $\epsilon_x$ on $x$ (through $\epsilon_x^0$ and $K$) and on $y$ (explicitly).

Equation (16.12) places no restriction on the material of the beam. To find $\sigma_x$, however, the appropriate stress-strain relation must be used. For a material which is linearly elastic, homogeneous, and isotropic, assuming that $\sigma_y = \sigma_z = 0$, it follows from Eqs. (14.12) and (16.12) that

$$\sigma_x = E\epsilon_x^0 - EKy. \tag{16.13}$$

Equation (16.13) gives $\sigma_x$ in terms of known quantities $E$ and $y$ and unknown parameters $\epsilon_x^0$ and $K$. The two unknown parameters are found in terms of $N$ and $M$ by expressing the mechanical equivalence of the force-couple system on a cross section to the normal-stress distribution there. By the first of Eqs. (8.29),

$$N = \iint_A \sigma_x \, dA,$$

so that

$$N = E\epsilon_x^0 \iint_A dA - EK \iint_A y \, dA.$$

The first integral in this equation is $A$, and the second is zero; therefore,

$$N = E\epsilon_x^0 A,$$

and

$$\epsilon_x^0 = \frac{N}{EA}. \tag{16.14}$$

By the last of Eqs. (8.29),

$$M = - \iint_A \sigma_x y \, dA$$

(the minus sign being used because a positive $\sigma_x$ and a positive $y$ contribute negatively to $M$), so that

$$M = -E\epsilon_x^0 \iint_A y \, dA + EK \iint_A y^2 \, dA.$$

The second integral here is the moment of inertia $I_z$ of the cross-sectional area, hereafter designated simply as $I$. Hence,

$$M = EKI,$$

and

$$K = \frac{M}{EI}. \tag{16.15}$$

Substituting Eqs. (16.14) and (16.15) into Eq. (16.13),

$$\sigma_x = \frac{N}{A} - \frac{My}{I}. \tag{16.16}$$

Equation (16.16) gives the normal stress $\sigma_x$ at any point in the beam (except points near a concentrated load) in terms of known quantities. The equation is called the *flexure formula*. Note that, when $M = 0$, Eq. (16.16) reduces to Eq. (14.9). On the other hand, when $N = 0$, a case called *pure bending*, $\sigma_x$ is proportional to $y$ on any cross section, and $\sigma_x = 0$ when $y = 0$. The line of zero stress on a cross section is called the *neutral axis;* thus, in pure bending, the $z$-axis is the neutral axis.

The stress given by Eq. (16.16) does not depend on the material of the beam, but the material must be linearly elastic to make the moment term in the equation correct. Furthermore, it can be shown through the use of a more complicated derivation that Eq. (16.16) is not changed by omitting the assumptions of small strains and a slender beam made above (although the basic assumption that plane sections remain plane usually becomes unrealistic when these other assumptions are violated). Equation (16.15), which is used later to find the deflection $u_y$ of the beam, does depend on these assumptions.

Equation (16.16) shows that the total stress $\sigma_x$ at any point in a linearly elastic beam is the sum of the stress caused by $N$ and that caused by $M$.

For a rectangular cross section of width $b$ and height $h$, from Fig. 10.8,

$$I = \tfrac{1}{12}bh^3,$$

so that

$$\sigma_x = \frac{N}{bh} - \frac{12My}{bh^3}.$$

A graph of this stress for positive $N$ and $M$ is plotted in two parts in Fig. 16.19, one part being the constant term and the other part the linear term. Note that the stress does not vary with $z$. For any other symmetrical cross section, the graph is similar.

Since there is only one normal stress in the beam, the subscript $x$ may be dropped and the stress designated simply as $\sigma$.

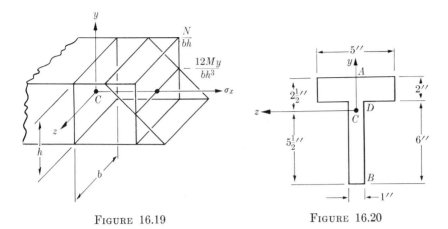

FIGURE 16.19                                      FIGURE 16.20

EXAMPLE 16.6.   A beam with the cross section of Example 10.4 (shown in
Fig. 16.20) is subjected to an internal-force system in which $M = -20$ ft-kips
and $N = 0$. Find the normal stress $\sigma$ at the "extreme fibers" above and below
the neutral axis, i.e., at $A$ and $B$.

*Solution.* From Example 10.4,

$$I = 81.3 \text{ in}^4,$$

so that, by Eq. (16.16),

$$\sigma_A = -\frac{(-20)(2.5)(12)}{81.3} = 7.38 \text{ ksi},$$

$$\sigma_B = -\frac{(-20)(-5.5)(12)}{81.3} = -16.24 \text{ ksi}.$$

The analysis of a beam in which there is also a normal force $N$ is illustrated in the following example.

EXAMPLE 16.7.   A beam with the same cross section as in Example 16.6 is
subjected to an internal-force system in which $M = -20$ ft-kips and $N =
-40$ kips. Find the normal stress at $A$ and $B$.

*Solution.* By Eq. (16.16) and the results of Example 16.6,

$$\sigma_A = -\tfrac{40}{16} + 7.38 = 4.88 \text{ ksi},$$

$$\sigma_B = -\tfrac{40}{16} - 16.24 = -18.74 \text{ ksi}.$$

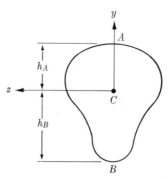

FIGURE 16.21

Since the maximum and minimum values of normal stress occur at the "extreme fibers," i.e., at the top and bottom of the beam, finding the allowable positive or negative bending moment for a cross section may require investigating both the top and the bottom, using the appropriate allowable stress in each case. If it is required to find the allowable positive bending moment on the cross section of Fig. 16.21, for example, the allowable moment $M_a^T$ as controlled by tension is found from Eq. (16.16) as follows:

$$M_a^T = -\frac{\sigma_a^T I}{-h_B},$$

while the moment $M_a^C$ as controlled by compression is given by

$$M_a^C = -\frac{\sigma_a^C I}{h_A}.$$

The actual allowable positive bending moment $M_a$ is the smaller of these two values. For negative bending moment, the denominators in the foregoing equations are interchanged, and the actual allowable negative bending moment is the smaller in absolute value of the two computed values $M_a^T$ and $M_a^C$.

EXAMPLE 16.8. The beam of Example 16.6 is subjected to pure bending such that the flange is in compression, that is, $M$ is positive. Find the allowable moment $M_a$ if $\sigma_a^T = 20$ ksi, $\sigma_a^C = -16$ ksi.

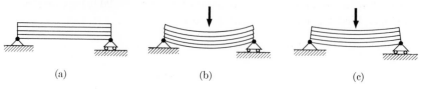

(a)  (b)  (c)

FIGURE 16.22

*Solution.* As controlled by the stress at $A$,

$$M_a^C = -\frac{(-16)(81.3)}{(2.5)(12)} = 43.3 \text{ ft-kips,}$$

and, by the stress at $B$,

$$M_a^T = -\frac{(20)(81.3)}{(-5.5)(12)} = 24.6 \text{ ft-kips.}$$

Hence,

$$M_a = 24.6 \text{ ft-kips.}$$

---

To make a beam strong in flexure without making it excessively heavy, it is desirable that the ratio of $I$ to $A$ be large. This is accomplished, for example, in the *wide-flange beam*, which has a cross section shaped like the area of Fig. 10.26.

**16.4 Shear stresses in beams.** The presence of shear stresses in a beam can be demonstrated by considering a stack of rectangular beams such as that in Fig. 16.22(a). If a transverse load is applied, the beams are found to slide with respect to each other at every point except the midspan, as in Fig. 16.22(b). Note in this figure that plane sections do not remain plane for the system of beams as a whole. If the individual pieces are connected to each other, however, in some way that prevents the relative slipping (e.g., by glue), then plane sections do remain nearly plane as in Fig. 16.22(c), and the beam is stiffer and stronger. Considering now a solid beam of the same height as the stack, we conclude that shear stresses $\tau_{xy}$ must act between layers of the beam to cause plane sections to remain plane, i.e., to make the beam act as a single member.

To determine the shear stresses quantitatively, consider an elemental length of beam as in Fig. 16.23(a). Figure 16.23(b) shows the cross section and indicates the height $y$ at which it is desired to evaluate $\tau_{xy}$.

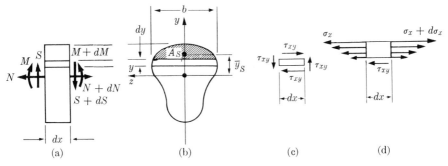

FIGURE 16.23

Figure 16.23(c) shows the element (as seen from the side of the beam) on which $\tau_{xy}$ acts, and Fig. 16.23(d) shows (again from the side) the portion of beam between the two cross sections of Fig. 16.23(a) and above the element of Fig. 16.23(c).

Applying the first equation of equilibrium to the free-body diagram of Fig. 16.23(d),

$$\Sigma F_x = \iint_{A_S} (\sigma_x + d\sigma_x)\, dA - \iint_{A_S} \sigma_x\, dA - \tau_{xy} b\, dx = 0,$$

where $A_S$ and $b$ are as shown in Fig. 16.23(b). It is assumed in this elementary theory that $\tau_{xy}$ does not vary with $z$. Rewriting the last equation,

$$\tau_{xy} b\, dx = \iint_{A_S} d\sigma_x\, dA.$$

From Eq. (16.16),

$$d\sigma_x = \frac{dN}{A} - \frac{(dM)y}{I},$$

so that

$$\tau_{xy} b\, dx = \frac{dN}{A} \iint_{A_S} dA - \frac{dM}{I} \iint_{A_S} y\, dA.$$

Hence,

$$\tau_{xy} b = \frac{dN}{dx} \frac{A_S}{A} - \frac{dM}{dx} \frac{A_S \bar{y}_S}{I}.$$

By Eqs. (16.1) and (16.3), therefore,

$$\tau_{xy} b = -q_x \frac{A_S}{A} - \frac{S A_S \bar{y}_S}{I}, \qquad (16.17)$$

and

$$\tau_{xy} = -\frac{q_x}{b} \frac{A_S}{A} - \frac{S A_S \bar{y}_S}{Ib}. \qquad (16.18)$$

In most practical problems, $q_x = 0$, so that

$$\tau_{xy} = -\frac{S A_S \bar{y}_S}{Ib}. \qquad (16.19)$$

From Eq. (16.19) it can be seen that $\tau_{xy}$ is a function of $x$ (through the shear $S$) and of $y$ (through $A_S$, $\bar{y}_S$, and $b$).

For the rectangular cross section of Fig. 16.24,

$$A_S = b\left(\frac{h}{2} - y\right), \qquad \bar{y}_S = \frac{1}{2}\left(\frac{h}{2} + y\right),$$

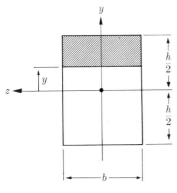

FIGURE 16.24

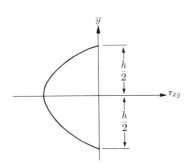

FIGURE 16.25

so that

$$A_s \bar{y}_s = \frac{b}{2}\left(\frac{h^2}{4} - y^2\right).$$

Hence,

$$\tau_{xy} = -\frac{6S}{bh^3}\left(\frac{h^2}{4} - y^2\right). \tag{16.20}$$

Thus, $\tau_{xy}$ is parabolic in $y$, and a graph of $\tau_{xy}$ vs. $y$ for positive $S$ is as shown in Fig. 16.25. (The negative sign of $\tau_{xy}$ is due to the difference in conventions for positive $S$ and positive $\tau_{xy}$. See Figs. 14.6 and 14.21.) The maximum absolute value of $\tau_{xy}$ occurs when $y = 0$ and is given by

$$|\tau_{xy}|_{\max} = \frac{3}{2}\frac{S}{bh} = \frac{3}{2}\frac{S}{A},$$

which is 1.5 times the "average" absolute value. A graph of $\tau_{xy}$ vs. $y$ for a wide-flange beam is shown in Fig. 16.26. For most standard cross

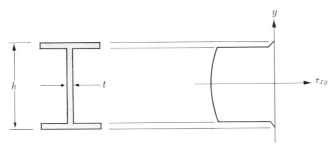

FIGURE 16.26

FIGURE 16.27

sections of this shape, the maximum absolute value of $\tau_{xy}$ is given approximately by

$$|\tau_{xy}|_{\max} = \frac{S}{th}.$$

For a solid circular cross section, it can be shown that

$$|\tau_{xy}|_{\max} = \frac{4}{3}\frac{S}{A}$$

and that this maximum shear stress occurs along the horizontal diameter of the cross section.

If a beam is "built up" by connecting plates, angles, or other sections to a solid beam by riveting, welding, etc., as in Fig. 16.27, the intensity of force per unit length of beam which the shear connection must transmit is given by

$$-\frac{SA_S\bar{y}_S}{I},$$

where the area $A_S$ is that shown crosshatched in Fig. 16.27.

Since there is only one shear stress in a beam, the subscripts $x$ and $y$ may be dropped and the shear stress designated simply as $\tau$.

---

EXAMPLE 16.9. Find the shear stress $\tau$ at $D$ in the beam of Example 16.6 if $S = -30$ kips.

*Solution.* By Eq. (16.19),

$$\tau = -\frac{(-30)(10)(1.5)}{(81.3)(1)} = 5.54\ \text{ksi}.$$

---

The following example shows the determination of allowable bending moment and shear for a given cross section. From Eq. (16.19),

$$S_a = \pm\frac{\tau_a I b}{A_S\bar{y}_S},$$

the plus sign being used for positive shear and the minus sign for negative.

EXAMPLE 16.10. Find the allowable negative bending moment and the allowable positive shear on the cross section shown in Fig. 16.28 if the beam is made of a grade of cast iron for which

$$\sigma_a^T = 3000 \text{ psi},$$

$$\sigma_a^C = -13,000 \text{ psi},$$

$$\tau_a = 3500 \text{ psi}.$$

For this cross section, $I_z = 58.0 \text{ in}^4$.

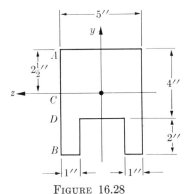

FIGURE 16.28

*Solution.* As controlled by the normal stress at $A$,

$$M_a^T = -\frac{(3000)(58.0)}{(2.5)(12)} = -5800 \text{ ft-lb},$$

and, by the normal stress at $B$,

$$M_a^C = -\frac{(-13,000)(58.0)}{(-3.5)(12)} = -17,950 \text{ ft-lb}.$$

Hence,

$$M_a = -5800 \text{ ft-lb}.$$

To investigate allowable shear, it is necessary to consider the shear stress at both $C$ (the centroidal axis) and $D$ (the point nearest the centroidal axis with a reduced width $b$). As controlled by the shear stress at $C$,

$$S_a^C = \frac{(3500)(58.0)(5)}{(5)(2.5)(1.25)} = 65,000 \text{ lb},$$

and, by the shear stress at $D$,

$$S_a^D = \frac{(3500)(58.0)(2)}{(5)(4)(0.5)} = 40,600 \text{ lb}.$$

Hence,

$$S_a = 40,600 \text{ lb}.$$

**16.5 Analysis and design of beams.** For a beam loaded by a single force **P** at a specified point, Eq. (15.1) gives the factor of safety of the beam. If, instead of a concentrated force, the beam carries a uniformly distributed force of intensity $q_0$ over a specified portion of beam, the factor of safety $n$ is given by

$$n = \frac{q_f}{q_a}, \tag{16.21}$$

where $q_f$ is the value of $q_0$ at failure, etc. The latter loading depends on a single parameter, the intensity $q_0$; for any other single-parameter loading (e.g., a linearly varying distributed force starting with zero intensity and extending over a specified length), $n$ is defined in a similar manner.

To define a factor of safety in terms of stresses, the following three equations for $n$ are written:

$$n = \frac{\sigma_f^T}{\sigma_a^T}, \qquad n = \frac{\sigma_f^C}{\sigma_a^C}, \qquad n = \frac{\tau_f}{\tau_a}, \qquad (16.22)$$

where the denominators, in analysis problems, are either the extreme actual values of the stresses anywhere in the beam under any loading conditions or the allowable values of the stresses, and, in design, are the allowable stresses. The factor of safety is then the smallest of those values of $n$ given by Eqs. (16.22). If there are several members in a structure, the actual safety factor is, as before, the smallest of those for all the members.

To find the extreme normal and shear stresses in a beam in which $N = 0$, it is usually necessary to first determine the maximum and minimum bending moment and the shear with the greatest absolute value. In all but the simplest cases, the latter operation is most effectively accomplished by drawing complete shear and bending-moment diagrams. Equations (16.16) and (16.19) are then used to compute the stresses.

---

EXAMPLE 16.11. A beam with the cross section of Example 16.6 is supported and loaded as shown in Fig. 16.29. Find the maximum tensile and compressive stresses and the maximum shear stress.

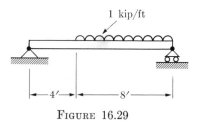

1 kip/ft

|←—4′—→|←———8′———→|

FIGURE 16.29

*Solution.* Figure 16.30 shows the shear and bending-moment diagrams as determined from Fig. 16.14(b). The maximum and minimum normal stresses are now found in the same manner as in Example 16.6, i.e.,

$$\sigma_{min} = -\frac{(14.22)(2.5)(12)}{81.3} = -5.25 \text{ ksi,}$$

$$\sigma_{max} = -\frac{(14.22)(-5.5)(12)}{81.3} = 11.55 \text{ ksi.}$$

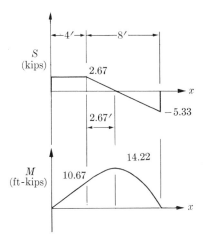

FIGURE 16.30

Since the width $b$ to be used in Eq. (16.19) is as small at the neutral axis as anywhere else on the cross section, the maximum absolute shear stress is at the neutral axis, and it is on that cross section having the greatest absolute shear, i.e.,

$$|\tau|_{max} = \frac{[5.33][(10)(1.5) + (0.5)(0.25)]}{(81.3)(1)} = 0.992 \text{ ksi.}$$

If a beam with no axial force carries several external loads, it is mentioned in Art. 16.2 that the shear and bending moment on a cross section may be obtained by adding the effects of the separate loads. Since the stresses $\sigma$ and $\tau$ are linear in $M$ and $S$, it is clear now that the normal or shear stress at any point in a linearly elastic beam carrying several loads is equal to the sum of the corresponding stresses due to the separate loads. This is called the *principle of superposition of stresses*. The principle is also valid for certain three-dimensional deformable bodies carrying multiple loads, but it is usually invalidated by effects such as inelasticity and large deformations.

In designing a beam having no axial force, the customary procedure is to design for the bending moment and then check the resulting beam for safety in shear. Since there are generally many cross sections of different shapes and sizes capable of withstanding the given applied forces, design problems do not have unique solutions. The final selection of a cross section may be made on the basis of economy, availability of standard shapes, and other factors. For a beam with a horizontal plane of symmetry, such

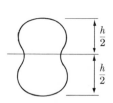 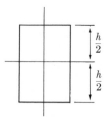 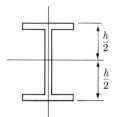

FIGURE 16.31

as those shown in Fig. 16.31, the maximum and minimum normal stresses on a cross section have equal absolute values, and it is therefore necessary to design the cross section only for that bending moment which has the greatest absolute value. By Eq. (16.16), the beam must be designed so that

$$|\sigma_a| = \frac{|M|_{\max}(h/2)}{I}.$$

By definition, the *section modulus Z* of the cross section is given by

$$Z = \frac{2I}{h}, \tag{16.23}$$

so that the required section modulus $Z_r$ of a beam being designed is

$$Z_r = \frac{|M|_{\max}}{|\sigma_a|}. \tag{16.24}$$

If the allowable stresses $\sigma_a$ in tension and compression have different absolute values, the smaller absolute value is used in Eq. (16.24). After $Z_r$ is computed, a cross section having at least that much section modulus must be selected to complete the design.

---

EXAMPLE 16.12. A timber beam to be supported and loaded as in Fig. 16.32 is to be designed with a rectangular cross section having $h = 2b$. If the allowable stresses for the grade of timber being considered are 1700 psi in tension and compression and 120 psi in shear, design the cross section.

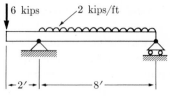

FIGURE 16.32

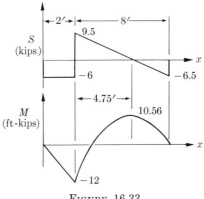

FIGURE 16.33

*Solution.* Shear and bending-moment diagrams for the beam are shown in Fig. 16.33. By Eq. (16.24),

$$Z_r = \frac{(12,000)(12)}{1700} = 84.7 \text{ in}^3.$$

For a rectangular cross section, by Eq. (16.23),

$$Z = bh^2/6.$$

Therefore,

$$\frac{b(2b)^2}{6} = 84.7, \qquad b = 5.03 \text{ in.}, \qquad h = 10.06 \text{ in.}$$

The smallest standard-size timber fulfilling the requirements of this problem is a nominal 6 in. by 12 in. (actual dimensions $5\frac{1}{2}$ in. by $11\frac{1}{2}$ in.). In practice, that is the cross section which would be specified. To illustrate the shear check, however, assume that a beam with actual dimensions 5 in. by 10 in. is to be used. Since the cross section is rectangular,

$$|\tau|_{\max} = \frac{3}{2} \frac{9500}{50} = 285 \text{ psi.}$$

The beam is therefore not safe in shear. The required cross-sectional area on the basis of shear is

$$A = \frac{3}{2} \frac{9500}{120} = 118.8 \text{ in}^2.$$

Thus,

$$b(2b) = 118.8, \qquad b = 7.71 \text{ in.}, \qquad h = 15.42 \text{ in.}$$

Many practical problems are concerned with beams having axial force as well as shear and bending moment. Two simple examples of beams with axial forces are shown in Figs. 16.34(a) and 16.34(b). The analysis and

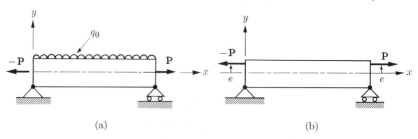

FIGURE 16.34

design of such beams is only slightly more complicated than when $N = 0$ provided that the deflection of the centerline is small enough to neglect the *change* in bending moment which occurs on any cross section during deformation. [This change is due to the change in the eccentricity $e$ of the load $\mathbf{P}$ in Fig. 16.34(b) and to the eccentricity itself in Fig. 16.34(a). The bending moment on a cross section changes because the lever arm of the force $\mathbf{P}$ changes.] Such a simplification is usually not permissible if the beam is very slender, in which case a more advanced theory including deflections must be used. For thick beams, on the other hand, fairly accurate computations can be made by computing $N$ and $M$ for the undeformed state and using the flexure formula as in Art. 16.3.

EXAMPLE 16.13. A cast-iron frame for a press is shaped as shown in Fig. 16.35. Forces $\mathbf{P}$ and $-\mathbf{P}$ are applied 14 in. from the edge of the vertical part of the frame. What is the allowable magnitude $P$ if the allowable normal stresses are 4 ksi in tension and 12 ksi in compression? Assume that cross section $A$–$A$, for which $I_z = 47.0$ in$^4$, is critical.

*Solution.* For cross section $A$–$A$,

$$N = P, \qquad M = -15.94P.$$

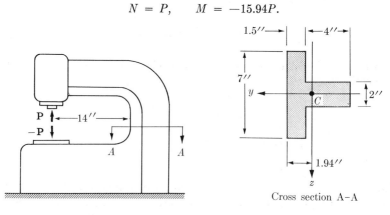

Cross section A–A

FIGURE 16.35

By Eq. (16.16),

$$\sigma_a^T = 4 = \frac{P_a^T}{18.5} - \frac{(-15.94P_a^T)(1.94)}{47.0},$$

from which

$$P_a^T = 5.62 \text{ kips},$$

and

$$\sigma_a^C = -12 = \frac{P_a^C}{18.5} - \frac{(-15.94P_a^C)(-3.56)}{47.0},$$

from which

$$P_a^C = 10.41 \text{ kips}.$$

Hence,

$$P_a = 5.62 \text{ kips}.$$

---

In the design of walls, pedestals, etc., to be constructed of concrete or masonry, the controlling factor is often that there be no tension anywhere on any cross section. Consider the eccentrically loaded compression block of Fig. 16.36. On any cross section, by Eq. (16.16),

$$\sigma = -\frac{P}{A} - \frac{Pey}{I}.$$

If the cross section is rectangular, as in Fig. 16.37, then

$$\sigma = -\frac{P}{bh} - \frac{12Pey}{bh^3}.$$

The maximum stress occurs at $y = -h/2$, so that

$$\sigma_{\max} = -\frac{P}{bh} + \frac{6Pe}{bh^2}$$

$$= -\frac{P}{bh}\left(1 - \frac{6e}{h}\right),$$

and $\sigma_{\max} = 0$ when

$$e = h/6.$$

If $e$ is negative, the maximum stress is at $y = h/2$, so that

$$\sigma_{\max} = -\frac{P}{bh}\left(1 + \frac{6e}{h}\right),$$

and $\sigma_{\max} = 0$ when

$$e = -h/6.$$

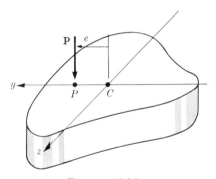

FIGURE 16.36

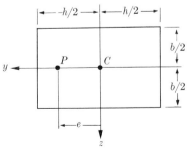

FIGURE 16.37

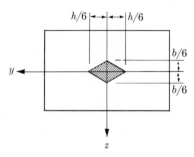

FIGURE 16.38

Thus, a compressive force anywhere on the $y$-axis within a distance of $h/6$ from the $z$-axis produces no tension anywhere in the block. It can be shown by considering bending moments about both the $y$- and $z$-axes that a force anywhere in the crosshatched area of Fig. 16.38 produces no tension anywhere in the block. Such an area is called the *core* or *kernel* of a cross section.

**16.6 Deflection of beams.** The deflection $u_y$ of a beam (Fig. 16.17) is a result of bending deformation (i.e., normal strains) and shear deformation (i.e., shear strains). To develop an elementary theory of deflections of beams, the assumptions of small strains and a slender beam made in Art. 16.3 are retained. Since shear deflection is found to be significant only for thick beams, the assumption of a slender beam makes it permissible to neglect that effect.

To find the bending deflection, it is assumed, in addition to the previous assumptions, that the slope of the deflected centerline is small, i.e., that

$$u_y' \ll 1.$$

Then, by Eq. (16.6),

$$K = u_y'',$$

and, by Eq. (16.15),

$$EIu_y'' = M. \tag{16.25}$$

Differentiating Eq. (16.25) twice and using Eqs. (16.2) and (16.3),

$$(EIu_y'')' = M' = S,$$

$$(EIu_y'')'' = S' = q_y.$$

If $EI$ is constant over some interval of $x$, then, for that interval,

$$EIu_y''' = S \tag{16.26}$$

and

$$EIu_y'''' = q_y. \tag{16.27}$$

The deflection $u_y$ can be found in any segment of a beam in which $EI$ is constant by expressing $M$ in terms of $x$ and substituting into Eq. (16.25). Upon integrating twice and evaluating the constants of integration by known values of $u_y'$ and $u_y$ at the ends of the segment (these values being called *boundary conditions*), we find an expression for $u_y$ as a function of $x$. The procedure is illustrated for a one-segment beam in the following example.

EXAMPLE 16.14. Determine the deflection curve of the cantilever beam pictured in Fig. 16.39 if $EI$ is constant.

*Solution.* At a general distance $x$ from the origin,

$$M = -Px.$$

By Eq. (16.25), therefore,

$$EIu_y'' = -Px,$$

and, by integration,

$$EIu_y' = -\tfrac{1}{2}Px^2 + C_1.$$

By the boundary condition at $x = L$,

$$EIu_y'(L) = 0 = -\tfrac{1}{2}PL^2 + C_1,$$

$$C_1 = \tfrac{1}{2}PL^2,$$

$$EIu_y' = -\tfrac{1}{2}Px^2 + \tfrac{1}{2}PL^2.$$

Integrating again,

$$EIu_y = -\tfrac{1}{6}Px^3 + \tfrac{1}{2}PL^2x + C_2,$$

and, using the other boundary condition at $x = L$,

$$EIu_y(L) = 0 = -\tfrac{1}{6}PL^3 + \tfrac{1}{2}PL^3 + C_2,$$

$$C_2 = -\tfrac{1}{3}PL^3,$$

$$EIu_y = -\tfrac{1}{6}Px^3 + \tfrac{1}{2}PL^2x - \tfrac{1}{3}PL^3.$$

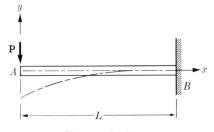

FIGURE 16.39

| | | |
|---|---|---|
| (a) | 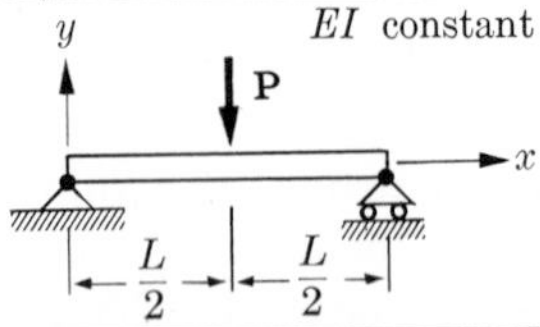y<br>EI constant<br>P<br>x<br>L/2<br>L/2 | $0 < x < \frac{L}{2}$:<br>$u_y = -\frac{PL^3}{48EI}\left[3\left(\frac{x}{L}\right) - 4\left(\frac{x}{L}\right)^3\right]$<br>$\frac{L}{2} < x < L$:<br>$u_y = -\frac{PL^3}{48EI}\left[-1 + 9\left(\frac{x}{L}\right) - 12\left(\frac{x}{L}\right)^2 + 4\left(\frac{x}{L}\right)^3\right]$ |
| (b) | 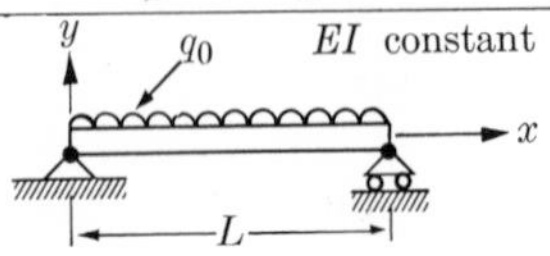y<br>$q_0$<br>EI constant<br>x<br>L | $u_y = -\frac{5q_0L^4}{384EI}\left[\frac{16}{5}\left(\frac{x}{L}\right) - \frac{32}{5}\left(\frac{x}{L}\right)^3 + \frac{16}{5}\left(\frac{x}{L}\right)^4\right]$ |
| (c) | 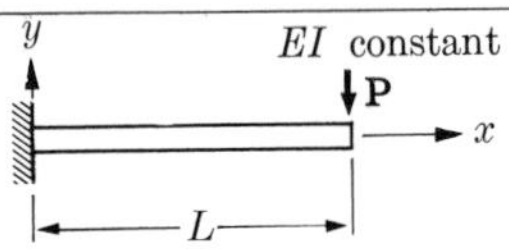y<br>EI constant<br>P<br>x<br>L | $u_y = -\frac{PL^3}{3EI}\left[\frac{3}{2}\left(\frac{x}{L}\right)^2 - \frac{1}{2}\left(\frac{x}{L}\right)^3\right]$ |
| (d) | 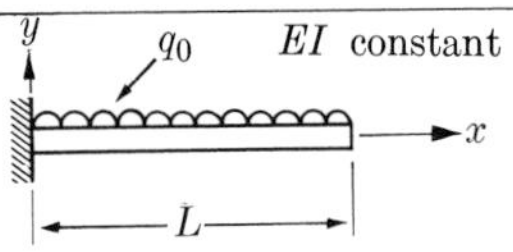y<br>$q_0$<br>EI constant<br>x<br>L | $u_y = -\frac{q_0L^4}{8EI}\left[2\left(\frac{x}{L}\right)^2 - \frac{4}{3}\left(\frac{x}{L}\right)^3 + \frac{1}{3}\left(\frac{x}{L}\right)^4\right]$ |
| (e) | 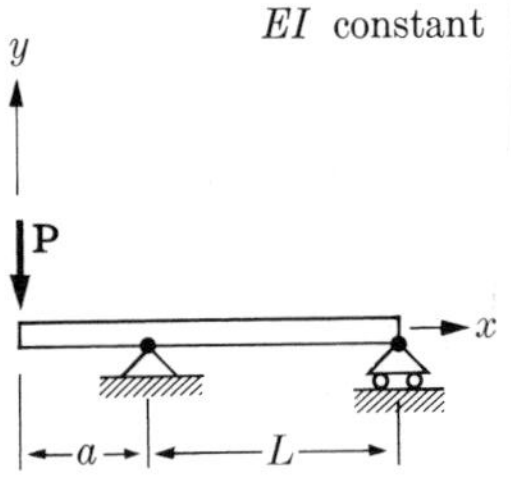EI constant<br>y<br>P<br>x<br>a<br>L | $0 < x < a$:<br>$u_y = -\frac{PL^3}{3EI}\left[\left(\frac{a}{L}\right)^2 + \left(\frac{a}{L}\right)^3 - \left(\frac{a}{L}\right)\left(\frac{x}{L}\right) - \frac{3}{2}\left(\frac{a}{L}\right)^2\left(\frac{x}{L}\right) + \frac{1}{2}\left(\frac{x}{L}\right)^3\right]$<br>$a < x < a + L$:<br>$u_y = \frac{PaL^2}{6EI}\left[-2\left(\frac{a}{L}\right) - 3\left(\frac{a}{L}\right)^2 - \left(\frac{a}{L}\right)^3 + 2\left(\frac{x}{L}\right) + 6\left(\frac{a}{L}\right)\left(\frac{x}{L}\right) + 3\left(\frac{a}{L}\right)^2\left(\frac{x}{L}\right) - 3\left(\frac{x}{L}\right)^2 - 3\left(\frac{a}{L}\right)\left(\frac{x}{L}\right)^2 + \left(\frac{x}{L}\right)^3\right]$ |
| (f) | 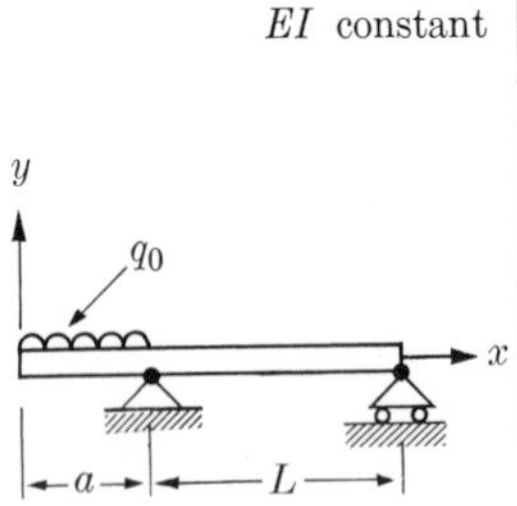EI constant<br>y<br>$q_0$<br>x<br>a<br>L | $0 < x < a$:<br>$u_y = -\frac{q_0L^4}{24EI}\left[4\left(\frac{a}{L}\right)^3 + 3\left(\frac{a}{L}\right)^4 - 4\left(\frac{a}{L}\right)^2\left(\frac{x}{L}\right) - 4\left(\frac{a}{L}\right)^3\left(\frac{x}{L}\right) + \left(\frac{x}{L}\right)^4\right]$<br>$a < x < a + L$:<br>$u_y = \frac{q_0a^2L^2}{12EI}\left[-2\left(\frac{a}{L}\right) - 3\left(\frac{a}{L}\right)^2 - \left(\frac{a}{L}\right)^3 + 2\left(\frac{x}{L}\right) + 6\left(\frac{a}{L}\right)\left(\frac{x}{L}\right) + 3\left(\frac{a}{L}\right)^2\left(\frac{x}{L}\right) - 3\left(\frac{x}{L}\right)^2 - 3\left(\frac{a}{L}\right)\left(\frac{x}{L}\right)^2 + \left(\frac{x}{L}\right)^3\right]$ |

FIGURE 16.40

Rewriting the equations for the deflection and slope,

$$u_y = -\frac{PL^3}{3EI}\left[\frac{1}{2}\left(\frac{x}{L}\right)^3 - \frac{3}{2}\left(\frac{x}{L}\right) + 1\right],$$

$$u_y' = \frac{PL^2}{2EI}\left[-\left(\frac{x}{L}\right)^2 + 1\right].$$

Since the slope $u_y'$ is everywhere small, it is essentially equal to the angle of rotation $\theta$ of the cross section at each point. At $x = 0$, then, denoting the deflection at $A$ by $\Delta_A$,

$$u_y(0) = \Delta_A = -\frac{PL^3}{3EI},$$

$$u_y'(0) = \theta_A = \frac{PL^2}{2EI}.$$

Figure 16.40 gives $u_y$ as a function of $x$ for some simple cases of beams with $EI$ constant throughout. When a beam has several segments, as in Figs. 16.40(a), 16.40(e), and 16.40(f), it is usually necessary to perform two integrations for each segment (using the appropriate expression for $M$). Some of the boundary conditions then occur at the junction of the two segments and express either the continuity or the differentiability of the function $u_y$ there. For example, the four boundary conditions for the beam in Fig. 16.40(e) are as follows:

$$u_{y1}(a) = 0, \qquad u_{y2}(a) = 0, \qquad u_{y2}(a + L) = 0,$$

$$u_{y1}'(a) = u_{y2}'(a).$$

Problems such as this often entail the solution of simple simultaneous equations during the evaluation of the constants.

The foregoing deflection theory is valid only for slender beams, and it is therefore impossible to use it for finding deflections when the beam carries both normal force and bending moment, since, for slender beams, the contribution of the normal force to the deflection cannot be neglected.

For a slender beam carrying several transverse forces, e.g., those of Figs. 16.40(e) and 16.40(f), but no axial forces, the total deflection at a point is the sum of the deflections caused there by the separate loads. This is called the *principle of superposition of deflections*. It depends on the linearity between $u_y''$ and $M$ of Eq. (16.25) and the previously established linearity between $M$ and the loads (Art. 16.2). The principle is not valid unless the beam is linearly elastic and unless the beam does not change shape appreciably when loaded.

**16.7 Moment-area theorems.** For problems where the deflection $\Delta$ and the angle of rotation $\theta$ are required only at particular points in a beam (e.g., at point $A$ in Fig. 16.39), it is usually more convenient to integrate Eq. (16.25) by means of definite integrals rather than indefinite. Doing this in a general way leads to equations which are suitable for finding deflections and rotations in beams with many segments and with variations in $I$, such problems being difficult to solve by the method of Art. 16.6.

Rewriting Eq. (16.25),

$$u_y''(x) = \frac{M}{EI}.$$

Integration between two points $x_1$ and $x_2$ now gives

$$u_y'(x_2) - u_y'(x_1) = \int_{x_1}^{x_2} \frac{M}{EI}\, dx, \qquad (16.28)$$

or

$$\theta_2 = \theta_1 + \int_{x_1}^{x_2} \frac{M}{EI}\, dx. \qquad (16.29)$$

Equation (16.29) states that the rotation at $x_2$ equals the rotation at $x_1$ plus the area under the $(M/EI)$-diagram between $x_1$ and $x_2$. This is called the *first moment-area theorem*. Because of the properties of the definite integral, this theorem applies to any two points of a beam, even if there are concentrated forces and couples and changes in $q_y$ and $I$ between the two points, as long as there are no hinges in the beam between the two points.

Applying Eq. (16.28) to $x_1$ and a general point $x$,

$$u_y'(x) = u_y'(x_1) + \int_{x_1}^{x} \frac{M}{EI}\, dx. \qquad (16.30)$$

The integral on the right-hand side of this equation is a function of $x$. Temporarily calling this function $A(x)$, we have

$$A(x) = \int_{x_1}^{x} \frac{M}{EI}\, dx, \qquad (16.31)$$

and

$$dA = \frac{M}{EI}\, dx. \qquad (16.32)$$

Equation (16.30) then becomes

$$u_y'(x) = u_y'(x_1) + A.$$

Another integration between points $x_1$ and $x_2$ now gives

$$u_y(x_2) - u_y(x_1) = [u'_y(x_1)][x_2 - x_1] + \int_{x_1}^{x_2} A \, dx. \qquad (16.33)$$

To put the integral of Eq. (16.33) into a more useful form, note, since

$$d(Ax) = A \, dx + x \, dA,$$

that

$$A \, dx = d(Ax) - x \, dA$$

and

$$\int A \, dx = Ax - \int x \, dA.$$

(This is called *integrating by parts*.)  Hence,

$$\int_{x_1}^{x_2} A \, dx = Ax \Big|_{x_1}^{x_2} - \int_{x_1}^{x_2} x \, dA$$

$$= [A(x_2)][x_2] - [A(x_1)][x_1] - \int_{x_1}^{x_2} x \, dA.$$

But, by Eq. (16.31),

$$A(x_1) = 0.$$

Therefore,

$$\int_{x_1}^{x_2} A \, dx = [A(x_2)][x_2] - \int_{x_1}^{x_2} x \, dA = \int_{x_1}^{x_2} (x_2 - x) \, dA,$$

and, using Eq. (16.32),

$$\int_{x_1}^{x_2} A \, dx = \int_{x_1}^{x_2} \frac{M}{EI} (x_2 - x) \, dx.$$

Finally, then, Eq. (16.33) becomes

$$\Delta_2 = \Delta_1 + \theta_1(x_2 - x_1) + \int_{x_1}^{x_2} \frac{M}{EI} (x_2 - x) \, dx. \qquad (16.34)$$

Equation (16.34) states that the deflection at $x_2$ equals the deflection at $x_1$ plus the product of the rotation at $x_1$ and the difference $x_2 - x_1$ plus the first moment of the area under the $(M/EI)$-diagram about the $x_2$-end of the diagram.  This is called the *second moment-area theorem*.  It also applies to any two points between which there are no hinges.

---

EXAMPLE 16.15.  Using the moment-area theorems, find $\theta_C$, $\theta_D$, and $\Delta_D$ for the beam of Fig. 16.41.

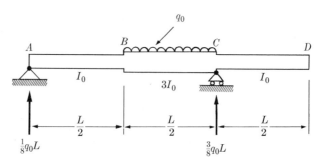

FIGURE 16.41

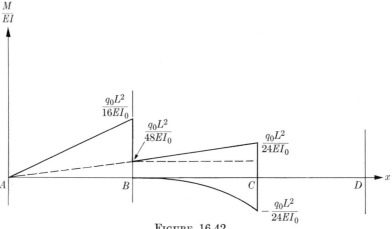

FIGURE 16.42

*Solution.* To facilitate the computation of areas and first moments, the $(M/EI)$-diagram is drawn *by parts* in Fig. 16.42 (i.e., the contribution of the reaction at $A$ is plotted separately from that of the distributed load). Applying Eq. (16.34) to points $A$ and $C$,

$$0 = \theta_A L + \frac{1}{2}\left(\frac{L}{2}\right)\left(\frac{q_0 L^2}{16EI_0}\right)\left(\frac{2L}{3}\right) + \left(\frac{L}{2}\right)\left(\frac{q_0 L^2}{48EI_0}\right)\left(\frac{L}{4}\right)$$

$$+ \frac{1}{2}\left(\frac{L}{2}\right)\left(\frac{q_0 L^2}{48EI_0}\right)\left(\frac{L}{6}\right) + \frac{1}{3}\left(\frac{L}{2}\right)\left(-\frac{q_0 L^2}{24EI_0}\right)\left(\frac{L}{8}\right).$$

[Note how the contribution of the negative part of the $(M/EI)$-diagram to the integral of Eq. (16.34) is properly accounted for by using the negative ordinate of the parabola at $C$.] Solving for $\theta_A$,

$$\theta_A = -\frac{5q_0 L^3}{384EI_0}.$$

By Eq. (16.29), then,

$$\theta_C = -\frac{5q_0L^3}{384EI_0} + \frac{1}{2}\left(\frac{L}{2}\right)\left(\frac{q_0L^2}{16EI_0}\right) + \left(\frac{L}{2}\right)\left(\frac{q_0L^2}{48EI_0}\right)$$

$$+ \frac{1}{2}\left(\frac{L}{2}\right)\left(\frac{q_0L^2}{48EI_0}\right) + \frac{1}{3}\left(\frac{L}{2}\right)\left(-\frac{q_0L^2}{24EI_0}\right)$$

$$= \frac{13q_0L^3}{1152EI_0}.$$

[Note again how the contribution of the negative bending moment to Eq. (16.29) is properly accounted for by using the negative ordinate.]

Applying Eq. (16.29) to points $C$ and $D$,

$$\theta_D = \theta_C = \frac{13q_0L^3}{1152EI_0},$$

and, applying Eq. (16.34) to the same two points,

$$\Delta_D = \theta_C\left(\frac{L}{2}\right) = \frac{13q_0L^4}{2304EI_0}.$$

## PROBLEMS

16.1 Find the shear and bending moment on cross section $C$ of the beam in Fig. 16.43.

16.2 It is desired to place a joint, in the beam shown in Fig. 16.44, at the point between $B$ and $C$ where the bending moment is zero. (a) Find expressions for $S$ and $M$ in terms of $x$ between $B$ and $C$. (b) Locate the point where $M$ is zero. (c) Find the shear which the joint must transmit.

[*Ans.*: (b) $x = 11.5$ ft; (c) $6.5$ kips.]

16.3 Draw shear and bending-moment diagrams for the beam in Fig. 16.45.

16.4 Verify the $S$- and $M$-diagrams given in Fig. 16.14(b).

16.5 Verify the $S$- and $M$-diagrams given in Fig. 16.14(d).

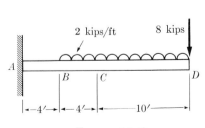

FIGURE 16.43

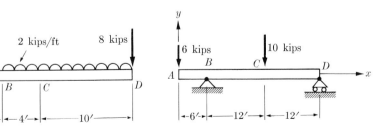

FIGURE 16.44

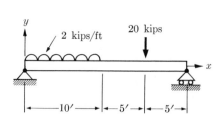

FIGURE 16.45

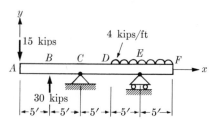

FIGURE 16.46

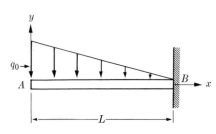

FIGURE 16.47

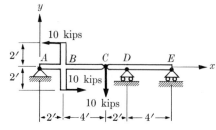

FIGURE 16.48

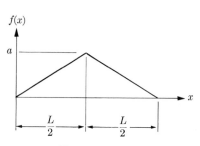

FIGURE 16.49

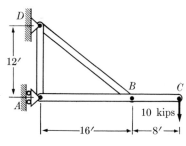

FIGURE 16.50

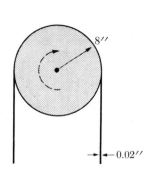

FIGURE 16.51

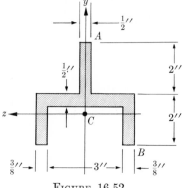

FIGURE 16.52

16.6 Draw shear and bending-moment diagrams for the beam shown in Fig. 16.46.

16.7 The beam in Fig. 16.47 carries a downward distributed load varying in intensity from $q_0$ at the free end to zero at the support. Draw the shear and bending-moment diagrams.

16.8 Draw shear and bending-moment diagrams for the beam $ABCDE$ in Fig. 16.48.

16.9 (a) If, in Fig. 16.49, $f$ is the bending moment, draw the beam and loading and the $S$-diagram. (b) If $f$ is the shear, draw a beam and loading which will give such an $S$-diagram, and also draw the $M$-diagram for that beam.

16.10 Draw $N$-, $S$-, and $M$-diagrams for member $ABC$ of the pin-connected frame shown in Fig. 16.50.

16.11 Draw $N$-, $S$-, and $M$-diagrams for the beam of Problem 11.22.

16.12 A band-saw blade which is 0.02 in. thick is driven by a wheel of 8-in. radius as shown in Fig. 16.51. If the blade is made of steel ($E = 30,000$ ksi), find the maximum flexural stress in the blade.

[*Ans.:* 37.5 ksi.]

16.13 A beam having rectangular cross section 6 in. wide and 12 in. deep is subjected to a positive bending moment of 20 ft-kips. Find the maximum and minimum stresses.

16.14 A beam having rectangular cross section 6 in. wide and 12 in. deep is subjected to a positive bending moment of 20 ft-kips and a positive normal force of 10 kips. Find the maximum and minimum stresses.

[*Ans.:* $\sigma_{max} = 1806$ psi, $\sigma_{min} = -1528$ psi.]

16.15 For a positive bending moment of 20 ft-kips on the cross section shown in Fig. 16.52, find the normal stress at $A$ and $B$.

16.16 The standard "tee" section shown in Fig. 16.53 is loaded as a beam in such a way that the flange is in tension. If the allowable stresses are 20 ksi in tension and 16 ksi in compression, what is the allowable negative bending moment for the section?

[*Ans.:* $-2.70$ ft-kips.]

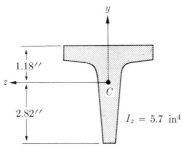

FIGURE 16.53

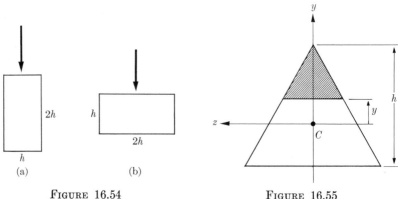

FIGURE 16.54                    FIGURE 16.55

16.17 In Fig. 16.54, compare the effectiveness of the two orientations (a) and (b) of a rectangular cross section by computing, for no axial force, the ratio of the allowable positive bending moment on (a) to that on (b).

16.18 An equilateral triangular cross section of height $h$ is oriented as shown in Fig. 16.55. (a) Find the absolute value of the shear stress at $y$ in terms of $S$, $h$, and $y$. (b) Find the $y$ necessary to maximize that absolute value. (c) What is the maximum absolute value?

$$\left[ Ans.: \text{ (a) } \sqrt{3}\, \frac{|S|}{h^4} \left( \frac{4}{3}\, h^2 + 2hy - 6y^2 \right); \text{ (b) } \frac{h}{6}; \text{ (c) } \frac{3\sqrt{3}}{2}\, \frac{|S|}{h^2}. \right]$$

16.19 A beam having rectangular cross section 6 in. wide and 12 in. deep is subjected to a positive shear of 4 kips. Find the maximum absolute value of the shear stress.

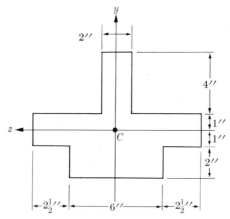

FIGURE 16.56

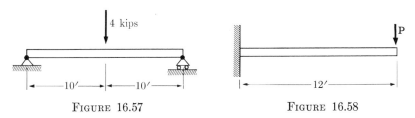

FIGURE 16.57                     FIGURE 16.58

16.20 Find the ratio of the allowable positive shears for the two orientations of cross section of Problem 16.17.

[*Ans.:* 1.]

16.21 Find the allowable positive bending moment and the allowable negative shear on the cross section shown in Fig. 16.56 if the allowable stresses are as given in Example 16.10.

16.22 The beam in Fig. 16.57 has a rectangular cross section 6 in. wide and 12 in. deep. Find the maximum tensile and compressive stresses and the maximum shear stress.

[*Ans.:* $\sigma_{max} = 1670$ psi, $\sigma_{min} = -1670$ psi, $|\tau|_{max} = 41.7$ psi.]

16.23 The cast-iron beam in Fig. 16.58 has the cross section of Example 16.10. Using the results of that example, determine the allowable value of $P$.

16.24 A standard wide-flange beam with properties shown at the right in Fig. 16.59 is to carry a uniform downward load on a 20-ft simple span. (a) If the allowable stresses are 20 ksi in tension and 18.2 ksi in compression, find the allowable value of $q_0$. (b) Compute the approximate maximum shear stress due to this load.

[*Ans.:* (a) 3.89 kips/ft; (b) 4.94 ksi.]

16.25 A standard wide-flange beam with properties shown at the right in Fig. 16.60 is to support the tracks for a railway as shown at the left in the figure. (a) If $P = 80$ kips, find the maximum tensile and compressive stresses in the beam. (b) If the allowable stresses are 20 ksi in tension and compression, what is the allowable value of $P$?

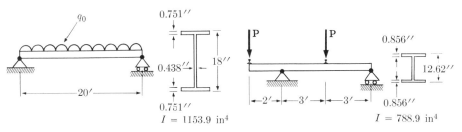

FIGURE 16.59                     FIGURE 16.60

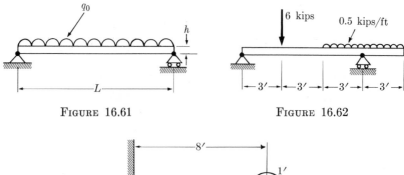

FIGURE 16.61

FIGURE 16.62

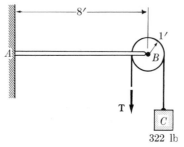

FIGURE 16.63

Centerline of channel

100 kips

100 kips

0.50″

2.24″

0.70″

FIGURE 16.64

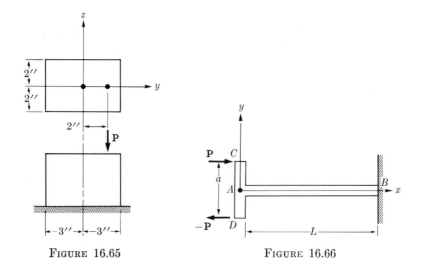

FIGURE 16.65

FIGURE 16.66

16.26 A timber beam with rectangular cross section of height $h$ is to be designed to carry a uniform downward load (Fig. 16.61). If the allowable stresses are 1200 psi in tension and compression and 112 psi in shear, find the minimum ratio $L/h$ such that flexure controls the design.

[*Ans.:* 10.7.]

16.27 It is desired to use a timber beam 8 in. wide to support the loads shown in Fig. 16.62. What height $h$ is required to limit the normal stress to an absolute value of 1200 psi?

16.28 The cast-iron beam shown in Fig. 16.63 has the cross section of Example 16.10. Using the results of that example, determine the maximum permissible upward acceleration that can be given to the weight $C$. Treat the rope and pulley as ideal.

[*Ans.:* 4.05 ft/sec².]

16.29 A standard, steel "channel" section for which $A = 6.03$ in² and $I = 3.90$ in⁴ is used as a tension member in a frame. It is connected at its ends by riveted lap joints to $\frac{1}{2}$-in.-thick steel plates as shown in Fig. 16.64. The member was designed to carry an axial load of 100 kips on the assumption that the load would act along the centerline of the member. (a) On the basis of the design assumption, what is the stress in the member? (b) If the load is actually applied along the centerline of the connecting plates, what is the maximum stress in the member?

16.30 A short, cast-iron compression block carries a vertical force **P** as shown in Fig. 16.65. (a) Is there any tension in the block? (b) If the allowable stresses are 4000 psi in tension and 13,000 psi in compression, find the allowable value of $P$.

[*Ans.:* (b) 96 kips.]

16.31 Design member $ABC$ of the pin-connected frame of Problem 16.10 as a square member if the allowable stresses are 30,000 psi in tension and compression and 15,000 psi in shear.

16.32 Considering the deflection at any point of any one of the beams of Fig. 16.40, compute the ratio of the deflections at the point for the two orientations of cross section of Problem 16.17.

[*Ans.:* $\frac{1}{4}$.]

16.33 Verify the formula for $u_y$ in Fig. 16.40(d).

16.34 (a) If $EI$ is constant for the beam $AB$ in Fig. 16.66, find $u_y$ and $u_y'$ for that beam in terms of $P$, $E$, $I$, $L$, $a$, and $x$. (b) If $P = 8$ kips, $E = 30,000$ ksi, $I = 216$ in⁴, $L = 12$ ft, and $a = 4$ ft, find $\Delta_A$ and $\theta_A$.

[*Ans.:* (b) $\Delta_A = 0.614$ in., $\theta_A = -0.00853$ rad.]

16.35 Find $\Delta_A$ and $\theta_A$ for the beam of Example 16.14 by the moment-area theorems.

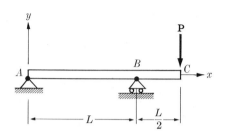

FIGURE 16.67

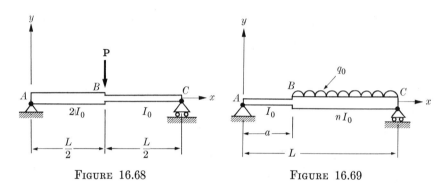

FIGURE 16.68              FIGURE 16.69

16.36 If $EI$ is constant for the beam shown in Fig. 16.67, find $\theta_C$ and $\Delta_C$ by the moment-area theorems.

$$\left[ Ans.:\ \theta_C = -\frac{7PL^2}{24EI}, \ \Delta_C = -\frac{PL^3}{8EI}. \right]$$

16.37 (a) Using the moment-area theorems, find $\Delta_B$ for the beam shown in Fig. 16.68. (b) Evaluate $\Delta_B$ if $P = 1200$ lb, $E = 2500$ ksi, $I_0 = 188$ in$^4$, and $L = 12$ ft.

16.38 Using the moment-area theorems, find $\Delta_B$ for the beam shown in Fig. 16.69.

$$\left[ Ans.:\ \Delta_B = -\frac{q_0 a(L-a)^3}{24nEI_0L^2}(4a^2n - 4a^2 + 3aL + L^2). \right]$$

# CHAPTER 17

## TORSION

**17.1 Introduction.** If all the external forces on the bar of Fig. 14.5 do not lie in the $xy$-plane, the cross section may carry, in addition to the two forces and one couple shown in Fig. 14.5, another shear force, another bending couple, and a torsional couple. The present chapter is concerned with the effect of the torsional couple, shown in Fig. 17.1. The algebraic scalar $T$ is commonly called the "torque."

**17.2 Circular torsion bars.** If a circular torsion bar of radius $b$ is subjected to a constant torque $T_0$ as shown in Fig. 17.2, an originally straight line $MN$ along its surface is found experimentally to deform into a space curve $MN'$ closely approximating a circular helix. Also, the end cross sections are found to remain nearly plane, and diameters on the end faces are found to remain nearly straight. For a bar of any cross section except a solid or hollow circle, on the other hand, the end cross sections do not remain plane, warping of the cross section being, in general, a major effect.

For any variation of $T$ along the bar of Fig. 17.2, the stresses and deformations in the bar can be found by studying the elemental length $dx$. The basic assumptions are that all cross sections remain plane and all

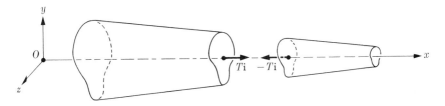

FIGURE 17.1

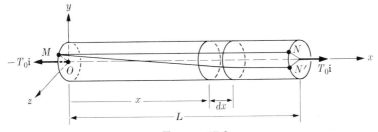

FIGURE 17.2

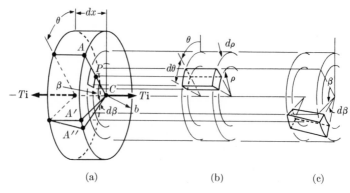

FIGURE 17.3

diameters remain straight. Figure 17.3(a) shows the elemental portion of the bar enlarged. The radial line $CA$ moves to a position $CA'$ due to rotation of the piece as a whole and further to $CA''$ due to deformation of the piece. Figure 17.3(b) shows an element of the bar in its original location at a general point $P$ defined by polar coordinates $\rho$, $\theta$, and Fig. 17.3(c) shows the same element after it is displaced and deformed by the torque. The angle $\beta$, called the *angle of twist*, is a function of $x$ and is therefore a dependent variable, while the polar angle $\theta$ is an independent variable.

Figure 17.4 shows the element of Fig. 17.3(c) as viewed along a radial line. By Eq. (14.7), the shear strain in the element is given by

$$\gamma_{\theta x} = \frac{\rho \, d\beta}{dx},$$

$\gamma_{\theta x}$ being equal to $\alpha$ if $\alpha$ is small. Up to this point, no restriction is made on the material of the bar. If the material is linearly elastic, etc., Eq. (14.17) applies, so that

$$\tau_{\theta x} = G\rho \frac{d\beta}{dx}.$$

By definition, the *rate of twist* or *unit twist* $\eta$ is given by

$$\eta = \frac{d\beta}{dx} \tag{17.1}$$

($\eta$ being, in general, a function of $x$), so that

$$\tau_{\theta x} = G\eta\rho. \tag{17.2}$$

For a given $x$, $\tau_{\theta x}$ is thus proportional to $\rho$, and the variation of $\tau_{\theta x}$ over the face of the elemental length is shown in Fig. 17.5. Since the stresses

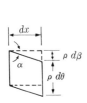

FIGURE 17.4

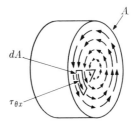

FIGURE 17.5

on the face are mechanically equivalent to the torque,

$$T = \iint_A \rho \tau_{\theta x}\, dA.$$

Hence, by Eq. (17.2),

$$T = G\eta \iint_A \rho^2\, dA,$$

and, by Eq. (10.4),

$$T = G\eta J_C, \tag{17.3}$$

where $J_C$ is the polar moment of inertia of the circular area about its center. For a hollow circular bar, $J_C$ is the polar moment of the net area. Rewriting Eq. (17.3),

$$\eta = \frac{T}{GJ_C}. \tag{17.4}$$

For any other cross section, it can be shown using advanced mechanics of deformable elastic bodies that

$$\eta = \frac{T}{GJ}, \tag{17.5}$$

where $J$ is a property of the cross-sectional area (but is *not* the polar moment of inertia).

Substituting Eq. (17.4) into Eq. (17.2),

$$\tau_{\theta x} = \frac{T\rho}{J_C}. \tag{17.6}$$

Note the dimensional similarity between the right-hand side of Eq. (17.6) and the bending-moment term of Eq. (16.16). Since there is only one shear stress in the bar, the subscripts may be dropped, but it is desirable, since a bar may be subjected to both torsion and flexure, to distinguish between the torsional shear stresses and the flexural shear stresses. Designating the former as $\tau_T$,

$$\tau_T = \frac{T\rho}{J_C},$$

and, on any cross section,

$$|\tau_T|_{\max} = \frac{|T|b}{J_C}.$$

In general the bar may be both tapered and hollow, in which case the maximum shear stress anywhere in the bar is found by applying the last equation to all cross sections which may be critical.

To find the angle of twist, note by Eqs. (17.1) and (17.4) that

$$\frac{d\beta}{dx} = \frac{T}{GJ_C}. \tag{17.7}$$

The angle of twist can be found by expressing $T$ and $J_C$ in terms of $x$ and integrating Eq. (17.7), evaluating the constant of integration by means of a boundary condition. Suppose, for example, that $T$ and $J_C$ are constant over the entire length of a bar and that $\beta(0) = 0$. Then, by integration,

$$\beta = \frac{T}{GJ_C} x, \tag{17.8}$$

and

$$\beta(L) = \frac{TL}{GJ_C}. \tag{17.9}$$

EXAMPLE 17.1. Bar $AB$ in Fig. 17.6 is a circular bar with 1-in. diameter. Find: (a) the maximum shear stress in the bar, (b) the vertical displacement of point $C$ if $CD$ is rigid and $G$ for $AB$ is 12,000 ksi.

*Solution.* (a) For bar $AB$,

$$J_C = \frac{\pi}{2}\left(\frac{1}{2}\right)^4 = 0.0982 \text{ in}^4.$$

Hence,

$$|\tau_T|_{\max} = \frac{(200)(0.5)(12)}{0.0982} = 12,220 \text{ psi.}$$

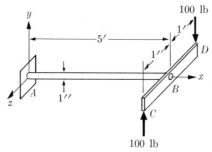

FIGURE 17.6

(b) By Eq. (17.9),

$$\beta(L) = \frac{(200)(5)(144)}{(12{,}000{,}000)(0.0982)} = 0.1220 \text{ rad.}$$

To a close approximation, therefore,

$$\Delta_C = (0.1220)(1) = 0.1220 \text{ ft.}$$

The following example illustrates a simple type of design problem involving a torsion bar.

EXAMPLE 17.2. A hollow torsion bar is to have a circular cross section with inside diameter of 1.5 in. and outside diameter of 2 in. The bar is to be designed so that, when one end is fixed, the other end can be rotated through an angle of 30° without exceeding a torsional shear stress of 10 ksi. Find the minimum length required for the bar if $G = 12{,}000$ ksi.

*Solution.* For the given cross section,

$$J_C = \frac{\pi}{2}[(1)^4 - (0.75)^4] = 1.074 \text{ in.}^4.$$

Using Eq. (17.6), the allowable torque $T_a$ is found as follows:

$$T_a = \frac{\tau_a J_C}{b} = \frac{(10)(1.074)}{1} = 10.74 \text{ in-kips.}$$

Thus, by Eq. (17.9), the required length $L_r$ is

$$L_r = \frac{\beta G J_C}{T_a} = \frac{(\pi/180)(30)(12{,}000)(1.074)}{(10.74)(12)} = 52.4 \text{ ft.}$$

**17.3 Combined torsion and flexure.** In many applications a bar is subjected to both twisting and bending, in which case the flexural and torsional shear stresses must be added at some points on the cross section.

EXAMPLE 17.3. The crank in Fig. 17.7 carries a force of 100-lb magnitude at $C$. Find: (a) the maximum shear stress in portion $AB$, (b) the deflection of $C$ if $E = 30{,}000$ ksi and $G = 12{,}000$ ksi.

*Solution.* (a) Figure 17.8 shows a cross section of member $AB$ as viewed in the negative $x$-direction. The greatest shear stress due to the combination of

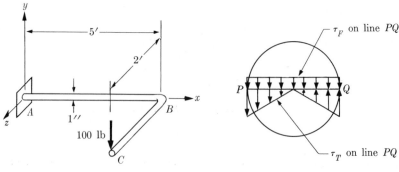

FIGURE 17.7    FIGURE 17.8

torsion and flexure occurs at point $P$ in the figure, where, by Eq. (17.6),

$$\tau_T = \frac{(200)(0.5)(12)}{0.0982} = 12{,}220 \text{ psi},$$

and, from Art. 16.4,

$$\tau_F = \frac{4}{3} \frac{100}{0.7854} = 170 \text{ psi}.$$

The total shear stress at $P$ is therefore

$$\tau = 12{,}390 \text{ psi},$$

although in this problem $\tau_F$ is virtually negligible as compared with $\tau_T$.

(b) Neglecting deformations due to flexural shear, the deflection at $C$ is caused by twisting in $AB$, bending in $AB$, and bending in $BC$. From the first effect, as in Example 17.1,

$$\Delta_C' = \frac{(200)(5)(144)(2)}{(12{,}000{,}000)(0.0982)} = 0.244 \text{ ft};$$

from the second effect, by Fig. 16.40(c),

$$\Delta_C'' = \frac{(100)(5)^3(144)}{3(30{,}000{,}000)(0.0491)} = 0.407 \text{ ft};$$

and, from the third effect, also by Fig. 16.40(c),

$$\Delta_C''' = \frac{(100)(2)^3(144)}{3(30{,}000{,}000)(0.0491)} = 0.026 \text{ ft}.$$

Hence, adding the three deflections,

$$\Delta_C = 0.677 \text{ ft}.$$

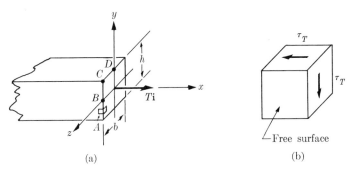

FIGURE 17.9

**17.4 Rectangular torsion bars.** For the rectangular torsion bar of Fig. 17.9(a), plane sections do not remain plane, and the elementary theory cannot be used to find the stresses and deformations. Consider, however, the surface element at $A$, which is shown enlarged in Fig. 17.9(b). It is obvious that there is no shear stress on the free surface and therefore that the shear stress must be in the direction indicated in Fig. 17.9(b). This implies that, at a corner such as $C$, the shear stress is zero. The advanced theory which takes into account warping of the cross section shows that, when $b < h$, the shear stress $\tau_T$ is greatest at point $B$ and is large at point $D$. The exact equation for the maximum shear stress is complicated, but the following approximate equation, valid when $b \leq h$, is accurate enough for most practical problems:

$$|\tau_T|_{\max} = \frac{|T|}{b^2 h}\left(3 + 1.8\frac{b}{h}\right).$$  (17.10)

For the case where $b = h$, Eq. (17.10) reduces to

$$|\tau_T|_{\max} = 4.8\,\frac{|T|}{b^3}.$$  (17.11)

The unit twist is given by Eq. (17.5), and, for a rectangular cross section with $b < h$, $J$ can be expressed as

$$J = kb^3 h,$$  (17.12)

where $k$ is a constant which has a value of 0.141 when $h/b = 1$, increases as $h/b$ increases, and approaches $\frac{1}{3}$ as $h/b$ approaches infinity.

## PROBLEMS

17.1 Steel shafting with an outside diameter $b$ of 6 in. and an inside diameter $a$ of 5 in. is used to drill through a rock stratum 1000 ft below the ground surface. It is found necessary to apply a torque of 15,000 ft-lb at the top of the shaft to maintain an angular speed of 30 rpm. (a) Neglecting the effect of the couplings, what is the maximum shear stress in the shaft? (b) What is the relative rotation in degrees of the ends of the shaft? Assume that $G = 12,000$ ksi.

17.2 A drive shaft 50 ft long is made of a steel for which $\tau_a = 13$ ksi. (a) What is the allowable torque if the shaft is hollow and has outside and inside diameters of 16 in. and 9 in., respectively? (b) What is the allowable torque if the shaft is solid but with the same cross-sectional area as the shaft of part (a)?

[*Ans.:* (a) 9410 in-kips; (b) 5910 in-kips.]

17.3 Find the diameter required for a solid circular bar which is to transmit a torque of 100 ft-kips without exceeding a shear stress of 12 ksi.

17.4 The two shafts shown in Fig. 17.10 are to carry the same torque with the same maximum shear stress. Find the ratio of the area of shaft (b) to the area of shaft (a).

[*Ans.:* 1.28.]

17.5 A circular, steel torsion bar 1 in. in diameter and 5 ft long is twisted through an angle of 6°. If $G = 12,000$ ksi, what is the maximum shear stress?

17.6 A copper wire for which $G = 6000$ ksi is to be twisted through one complete revolution without exceeding a shear stress of 4000 psi. If the length of the wire is 30 ft, determine its maximum diameter.

[*Ans.:* 0.0764 in.]

17.7 A coupling for a 5-in.-diameter steel shaft consists of six 1-in.-diameter bolts in a circle as shown in Fig. 17.11. The allowable shear stresses are 9000 psi in the bolts and 12,000 psi in the shaft. What must be the radius $b_0$ of the bolt circle in order for the coupling to have the same torsional strength as the shaft?

17.8 A 1288-lb weight is to be raised 40 ft from rest in 4 sec by a windlass, of which part is shown in Fig. 17.12. If the acceleration of the weight is constant, find the maximum torsional shear stress in the 2-in.-diameter shaft.

[*Ans.:* 5680 psi.]

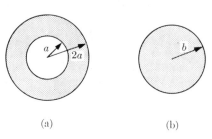

(a)                    (b)

FIGURE 17.10

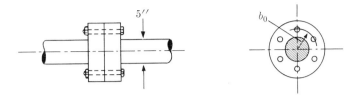

FIGURE 17.11

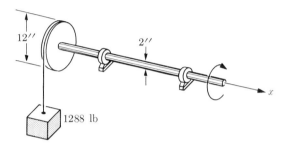

FIGURE 17.12

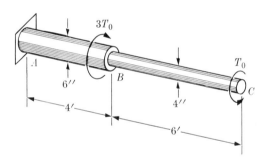

FIGURE 17.13

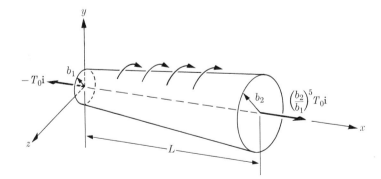

FIGURE 17.14

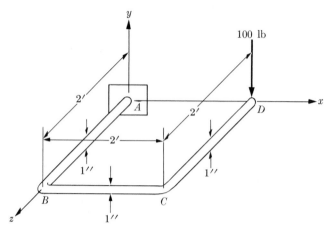

FIGURE 17.15

17.9 The stepped shaft shown in Fig. 17.13 is fixed at end $A$. Torques $3T_0$ and $T_0$ are to be applied at $B$ and $C$, respectively, with $T_0$ having a value such that the maximum shear stress anywhere in the shaft is 13 ksi. What is the angle of twist at $C$?

17.10 Find $\beta(L)$ for the bar shown in Fig. 17.14 if $\beta(0) = 0$ and

$$T = \frac{\{b_1[1 - (x/L)] + b_2(x/L)\}^5}{b_1^5} T_0.$$

$$\left[ Ans.: \frac{T_0L(b_1 + b_2)}{\pi G b_1^5} . \right]$$

17.11 Find the deflection at $D$ in Fig. 17.15 if $E = 30{,}000$ ksi and $G = 12{,}000$ ksi.

# CHAPTER 18

## STATICALLY INDETERMINATE SYSTEMS

**18.1 Applied axial forces.** To analyze a mechanical system which is statically indeterminate (such as that in Fig. 4.8), it is necessary to eliminate the idealizations of inextensibility, rigidity, etc., in some parts of the system and to consider deformations in those parts.

Table 18.1 gives typical values of the modulus of elasticity $E$ and the coefficient of linear expansion $\alpha$ for some common materials, and these values may be used in the problems of this chapter (although variations in materials make them unreliable for any purpose except illustration).

The systems of Examples 14.1 and 14.2 are statically determinate in the sense that the normal force in each member is known from statics (although deformations must be considered to find the quantities required in those examples). But consider the problem of finding the normal force in the members of Figs. 18.1 and 18.2 if the blocks are rigid. In Fig. 18.1, if $\delta$ is known and $N$ unknown, then, from Eq. (14.14),

$$N = \frac{EA}{L}\delta \quad \text{if} \quad \delta < \frac{WL}{EA},$$

and

$$N = W \quad \text{if} \quad \delta \geq \frac{WL}{EA}.$$

In Fig. 18.2, if $\delta_T$ is known, then

$$N_1 = N_2 = N_3 = N, \tag{18.1}$$

and, if $W$ is large enough to close the gap,

$$\delta_1 + \delta_2 + \delta_3 = \delta_T. \tag{18.2}$$

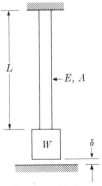

FIGURE 18.1

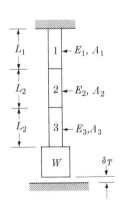

FIGURE 18.2

377

TABLE 18.1

| Material | $E$, ksi | $\alpha$, 1/°F |
|----------|----------|----------------|
| Aluminum | 10,500 | 0.0000128 |
| Brass | 14,000 | 0.0000104 |
| Cast Iron | 12,000 | 0.0000060 |
| Concrete | 3000 | 0.0000060 |
| Copper | 15,000 | 0.0000093 |
| Steel | 30,000 | 0.0000065 |
| Timber | 2000 | 0.0000030 |

Thus, from Eq. (14.14),

$$\frac{NL_1}{E_1 A_1} + \frac{NL_2}{E_2 A_2} + \frac{NL_3}{E_3 A_3} = \delta_T,$$

and

$$N = \frac{\delta_T}{(L_1/E_1 A_1) + (L_2/E_2 A_2) + (L_3/E_3 A_3)}$$

if

$$\delta_T < \frac{WL_1}{E_1 A_1} + \frac{WL_2}{E_2 A_2} + \frac{WL_3}{E_3 A_3}.$$

If the gap does not close, i.e., if the last inequality is not satisfied, then

$$N = W.$$

The system of Fig. 18.2 has three members in *series*. Indeterminate problems also occur when members are in *parallel*. In Fig. 18.3 three wires of equal length are used to pick up a weight $W$. In this case,

$$N_1 + N_2 + N_3 = W, \qquad (18.3)$$

and

$$\delta_1 = \delta_2 = \delta_3 = \delta, \qquad (18.4)$$

where $\delta$ is the unknown common elongation of the wires. By Eq. (14.14), therefore,

$$\frac{N_2 L}{E_2 A_2} = \frac{N_1 L}{E_1 A_1}, \qquad \frac{N_3 L}{E_3 A_3} = \frac{N_2 L}{E_2 A_2}.$$

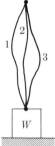

FIGURE 18.3

These two equations, along with Eq. (18.3), are three equations on the three unknowns $N_1$, $N_2$, $N_3$.

EXAMPLE 18.1.  Two steel wires and one copper wire are used to support a
rigid weight of 150 lb as in Fig. 18.4.  Each of the wires has a cross-sectional
area of 0.00307 in². (a) If the wires are all originally of the same length, find
the stresses in the steel and in the copper.  (b) If the copper wire is originally
0.01 in. longer than the steel wires, what must be the original length $L$ of the
steel wires to have the load produce a stress of 5000 psi in the copper?

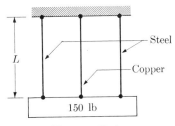

FIGURE 18.4

*Solution.*  In either case,

$$N_S + N_C = 150.$$

(a) In this case,

$$\frac{N_S L}{E_S A_S} = \frac{N_C L}{E_C A_C},$$

and, since $A_S = 2A_C$,

$$N_S = 2N_C \left(\frac{E_S}{E_C}\right) = 4N_C.$$

Thus,

$$N_S = 120 \text{ lb}, \qquad N_C = 30 \text{ lb},$$

and

$$\sigma_S = 19{,}540 \text{ psi}, \qquad \sigma_C = 9770 \text{ psi}.$$

(b) In this case,

$$\frac{N_S L}{E_S A_S} = \frac{N_C L}{E_C A_C} + 0.01.$$

Since $\sigma_C = 5000$ psi,

$$N_C = (5000)(0.00307) = 15.35 \text{ lb},$$

and

$$N_S = 150 - 15.35 = 134.65 \text{ lb}.$$

Hence,

$$\frac{134.65L}{(30{,}000{,}000)(0.00614)} = \frac{15.35L}{(15{,}000{,}000)(0.00307)} + 0.01,$$

from which

$$L = 25.2 \text{ in.}$$

**18.2 Temperature changes.** Even when there are no applied loads, statically indeterminate stresses can be induced by temperature changes. Such stresses are called *thermal stresses*. If the bar of Fig. 18.5 fits exactly between two immovable walls when the temperature is $T_0$, then, at temperature $T$, it follows from Eq. (14.11) and the first of Eqs. (14.19) that

$$\epsilon_x = \frac{\delta}{L} = \frac{\sigma_x}{E} + \alpha(T - T_0) = 0,$$

from which

$$\sigma_x = -E\alpha(T - T_0). \tag{18.5}$$

When there is a gap $\delta$, as shown in Fig. 18.6, then $\epsilon_x \neq 0$, $\delta$ being the actual elongation of the bar if $T - T_0$ is great enough to close the gap. In this case,

$$\epsilon_x = \frac{\delta}{L} = \frac{\sigma_x}{E} + \alpha(T - T_0),$$

from which

$$\sigma_x = E\left[-\alpha(T - T_0) + \frac{\delta}{L}\right]. \tag{18.6}$$

Hence, $\sigma_x < 0$ if

$$\delta < \alpha(T - T_0)L.$$

If, however,

$$\delta \geq \alpha(T - T_0)L,$$

then $\sigma_x = 0$.

Now consider three members in series as in Fig. 18.7. Assume that the temperature change is the same for all three members and that

$$\delta_T < \alpha_1(T - T_0)L_1 + \alpha_2(T - T_0)L_2 + \alpha_3(T - T_0)L_3.$$

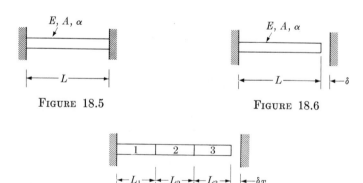

FIGURE 18.5          FIGURE 18.6

FIGURE 18.7

In this case,

$$N_1 = N_2 = N_3 = N, \qquad (18.7)$$

where $N$ is unknown, and

$$\delta_1 + \delta_2 + \delta_3 = \delta_T, \qquad (18.8)$$

where $\delta_T$ is known. Hence,

$$\frac{NL_1}{E_1 A_1} + \alpha_1(T - T_0)L_1 + \frac{NL_2}{E_2 A_2} + \alpha_2(T - T_0)L_2$$

$$+ \frac{NL_3}{E_3 A_3} + \alpha_3(T - T_0)L_3 = \delta_T,$$

and this equation can be solved for $N$ (or for some other unknown).

EXAMPLE 18.2. An aluminum cylinder and a brass cylinder have lengths of 20 in. and 10 in., respectively, and the same cross-sectional area $A$. They are placed end to end between two walls. If one wall yields 0.01 in. when the temperature is raised, what must be the temperature increase to develop a compressive stress of 5 ksi in the bars?

*Solution.* In this example,

$$N_A = N_B = N = -5A,$$

and

$$\delta_A + \delta_B = 0.01.$$

Hence,

$$\frac{(-5)(20)}{10,500} + (0.0000128)(20)(T - T_0) + \frac{(-5)(10)}{14,000}$$

$$+ (0.0000104)(10)(T - T_0) = 0.01,$$

from which

$$T - T_0 = 64.2°F.$$

Figure 18.8 shows three concentric cylinders welded to two rigid plates, this being a system of three members in parallel. For this arrangement,

$$N_1 + N_2 + N_3 = 0, \qquad (18.9)$$

and

$$\delta_1 = \delta_2 = \delta_3 = \delta, \qquad (18.10)$$

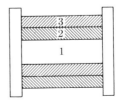

FIGURE 18.8

where $\delta$ is the unknown common elongation. Hence,

$$\frac{N_2 L}{E_2 A_2} + \alpha_2 (T - T_0)L = \frac{N_1 L}{E_1 A_1} + \alpha_1 (T - T_0)L,$$

$$\frac{N_3 L}{E_3 A_3} + \alpha_3 (T - T_0)L = \frac{N_2 L}{E_2 A_2} + \alpha_2 (T - T_0)L.$$

These two equations, along with Eq. (18.9), are three equations on the three unknowns $N_1$, $N_2$, $N_3$.

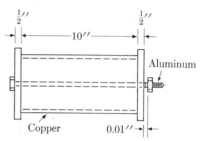

FIGURE 18.9

EXAMPLE 18.3. An aluminum bolt is heated to 250°F, inserted into a covered copper cylinder of equal area which is at 70°F, tightened down until a clearance of 0.01 in. remains, and then allowed to cool to 70°F. (See Fig. 18.9.) If the washers are rigid, find the stress in the copper tube.

*Solution.* In this example, $T_0$ for the bolt is 250°F, while $T_0$ for the cylinder is 70°F. By Eq. (18.9),

$$N_A + N_C = 0$$

in the final state. Since $\delta_A$ and $\delta_C$ are both negative,

$$\delta_C = \delta_A + 0.01.$$

Hence,

$$\frac{10 N_C}{15,000 A} = \frac{-11 N_C}{10,500 A} + 0.0000128(-180)(11) + 0.01,$$

and

$$\sigma_C = \frac{N_C}{A} = -8.95 \text{ ksi}.$$

If the system of Fig. 18.8 is placed between two rigid walls with a known clearance $\delta$ that is smaller than the unknown $\delta$ of Eq. (18.10), then Eqs. (18.9) and (18.10) become, respectively,

$$N_1 + N_2 + N_3 = -P,$$

where $P$ is the unknown magnitude of the total compressive force, and

$$\delta_1 = \delta_2 = \delta_3 = \delta.$$

Although $P$ is unknown, $\delta$ is now known, and $N_1$, $N_2$, $N_3$ can again be determined.

**18.3 Combined applied forces and temperature changes.** If the series system of Fig. 18.2 is subjected to a temperature change in addition to the applied force **W**, then Eqs. (18.1) and (18.2) still hold for any combination of effects which closes the gap. Now, however, for any one of the members,

$$\delta_i = \frac{NL_i}{E_iA_i} + \alpha_i(T - T_0)L_i,$$

so that

$$N = \frac{\delta_T - \alpha_1(T - T_0)L_1 - \alpha_2(T - T_0)L_2 - \alpha_3(T - T_0)L_3}{(L_1/E_1A_1) + (L_2/E_2A_2) + (L_3/E_3A_3)}$$

if

$$\delta_T < \frac{WL_1}{E_1A_1} + \alpha_1(T - T_0)L_1 + \frac{WL_2}{E_2A_2} + \alpha_2(T - T_0)L_2$$

$$+ \frac{WL_3}{E_3A_3} + \alpha_3(T - T_0)L_3,$$

and

$$N = W$$

otherwise.

For three members in parallel carrying forces **P** and $-$**P** as in Fig. 18.10, Eqs. (18.9) and (18.10) become, respectively,

$$N_1 + N_2 + N_3 = P \tag{18.11}$$

and

$$\delta_1 = \delta_2 = \delta_3 = \delta, \tag{18.12}$$

where $\delta$ is again unknown. As before, there are three equations on the three unknowns $N_1$, $N_2$, $N_3$.

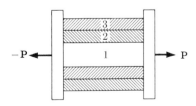

FIGURE 18.10

EXAMPLE 18.4. If the wires of Example 18.1 are originally of the same length, what temperature change is necessary to reduce the stress in the copper wire to zero?

*Solution.* In this problem,

$$N_S = 150 \text{ lb}, \qquad N_C = 0.$$

Thus,

$$\frac{150L}{(30,000,000)(2)(0.00307)} + (0.0000065)(T - T_0)L$$
$$= (0.0000093)(T - T_0)L,$$

from which

$$T - T_0 = 291°F.$$

**18.4 Flexure.** To find the reactions on an indeterminate beam, it is necessary to investigate the deflections of the beam by a method such as that of Art. 16.6. Consider first, however, the determinate beam of Fig. 18.11(a). A complete analysis of this beam involves four unknowns: the two reactions at $A$ and the two constants of integration in the deflection analysis. But there are four equations available: the two equations of equilibrium and the two boundary conditions at $A$. Adding one "redundant" support to the beam as in Fig. 18.11(b) creates another unknown reaction (at $B$) but provides another boundary condition, so that there are now five equations and five unknowns. Adding two redundants as in Fig. 18.11(c) creates two additional unknown reactions but gives two new boundary conditions for a total of six equations and six unknowns. In general, there are enough equations to completely analyze any indeterminate beam.

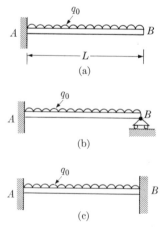

FIGURE 18.11

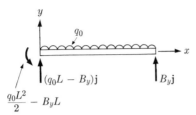

FIGURE 18.12

EXAMPLE 18.5. Find the reaction $B_y$ on the beam of Fig. 18.11(b).

*Solution.* Figure 18.12 shows a free-body diagram of the beam with the two reactions at $A$ expressed in terms of the redundant $B_y$. At a general distance $x$ from the origin,

$$M = -\frac{q_0}{2}x^2 + (q_0 L - B_y)x - \left(\frac{q_0 L^2}{2} - B_y L\right).$$

By Eq. (16.25), therefore,

$$EIu_y'' = -\frac{q_0}{2}x^2 + (q_0 L - B_y)x - \left(\frac{q_0 L^2}{2} - B_y L\right).$$

Integrating and using the boundary condition on $u_y'$ at $A$,

$$EIu_y' = -\frac{q_0}{6}x^3 + \frac{1}{2}(q_0 L - B_y)x^2 - \left(\frac{q_0 L^2}{2} - B_y L\right)x.$$

Integrating again and using the boundary condition on $u_y$ at $A$,

$$EIu_y = -\frac{q_0}{24}x^4 + \frac{1}{6}(q_0 L - B_y)x^3 - \frac{1}{2}\left(\frac{q_0 L^2}{2} - B_y L\right)x^2.$$

Using now the boundary condition on $u_y$ at $B$,

$$EIu_y(L) = 0 = -\frac{q_0 L^4}{24} + \frac{1}{6}(q_0 L - B_y)L^3 - \frac{1}{2}\left(\frac{q_0 L^2}{2} - B_y L\right)L^2,$$

from which

$$B_y\left(\frac{L^3}{2} - \frac{L^3}{6}\right) = \frac{q_0 L^4}{24} - \frac{q_0 L^4}{6} + \frac{q_0 L^4}{4},$$

$$B_y = \tfrac{3}{8}q_0 L.$$

Knowing $B_y$, it is possible to find the reactions at $A$ and the quantities $u_y$, $u_y'$, $S$, and $M$ at any point in the beam.

The moment-area theorems (Art. 16.7) offer a convenient method of analyzing indeterminate beams, as illustrated in the following example.

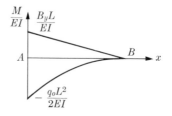

FIGURE 18.13

EXAMPLE 18.6. Solve Example 18.5 by the moment-area theorems.

*Solution.* Figure 18.13 shows the $(M/EI)$-diagram drawn by parts. The application of Eq. (16.34) to points $A$ and $B$ gives

$$0 = \frac{1}{2}(L)\left(\frac{B_y L}{EI}\right)\left(\frac{2L}{3}\right) + \frac{1}{3}(L)\left(-\frac{q_0 L^2}{2EI}\right)\left(\frac{3L}{4}\right),$$

from which

$$B_y = \tfrac{3}{8}q_0 L.$$

## PROBLEMS

18.1 A composite member 15 in. long is made by bonding two $\frac{1}{4}$-in.-thick brass bars to a $\frac{1}{4}$-in.-thick steel bar as shown in Fig. 18.14. If the member carries a tensile force of 4000 lb, find the stresses in the brass and in the steel.

18.2 A rigid beam is supported as shown in Fig. 18.15 by a copper bar having a cross-sectional area of 2 in$^2$ and by two steel wires having a cross-sectional area of 0.005 in$^2$ each. If the beam is subjected to a load **P** of 10-kip magnitude, determine: (a) the stresses in the steel and in the copper, and (b) the downward displacement of the beam.

[*Ans.:* (a) $\sigma_S = 7.44$ ksi, $\sigma_C = -4.96$ ksi; (b) 0.00496 in.]

18.3 Referring to Example 15.3, determine the location of **P** required to have the platform remain horizontal.

18.4 After all parts of the assembly of Problem 14.7 are in contact, the nuts are given $\frac{1}{4}$ turns each. (a) Find the stresses in the aluminum tube and in the steel bolts. (b) How much does the tube shorten?

[*Ans.:* (a) $\sigma_A = -4400$ psi, $\sigma_S = 14,000$ psi; (b) 0.0126 in.]

FIGURE 18.14

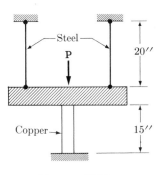

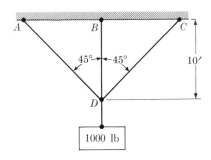

FIGURE 18.15          FIGURE 18.16

18.5 The three wires of Fig. 18.3 are steel wires with cross-sectional areas of 0.01 in² each. The lengths of the wires are as follows:

$$L_1 = 10.000 \text{ ft,}$$
$$L_2 = 10.005 \text{ ft,}$$
$$L_3 = 10.010 \text{ ft.}$$

If a weight $W$ of 200 lb is picked up by the wires, what is the stress in each wire?

18.6 Three elastic ropes having the same cross-sectional area support a 1000-lb load as shown in Fig. 18.16. Assuming small deformations, find the tension in each rope.

[*Ans.*: $T_A = T_C = 293$ lb, $T_B = 586$ lb.]

18.7 Three wires having the same cross-sectional area are tied between unyielding walls as shown in Fig. 18.17. (a) If the temperature is decreased 50°F, find the stress in the wires. (b) If the wires have an initial tensile stress of 10,000 psi and the temperature is increased 50°F, find the stress in the wires. (c) If the wires have an initial tensile stress of 5000 psi and the temperature is increased 50°F, what is the stress in the wires?

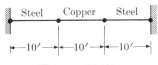

FIGURE 18.17

18.8 If the composite member of Problem 18.1 is subjected to a temperature increase of 100°F but no force, what are the stresses in the brass and in the steel?

[*Ans.*: $\sigma_B = -2820$ psi, $\sigma_S = 5650$ psi.]

18.9 Referring to Example 15.3, determine the temperature change necessary to make the platform horizontal if **P** is located as in Fig. 15.4.

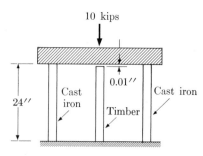

FIGURE 18.18

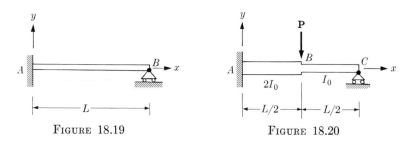

FIGURE 18.19                           FIGURE 18.20

18.10 Find the temperature change needed to relieve the stresses of Problem 18.4.

[*Ans.:* −252°F.]

18.11 The composite member of Problem 18.1 is subjected to a tensile force of 4000 lb and a simultaneous temperature increase of 100°F. Find the stresses in the brass and in the steel.

18.12 The system shown in Fig. 18.18 is assembled at 70°F with a clearance of 0.01 in. between the timber and the rigid beam. A load of 10-kip magnitude is then applied to the beam. If the timber is 4 in. by 4 in. in cross section and the cast-iron members each have a cross-sectional area of 2 in², to what must the temperature be changed to have a compressive stress of 500 psi in the timber?

[*Ans.:* −138°F.]

18.13 Using integration, find the reactions at $A$ for the beam of Fig. 18.11(c).

18.14. Using integration, find the reaction at $B$ in Fig. 18.19 if the support at $B$ moves up a known distance $\Delta_B$ but there are no loads on the beam. Assume that $EI$ is constant.

$$\left[ Ans.:\ B_y \ = \ \frac{3EI\,\Delta_B}{L^3} \,. \right]$$

18.15 Using the moment-area theorems, find the reaction at $C$ for the beam shown in Fig. 18.20.

18.16 Solve Problem 18.14 by the moment-area theorems.

*Part 4*

# THE CONCEPTS OF
# MOMENTUM AND ENERGY

# CHAPTER 19

## IMPULSE AND MOMENTUM

**19.1 Introduction.** In the foregoing chapters of this book, the subject of kinetics is developed by starting with Newton's Second Law, Eq. (6.1), differentiating the momentum $m\mathbf{v}$ for a constant mass to obtain Eq. (6.2), and then using Eq. (6.2) thereafter to solve problems involving a single particle and to generalize the theory to systems of particles and rigid bodies. An alternative approach is to integrate Eq. (6.1) in accordance with the methods of Art. 5.1 and obtain an integrated form of Newton's Second Law. This operation introduces no new theory but leads to equations that are useful for solving certain types of problems in which accelerations are not of primary interest.

**19.2 Single particle.** Consider the single particle $P$ of Fig. 19.1. In this figure, $m$ is the mass of the particle, $\mathbf{R}$ is the resultant force, and $\mathbf{r}$, $\mathbf{v}$, and $\mathbf{a}$ are the position vector, velocity, and acceleration, respectively. By Eq. (6.1),

$$\mathbf{R} = \frac{d}{dt}(m\mathbf{v}),$$

where $\mathbf{R}$ and $\mathbf{v}$ are vector functions of time and $m\mathbf{v}$ is the momentum of the particle. Integrating in accordance with Eq. (5.13), we obtain

$$\int \mathbf{R}\, dt = m\mathbf{v} + \mathbf{C}.$$

For two positions $P_1$ and $P_2$ on the path, the definite integral may be

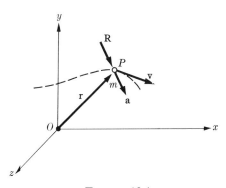

FIGURE 19.1

391

used, i.e.,

$$\int_{t_1}^{t_2} \mathbf{R}\, dt = m\mathbf{v}(t_2) - m\mathbf{v}(t_1). \tag{19.1}$$

It is convenient now to have a symbol for the momentum. Designating it by $\mathbf{N}$, Eq. (19.1) becomes

$$\mathbf{N}(t_2) - \mathbf{N}(t_1) = \int_{t_1}^{t_2} \mathbf{R}\, dt. \tag{19.2}$$

The integral on the right-hand side of Eq. (19.2) is called the *impulse* of $\mathbf{R}$ during the time interval from $t_1$ to $t_2$. Equation (19.2) thus states that the change in momentum of a particle is equal to the impulse of the resultant force. This is called the *principle of momentum for a single particle*. By Eq. (5.14),

$$\int_{t_1}^{t_2} \mathbf{R}\, dt = \int_{t_1}^{t_2} \mathbf{F}_1\, dt + \int_{t_1}^{t_2} \mathbf{F}_2\, dt + \cdots + \int_{t_1}^{t_2} \mathbf{F}_N\, dt,$$

i.e., the impulse of the resultant equals the sum of the impulses of the individual forces.

Since, by Eq. (5.17),

$$\int_{t_1}^{t_2} \mathbf{R}\, dt = \mathbf{i}\int_{t_1}^{t_2} R_x\, dt + \mathbf{j}\int_{t_1}^{t_2} R_y\, dt + \mathbf{k}\int_{t_1}^{t_2} R_z\, dt,$$

Eq. (19.2) may be replaced by the following three scalar equations:

$$N_x(t_2) - N_x(t_1) = \int_{t_1}^{t_2} R_x\, dt,$$

$$N_y(t_2) - N_y(t_1) = \int_{t_1}^{t_2} R_y\, dt, \tag{19.3}$$

$$N_z(t_2) - N_z(t_1) = \int_{t_1}^{t_2} R_z\, dt.$$

For rectilinear-motion problems, only the first of Eqs. (19.3) is used, and the right-hand side of that equation is the area under the $R_x$-$t$ curve between $t_1$ and $t_2$. The following example shows how to find impulses and how to use the principle of momentum.

---

EXAMPLE 19.1. The 100-lb block in Fig. 19.2 is subjected to a horizontal force $\mathbf{P}$ such that

$$P = 40 + 30t^2,$$

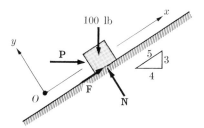

FIGURE 19.2

where $P$ is in lb and $t$ is in sec. At $t = 0$, the velocity $v_x$ is $-30$ ft/sec, and the coefficient of kinetic friction is 0.25. (a) Find the impulse of **P** between $t = 0$ and $t = 2$ sec. (b) Assuming that the block does not reverse its direction of motion, find the impulse of **R** between $t = 0$ and $t = 2$ sec. (c) Find $v_x$ at $t = 2$ sec.

*Solution.* (a) By the methods of Chapter 3,

$$\mathbf{P} = \tfrac{4}{5}P\mathbf{i} - \tfrac{3}{5}P\mathbf{j} = (32 + 24t^2)\mathbf{i} - (24 + 18t^2)\mathbf{j}.$$

Therefore,

$$\int_{t_1}^{t_2} \mathbf{P}\, dt = \mathbf{i}\int_0^2 (32 + 24t^2)\, dt - \mathbf{j}\int_0^2 (24 + 18t^2)\, dt$$

$$= 128\mathbf{i} - 96\mathbf{j} \text{ lb-sec.}$$

(b) By the equation of equilibrium in the $y$-direction,

$$N = 80 + \tfrac{3}{5}P,$$

and, by the law of kinetic friction,

$$F = 0.25N = 20 + \tfrac{3}{20}P.$$

Thus,

$$\mathbf{R} = [\tfrac{4}{5}P + (20 + \tfrac{3}{20}P) - 60]\mathbf{i} = (\tfrac{19}{20}P - 40)\mathbf{i},$$

and

$$\int_{t_1}^{t_2} \mathbf{R}\, dt = \mathbf{i}\int_0^2 [\tfrac{19}{20}(40 + 30t^2) - 40]\, dt = 72\mathbf{i} \text{ lb-sec.}$$

(c) By the first of Eqs. (19.3),

$$\frac{100}{32.2}[v_x(2)] - \frac{100}{32.2}[-30] = 72,$$

and, from this,

$$v_x(2) = \frac{32.2}{100}(72) - 30 = -6.82 \text{ ft/sec.}$$

Note that the expression for $\mathbf{R}$ in part (b) is valid only when $\mathbf{F}$ is in the positive $x$-direction. If the block had reversed its direction of motion in the time interval (as would have been indicated by a positive final velocity), the impulse of $\mathbf{R}$ would not be 72i lb-sec, and the problem would require a new solution, obtained by subdividing the time interval at the time when $v_x = 0$. The first of Eqs. (19.3) could be used, of course, to find that time.

---

In the case where $\mathbf{R} = \mathbf{0}$ throughout a time interval, it follows from Eq. (19.2) that

$$\mathbf{N}(t_2) = \mathbf{N}(t_1). \qquad (19.4)$$

This fact is called the *principle of conservation of momentum for a single particle;* it is simply an alternative way of stating that the velocity is a constant vector when $\mathbf{R} = \mathbf{0}$. If any component of $\mathbf{R}$ is zero in a time interval, the corresponding component of $\mathbf{N}$ is conserved. For example, if $R_x = 0$, then, by the first of Eqs. (19.3),

$$N_x(t_2) = N_x(t_1).$$

Another useful concept is the *moment of momentum* or *angular momentum* of a particle with respect to a fixed point $O$, designated by $\mathbf{H}$. (The quantity $\mathbf{N}$ is often called the "linear" momentum to distinguish it from the angular momentum.) By definition, referring to Fig. 19.1,

$$\mathbf{H} = \mathbf{r} \times \mathbf{N}. \qquad (19.5)$$

To make this definition meaningful, the momentum $\mathbf{N}$ must be considered as having a line of action through the particle itself. Differentiating Eq. (19.5) in accordance with Eq. (7.30),

$$\frac{d\mathbf{H}}{dt} = \mathbf{r} \times \left( m\frac{d\mathbf{v}}{dt} \right) + \frac{d\mathbf{r}}{dt} \times (m\mathbf{v}).$$

By Eqs. (5.18) and (5.19), therefore,

$$\frac{d\mathbf{H}}{dt} = \mathbf{r} \times (m\mathbf{a}) + \mathbf{v} \times (m\mathbf{v}),$$

and the second term on the right is null by Eqs. (7.16) and (7.18). Thus,

$$\frac{d\mathbf{H}}{dt} = \mathbf{r} \times \mathbf{R},$$

and, by Varignon's theorem,

$$\frac{d\mathbf{H}}{dt} = \mathbf{T}, \qquad (19.6)$$

where **T** is the total moment of all the forces about $O$. Integrating Eq. (19.6), we obtain

$$\mathbf{H}(t_2) - \mathbf{H}(t_1) = \int_{t_1}^{t_2} \mathbf{T} \, dt. \tag{19.7}$$

Equation (19.7), the angular counterpart of Eq. (19.2), is called the *principle of angular momentum for a single particle*, and the integral on the right-hand side is called the *angular impulse* of **R**. As usual, Eq. (19.7) may be written as three scalar equations, i.e.,

$$H_x(t_2) - H_x(t_1) = \int_{t_1}^{t_2} T_x \, dt,$$

$$H_y(t_2) - H_y(t_1) = \int_{t_1}^{t_2} T_y \, dt, \tag{19.8}$$

$$H_z(t_2) - H_z(t_1) = \int_{t_1}^{t_2} T_z \, dt.$$

If **T** $=$ **0** throughout a time interval, then

$$\mathbf{H}(t_2) = \mathbf{H}(t_1), \tag{19.9}$$

this being called the *principle of conservation of angular momentum for a single particle*. If $T_x = 0$ in a time interval, then

$$H_x(t_2) = H_x(t_1),$$

or, using Eqs. (7.21) and (19.5),

$$m[y(t_2)\dot{z}(t_2) - z(t_2)\dot{y}(t_2)] = m[y(t_1)\dot{z}(t_1) - z(t_1)\dot{y}(t_1)].$$

---

EXAMPLE 19.2. A particle of weight $W$ is attached to an ideal string and travels on a smooth, horizontal plane. The string runs through a hole $O$ in the plane where a force $\mathbf{P}_1$ acts to keep the particle moving on a circular path of radius $L_1$ at a constant speed $v_1$, as shown in Fig. 19.3. The string is then pulled through the hole so as to reduce the radius of the circle from $L_1$ to $L_2$. Find the new speed $v_2$ in terms of $v_1$, and the new magnitude $P_2$ in terms of $P_1$.

*Solution.* Since the string force on the particle intersects the $y$-axis at all times, it follows that $T_y = 0$ throughout the process and, by the second of Eqs. (19.8), that

$$H_y(t_2) = H_y(t_1).$$

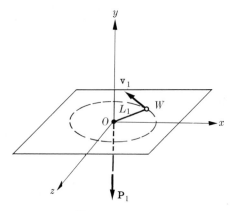

FIGURE 19.3

Therefore,

$$L_2 \frac{W}{g} v_2 = L_1 \frac{W}{g} v_1,$$

and

$$v_2 = \frac{L_1}{L_2} v_1.$$

At $t_1$,

$$\sum F_\rho = -P_1 = -\frac{W}{g} \frac{v_1^2}{L_1},$$

and, at $t_2$,

$$\sum F_\rho = -P_2 = -\frac{W}{g} \frac{v_2^2}{L_2}.$$

Therefore,

$$P_2 = \frac{W}{gL_2} \left(\frac{L_1}{L_2} v_1\right)^2 = \left(\frac{L_1}{L_2}\right)^3 \frac{W}{g} \frac{v_1^2}{L_1} = \left(\frac{L_1}{L_2}\right)^3 P_1.$$

Note that the way in which the quantities **P** and **v** vary during the change of radius is immaterial. The efficacy of the momentum approach to this type of problem stems from the fact that only the times $t_1$ and $t_2$ need be considered when angular momentum is conserved.

**19.3 System of particles.** For any particle $m_i$ of the system of particles of Fig. 19.4,

$$\mathbf{R}_i = \frac{d}{dt}(m_i \mathbf{v}_i).$$

Adding for all the particles and using Eq. (11.3),

$$\mathbf{R} = \frac{d}{dt}(m_1 \mathbf{v}_1 + m_2 \mathbf{v}_2 + \cdots + m_n \mathbf{v}_n), \qquad (19.10)$$

where **R** is the resultant of all the forces on all the particles. By definition, the total momentum **N** of the system of particles is obtained by
adding the momenta of the individual particles, i.e.,

$$\mathbf{N} = m_1\mathbf{v}_1 + m_2\mathbf{v}_2 + \cdots + m_n\mathbf{v}_n. \tag{19.11}$$

Therefore, integrating Eq. (19.10), we obtain

$$\mathbf{N}(t_2) - \mathbf{N}(t_1) = \int_{t_1}^{t_2} \mathbf{R}\, dt. \tag{19.12}$$

This equation has the same form as Eq. (19.2), but now **R** may be interpreted as the resultant of all the *external* forces, in accordance with
Eq. (11.7). The integral on the right is called the *total impulse* of all the
external forces, and Eq. (19.12) is called the *principle of momentum for a
system of particles*. It may be written in scalar form by equations such as
Eqs. (19.3), where, now,

$$N_x(t_2) = \sum_{i=1}^{n} m_i \dot{x}_i(t_2),$$

etc. This principle is applicable in certain problems of fluid mechanics, a
particularly simple type of which is illustrated in the following example.

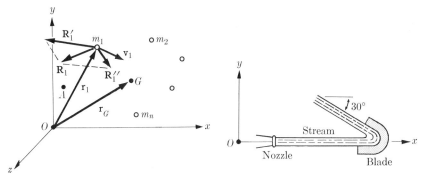

FIGURE 19.4                              FIGURE 19.5

EXAMPLE 19.3. A stream of water with cross-sectional area of $1\,\mathrm{in}^2$ is deflected
by a smooth, stationary turbine blade as shown in Fig. 19.5. All particles of the
stream are assumed to have the same constant speed $v$ of 200 ft/sec. Find the
resultant force exerted on the blade by the water.

*Solution.* The mechanical system to be studied can be taken as all the particles of water passing the blade in a time interval $\Delta t$. The total mass of the system is then the product of the volume and the density, i.e.,

$$m = Av\,\Delta t\,\frac{\gamma}{g} = \frac{(1)(200)}{144}\,\frac{62.4}{32.2}\,\Delta t = 2.69\,\Delta t.$$

Since all the particles have the same speed, the components of the total momentum may be computed by multiplying the total mass by the common velocity components. The principle of momentum then gives

$$m[\dot{x}(t_2) - \dot{x}(t_1)] = R_x \Delta t,$$

$$m[\dot{y}(t_2) - \dot{y}(t_1)] = R_y \Delta t,$$

the right-hand sides being impulse components for a constant $\mathbf{R}$. Thus,

$$2.69 \,\Delta t[-(200)(0.866) - 200] = R_x \Delta t,$$

$$2.69 \,\Delta t[(200)(0.500)] = R_y \Delta t,$$

from which

$$\mathbf{R} = -1004\mathbf{i} + 269\mathbf{j} \text{ lb.}$$

The force on the blade is

$$-\mathbf{R} = 1004\mathbf{i} - 269\mathbf{j} \text{ lb.}$$

-------

If $\mathbf{R} = \mathbf{0}$ throughout a time interval, then

$$\mathbf{N}(t_2) = \mathbf{N}(t_1). \tag{19.13}$$

This is the *principle of conservation of momentum for a system of particles.* If $R_x = 0$ in a time interval, then

$$\sum_{i=1}^{n} m_i \dot{x}_i(t_2) = \sum_{i=1}^{n} m_i \dot{x}_i(t_1). \tag{19.14}$$

An important application of Eq. (19.14) is to impact problems, as illustrated in Art. 19.5.

The *total moment of momentum* or *total angular momentum* of a system of particles with respect to a fixed point $O$ is obtained by adding the angular momenta of the individual particles, i.e.,

$$\mathbf{H} = \mathbf{r}_1 \times (m_1\mathbf{v}_1) + \mathbf{r}_2 \times (m_2\mathbf{v}_2) + \cdots + \mathbf{r}_n \times (m_n\mathbf{v}_n). \tag{19.15}$$

Proceeding as for the single particle,

$$\frac{d\mathbf{H}}{dt} = \mathbf{r}_1 \times \mathbf{R}_1 + \mathbf{r}_2 \times \mathbf{R}_2 + \cdots + \mathbf{r}_n \times \mathbf{R}_n,$$

where $\mathbf{R}_i$ is the resultant of all the forces on the $i$th particle. Thus,

$$\frac{d\mathbf{H}}{dt} = \mathbf{T}_1 + \mathbf{T}_2 + \cdots + \mathbf{T}_n,$$

where $T_i$ is the total moment about $O$ of all the forces on the $i$th particle. By Eq. (11.11),

$$\frac{d\mathbf{H}}{dt} = \mathbf{T}, \tag{19.16}$$

where $\mathbf{T}$ is the total moment of all the forces on all the particles. Integrating Eq. (19.16), we obtain

$$\mathbf{H}(t_2) - \mathbf{H}(t_1) = \int_{t_1}^{t_2} \mathbf{T} \, dt. \tag{19.17}$$

This equation has the same form as Eq. (19.7), but now $\mathbf{T}$ may be interpreted as the total moment of all the *external* forces, in accordance with Eq. (11.14). The integral on the right is called the *total angular impulse* of all the external forces, and Eq. (19.17) is called the *principle of angular momentum for a system of particles*. It may be written in scalar form by equations such as Eqs. (19.8), where, now,

$$H_x(t_2) = \sum_{i=1}^{n} m_i [y_i(t_2)\dot{z}_i(t_2) - z_i(t_2)\dot{y}_i(t_2)], \qquad \text{etc.}$$

If $\mathbf{T} = \mathbf{0}$ throughout a time interval, then

$$\mathbf{H}(t_2) = \mathbf{H}(t_1).$$

This is called the *principle of conservation of angular momentum for a system of particles*.

The question now arises as to whether Eq. (19.16) would hold if some moving point were used as a reference point for $\mathbf{H}$ and $\mathbf{T}$ instead of the fixed point $O$. It happens that the equation does not hold for a general moving point $A$, but, for the particular moving point $G$, the expression for the angular momentum is

$$\mathbf{H}^G = (\mathbf{r}_1 - \mathbf{r}_G) \times (m_1\mathbf{v}_1) + (\mathbf{r}_2 - \mathbf{r}_G) \times (m_2\mathbf{v}_2) + \cdots$$
$$+ (\mathbf{r}_n - \mathbf{r}_G) \times (m_n\mathbf{v}_n),$$

and, differentiating this equation with respect to $t$, we can show that

$$\frac{d\mathbf{H}^G}{dt} = \mathbf{T}^G, \tag{19.18}$$

where $\mathbf{T}^G$ is the total moment of all the external forces about $G$.

**19.4 Rigid bodies in plane motion.** If a rigid body in plane motion (Fig. 19.6) carries $N$ external forces, then

$$\mathbf{R} = \mathbf{F}_1 + \mathbf{F}_2 + \cdots + \mathbf{F}_N, \qquad \mathbf{T} = \mathbf{M}_1 + \mathbf{M}_2 + \cdots + \mathbf{M}_N,$$

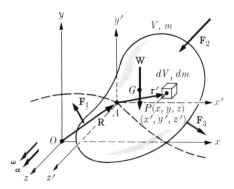

FIGURE 19.6

where the subscripts now refer to the forces ($\mathbf{M}_i$ being the moment of $\mathbf{F}_i$ about $O$), and the $N$ forces include $\mathbf{W}$ and any other equivalent concentrated forces. Adapting Eq. (19.10) to this special system of particles,

$$\mathbf{R} = \frac{d}{dt} \iiint_V \mathbf{v}\mu \, dV,$$

where $\mathbf{v}$ is the velocity of point $P$ and $\mu$ is the density at $P$. Hence,

$$\mathbf{R} = \frac{d}{dt}\left(\mathbf{i}\iiint_V \dot{x}\mu \, dV + \mathbf{j}\iiint_V \dot{y}\mu \, dV\right)$$

$$= \frac{d}{dt}\left(\mathbf{i}\frac{d}{dt}\iiint_V x\mu \, dV + \mathbf{j}\frac{d}{dt}\iiint_V y\mu \, dV\right).$$

By Eqs. (9.26), therefore,

$$\mathbf{R} = \frac{d}{dt}\left[\mathbf{i}\frac{d}{dt}(mx_G) + \mathbf{j}\frac{d}{dt}(my_G)\right]$$

$$= \frac{d}{dt}[m(\dot{x}_G\mathbf{i} + \dot{y}_G\mathbf{j})] = \frac{d}{dt}(m\mathbf{v}_G).$$

Integrating, we obtain

$$m\mathbf{v}_G(t_2) - m\mathbf{v}_G(t_1) = \int_{t_1}^{t_2} \mathbf{R} \, dt. \qquad (19.19)$$

The quantity $m\mathbf{v}_G$ is called the *momentum of a rigid body*, and Eq. (19.19) is called the *principle of momentum for a rigid body*. If the rigid body is in general motion, a derivation similar to the foregoing results in the same equation, Eq. (19.19), which means that the principle is not restricted to plane motion.

The *angular momentum* of the body of Fig. 19.6 about $A$ (any point fixed in the body) is defined as follows:

$$\mathbf{H}^A = \iiint_V \mathbf{r}' \times (\mathbf{v}\mu \, dV).$$

Hence, in general,

$$H_x^A = \iiint_V [(y - y_A)\dot{z} - (z - z_A)\dot{y}]\mu \, dV,$$

$$H_y^A = \iiint_V [(z - z_A)\dot{x} - (x - x_A)\dot{z}]\mu \, dV,$$

$$H_z^A = \iiint_V [(x - x_A)\dot{y} - (y - y_A)\dot{x}]\mu \, dV,$$

and, for the particular case of plane motion,

$$H_x^A = \iiint_V -(z - z_A)\dot{y}\mu \, dV,$$

$$H_y^A = \iiint_V (z - z_A)\dot{x}\mu \, dV,  \tag{19.20}$$

$$H_z^A = \iiint_V [(x - x_A)\dot{y} - (y - y_A)\dot{x}]\mu \, dV.$$

The way in which $\dot{x}$ and $\dot{y}$ vary throughout the body is known from Eqs. (12.19), i.e.,

$$\dot{x} = \dot{x}_A - \omega_z(y - y_A), \qquad \dot{y} = \dot{y}_A + \omega_z(x - x_A).$$

Substituting these equations into Eqs. (19.20) and proceeding as in Art. 13.2, we obtain the following equations:

$$H_x^A = -m\dot{y}_A(z_G - z_A) - I_{zx}^A \omega_z,$$

$$H_y^A = m\dot{x}_A(z_G - z_A) - I_{yz}^A \omega_z,  \tag{19.21}$$

$$H_z^A = m\dot{y}_A(x_G - x_A) - m\dot{x}_A(y_G - y_A) + I_z^A \omega_z.$$

If the $x'y'$-plane is a plane of symmetry of shape and density distribution, then, as in Art. 13.2,

$$H_x^A = 0, \qquad H_y^A = 0,$$
$$H_z^A = m\dot{y}_A(x_G - x_A) - m\dot{x}_A(y_G - y_A) + I_z^A \omega_z.  \tag{19.22}$$

In many problems, it is convenient to take $G$ as the reference point $A$, in which case the last of Eqs. (19.22) reduces to

$$H_z^G = I_z^G \omega_z. \qquad (19.23)$$

Using Eq. (13.15), we find that

$$T_z^G = I_z^G \alpha_z = I_z^G \frac{d\omega_z}{dt} = \frac{d}{dt}(I_z^G \omega_z) = \frac{dH_z^G}{dt},$$

which is in agreement with Eq. (19.18), and, integrating, we obtain

$$H_z^G(t_2) - H_z^G(t_1) = \int_{t_1}^{t_2} T_z^G \, dt. \qquad (19.24)$$

Equation (19.24) is the *principle of angular momentum for a rigid body in plane motion*. The principle also holds for a fixed point $O$, although it is not often used in that form for solving problems unless the body is in pure rotation about a fixed axis through $O$, in which case

$$H_z = I_z \omega_z, \qquad (19.25)$$

and

$$H_z(t_2) - H_z(t_1) = \int_{t_1}^{t_2} T_z \, dt. \qquad (19.26)$$

For the instantaneous center of null velocity $C$,

$$H_z^C = I_z^C \omega_z,$$

and, provided that $x_G = x_C$ and $\ddot{x}_C = 0$, it follows from Eq. (13.23) that

$$H_z^C(t_2) - H_z^C(t_1) = \int_{t_1}^{t_2} T_z^C \, dt.$$

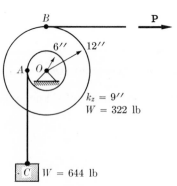

FIGURE 19.7

EXAMPLE 19.4. The pulley in Fig. 19.7 starts from rest at $t_1 = 0$. It is then subjected to a horizontal force **P** such that

$$P = 322 + 161t,$$

where $P$ is in lb and $t$ is in sec. Neglecting friction in the bearings at $O$, find the time $t_2$ at which the block attains a speed of 10 ft/sec.

*Solution.* Letting $S$ be the tension in the rope and applying the principle of momentum to the block,

$$\frac{644}{32.2}(10) = \int_0^{t_2} (S - 644)\, dt,$$

from which

$$\int_0^{t_2} S\, dt = 200 + 644t_2.$$

Writing the second of Eqs. (12.19) for points $O$ and $A$,

$$\dot{y}_A(t_2) = 10 = [\omega_z(t_2)][-0.5],$$

from which

$$\omega_z(t_2) = -\frac{10}{0.5} = -20 \text{ rad/sec},$$

and, applying the principle of angular momentum to the pulley,

$$\frac{322}{32.2}(0.75)^2(-20) = \int_0^{t_2} (0.5S - P)\, dt,$$

$$-112.5 = 0.5 \int_0^{t_2} S\, dt - \int_0^{t_2} (322 + 161t)\, dt$$

$$= 0.5 \int_0^{t_2} S\, dt - 322t_2 - 80.5t_2^2.$$

Finally, substituting the previously determined value of the impulse of $S$,

$$-112.5 = 0.5(200 + 644t_2) - 322t_2 - 80.5t_2^2,$$

$$80.5t_2^2 = 212.5,$$

$$t_2^2 = 2.64,$$

$$t_2 = 1.62 \text{ sec}.$$

This problem can also be solved without considering the impulse of the tension $S$ by applying the principle of angular momentum to the combined system of block and pulley, for which the tension in rope $AC$ is an internal force. Since the momentum of the block at $t_2$ has a clockwise (i.e., negative) moment about $O$,

$$\frac{322}{32.2}(0.75)^2(-20) - \frac{644}{32.2}(10)(0.5) = \int_0^{t_2} [0.5(644) - P] \, dt,$$

which yields the same value of $t_2$ as before.

**19.5 Impact.** Suppose that two blocks are traveling toward each other with known velocities on a smooth plane as in Fig. 19.8(a). Assume that the blocks are equipped with a mechanism that causes them to become coupled during the collision, which is shown in Fig. 19.8(b). The blocks then travel away together as in Fig. 19.8(c) with some unknown velocity. By Eq. (19.14),

$$(m_1 + m_2)\dot{x}' = m_1\dot{x}_1 + m_2\dot{x}_2,$$

where the primed velocity is that immediately after impact and the un-primed velocities are those immediately before impact. Equation (19.14) applies here because there are no external forces acting in the $x$-direction during impact. Since, during the collision, both blocks undergo finite changes in velocity in a very short time, however, their accelerations must attain very large absolute values during impact, indicating that the internal force between them attains a very large magnitude during impact. Such a force is called an *impulsive force*. The way in which its magnitude varies during impact is difficult to determine, but the principle of conservation of momentum yields the final velocity without regard to that variation.

Consider next the two blocks in Fig. 19.9(a), which collide as in Fig. 19.9(b) and then travel away with *different* unknown final velocities as

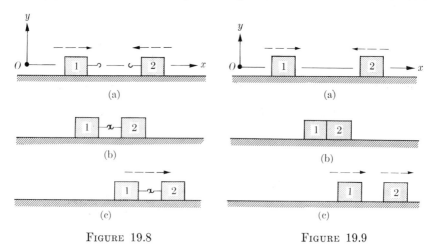

(a)

(b)

(c)

FIGURE 19.8          FIGURE 19.9

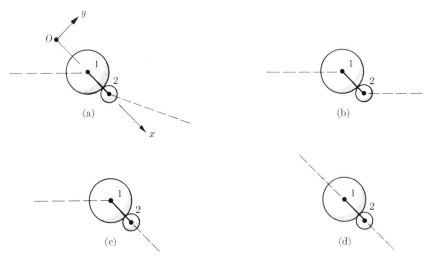

FIGURE 19.10

in Fig. 19.9(c). Since there are two unknowns, Eq. (19.14) is not adequate for solving the problem completely. In fact, the final velocities depend in this case on the amount of deformation and recovery of the blocks during impact and hence on the materials of which they are made. As before, the force between them attains very large magnitudes during impact (since the blocks remain in contact a very short time).

A classification of types of impact can be made by considering two homogeneous, translating spheres colliding as in Fig. 19.10(a). The dashed lines indicate the paths of their centers before impact (with both paths assumed in the $xy$-plane), and the solid line between their centers is called the *line of impact*. In general, the line of impact is a line through the point of contact and perpendicular to the tangent plane at the point of contact. The special case under consideration in which the line of impact contains both mass centers is called *central impact*. For bodies other than spheres, the impact may be *eccentric*.

Figure 19.10(b) shows a special case of the preceding one in which both paths are parallel, and Fig. 19.10(c) shows another special case in which one path coincides with the line of impact. Finally, Fig. 19.10(d) shows the case where both paths coincide with the line of impact. The last case is called *direct central impact*, while the other three are called *oblique central impact*.

Taking the $x$-axis along the line of impact as shown in Fig. 19.10(a), it follows from Eq. (19.14) that

$$m_1 \dot{x}_1' + m_2 \dot{x}_2' = m_1 \dot{x}_1 + m_2 \dot{x}_2. \tag{19.27}$$

The material properties of the two spheres are represented by a quantity $e$ called the *coefficient of restitution*, where, by definition,

$$e = -\frac{\dot{x}'_1 - \dot{x}'_2}{\dot{x}_1 - \dot{x}_2}. \tag{19.28}$$

This coefficient depends on the materials and shapes of both bodies involved, and its value can be found in most cases only by experiment. If $e$ is given in a problem, Eqs. (19.27) and (19.28) allow the determination of two unknowns, e.g., $\dot{x}'_1$ and $\dot{x}'_2$, in any of the four cases pictured in Fig. 19.10. For oblique central impact, two additional equations may be written on $y$-components by assuming that the spheres are smooth and hence that there is no impulsive force on either sphere in the $y$-direction, i.e.,

$$m_1\dot{y}'_1 = m_1\dot{y}_1, \qquad m_2\dot{y}'_2 = m_2\dot{y}_2. \tag{19.29}$$

Solving Eqs. (19.27), (19.28), and (19.29) for the final velocity components,

$$\dot{x}'_1 = \frac{(m_1 - em_2)\dot{x}_1 + (1 + e)m_2\dot{x}_2}{m_1 + m_2},$$

$$\dot{x}'_2 = \frac{(m_2 - em_1)\dot{x}_2 + (1 + e)m_1\dot{x}_1}{m_1 + m_2}, \tag{19.30}$$

$$\dot{y}'_1 = \dot{y}_1,$$

$$\dot{y}'_2 = \dot{y}_2.$$

If $e = 0$,

$$\dot{x}'_1 = \dot{x}'_2 = \frac{m_1\dot{x}_1 + m_2\dot{x}_2}{m_1 + m_2}. \tag{19.31}$$

This case is called *plastic impact*. It is exemplified by two balls of putty-like material, by a bullet becoming embedded in a block on impact, or by the two previously mentioned blocks which become coupled. If $e = 1$,

$$\dot{x}'_1 = \frac{(m_1 - m_2)\dot{x}_1 + 2m_2\dot{x}_2}{m_1 + m_2},$$

$$\dot{x}'_2 = \frac{(m_2 - m_1)\dot{x}_2 + 2m_1\dot{x}_1}{m_1 + m_2}. \tag{19.32}$$

This case is called *elastic impact*, since it can be shown that two elastic spheres behave in such a way that $e = 1$. Approximately, then, so do steel or ivory spheres. For any situation other than the two limiting cases just discussed,

$$0 < e < 1.$$

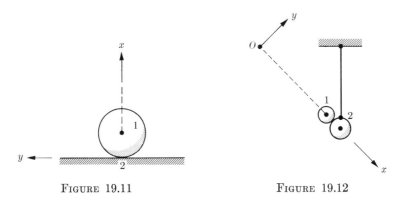

FIGURE 19.11                          FIGURE 19.12

If a ball is dropped to the floor as in Fig. 19.11, a small amount of the momentum of the ball is imparted to the floor or, if the floor is rigidly attached to the earth, to the earth itself. Thus the velocity of the ball after impact may depend on the mass of the earth. The disturbance to the earth resulting from a dropped ball is so slight, however, that it is completely negligible; hence, for all practical purposes, Eq. (19.28) becomes

$$e = -\frac{\dot{x}'_1}{\dot{x}_1} \qquad (19.33)$$

for this case. If Eq. (19.33) is used, the velocity $\dot{x}'_1$ depends only on $e$ and $\dot{x}_1$ and not on the mass of the earth.

More complicated impact problems beyond the scope of this book occur when one of the spheres is constrained. In Fig. 19.12, a stationary sphere supported on a string is struck by a moving sphere. Since there is an impulsive external reaction in the string, only the horizontal component of the total momentum is conserved during impact. This problem is complicated by the fact that, if Eq. (19.28) is to be used, the value of $e$ is influenced by the presence of the string and is not the same as when the two spheres are unconstrained.

Problems of eccentric impact, such as that shown in Fig. 19.13, are also complicated, and they are solved by applying the principles of momentum and angular momentum to each body and writing an equation similar to Eq. (19.28) for the two contact points $A$ and $B$.

There is one case of eccentric impact simple enough to be considered, namely the problem of the so-called "ballistic" pendulum, pictured in Fig. 19.14. In this problem, a bullet of mass $m_0$ is fired with a large speed $v_0$ into a heavy block of wood. The block is attached to a bar, and the bar is supported at a fixed point $O$. Unless the bullet strikes the pendulum at its center of percussion, there is an impulsive reaction at $O$, but using $O$ as a reference point for the principle of angular momentum eliminates

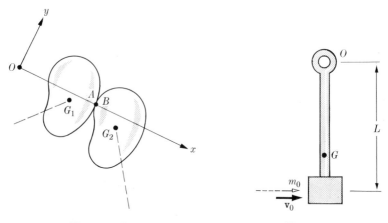

FIGURE 19.13                              FIGURE 19.14

that reaction from the problem. The fact that the impact is plastic further simplifies the problem. Applying Eq. (19.26) to the combined system during the impact,

$$I_z\omega'_z - Lm_0v_0 = 0,$$

where $I_z$ is the combined moment of inertia of the bullet and pendulum. Hence,

$$v_0 = \frac{I_z\omega'_z}{Lm_0}.$$

### PROBLEMS

19.1 Find the impulse of

$$\mathbf{F} = 100t\mathbf{i} + 100\sin\left(\frac{\pi}{2}t\right)\mathbf{j} - 40t^3\mathbf{k},$$

where $F$ is in lb and $t$ is in sec, between $t = 1$ sec and $t = 4$ sec.

19.2 Solve Problem 6.3(a) by the principle of momentum.

[*Ans.*: 40 sec.]

19.3 Solve Problem 6.7 by the principle of momentum.

19.4 The coefficient of kinetic friction between the block and plane in Fig. 19.15 is 0.1. Find the time it takes for the block to attain a velocity $v_x$ of 30 ft/sec to the right if: (a) $v_x(0) = 10$ ft/sec, (b) $v_x(0) = -10$ ft/sec.

[*Ans.*: (a) 1.16 sec; (b) 2.13 sec.]

19.5 A projectile is fired at $t = 0$ with an initial velocity $\mathbf{v}_0$ (Fig. 19.16). (a) What is $t$ when the projectile reaches its maximum height? (b) What is the speed of the projectile when $t$ is three times the value obtained in part (a)?

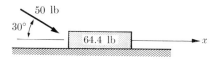

FIGURE 19.15

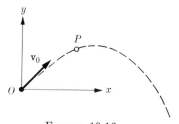

FIGURE 19.16

19.6 A particle with mass of 2 slugs moves in space in such a way that

$$x = 20t, \qquad y = -\tfrac{5}{2}t^2, \qquad z = \tfrac{1}{3}t^3,$$

where $x$, $y$, $z$ are in ft and $t$ is in sec. Find $\mathbf{N}$ and $\mathbf{H}$ when $t = 6$ sec.

[*Ans.:* $\mathbf{N}(6) = 40\mathbf{i} - 60\mathbf{j} + 72\mathbf{k}$ lb-sec, $\mathbf{H}(6) = -2160\mathbf{i} - 5760\mathbf{j} - 3600\mathbf{k}$ ft-lb-sec.]

19.7 Solve Problem 6.21 by the principle of angular momentum.

19.8 In Fig. 19.17, the string from a conical pendulum runs through a hole in a fixed plane, where a force $\mathbf{P}_1$ acts to keep the particle moving on a circular path of radius $b_1$ at a constant speed $v_1$. The string is then pulled through the hole so as to reduce the projecting length from $L_1$ to $L_2$. What must $L_2$ be to double the speed of the particle?

[*Ans.:* $L_2 = \sqrt{(1/256)(L_1^2 + 63b_1^2)}.$]

19.9 In the system shown in Fig. 19.18, the pulley is weightless and frictionless, and the string is inextensible. The coefficient of kinetic friction between

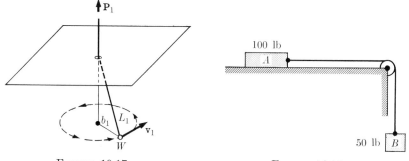

FIGURE 19.17      FIGURE 19.18

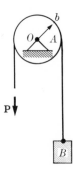

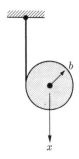

FIGURE 19.19                          FIGURE 19.20

block $A$ and the horizontal plane is 0.25. If block $A$ has an initial velocity of 40 ft/sec to the left, determine its velocity after 2 sec.

19.10  The 32.2-lb body $B$ in Fig. 19.19 is connected to a rope running over the solid, homogeneous cylinder $A$. The cylinder weighs 64.4 lb and rotates about a fixed axis through $O$. If there is no slipping between rope and cylinder, find the magnitude of the constant force $P$ required to change the velocity of $B$ from 10 ft/sec downward to 20 ft/sec upward in 2 sec.

[*Ans.:* 62.2 lb.]

19.11  Solve Problem 13.9(c) by the principle of angular momentum.

19.12  A solid, homogeneous cylinder of weight $W$ and radius $b$ has a string wound around its middle. One end of the string is fixed as shown in Fig. 19.20. The cylinder is released from rest and falls vertically, unwinding the string. Find the velocity of the cylinder's axis after 3 sec.

[*Ans.:* 64.4 ft/sec.]

19.13  For the two cars shown in Fig. 19.21,

$$m_1 = m_0, \qquad m_2 = 2m_0, \qquad \dot{x}_1 = v_0, \qquad \dot{x}_2 = -v_0.$$

Assuming that $e = 0.5$, determine the change in speed of each car during a head-on collision.

19.14  For the two cars in Fig. 19.21,

$$m_1 = m_0, \qquad m_2 = m_0, \qquad \dot{x}_1 = v_0, \qquad \dot{x}_2 = -2v_0.$$

Assuming that $e = 0.5$, determine the change in speed of each car during a head-on collision.

[*Ans.:* $\Delta v_1 = \Delta v_2 = 2.25v_0$.]

FIGURE 19.21

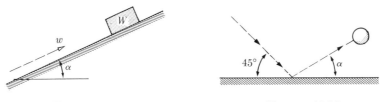

FIGURE 19.22            FIGURE 19.23

19.15 A wooden block of weight $W$ slides down a smooth plane of inclination $\alpha$ (Fig. 19.22). At the instant when the block has a speed $v$ down the plane, a bullet of weight $w$ is fired up the plane and into the block. Find the speed of the bullet necessary to reverse the direction of motion of the block and give it a speed $v$ up the plane.

19.16 A ball is bounced on the floor at an angle of 45° as shown in Fig. 19.23. If $e = 0.8$, determine the angle $\alpha$ at which the ball rebounds.

[*Ans.:* 38.7°.]

## CHAPTER 20

## WORK AND ENERGY

**20.1 Introduction.** The energy approach to mechanics represents still another formulation of the subject, useful for the solution of another class of problems. Furthermore, the energy methods are of fundamental importance and wide applicability in advanced mechanics. In many cases they provide valuable insight into the behavior of mechanical systems.

The historical development of the energy concept, in addition to its influence on Newtonian mechanics, led to the evolution of other branches of physics such as thermodynamics and laid the foundation for much of modern physics and chemistry.

**20.2 Work.** Figure 20.1 shows a particle $P$ moving along a path in space, so that

$$x = f_1(t), \qquad y = f_2(t), \qquad z = f_3(t).$$

The displacement $\mathbf{u}$ is measured from some initial point $A_1$ on the path, with $\Delta\mathbf{u}$ being the change in $\mathbf{u}$ in a time interval $\Delta t$. The vector $d\mathbf{u}$ is the differential of $\mathbf{u}$, that is,

$$d\mathbf{u} = \frac{d\mathbf{u}}{dt}\,\Delta t = \left(\lim_{\Delta t \to 0} \frac{\Delta\mathbf{u}}{\Delta t}\right)\Delta t.$$

It is known from Art. 5.1 that this vector is tangent to the path at $P$. In terms of $\mathbf{i}$, $\mathbf{j}$, $\mathbf{k}$,

$$\Delta\mathbf{u} = \Delta x\mathbf{i} + \Delta y\mathbf{j} + \Delta z\mathbf{k}, \qquad d\mathbf{u} = dx\mathbf{i} + dy\mathbf{j} + dz\mathbf{k}.$$

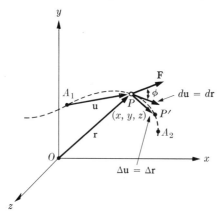

FIGURE 20.1

412

By definition, the *differential work* $dw$ done by a force $\mathbf{F}$ acting on the particle during the time interval $\Delta t$ is given by

$$dw = \mathbf{F} \cdot d\mathbf{u}. \tag{20.1}$$

By Eq. (7.1),

$$dw = F \cos \phi \, du, \tag{20.2}$$

where $du$ is the magnitude of $d\mathbf{u}$, and from this it follows that $dw = F \, du$ if $\phi = 0$, $dw = -F \, du$ if $\phi = 180°$, and $dw = 0$ if $\phi = 90°$.

From Eq. (20.1), the *work* $w$ done by $\mathbf{F}$ as the particle travels from $A_1$ to $A_2$ is

$$w = \int_{A_1}^{A_2} \mathbf{F} \cdot d\mathbf{u}, \tag{20.3}$$

the integral being a line integral which in general depends on the locations of $A_1$ and $A_2$ and on the path. Such a line integral is defined by subdividing the path between $A_1$ and $A_2$ into $n$ parts and selecting an arbitrary point $(x_i, y_i, z_i)$ in each part, so that

$$w = \lim_{n \to \infty} \sum_{i=1}^{n} \mathbf{F}(x_i, y_i, z_i) \cdot \Delta_i \mathbf{u}. \tag{20.4}$$

Using Eq. (7.1) again, we obtain

$$w = \lim_{n \to \infty} \sum_{i=1}^{n} F(x_i, y_i, z_i) \cos \phi(x_i, y_i, z_i) \sqrt{(\Delta_i x)^2 + (\Delta_i y)^2 + (\Delta_i z)^2},$$

and now the right-hand side conforms to the basic definition of a line integral.

To better understand and to evaluate $w$, it is convenient to rewrite Eq. (20.4) using Eq. (7.7), i.e.,

$$w = \lim_{n \to \infty} \sum_{i=1}^{n} F_x(x_i, y_i, z_i) \, \Delta_i x + \lim_{n \to \infty} \sum_{i=1}^{n} F_y(x_i, y_i, z_i) \, \Delta_i y$$

$$+ \lim_{n \to \infty} \sum_{i=1}^{n} F_z(x_i, y_i, z_i) \, \Delta_i z. \tag{20.5}$$

The three terms on the right-hand side are also line integrals, so that

$$w = \int_{A_1}^{A_2} F_x(x, y, z) \, dx + \int_{A_1}^{A_2} F_y(x, y, z) \, dy + \int_{A_1}^{A_2} F_z(x, y, z) \, dz, \tag{20.6}$$

although these line integrals are of a different type from that of Eq. (20.3). If the path of the particle is mathematically defined in such a way that any two coordinates of $P$ can be expressed as functions of the other one, then Eq. (20.5) can be rewritten as follows:

$$w = \lim_{n \to \infty} \sum_{i=1}^{n} F_x[x_i, y(x_i), z(x_i)]\, \Delta_i x + \lim_{n \to \infty} \sum_{i=1}^{n} F_y[x(y_i), y_i, z(y_i)]\, \Delta_i y$$

$$+ \lim_{n \to \infty} \sum_{i=1}^{n} F_z[x(z_i), y(z_i), z_i]\, \Delta_i z.$$

The three terms on the right-hand side are now ordinary integrals, so that

$$w = \int_{x_1}^{x_2} F_x[x, y(x), z(x)]\, dx + \int_{y_1}^{y_2} F_y[x(y), y, z(y)]\, dy$$

$$+ \int_{z_1}^{z_2} F_z[x(z), y(z), z]\, dz. \quad (20.7)$$

If the path of the particle is defined in terms of a parameter $t$ (which may be time), then Eq. (20.5) can be rewritten as follows:

$$w = \lim_{n \to \infty} \sum_{i=1}^{n} F_x[x(t_i), y(t_i), z(t_i)] \frac{\Delta_i x}{\Delta_i t} \Delta_i t + \cdots .$$

The three terms are now ordinary integrals on $t$, that is,

$$w = \int_{t_1}^{t_2} F_x[x(t), y(t), z(t)] \frac{dx}{dt}\, dt + \cdots . \quad (20.8)$$

Equations (20.7) and (20.8) are usually adequate for computing the work done by a force in practical problems.

It is important to understand that work is a scalar quantity, and that what causes the displacement and whether or not the particle accelerates are immaterial (a force and a displacement being the only two essential phenomena to the doing of work).

---

EXAMPLE 20.1. The particle $P$ in Fig. 20.2 carries a force $\mathbf{F}$ with a magnitude of 100 lb and a line of action always through point $B$. Find the work done by $\mathbf{F}$ as $P$ moves: (a) from $O$ to $A$, and (b) from $A$ to $O$.

*Solution.* By trigonometry,

$$F_x = \frac{x}{\sqrt{x^2 + 9}} (100).$$

(a) By Eq. (20.7),

$$w = \int_0^4 \frac{100x}{\sqrt{x^2 + 9}}\, dx = 100\sqrt{x^2 + 9}\,\Big|_0^4 = 200 \text{ ft-lb.}$$

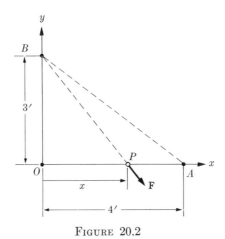

FIGURE 20.2

(b) By Eq. (20.7),

$$w = \int_4^0 \frac{100x}{\sqrt{x^2 + 9}}\, dx = -200 \text{ ft-lb.}$$

The $y$-component of $\mathbf{F}$, another function of $x$, does no work because, in the second integral of Eq. (20.7), $x$ is not a function of $y$ and both limits are zero.

It is frequently necessary in problems to find the work done by a weight force during a displacement. If a block of weight $W$ moves up a vertical distance $h$ in either of the two ways shown in Figs. 20.3(a) and (b), then

$$F_y = -W$$

at all times, and

$$w = \int_{y_A}^{y_B} -W\, dy = -W(y_B - y_A) = -Wh.$$

Since $\mathbf{W}$ is a constant force, the way in which $x$ varies with $y$ along the path does not affect the total work.

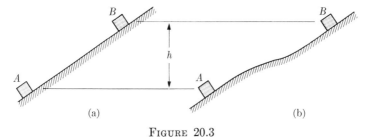

(a)                                              (b)

FIGURE 20.3

Another important type of force component is one which is a linear function of a coordinate. Consider, for example, the block and spring of Fig. 20.4(a). Take the origin at the center of the block when the spring is in its relaxed state, as shown in Fig. 20.4(a). For the general displacement $x$ of Fig. 20.4(c), if the spring is a *linear spring*, the spring force exerted on the block has an $x$-component given by

$$F_x = -kx$$

for either positive or negative $x$. The constant $k$ has units of force/length and is called the *spring constant*. As the block moves from the position of Fig. 20.4(b) to that of Fig. 20.4(d), the work done by $\mathbf{F}$ is

$$w = \int_{x_1}^{x_2} -kx\, dx = -\left. \tfrac{1}{2}kx^2 \right|_{x_1}^{x_2} = -\tfrac{1}{2}k(x_2^2 - x_1^2),$$

where $x_1$ and $x_2$ may have any values, positive or negative.

The differential work done by $N$ concurrent forces having a point of concurrency with displacement $\mathbf{u}$ is given by

$$dw = \mathbf{F}_1 \cdot d\mathbf{u} + \mathbf{F}_2 \cdot d\mathbf{u} + \cdots + \mathbf{F}_N \cdot d\mathbf{u}.$$

Factoring out $d\mathbf{u}$, we obtain

$$dw = (\mathbf{F}_1 + \mathbf{F}_2 + \cdots + \mathbf{F}_N) \cdot d\mathbf{u}.$$

Hence,

$$dw = \mathbf{R} \cdot d\mathbf{u}, \tag{20.9}$$

where $\mathbf{R}$ is the resultant. For a nonconcurrent system, the total work is obtained by adding algebraically the works of the separate forces.

There are many situations in mechanics where particles or bodies are constrained in such a way that certain forces or sets of forces do no work. (Constraints of this type are called *workless constraints*.) Among these forces are the following:

(1) The reaction on a moving body in smooth contact with a fixed body. See Figs. 20.5(a) and (b).

(2) The reaction on a body rolling without slipping on a fixed body, even with friction. See Fig. 20.6.

(3) The pair of internal forces between two particles of a rigid body.

(4) The pair of internal forces between two bodies connected by a smooth pin.

(5) The pair of internal forces in an ideal string.

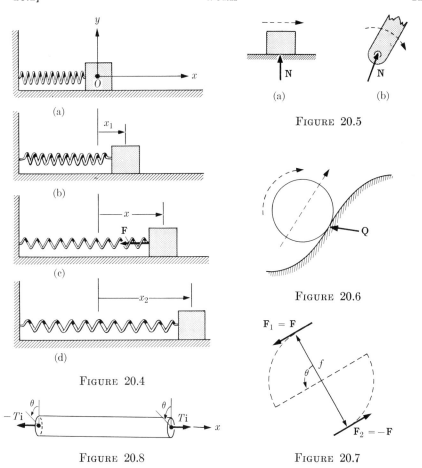

FIGURE 20.5

FIGURE 20.6

FIGURE 20.4

FIGURE 20.8                                  FIGURE 20.7

To find the work done by a constant couple during rotation (Fig. 20.7), note that

$$dw = 2F\left(\frac{f}{2}\,d\theta\right) = Ff\,d\theta.$$

Therefore,

$$w = \int_0^\theta Ff\,d\theta = Ff\theta.$$

Using Eq. (8.21),

$$w = C\theta, \tag{20.10}$$

where $\theta$ is in rad. For a rigid shaft rotating with a constant torque $T$ through an angle $\theta$, as in Fig. 20.8, the work delivered at the right end of the shaft is given by

$$w = T\theta.$$

By definition, the *power p* of a force or couple is the rate of doing work, i.e.,

$$p = \frac{dw}{dt}. \tag{20.11}$$

Thus, the power delivered at the right end of the shaft of Fig. 20.8 is

$$p = T\frac{d\theta}{dt} = T\omega_x, \tag{20.12}$$

where $\omega_x$ is the angular velocity of the shaft.

The differential work done by all the forces acting on a system of $n$ particles may be divided into work done by external forces and work done by internal forces, i.e.,

$$dw = dw_E + dw_I$$
$$= (\mathbf{R}_1' \cdot d\mathbf{u}_1 + \mathbf{R}_2' \cdot d\mathbf{u}_2 + \cdots + \mathbf{R}_n' \cdot d\mathbf{u}_n)$$
$$+ (\mathbf{R}_1'' \cdot d\mathbf{u}_1 + \mathbf{R}_2'' \cdot d\mathbf{u}_2 + \cdots + \mathbf{R}_n'' \cdot d\mathbf{u}_n).$$

The internal work $dw_I$ is zero if the system is a rigid body or a group of rigid bodies connected by smooth pins, inextensible strings, etc., but it is not zero in general.

**20.3 Kinetic energy.** The *kinetic energy $T$* of a particle is defined by

$$T = \tfrac{1}{2}mv^2, \tag{20.13}$$

where $v$ is the speed, so that

$$T = \tfrac{1}{2}m\dot{x}^2 + \tfrac{1}{2}m\dot{y}^2 + \tfrac{1}{2}m\dot{z}^2.$$

For a system of $n$ particles each having a kinetic energy $T_i$,

$$T = \sum_{i=1}^{n} T_i = \sum_{i=1}^{n} \tfrac{1}{2}m_i v_i^2$$
$$= \sum_{i=1}^{n} \tfrac{1}{2}m_i \dot{x}_i^2 + \sum_{i=1}^{n} \tfrac{1}{2}m_i \dot{y}_i^2 + \sum_{i=1}^{n} \tfrac{1}{2}m_i \dot{z}_i^2.$$

For a rigid body in plane motion,

$$T = \iiint\limits_{V} \tfrac{1}{2}v^2 \mu \, dV = \iiint\limits_{V} \tfrac{1}{2}(\dot{x}^2 + \dot{y}^2)\mu \, dV.$$

By Eqs. (12.19),

$$\dot{x}^2 + \dot{y}^2 = \dot{x}_A^2 + \dot{y}_A^2 + \omega_z^2[(x - x_A)^2 + (y - y_A)^2]$$
$$-2\dot{x}_A\omega_z(y - y_A) + 2\dot{y}_A\omega_z(x - x_A).$$

Substituting into the equation for $T$ and proceeding as in Art. 13.2, we obtain

$$T = \tfrac{1}{2}mv_A^2 + \tfrac{1}{2}I_z^A\omega_z^2 - m\dot{x}_A\omega_z(y_G - y_A) + m\dot{y}_A\omega_z(x_G - x_A). \qquad (20.14)$$

If $A$ is $G$,

$$T = \tfrac{1}{2}mv_G^2 + \tfrac{1}{2}I_z^G\omega_z^2, \qquad (20.15)$$

which shows that the total kinetic energy may be divided into two parts, that of translation and that of rotation. If $A$ is a point $O$ on a fixed axis of rotation,

$$T = \tfrac{1}{2}I_z\omega_z^2, \qquad (20.16)$$

and a similar equation holds for the instantaneous center of null velocity $C$. If the body is in translation,

$$T = \tfrac{1}{2}mv^2, \qquad (20.17)$$

where $v$ is the common speed of all points in the body.

For a system of $n$ rigid bodies each having a kinetic energy $T_i$,

$$T = \sum_{i=1}^{n} T_i.$$

---

EXAMPLE 20.2.   The solid, homogeneous cylinder of Fig. 20.9 rolls without slipping on the inclined plane. Find $T$ in terms of the speed $v_G$ of point $G$.

*Solution.* By Eq. (20.15),

$$T = \frac{1}{2}\frac{W}{g}v_G^2 + \frac{1}{2}\left(\frac{1}{2}\frac{W}{g}b^2\right)\omega_z^2.$$

But, by kinematics,

$$\omega_z^2 = \frac{v_G^2}{b^2}.$$

Thus,

$$T = \frac{1}{2}\frac{W}{g}v_G^2 + \frac{1}{4}\frac{W}{g}v_G^2 = \frac{3}{4}\frac{W}{g}v_G^2.$$

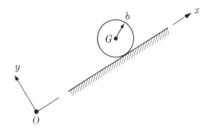

FIGURE 20.9

**20.4 Principle of kinetic energy.** For a particle acted upon by several forces, the differential work done by all the forces, by Eq. (20.9), is

$$dw = \mathbf{R} \cdot d\mathbf{u}.$$

Hence,

$$dw = \mathbf{R} \cdot d\mathbf{r} = \left(m\frac{d\mathbf{v}}{dt}\right) \cdot \left(\frac{d\mathbf{r}}{dt}dt\right) = \left(m\mathbf{v} \cdot \frac{d\mathbf{v}}{dt}\right)dt$$

$$= d(\tfrac{1}{2}m\mathbf{v} \cdot \mathbf{v}) = d(\tfrac{1}{2}mv^2) = dT.$$

Integrating, we obtain

$$w = T_2 - T_1, \tag{20.18}$$

i.e., the total work done by all the forces equals the change in kinetic energy. This is called the *principle of kinetic energy*. It can be used to find velocities directly, without first finding accelerations. While the momentum principles are advantageous for problems involving velocity and time, the principle of kinetic energy is advantageous for those involving velocity and distance.

If the particle is in rectilinear motion,

$$\tfrac{1}{2}m[\dot{x}(x_2)]^2 - \tfrac{1}{2}m[\dot{x}(x_1)]^2 = \int_{x_1}^{x_2} R_x \, dx. \tag{20.19}$$

Equation (20.19) is useful when $R_x$ (or $a_x$) is given as a function of $x$ instead of $t$. The integral in Eq. (20.19) is the area under the $R_x$-$x$ graph between $x_1$ and $x_2$. For a comparison between energy and momentum, note that, for rectilinear motion,

$$R_x = \frac{dT}{dx} = \frac{dN_x}{dt}.$$

---

EXAMPLE 20.3. A "ballistic" missile is to be launched vertically from the earth's surface as shown in Fig. 20.10. Find the initial speed $v_0$ necessary for the missile to reach an altitude $h$.

*Solution.* By Eq. (6.18),

$$W = \frac{r_0^2}{x^2} mg_0,$$

where $m$ is the mass of the missile and $g_0$ is 32.2 ft/sec$^2$. By Eq. (20.19), since the final velocity is zero,

$$-\tfrac{1}{2}mv_0^2 = \int_{r_0}^{r_0+h} -\frac{r_0^2}{x^2} mg_0 \, dx$$

$$= \frac{r_0^2}{x} mg_0 \Big|_{r_0}^{r_0+h}.$$

Therefore,

$$-\tfrac{1}{2}v_0^2 = \frac{r_0^2 g_0}{r_0 + h} - r_0 g_0,$$

and

$$v_0^2 = 2r_0 g_0 - \frac{2r_0^2 g_0}{r_0 + h}.$$

The foregoing result may be used to find the *escape speed* (i.e., the initial speed required to have the missile continue indefinitely upward) by letting $h$ approach infinity, whereupon

$$v_0^2 = 2r_0 g_0 = 2(3960) \left( \frac{32.2}{5280} \right) = 48.3,$$

and

$$v_0 = 6.95 \, \text{mi/sec.}$$

If a particle is in curvilinear motion,

$$\tfrac{1}{2}mv_2^2 - \tfrac{1}{2}mv_1^2 = \int_{A_1}^{A_2} R_x \, dx + \int_{A_1}^{A_2} R_y \, dy + \int_{A_1}^{A_2} R_z \, dz. \quad (20.20)$$

Equation (20.20) is useful when the speed of the particle is of more interest than its velocity.

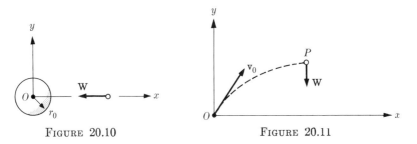

FIGURE 20.10                    FIGURE 20.11

EXAMPLE 20.4. A missile of weight $W$ is launched at the origin as shown in Fig. 20.11. Assuming that **W** does not change in magnitude or direction, find the speed as a function of the altitude $y$.

*Solution.* By Eq. (20.20),

$$\frac{1}{2} \frac{W}{g} (v^2 - v_0^2) = \int_0^y -W \, dy = -Wy,$$

so that

$$v^2 = v_0^2 - 2gy, \qquad v = \sqrt{v_0^2 - 2gy}.$$

By summation, Eq. (20.18) also holds for a system of particles if $w$ is the work done by all the forces and $T$ is the kinetic energy of the entire system. The principle is especially useful when there are workless constraints, since the total work is then easily computed.

EXAMPLE 20.5. The blocks $A$ and $B$ in Fig. 20.12 weigh 966 lb and 644 lb, respectively, and they are connected together by an ideal rope running over a weightless pulley. If the system is released from rest, how far must block $A$ travel before it acquires a speed of 10 ft/sec?

*Solution.* The total kinetic energy of the system is zero initially and is the sum of the kinetic energies of the two blocks finally. The only forces which do work are the weight force of $B$ and the friction force on $A$. Calling the unknown distance $d$, therefore,

$$644d - 0.3(966)d = \frac{1}{2}\frac{966}{32.2}(10)^2 + \frac{1}{2}\frac{644}{32.2}(10)^2,$$

$$354d = 2500,$$

$$d = 7.06 \text{ ft.}$$

Equation (20.18) can also be used to solve rigid-body problems, in which case $w$ is the work done by the external forces and $T$ is given by an expression such as Eq. (20.15).

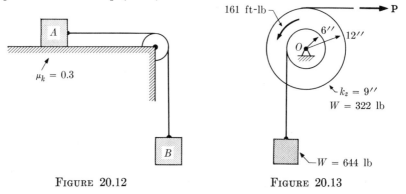

FIGURE 20.12          FIGURE 20.13

EXAMPLE 20.6. The system in Fig. 20.13 starts from rest and is accelerated by a force $P$ such that

$$P = 644 + 322x,$$

where $x$ is the displacement of $P$ from its initial position in ft and $P$ is in lb. The bearings produce a constant frictional couple of 161 ft-lb. Find the angular speed of the pulley when $x = 2$ ft.

*Solution.* The forces which do work are the weight force of the block, the frictional couple, and $P$. Since the linear displacement of $P$ is the product of the angular displacement in rad of the pulley and its outer radius, and since the linear displacement of the block is one-half that of $P$, the total work is

$$w = -644(1) - 161(2) + \int_0^2 (644 + 322x)\,dx = 966 \text{ ft-lb.}$$

Since the speed of the block is the product of the angular speed $\omega$ of the pulley and its inner radius, the final kinetic energy of the system is

$$T_2 = \frac{1}{2}\left[\frac{322}{32.2}\,(0.75)^2\right]\omega_2^2 + \frac{1}{2}\,\frac{644}{32.2}\,\frac{\omega_2^2}{4} = 5.31\omega_2^2.$$

By Eq. (20.18), therefore,

$$5.31\omega_2^2 = 966, \qquad \omega_2^2 = 181.9, \qquad \omega_2 = 13.49\,\text{rad/sec}.$$

**20.5 Potential energy in two dimensions.** Assume that a particle $P$ in the $xy$-plane is acted upon by a force $\mathbf{F}$ in the plane as in Fig. 20.14, and suppose that $\mathbf{F}$ depends only upon the position of the particle (not upon its speed, etc.). Assume further that $F_x(x, y)$ and $F_y(x, y)$ are finite, continuous, and single-valued functions. If

$$\frac{\partial F_x}{\partial y} = \frac{\partial F_y}{\partial x}, \tag{20.21}$$

then $\mathbf{F}$ is said to be a *conservative force*. From the calculus, Eq. (20.21) is a necessary and sufficient condition for the existence of a differentiable function $\phi$ of $x$ and $y$ such that

$$d\phi = F_x\,dx + F_y\,dy, \tag{20.22}$$

where

$$F_x = \frac{\partial \phi}{\partial x}, \qquad F_y = \frac{\partial \phi}{\partial y}. \tag{20.23}$$

The work done by $\mathbf{F}$ as $P$ goes from $A_1$ to $A_2$ is, from Eq. (20.6),

$$w = \int_{A_1}^{A_2} (F_x\,dx + F_y\,dy) = \int_{A_1}^{A_2} d\phi = \phi_2 - \phi_1.$$

Thus, the work done by a conservative force depends on the endpoints

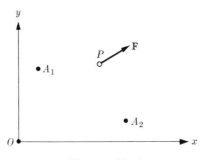

FIGURE 20.14

but not on the path, while, if $\phi$ did not exist, the work would still be given by

$$w = \int_{A_1}^{A_2} (F_x \, dx + F_y \, dy),$$

but $w$ would in general depend on the path followed.

The function $\phi(x, y)$ is called a *potential*, which means that other quantities (here $F_x$ and $F_y$) can be derived from it by partial differentiation. If the functions $F_x$ and $F_y$ are given, and if they satisfy Eq. (20.21), then $\phi$ can be determined by integrating Eq. (20.22), but only to within an arbitrary constant.

By definition, the *potential energy* $V$ of the particle with respect to **F** is given by

$$V = -\phi, \tag{20.24}$$

and $V$ is defined only if $\phi$ exists, i.e., only if **F** is a conservative force. Using Eqs. (20.22), (20.23), and (20.24),

$$dV = -d\phi = -F_x \, dx - F_y \, dy, \tag{20.25}$$

and

$$F_x = -\frac{\partial V}{\partial x}, \qquad F_y = -\frac{\partial V}{\partial y}. \tag{20.26}$$

It follows from Eq. (20.25) that

$$dV = -dw, \tag{20.27}$$

or, by integration,

$$V_2 - V_1 = \int_{A_1}^{A_2} -dw = -w, \tag{20.28}$$

i.e., the change in potential energy as the particle goes from $A_1$ to $A_2$ equals the negative of the work done.

Using the origin as an arbitrarily chosen reference position at which $V = 0$ (called the *standard configuration*) and integrating Eq. (20.27),

$$V_1 = \int_{A_1}^{O} dw, \qquad V_2 = \int_{A_2}^{O} dw,$$

or, for any point $A$ (called the *general configuration*),

$$V = \int_{A}^{O} dw,$$

i.e., the potential energy at the general configuration equals the work done

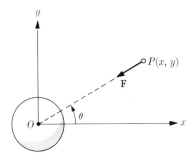

FIGURE 20.15

by **F** as the particle goes from the general configuration to the standard configuration along any path. Thus, $V$ is a function of the coordinates $x$, $y$ of $A$ and is the "capacity" of the conservative force **F** for doing work.

EXAMPLE 20.7. The gravitational force **F** on a particle (Fig. 20.15), by Eq. (6.15), has a magnitude given by

$$F = \frac{K}{x^2 + y^2},$$

where $K$ is a constant. Find expressions for $F_x$ and $F_y$ and show that **F** is a conservative force.

*Solution.* By trigonometry,

$$\cos\theta = \frac{x}{(x^2 + y^2)^{1/2}}, \qquad \sin\theta = \frac{y}{(x^2 + y^2)^{1/2}},$$

so that

$$F_x = -\frac{Kx}{(x^2 + y^2)^{3/2}}, \qquad F_y = -\frac{Ky}{(x^2 + y^2)^{3/2}}.$$

Differentiating,

$$\frac{\partial F_x}{\partial y} = \frac{3Kxy}{(x^2 + y^2)^{5/2}}, \qquad \frac{\partial F_y}{\partial x} = \frac{3Kxy}{(x^2 + y^2)^{5/2}}.$$

By Eq. (20.21), therefore, the force is conservative.

The total potential energy $V$ of a particle with respect to all the forces is defined as the sum of the potential energies with respect to the individual forces (if all of them are conservative). Since Eq. (20.25) holds for each force, and since the work done by a group of concurrent forces equals the work done by $R$, it follows that

$$dV = -R_x \, dx - R_y \, dy \qquad (20.29)$$

and

$$R_x = -\frac{\partial V}{\partial x}, \qquad R_y = -\frac{\partial V}{\partial y}. \qquad (20.30)$$

If $w$ is the work done by $R$ as the particle goes from $A_1$ to $A_2$, then, from Eq. (20.29),

$$dV = -dw, \qquad (20.31)$$

and, by integration,

$$w = -(V_2 - V_1). \qquad (20.32)$$

By analogy with Eq. (20.18), Eq. (20.32) may be called the *principle of potential energy*.

By summation, Eqs. (20.31) and (20.32) also hold for a system of particles if $w$ is the work done by all the forces and $V$ is the potential energy of the entire system. For a system of particles, a configuration is a set of positions for all the particles, and the potential energy of the entire system is the work done by all the forces as the system goes from the general configuration to the standard configuration.

For a rigid body, Eqs. (20.31) and (20.32) may be used if all the external forces are conservative. In this case, $w$ is the work done by the external forces and $V$ is the sum of the potential energies of the external forces.

**20.6 Principle of conservation of mechanical energy.** For any mechanical system in which all the forces are conservative, it follows from Eqs. (20.18) and (20.32) that

$$T_2 - T_1 = w = -(V_2 - V_1)$$

or

$$T_2 + V_2 = T_1 + V_1. \qquad (20.33)$$

Defining the *total mechanical energy $E$* as

$$E = T + V, \qquad (20.34)$$

Eq. (20.33) may be written

$$E_2 = E_1. \qquad (20.35)$$

This is called the *principle of conservation of mechanical energy*. A mechanical system for which Eq. (20.35) holds is called a *conservative system*. Generally, systems acted upon by nonconservative forces such as friction, air resistance, etc., are not conservative systems. If a system has work-less constraints, but all the forces which do work are conservative, the system itself may be regarded as conservative. For any conservative system, Eq. (20.35) can be used to find one unknown.

---

EXAMPLE 20.8.   Under the action of gravity alone, a particle of weight $W$ is traveling on a vertical circular path at the end of a string of length $L$ as in Fig. 20.16. If the tension $S$ in the string is zero at $A_1$, find $S$ at $A_2$.

*Solution.* At $A_1$,

$$\sum F_\rho = -W = -\frac{W}{g}\frac{v_1^2}{L}, \qquad v_1^2 = gL.$$

Applying Eq. (20.33), with $A_2$ taken as the standard configuration,

$$\frac{1}{2}\frac{W}{g}v_2^2 = \frac{1}{2}\frac{W}{g}v_1^2 + 2WL,$$

$$v_2^2 = v_1^2 + 4gL = 5gL.$$

Thus, at $A_2$,

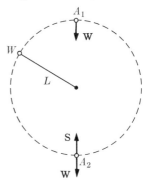

FIGURE 20.16

$$\sum F_\rho = W - S = -\frac{W}{g}\frac{5gL}{L} = -5W, \qquad S = 6W.$$

## PROBLEMS

20.1  The 100-lb force acting on particle $P$ in Fig. 20.17 always makes an angle of 30° with the $x$-direction. Find the work done by the force as $P$ moves from $A$ to $B$ along a circular path of 2-ft radius.

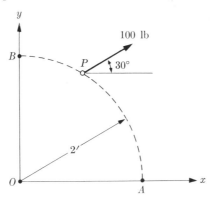

FIGURE 20.17

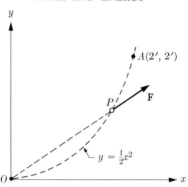

FIGURE 20.18

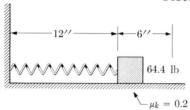

FIGURE 20.19

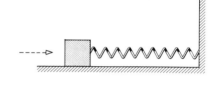

FIGURE 20.20

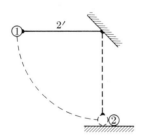

FIGURE 20.21

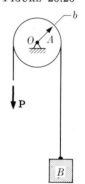

FIGURE 20.22

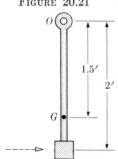

FIGURE 20.23

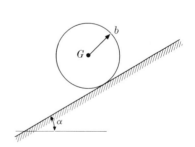

FIGURE 20.24

20.2  The line of action of the force $\mathbf{F}$ acting on particle $P$ in Fig. 20.18 is always through $O$. If

$$F = 100\sqrt{x^2 + y^2},$$

where $F$ is in lb and $x$ and $y$ are in ft, find the work done as $P$ moves from $O$ to $A$.

[*Ans.*: 400 ft-lb.]

20.3  Solve Problem 6.5 by the principle of kinetic energy.

20.4  A particle starts from a point $x = x_0$ with initial velocity $v_{x0} = cx_0$ (where $c$ is a constant) and travels on the $x$-axis in such a way that

$$a_x = c^2 x.$$

Find $v_x$ as a function of $x$.

[*Ans.*: $v_x = cx$.]

20.5  Starting from rest, a rocket of weight $W_0$ at the earth's surface is launched vertically from the surface. The thrust developed by the rocket is constant and equal to $5W_0/4$. Neglecting air resistance and the motion of the earth, find the speed of the rocket as a function of the distance $r$ from the center of the earth.

20.6  A spring which is 18 in. long in its relaxed state and which has a spring constant of 8 lb/in. is used to project a block along a rough, horizontal plane (Fig. 20.19). The spring is initially compressed to a length of 12 in., and the system is then released from rest. What is the velocity of the block when the spring reaches its full length?

[*Ans.*: 2.36 ft/sec.]

20.7  A target is mounted on a block of wood which weighs 64.2 lb and rests on a smooth plane. The block is attached to a spring with spring constant of 13.5 lb/in. (See Fig. 20.20.) If a 0.2-lb bullet is fired into the block with a speed of 1288 ft/sec, determine the maximum displacement of the block.

20.8  A particle attached to an ideal string is released from rest in the position shown in Fig. 20.21. At the bottom of its path, it strikes another particle of the same mass such that $e = 0.8$. Determine the velocity of the second particle after impact.

[*Ans.*: 10.2 ft/sec.]

20.9  The 32.2-lb body $B$ in Fig. 20.22 is raised starting from rest by a force $\mathbf{P}$ of 62.2-lb magnitude applied to a rope running over the solid, homogeneous cylinder $A$. The cylinder weighs 64.4 lb and rotates about a fixed axis through $O$. If there is no slipping between rope and cylinder, find the velocity of $B$ after it moves 10 ft upward.

20.10  The ballistic pendulum shown in Fig. 20.23 has a total weight of 120 lb and a moment of inertia about $O$ of 10 slug-ft$^2$. A bullet weighing 2 oz is fired into the block with a speed of 1288 ft/sec. Find the angular deviation of the pendulum.

[*Ans.*: 13.5°.]

20.11  A solid, homogeneous cylinder of weight $W$ is released from rest on a rough plane having inclination $\alpha$ (Fig. 20.24). If the cylinder rolls without slipping, find the speed $v_G$ of point $G$ as a function of the distance $d$ traveled by $G$.

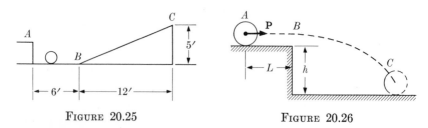

FIGURE 20.25               FIGURE 20.26

20.12 The ramp shown in Fig. 20.25 is for loading cylindrical rolls into a truck at $C$. When the rolls come out of a chute at $A$, their centers have a velocity $v_0$ to the right, and they roll without slipping from $A$ to $B$ and from $B$ to $C$. Each roll is 3 ft long and 1 ft in diameter and weighs 64.4 lb. Treating the rolls as solid, homogeneous cylinders, find the minimum initial speed $v_0$ of their centers if the rolls are to reach $C$.

[*Ans.:* 14.65 ft/sec.]

20.13 A solid, homogeneous cylinder (Fig. 20.26) of radius $b$ and weight $W$ starts from rest at $A$ and rolls without slipping to $B$ due to a constant, horizontal force $\mathbf{P}$ applied at its center. The force is removed at $B$. Find the number of revolutions the cylinder turns through between $B$ and $C$.

20.14 Given:

$$\mathbf{F} = \frac{2F_0}{ab}\,xy\mathbf{i} + \frac{F_0}{ab}\,x^2\mathbf{j}.$$

(a) Using Eq. (20.21), show that $\mathbf{F}$ is conservative. (b) Verify that the work is independent of the path by computing the work done by $\mathbf{F}$ on a particle that goes from $A$ to $O$ along the paths $AO$ and $ABO$ (Fig. 20.27).

[*Ans.:* (b) $w = -F_0 a$ in either case.]

20.15 A linear spring of unstretched length $L_0$ and spring constant $k$ exerts a force $\mathbf{F}$ on a particle (Fig. 20.28). Derive expressions for $F_x$ and $F_y$ in terms of $x$ and $y$ and show that $\mathbf{F}$ is a conservative force.

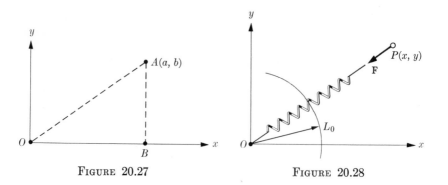

FIGURE 20.27               FIGURE 20.28

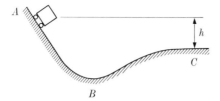

FIGURE 20.29

20.16 A small car of weight $W$ starts from rest at $A$ and rolls without friction to $C$ (Fig. 20.29). Using the principle of conservation of mechanical energy, find the speed of the car at $C$.

[*Ans.*: $v_C = \sqrt{2gh}$.]

20.17 Show by Eqs. (19.27) and (19.28) that energy is conserved during central impact of two spheres if $e = 1$.

# CHAPTER 21

## ENERGY METHODS FOR EQUILIBRIUM

**21.1 Particles and rigid bodies.** Using more advanced mathematics, we can also define conservative forces in three dimensions and show that the work done by such a force is independent of the path. The potential energy $V$ of a particle with respect to a force having three components is the work done as the particle goes from the general configuration to the standard configuration and is a function of all three coordinates at the general configuration. For a particle acted upon by a three-dimensional set of conservative forces with resultant $\mathbf{R}$, Eq. (20.29) becomes

$$dV = -R_x\, dx - R_y\, dy - R_z\, dz, \qquad (21.1)$$

and Eqs. (20.30) become

$$R_x = -\frac{\partial V}{\partial x}, \qquad R_y = -\frac{\partial V}{\partial y}, \qquad R_z = -\frac{\partial V}{\partial z}, \qquad (21.2)$$

while Eqs. (20.31) and (20.32) hold without change.

When we compare Eqs. (4.2) and (21.2), it is clear that the following equations are a set of necessary and sufficient conditions for equilibrium of the particle:

$$\frac{\partial V}{\partial x} = 0, \qquad \frac{\partial V}{\partial y} = 0, \qquad \frac{\partial V}{\partial z} = 0. \qquad (21.3)$$

This is called the *principle of stationary potential energy*, since, at a point where Eqs. (21.3) hold, the function $V$ is said to have a *stationary value*.

Equations (21.3) are also necessary conditions for the equilibrium of any conservative mechanical system, since, when the potential energy of each particle is stationary, the total potential energy must be stationary. If there are enough constraints so that the position of all the particles can be specified by a single parameter $p$, then

$$\frac{dV}{dp} = 0 \qquad (21.4)$$

when the system is in equilibrium. If, for that value of $p$ for which the system is in equilibrium,

$$\frac{d^2V}{dp^2} > 0, \qquad (21.5)$$

the system is said to be in *stable equilibrium*, which means physically that

432

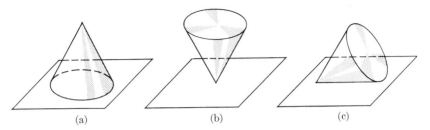

FIGURE 21.1

a small displacement $\Delta p$ from the equilibrium configuration results in a nonequilibrium configuration accompanied by forces and moments which tend to restore the system to its equilibrium position. A right circular cone resting on a horizontal plane as in Fig. 21.1(a) is in stable equilibrium. If, for the equilibrium $p$,

$$\frac{d^2 V}{dp^2} < 0, \tag{21.6}$$

the system is said to be in *unstable equilibrium*, which means physically that a small displacement $\Delta p$ results in a nonequilibrium configuration accompanied by forces and moments which tend to accelerate the system and increase the displacement. See Fig. 21.1(b). Finally, if

$$\frac{d^2 V}{dp^2} = 0, \tag{21.7}$$

the equilibrium is *neutral equilibrium*, as in Fig. 21.1(c). When the cone is in this position, a small displacement $\Delta p$ that preserves the contact with the plane results in another equilibrium position.

---

EXAMPLE 21.1.   For the ideal system shown in Fig. 21.2, find the angle $\theta$ between 0 and 180° at which the system is in equilibrium, and determine whether the equilibrium is stable, unstable, or neutral.

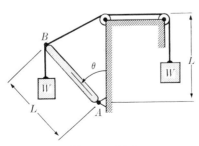

FIGURE 21.2

*Solution.* Let the configuration when $\theta = 0$ be the standard one. The potential energy of the system is then the work done by the two weight forces (the only forces which do work) as $\theta$ changes from its general value to zero, i.e.,

$$V = W\left(2L \sin \frac{\theta}{2}\right) - W(L - L \cos \theta)$$

$$= -WL + 2WL \sin \frac{\theta}{2} + WL \cos \theta.$$

By Eq. (21.4),

$$\frac{dV}{d\theta} = WL \cos \frac{\theta}{2} - WL \sin \theta = 0,$$

from which

$$\cos \frac{\theta}{2} = \sin \theta = 2 \sin \frac{\theta}{2} \cos \frac{\theta}{2},$$

$$\sin \frac{\theta}{2} = \frac{1}{2}.$$

Thus, at equilibrium,

$$\frac{\theta}{2} = 30°, \qquad \theta = 60°.$$

To investigate stability,

$$\frac{d^2 V}{d\theta^2} = -\frac{1}{2} WL \sin \frac{\theta}{2} - WL \cos \theta$$

$$= WL\left(-\frac{1}{2} \sin \frac{\theta}{2} - \cos \theta\right).$$

At $\theta = 60°$, therefore,

$$\frac{d^2 V}{d\theta^2} = WL\left[-\frac{1}{2}\left(\frac{1}{2}\right) - \frac{1}{2}\right] < 0,$$

which means that the equilibrium is unstable.

---

Another important principle which can be used to solve problems such as that of the previous example is the following:

PRINCIPLE OF VIRTUAL WORK: *A system with workless constraints is in equilibrium if and only if zero work is done by the active forces during any arbitrary, infinitesimal displacement satisfying the constraints.*

A displacement of the type described is called a *virtual displacement,* and the work done is called *virtual work.* The principle applies even for nonconservative systems; hence, it is a more general principle than the principle of stationary potential energy. The principle of virtual work also applies without the restriction of workless constraints if the work of all the forces is included. Since the forces of constraint (i.e., the reactions and internal forces) are usually unknown in a problem, however, the principle is most useful when the forces of constraint do no work and do not appear in the solution.

To prove the principle of virtual work, consider first a *free particle* (i.e., one with no constraints) acted upon by a concurrent force system. Let the particle undergo a virtual displacement $\delta\mathbf{u}$, which is symbolized in this manner to distinguish it from a real displacement $\Delta\mathbf{u}$ (which need not be infinitesimal) and from the real differential $d\mathbf{u}$ (to which it is very similar). The virtual work resembles differential work, but, to distinguish it from the real differential work of Eq. (20.9), we symbolize it by $\delta w$. By Eq. (20.9), with $\delta\mathbf{u}$ replacing $d\mathbf{u}$,

$$\delta w = \mathbf{R} \cdot \delta\mathbf{u},$$

this equation implying that the virtual work is computed by assuming that $\mathbf{R}$ remains constant during the virtual displacement. Since

$$\delta\mathbf{u} = \delta x\mathbf{i} + \delta y\mathbf{j} + \delta z\mathbf{k},$$

it follows that

$$\delta w = R_x\,\delta x + R_y\,\delta y + R_z\,\delta z.$$

If the particle is in equilibrium, then, by Eqs. (4.2),

$$\delta w = 0. \tag{21.8}$$

Conversely, if Eq. (21.8) holds, then, since $\delta x$, $\delta y$, $\delta z$ are arbitrary, Eq. (4.2) must be satisfied and the particle must be in equilibrium.

For a constrained particle (e.g., one moving on a fixed surface or one attached to a string), the sufficiency of Eq. (21.8) for equilibrium is more difficult to prove, but the necessity is easily proved by dividing the virtual work $\delta w$ into work done by the active forces and work done by the forces of constraint. As before, the work done by all the forces is zero if the particle is in equilibrium. If, in addition, the constraints are workless, then the remaining work (i.e., that done by the active forces) must be zero.

The principle of virtual work can be extended to a system of particles, to a rigid body, and to a system of rigid bodies.

To solve Example 21.1 by the principle of virtual work, assume an equilibrium position, and let a virtual displacement $\delta\theta$ occur. Since $\delta\theta$ is small, the virtual work is

$$\delta w = WL\,\delta\theta\sin\theta - WL\,\delta\theta\cos\frac{\theta}{2}.$$

By Eq. (21.8), therefore,

$$\sin \theta = \cos \frac{\theta}{2},$$

which yields the same value of $\theta$ as previously. Note that, since the displacement is infinitesimal, no line integrals need be evaluated when computing the virtual work.

The principle of virtual work is very useful for finding reactions on certain types of pin-connected frames, as illustrated in the next example.

---

EXAMPLE 21.2. For the pin-connected frame of Fig. 21.3, find the magnitude of the horizontal reaction $Q$ at $F$.

*Solution.* It is first necessary to replace the hinge at $F$ by a roller in order to make the unknown reaction $Q$ into an active force and to make a displacement possible. Then, taking coordinate axes with origin at $E$,

$$y_A = 3L \cos \theta, \qquad x_F = 2L \sin \theta.$$

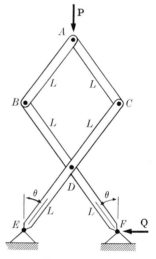

For a virtual displacement $\delta\theta$, then,

$$\delta y_A = -3L \sin \theta \, \delta\theta,$$
$$\delta x_F = 2L \cos \theta \, \delta\theta,$$

and

$$\delta w = 3PL \sin \theta \, \delta\theta - 2QL \cos \theta \, \delta\theta.$$

Using Eq. (21.8),

$$3P \sin \theta = 2Q \cos \theta,$$

and

$$Q = \tfrac{3}{2}P \tan \theta.$$

FIGURE 21.3

Compare this method with that of Chapter 11, in which the members must be disconnected and analyzed separately.

---

The principle of virtual work as applied to a conservative system may be interpreted as an alternative way of specifying that $V$ has a stationary value. By Eq. (20.31),

$$\delta V = -\delta w.$$

But

$$\delta V = \frac{dV}{dp} \, \delta p,$$

where $p$ is the parameter of Eq. (21.4) and $\delta p$ represents a virtual displacement. Therefore,

$$-\delta w = \frac{dV}{dp}\,\delta p.$$

Since $\delta p$ is arbitrary, the last equation shows that Eq. (21.8) is a necessary and sufficient condition for Eq. (21.4).

**21.2 Deformable bodies.** For a deformable body, it is convenient to divide the potential energy into two parts, that of the external forces and that of the internal forces, as follows:

$$V = V_E + V_I. \tag{21.9}$$

If the undeformed state is taken as the standard configuration for $V_I$, then $V_I$ is called the *potential energy of deformation* or *strain energy* and is designated by $U$, so that

$$V = V_E + U. \tag{21.10}$$

The strain energy $U$ is an important quantity in the mechanics of deformable bodies.

A body must be elastic to be a conservative system, and the strain energy is the work that the deformed body is capable of doing in returning to its undeformed state. As an example of the strain energy in a *linearly elastic body*, consider the linear spring discussed in Art. 20.2. With the undeformed state as the standard configuration, the strain energy of the spring when it is stretched an amount $\delta$ is the work done by the spring force as the spring goes from the stretched position to the unstretched, i.e., from Art. 20.2,

$$U = \tfrac{1}{2}k\,\delta^2.$$

When the spring is compressed (i.e., when it has a negative elongation $\delta$), the strain energy is still positive and is given by the same equation.

Applying the principle of conservation of mechanical energy to an elastic body which is stationary before and after deformation,

$$V_2 = V_1,$$

or, by Eq. (21.10),

$$V_{E2} + U = V_{E1}$$

and

$$U = -(V_{E2} - V_{E1}). \tag{21.11}$$

The term in parentheses is the change in potential energy of the external forces during the deformation. Let us now divide the work done in the same manner as is used above for the potential energy, so that

$$w = w_E + w_I.$$

By Eq. (20.32), which applies to any set of forces,

$$w_E = -(V_{E2} - V_{E1}),$$

so that Eq. (21.11) becomes

$$U = w_E. \tag{21.12}$$

In words, the strain energy equals the net work done by the external forces in deforming the body.

When $w_E$ can be computed, Eq. (21.12) can be used to evaluate $U$. Considering the linear spring of Fig. 20.4(c) again, for example, $U$ is equal to the work done on the spring by a force $-\mathbf{F}$ during the deformation, i.e.,

$$U = \int_0^\delta kx\, dx = \tfrac{1}{2}kx^2 \Big|_0^\delta = \tfrac{1}{2}k\delta^2$$

for either positive or negative $\delta$, and this agrees with the previous computation of $U$.

For a three-dimensional body, Eq. (21.12) can be used to find one unknown (e.g., the displacement of one of the external forces) if $U$ can be evaluated. To obtain a formula for $U$, an element of the body is isolated as in Fig. 14.9. The differential of $U$ is found by computing the differential work done by the forces on the element during a change in the strains, i.e.,

$$
\begin{aligned}
dU = {} & (\sigma_x\, dy\, dz)(d\epsilon_x\, dx) + (\sigma_y\, dz\, dx)(d\epsilon_y\, dy) \\
& + (\sigma_z\, dx\, dy)(d\epsilon_z\, dz) + (\tau_{yz}\, dz\, dx)(d\gamma_{yz}\, dy) \\
& + (\tau_{zx}\, dx\, dy)(d\gamma_{zx}\, dz) + (\tau_{xy}\, dy\, dz)(d\gamma_{xy}\, dx).
\end{aligned}
$$

Hence, during the entire deformation and throughout the entire body,

$$
\begin{aligned}
U = \iiint_V \Big( & \int_0^{\epsilon_x} \sigma_x\, d\epsilon_x + \int_0^{\epsilon_y} \sigma_y\, d\epsilon_y + \int_0^{\epsilon_z} \sigma_z\, d\epsilon_z \\
& + \int_0^{\gamma_{yz}} \tau_{yz}\, d\gamma_{yz} + \int_0^{\gamma_{zx}} \tau_{zx}\, d\gamma_{zx} + \int_0^{\gamma_{xy}} \tau_{xy}\, d\gamma_{xy} \Big)\, dV.
\end{aligned}
\tag{21.13}
$$

The integrand of the triple integral is called the *strain energy density* and is often symbolized by $u$. For a linearly elastic body, it can be shown that Eq. (21.13) becomes

$$
\begin{aligned}
U = \iiint_V ( & \tfrac{1}{2}\sigma_x\epsilon_x + \tfrac{1}{2}\sigma_y\epsilon_y + \tfrac{1}{2}\sigma_z\epsilon_z + \tfrac{1}{2}\tau_{yz}\gamma_{yz} \\
& + \tfrac{1}{2}\tau_{zx}\gamma_{zx} + \tfrac{1}{2}\tau_{xy}\gamma_{xy})\, dV.
\end{aligned}
\tag{21.14}
$$

The strain energy can be expressed in terms of stresses alone by assuming that the temperature of the body does not change. (If the body is heated or cooled, mechanical energy is not conserved.) Letting $T - T_0 = 0$ and using Eqs. (14.19), we obtain

$$U = \iiint_V \left\{ \frac{1}{2} \frac{\sigma_x}{E} [\sigma_x - \nu(\sigma_y + \sigma_z)] + \cdots + \frac{1}{2} \frac{\tau_{yz}^2}{G} + \cdots \right\} dV. \qquad (21.15)$$

As an example of the use of Eq. (21.15), consider a linearly elastic bar carrying normal force and bending moment but no shear or torsion. By Eq. (16.16),

$$\sigma_x = \frac{N}{A} - \frac{My}{I},$$

and

$$\sigma_y = \sigma_z = \tau_{yz} = \tau_{zx} = \tau_{xy} = 0.$$

Substituting these stresses into Eq. (21.15),

$$U = \frac{1}{2} \int_L \frac{N^2}{EA} \, dx + \frac{1}{2} \int_L \frac{M^2}{EI} \, dx. \qquad (21.16)$$

A linearly elastic bar carrying normal force only can be used to study the computation of $w_E$ for Eq. (21.12) and to illustrate the computation of $U$ by Eq. (21.16), as well as to show the validity of Eq. (21.12) for a special case. Assume that the bar of Fig. 21.4(a) is subjected to a *gradually applied force* **P** which produces an elongation $\delta$ as in Fig. 21.4(c) without any resulting vibrations in the free end of the bar. During the deformation process, the varying force **F** of Fig. 21.4(b) has an $x$-component given, from Eq. (14.14), by

$$F_x = \frac{EA}{L} \, x.$$

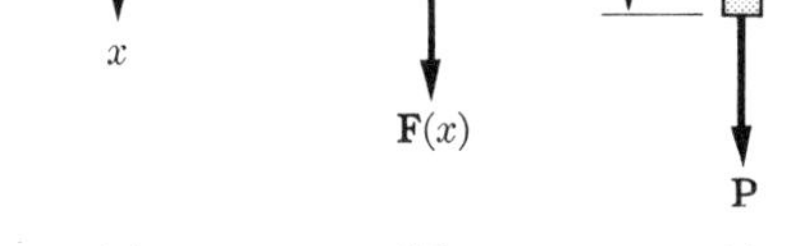

FIGURE 21.4

Hence, neglecting the weight of the bar,

$$w_E = \int_0^\delta \frac{EA}{L} x \, dx = \frac{1}{2} \frac{EA}{L} x^2 \Big|_0^\delta = \frac{1}{2} \frac{EA}{L} \delta^2.$$

But, also from Eq. (14.14),

$$P = \frac{EA}{L} \delta,$$

so that

$$w_E = \tfrac{1}{2} P \delta.$$

(For a linearly elastic body subjected to $N$ forces $\mathbf{P}_i$, it can be shown that

$$w_E = \sum_{i=1}^N \tfrac{1}{2} P_i \Delta_i,$$

where $\Delta_i$ is the component of the displacement of the point of application of $\mathbf{P}_i$ in the direction of $\mathbf{P}_i$.) From Eq. (21.16), at the deformed state of Fig. 21.4(c),

$$U = \frac{1}{2} \int_0^L \frac{P^2}{EA} \, dx = \frac{1}{2} \frac{P^2}{EA} L = \frac{1}{2} P\delta.$$

Hence, Eq. (21.12) is verified for this simple case.

Consider now a *suddenly applied weight* $W$ being added to the bar of Fig. 21.4(a). After the bar has stretched an amount $\delta$, where

$$\delta = \frac{WL}{EA},$$

the strain energy is, as before, $\tfrac{1}{2} W \delta$, but the work done by the weight force is $W\delta$, so that Eq. (21.12) does not apply. The reason for this is that the system is not stationary after the deformation $\delta$. In fact, the weight vibrates about the position $x = \delta$ and has kinetic energy of $\tfrac{1}{2} W \delta$ when $x = \delta$, so that the total mechanical energy is conserved. In a real system, the vibrations damp out after a period of time and the weight comes to rest at $x = \delta$. This means that an amount of energy $\tfrac{1}{2} W \delta$ is lost through internal friction, air resistance, and other nonconservative effects.

As a final case, a *gradually applied weight* $W$ may be added to the bar of Fig. 21.4(a), in which case the system is at rest in its final position. As before, the strain energy in the bar is $\tfrac{1}{2} W \delta$ and the loss of potential energy of the weight is $W\delta$. The difference here is accounted for by the work $-\tfrac{1}{2} W \delta$ done by the external agency adding the weight to the system.

If a structure carries a single applied force, Eqs. (21.12) and (21.16) can be used to find the displacement $\Delta$ of the point of application of the

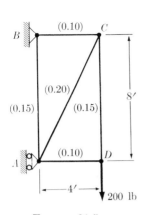

FIGURE 21.5

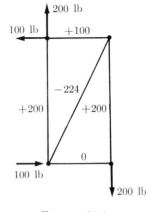

FIGURE 21.6

force in the direction of the force (called the *deflection* of the structure at the point). The procedure is illustrated for a truss in the following example.

EXAMPLE 21.3. Find the vertical deflection $\Delta_{DV}$ at point $D$ of the truss shown in Fig. 21.5 if the load is applied gradually. The cross-sectional areas of the members in $\text{in}^2$ are shown in parentheses. Assume that $E = 10,000$ ksi.

*Solution.* Figure 21.6 shows the axial forces in lb in the members as obtained by the methods of Art. 15.3. By Eq. (21.12),

$$\tfrac{1}{2}(200)\,\Delta_{DV} = U.$$

The total strain energy $U$ stored in the truss is the sum of the energies stored in the separate members, i.e., by Eq. (21.16),

$$U = \sum \frac{1}{2} \frac{N^2 L}{EA},$$

or, since $E$ is the same for all members,

$$U = \frac{1}{2E} \sum \frac{N^2 L}{A}.$$

Table 21.1 shows the computation of the summation in the last equation. Hence,

$$\tfrac{1}{2}(200)\,\Delta_{DV} = \frac{(6,900,000)(12)}{2(10,000,000)},$$

and

$$\Delta_{DV} = 0.0414 \text{ in. downward.}$$

TABLE 21.1

| Member | $N$, lb | $N^2$, lb$^2$ | $L$, ft | $A$, in$^2$ | $N^2L/A$, kips$^2$-ft/in$^2$ |
|--------|---------|---------------|---------|-------------|------------------------------|
| $AB$ | 200 | 40,000 | 8 | 0.15 | 2.13 |
| $BC$ | 100 | 10,000 | 4 | 0.10 | 0.40 |
| $CD$ | 200 | 40,000 | 8 | 0.15 | 2.13 |
| $AD$ | 0 | 0 | 4 | 0.10 | 0 |
| $AC$ | $-224$ | 50,000 | 8.96 | 0.20 | 2.24 |
| | | | | | Total 6.90 |

Equations (21.12) and (21.16) can also be used to solve certain beam-deflection problems, as illustrated in the following example.

EXAMPLE 21.4. Find the deflection of the free end of the beam of Fig. 16.40(c) if the load is applied gradually.

*Solution.* From Fig. 16.14(c),

$$M(x) = -P(L - x).$$

Hence, by Eq. (21.16),

$$U = \frac{1}{2} \int_0^L \frac{P^2(L^2 - 2Lx + x^2)}{EI} \, dx = \frac{P^2L^3}{6EI},$$

and, by Eq. (21.12),

$$-\tfrac{1}{2}P\Delta = \frac{P^2L^3}{6EI},$$

where $\Delta$ is the upward deflection. Thus,

$$\Delta = -\frac{PL^3}{3EI},$$

and this agrees with the value given by the formula of Fig. 16.40(c).

The principle of virtual work for deformable bodies is a most important theorem. Although its proof is too complicated to be included in this book, the principle may be stated briefly in the following way: Consider a body already deformed and in equilibrium under a set of forces. Suppose that the body then undergoes a virtual displacement consisting of translation and rotation and a virtual deformation consisting of dilatation (change in size) and distortion (change in shape). Both effects must be small. Then,

$$\delta w_E = \delta w_I, \qquad (21.17)$$

i.e., the virtual work of the external forces during the displacements of these forces equals the virtual work of the stresses during the occurrence of the strains. The works in Eq. (21.17) are computed by assuming that the forces and stresses (produced by the forces) remain constant while the displacements and strains (associated with the displacements) vary. The displacements and strains are completely independent of the forces and stresses and are quite arbitrary (e.g., they may be produced by another set of forces, they may be caused by temperature changes, or they may simply be imagined to occur without any cause). This principle is perfectly general, applying regardless of the material of which the body is made and regardless of the size of the original deformations. It is restricted to bodies in equilibrium and to small virtual displacements and deformations.

The principle of virtual work, Eq. (21.17), has the advantage over the principle of conservation of mechanical energy, Eq. (21.12), that it can be used to find the deflection at any point in a structure carrying any number of loads even if there are temperature changes and support movements.

For a rigid body, the right-hand side of Eq. (21.17) is zero, and the equation reduces to the principle of virtual work for a rigid body of Art. 21.1.

## Problems

21.1- Solve Example 21.1 if the homogeneous bar $AB$ has a weight $W$.

21.2 (a) Find the angle $\alpha$ required for equilibrium of the system shown in Fig. 21.7. (b) Determine whether the equilibrium is stable or unstable.

[*Ans.:* (a) $\alpha = 75.5°$.]

21.3 The framework shown in Fig. 21.8 is supported by hinges at $A$ and $B$. Find the vertical component of the reaction at $A$ produced by the load **P**.

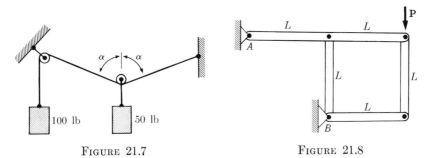

FIGURE 21.7           FIGURE 21.8

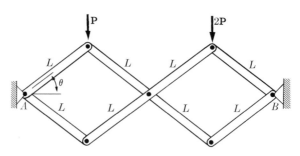

FIGURE 21.9

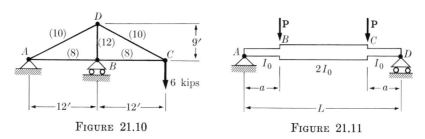

FIGURE 21.10          FIGURE 21.11

21.4 For the pin-connected frame shown in Fig. 21.9, find the horizontal and vertical components of the reaction at $B$.

[*Ans.:* $B_x = -\frac{3}{4}P \cot \theta$, $B_y = \frac{7}{4}P$.]

21.5 Compute the vertical deflection of point $C$ of the truss shown in Fig. 21.10. The cross-sectional areas of the members in $\text{in}^2$ are shown in parentheses, and $E = 2000$ ksi for all members.

21.6 Find the deflection $\Delta_C$ of the beam of Problem 16.36 by the principle of conservation of mechanical energy.

21.7 Using the principle of conservation of mechanical energy, find the deflection of each load $\mathbf{P}$ on the symmetrical beam shown in Fig. 21.11.

*Appendix*

# ELEMENTS OF SCALAR CALCULUS

# APPENDIX

## ELEMENTS OF SCALAR CALCULUS

**A.1 The concept of function.** Let $x$ be a quantity which can assume any value, i.e., can vary continuously, in an interval $a \leq x \leq b$. If each value of the variable $x$ in the interval determines a value of another variable $y$ according to some definite law, $y$ is said to be a *function* of $x$. This relationship is symbolized by writing the equation

$$y = f(x) \tag{A.1}$$

or, more simply, by writing

$$y(x).$$

The value of a function $f(x)$ for a particular value $x_0$ of $x$ is represented by the symbol $f(x_0)$, and two different functions of $x$ are distinguished by the use of two symbols such as $f(x)$ and $\phi(x)$.

The variables $x$ and $y$, called the *independent variable* and the *dependent variable*, respectively, are not to be confused with the coordinates $x$ and $y$ used in mechanics. In the calculus these symbols may represent quantities of any type whatever. For example, $y$ may be the pressure and $x$ the temperature of a specimen of gas in a constant-volume container, the pressure being a function of the temperature. If the gas remains within a certain range of temperature (or, more precisely, if the gas is an "ideal" gas), the functional relationship may be expressed by a mathematical equation based on a law of elementary physics, but the existence of a mathematical equation is not essential to the existence of the function.

Some examples of functions defined by mathematical equations are the following:

(1) The length $L$ of a rod is a function of the temperature $T$ of the rod. If the length is $L_0$ at $T = 0$, then $L$ is given, from elementary physics, by the equation

$$L = L_0(1 + \alpha T),$$

where $\alpha$ is the "coefficient of linear expansion." This type of function, because of its resemblance to the equation of a straight line in analytic geometry, is called a *linear function*.

(2) The length $c$ of one side of a triangle, from elementary trigonometry, is given in terms of the lengths $a$ and $b$ of the other two sides and the angle $\gamma$ between them by

$$c = \sqrt{a^2 + b^2 - 2ab \cos \gamma}.$$

447

If $a$ and $b$ are fixed, then $c$ is a function of the single independent variable $\gamma$. If $a$ and $b$ can also be varied, then $c$ is a function of three independent variables, symbolized in general by the equation

$$c = f(\gamma, a, b)$$

or, still more generally, by

$$w = f(x, y, z).$$

(3) The equation of a parabola with its vertex at the origin of an $xy$-coordinate system and its axis along the $y$-axis is, from analytic geometry,

$$y = cx^2,$$

where $c$ is a constant. Thus, the $y$-coordinate of any point on the curve is a function of the $x$-coordinate.

(4) The equation of a circle with its center at the origin is

$$x^2 + y^2 = c^2,$$

where $c$ is a constant. Solving for $y$, we find that

$$y = \pm\sqrt{c^2 - x^2},$$

and it is obvious that any given value of $x$ in the interval $-c < x < c$ determines two values for $y$ (a positive and a negative value). A function of this type is called a *multiple-valued* function. Henceforth only *single-valued* functions are considered.

Any one of the foregoing functions can be represented graphically by plotting the independent variable as the abscissa and the dependent variable as the ordinate. Figures A.1 and A.2 show the functions discussed in (1) and (3) above.

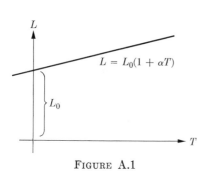

FIGURE A.1

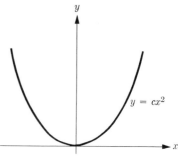

FIGURE A.2

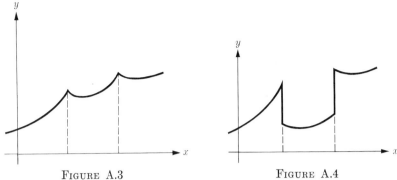

FIGURE A.3          FIGURE A.4

Much simplification is introduced into the calculus if only those functions are considered which are *continuous* throughout the interval of definition. To say that a function is continuous at a point means that any small change in $x$ at the point causes only a small change in $y$, not a sudden jump in $y$. More exactly, continuity means that the change in $y$ can be made *arbitrarily* small by letting the change in $x$ be small enough. The meaning of continuity can be stated in a still more precise fashion, but the foregoing suffices for this introduction to the calculus. The functions plotted in Figs. A.1 and A.2 are continuous everywhere. The function in Fig. A.3 is continuous everywhere, while the function in Fig. A.4 is *discontinuous* at two points.

**A.2 The derivative.** Consider a single-valued, continuous function $y = f(x)$ such as that shown graphically in Fig. A.5. Let $P$ be a point on the curve with coordinates $x$ and $y$. If a change $\Delta x$ is imagined to occur in the independent variable $x$, there is a corresponding change $\Delta y$ in the dependent variable $y$, represented graphically by the movement of point $P$ to a new location $P'$. If point $P'$ is now imagined to approach $P$ along the curve, both $\Delta x$ (called the *increment of x*) and $\Delta y$ (called the *increment of y*) approach zero as a limit, but their ratio $\Delta y/\Delta x$ in general approaches a

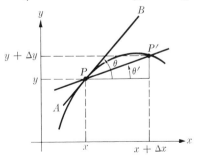

FIGURE A.5

number other than zero. (The number which this ratio approaches is itself usually a function of $x$.) If the limit of $\Delta y/\Delta x$ exists and is the same regardless of how $\Delta x$ is made to approach zero, then, by definition, the *derivative* of $y$ with respect to $x$, symbolized by $dy/dx$, $df/dx$, $y'(x)$, or $f'(x)$, is given by

$$\frac{dy}{dx} = \lim_{\Delta x \to 0} \frac{\Delta y}{\Delta x}. \tag{A.2}$$

The symbol $dy/dx$ is not to be interpreted as a fraction but rather as a single symbol defined by Eq. (A.2). The limiting process described in the equation is of the same type as the following familiar limits from elementary trigonometry and geometry:

(1) $\lim\limits_{\theta \to 0} \sin \theta = \lim\limits_{y \to 0} \dfrac{y}{\sqrt{x^2 + y^2}} = 0.$

(2) $\lim\limits_{\theta \to 0} \cos \theta = \lim\limits_{y \to 0} \dfrac{x}{\sqrt{x^2 + y^2}} = 1.$

(3) The length of a circular arc is the limit of the sum of the lengths of a series of chords (with their endpoints on the arc) as the number of chords approaches infinity (with the length of the longest chord approaching zero).

The precise meaning of a limit can be established only by extensive study of limits and various theorems on limits, but the concepts of the calculus can be developed in an intuitive way without such a rigorous background and put to use in mechanics and other branches of physics.

During the limiting process, the secant $PP'$ in Fig. A.5 approaches a line $AB$, which is called the *tangent* to the curve at $P$. Since

$$\frac{\Delta y}{\Delta x} = \tan \theta',$$

it is clear that, in the limit,

$$\frac{dy}{dx} = \tan \theta,$$

and thus the derivative has geometrical significance as the *slope* of the tangent. (The derivative, of course, is negative when the angle $\theta$ is negative.) It also has physical significance as the *rate* of change of $y$ with respect to $x$.

To ensure that the limit in Eq. (A.2) exists and is the same for any manner in which $\Delta x$ approaches zero, it is essential that the curve have no vertical tangents (since in this case $\Delta y/\Delta x$ approaches infinity) and no sharp points of the type in Fig. A.3 (since in this case $\Delta y/\Delta x$ approaches a different limit from the left than from the right). If these conditions are fulfilled, the function is said to be *differentiable* throughout the interval of definition, and the curve is said to be *smooth* and to have no vertical tangents.

It can be shown that continuity is a necessary condition but not a sufficient condition for differentiability.

A useful formula for the derivative is obtained by substituting into Eq. (A.2) the following expression for $\Delta y$:

$$\Delta y = f(x + \Delta x) - f(x).$$

This gives

$$\frac{dy}{dx} = \lim_{\Delta x \to 0} \frac{f(x + \Delta x) - f(x)}{\Delta x}. \tag{A.3}$$

**A.3 Formulas for the derivative.** Using Eq. (A.3) and a procedure called the "$\Delta$-process," we can derive many formulas for finding the derivative (an operation known as *differentiation*). For example, if $y$ is the sum of two differentiable functions of $x$, that is,

$$y(x) = y_1(x) + y_2(x),$$

then

$$\frac{\Delta y}{\Delta x} = \frac{y(x + \Delta x) - y(x)}{\Delta x}$$

$$= \frac{[y_1(x + \Delta x) + y_2(x + \Delta x)] - [y_1(x) + y_2(x)]}{\Delta x}$$

$$= \frac{y_1(x + \Delta x) - y_1(x)}{\Delta x} + \frac{y_2(x + \Delta x) - y_2(x)}{\Delta x}.$$

One theorem on limits states that the limit of a sum equals the sum of the limits. Hence,

$$\frac{dy}{dx} = \lim_{\Delta x \to 0} \frac{\Delta y}{\Delta x} = \frac{dy_1}{dx} + \frac{dy_2}{dx}.$$

If $y$ is the product of two differentiable functions, i.e.,

$$y(x) = y_1(x)y_2(x),$$

then

$$\frac{\Delta y}{\Delta x} = \frac{(y_1 + \Delta y_1)(y_2 + \Delta y_2) - y_1 y_2}{\Delta x}$$

$$= \frac{y_1 y_2 + y_1 \Delta y_2 + y_2 \Delta y_1 + \Delta y_1 \Delta y_2 - y_1 y_2}{\Delta x}$$

$$= y_1 \frac{\Delta y_2}{\Delta x} + y_2 \frac{\Delta y_1}{\Delta x} + \Delta y_1 \frac{\Delta y_2}{\Delta x}.$$

## TABLE A.1

### FUNCTIONS AND THEIR DERIVATIVES

| $y$ | $dy/dx$ |
|---|---|
| (1) $y_1(x) + y_2(x)$ | $\dfrac{dy_1}{dx} + \dfrac{dy_2}{dx}$ |
| (2) $y_1(x)y_2(x)$ | $y_1 \dfrac{dy_2}{dx} + y_2 \dfrac{dy_1}{dx}$ |
| (3) $\dfrac{y_1(x)}{y_2(x)}$ | $\dfrac{y_2\,(dy_1/dx) - y_1\,(dy_2/dx)}{y_2^2}$ |
| (4) $c\phi(x)$    ($c$ any constant) | $c\,\dfrac{d\phi}{dx}$ |
| (5) $-\phi(x)$ | $-\dfrac{d\phi}{dx}$ |
| (6) $f[\phi(x)]$ | $\dfrac{df}{d\phi}\dfrac{d\phi}{dx}$ |
| (7) $c$ | $0$ |
| (8) $x$ | $1$ |
| (9) $cx$ | $c$ |
| (10) $x^2$ | $2x$ |
| (11) $x^n$ | $nx^{n-1}$ |
| (12) $\dfrac{x^{n+1}}{n+1}$ | $x^n$ |
| (13) $\sin x$ $\Big\}$   ($x$ in radians) | $\cos x$ |
| (14) $\cos x$ | $-\sin x$ |
| (15) $\tan x$ | $\sec^2 x$ |
| (16) $e^x$ | $e^x$ |
| (17) $\log_e x$ | $\dfrac{1}{x}$ |
| (18) $\arcsin x$   ($x$ dimensionless) | $\dfrac{1}{\sqrt{1-x^2}}$ |
| (19) $\arccos x$ | $-\dfrac{1}{\sqrt{1-x^2}}$ |
| (20) $\arctan x$ | $\dfrac{1}{1+x^2}$ |

As $\Delta x$ approaches zero, both $\Delta y_1$ and $\Delta y_2$ also approach zero, since $y_1(x)$ and $y_2(x)$ are continuous functions. Another theorem on limits states that the limit of a product equals the product of the limits, so that

$$\lim_{\Delta x \to 0} \Delta y_1 \frac{\Delta y_2}{\Delta x} = \lim_{\Delta x \to 0} \Delta y_1 \lim_{\Delta x \to 0} \frac{\Delta y_2}{\Delta x} = (0)\left(\frac{dy_2}{dx}\right) = 0.$$

Hence,

$$\frac{dy}{dx} = y_1 \frac{dy_2}{dx} + y_2 \frac{dy_1}{dx}.$$

The derivative of many specific functions can be obtained by the $\Delta$-process. For example, if

$$y = cx,$$

where $c$ is any constant, then

$$\frac{\Delta y}{\Delta x} = \frac{c(x + \Delta x) - cx}{\Delta x} = c \frac{\Delta x}{\Delta x} = c.$$

Thus,

$$\frac{dy}{dx} = c.$$

Table A.1 is a list of some important types of functions and their derivatives. Some of these expressions can be derived from others already established by the $\Delta$-process. For example, the derivative of (12) is found from the derivatives of (4) and (11) by replacing $n$ by $n + 1$ and letting $c = 1/(n + 1)$.

The derivatives of many specific functions are found by a combination of the formulas in Table A.1. For example, if

$$y = \sin 4x,$$

then, letting

$$\phi(x) = 4x$$

and

$$f(\phi) = \sin \phi,$$

it follows from (9) that

$$\frac{d\phi}{dx} = 4$$

and from (13) that

$$\frac{df}{d\phi} = \cos \phi = \cos 4x.$$

Hence, by (6),

$$\frac{dy}{dx} = 4 \cos 4x.$$

Note in this example that

$$y = \sin \phi,$$

and thus, by (13) alone, the derivative of $y$ with respect to $\phi$ is given by

$$\frac{dy}{d\phi} = \cos \phi.$$

As for the derivative of $y$ with respect to $x$, however,

$$\frac{dy}{dx} = 4 \cos \phi \neq \cos \phi.$$

As another example, if

$$y = \sin^3 x,$$

then, letting

$$\phi(x) = \sin x$$

and

$$f(\phi) = \phi^3,$$

it follows from (6), (11), and (13) that

$$\frac{dy}{dx} = 3 \sin^2 x \cos x.$$

Finally, if

$$y = \sin^3 4x,$$

then

$$\frac{dy}{dx} = 12 \sin^2 4x \cos 4x.$$

Since the derivative is itself a function of $x$, it can be differentiated with respect to $x$ to obtain what is called the *second derivative* of $y$ with respect to $x$, symbolized by $d^2y/dx^2$ or $f''(x)$. By definition,

$$\frac{d^2y}{dx^2} = \frac{d}{dx}\left(\frac{dy}{dx}\right).$$

Similarly,

$$\frac{d^n y}{dx^n} = \frac{d}{dx}\left(\frac{d^{n-1}y}{dx^{n-1}}\right).$$

Since the derivative is a function of $x$, it can also be plotted against $x$ to give a graph of the slope of the curve $y = f(x)$, as shown in Fig. A.6. This figure shows the various properties of the curve for $f(x)$ which are reflected in the curve for $f'(x)$. At $A$, for example, the slope of $f(x)$ is zero. Between $A$ and $B$ the slope is positive and increasing, and between $B$ and

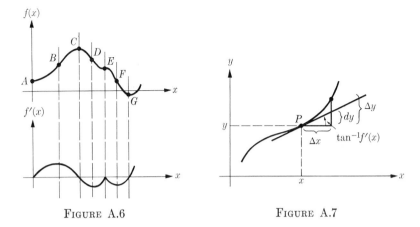

FIGURE A.6                              FIGURE A.7

$C$ it is positive and decreasing. At $C$ the function $f(x)$ has a *relative maximum*, which means that $f'(x)$ is zero there. Between $C$ and $D$ the slope is negative and decreasing, while between $D$ and $E$ it is negative and increasing. At $E$ the slope is zero again. The portion of curve between $E$ and $G$ has a similar slope variation to the portion between $C$ and $E$. At $G$ a *relative minimum* occurs, which means that $f'(x)$ is again zero. Two important facts emerge from a study of Fig. A.6:

(1) Zero derivative is a necessary condition but not a sufficient condition for a relative maximum or a relative minimum.

(2) Differentiability of $f(x)$ does not guarantee differentiability of $f'(x)$.

Since the derivative is a function of $x$, setting the derivative equal to zero gives an equation on $x$ which, if solved, yields the value of $x$ at which a horizontal slope occurs in the curve for $f(x)$.

**A.4 The differential.** By definition, the *differential* $dy$ of the function $y = f(x)$ is given by

$$dy = f'(x)\,\Delta x, \qquad (A.4)$$

where $\Delta x$ is an arbitrarily chosen increment of $x$. Since $f'(x)$ is the slope of the tangent at $x$, $dy$ is as shown in Fig. A.7. Denoting as previously the increment of $y$ which corresponds to $\Delta x$ by $\Delta y$, it is clear that, in general,

$$dy \neq \Delta y,$$

even though both $dy$ and $\Delta y$ are functions of the two independent variables $x$ and $\Delta x$. By Eq. (A.4),

$$f'(x) = \frac{dy}{\Delta x},$$

so that the derivative may be expressed as the ratio of $dy$, the differential of $y$, to $\Delta x$, the increment of $x$. This ratio is completely different from the ratio $\Delta y/\Delta x$, which becomes equal to $f'(x)$ only after it is taken to the limit.

To find $\Delta y$ and $dy$ for a specific function, consider the parabola $y = cx^2$. In this case,

$$\Delta y = f(x + \Delta x) - f(x) = c(x + \Delta x)^2 - cx^2$$
$$= 2cx(\Delta x) + c(\Delta x)^2,$$

while

$$dy = f'(x)\,\Delta x = 2cx(\Delta x).$$

If $\Delta x$ is very small as compared with $2x$, the term $c(\Delta x)^2$ may be negligible in comparison with $2cx(\Delta x)$, in which case $dy$ is a suitable approximation to $\Delta y$.

One case in which $dy$ is equal to $\Delta y$ is the linear function $y = ax + b$, for which

$$\Delta y = [a(x + \Delta x) + b] - [ax + b] = a\,\Delta x,$$

and

$$dy = a\,\Delta x.$$

It is customary to write $dx$ instead of $\Delta x$ for the arbitrarily chosen increment of $x$, so that Eq. (A.4) becomes

$$dy = f'(x)\,dx,$$

and thus

$$f'(x) = \frac{dy}{dx},$$

where $dy/dx$ is now the ratio of the differential $dy$ to the increment $dx$. It can now be seen that the symbol $dy/dx$ used for the derivative may be considered a fraction provided that the correct interpretation is placed on the numerator and denominator.

The differential $dy$ of any of the functions $y$ in Table A.1 can be obtained by multiplying the derivative $dy/dx$ by the increment $dx$.

**A.5 The indefinite integral.** Consider a function $f(x)$ to which any constant $C$ is added to give a new function $f(x) + C$. If $f'(x)\,dx$ is the differential of $f(x)$, then it is also the differential of $f(x) + C$. The function $f(x) + C$ is said to be the *indefinite integral* of $f'(x)\,dx$, and the operation of *integration*, which is the inverse of finding the differential, consists of determining a function the derivative of which is given. The operation is symbolized by the integral sign $\int$, so that, if $g(x)$ is a specific function such

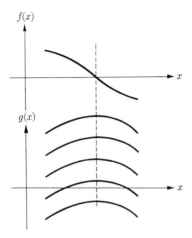

FIGURE A.8

that $g'(x) = f(x)$, then

$$\int f(x)\, dx = g(x) + C,$$

the function $f(x)$ being called the *integrand*.

The arbitrary constant $C$, called the *constant of integration*, must be added to $g(x)$ because the family of functions $g(x) + C$, which differ from each other by constants, all have the same differential or derivative. This situation is shown in Fig. A.8. The physical problems in which integration is used often impose a condition on the integrated function $g(x) + C$ which singles out one of the family of curves as being the one applicable to the problem, which means that the constant $C$ is ultimately evaluated.

If the notation $dy/dx$ is used for the derivative, the process of finding $y$ when $dy/dx$ is a given function $f(x)$ is as follows:

$$\frac{dy}{dx} = f(x), \qquad dy = f(x)\, dx, \qquad y = \int f(x)\, dx = g(x) + C.$$

Finding the differential of a function and finding the integral of a function may be thought of in a purely operational way. Just as the operator "sin" applied to any angle $x$ gives a number $y$, while the inverse operator "arc-sin" applied to $y$ gives $x$ again, so the operator $d$ applied to any function $g(x) + C$ gives the differential $f(x)\, dx$, while the inverse operator $\int$ applied to $f(x)\, dx$ gives $g(x) + C$ again.

Any one of the functions or combinations of functions in the right-hand column of Table A.1 can be multiplied by $dx$ and integrated to obtain the corresponding function or combination of functions in the left-hand column, provided that the arbitrary constant is added wherever necessary.

For example, by (12),

$$\int x^n \, dx = \frac{x^{n+1}}{n+1} + C.$$

By (4) and (10),

$$\int x \, dx = \frac{x^2}{2} + C.$$

This result, of course, could have been obtained from the preceding example by letting $n = 1$. By (5) and (14),

$$\int \sin x \, dx = -\cos x + C.$$

To find the integral of the sum of two functions $f_1(x)$ and $f_2(x)$, assume that $y_1$ and $y_2$ are two other functions such that

$$\frac{dy_1}{dx} = f_1(x), \qquad \frac{dy_2}{dx} = f_2(x).$$

Then,

$$\int [f_1(x) + f_2(x)] \, dx = \int \left( \frac{dy_1}{dx} + \frac{dy_2}{dx} \right) dx,$$

and hence, by (1) of Table A.1,

$$\int [f_1(x) + f_2(x)] \, dx = y_1 + y_2 + C.$$

Thus,

$$\int [f_1(x) + f_2(x)] \, dx = \int f_1(x) \, dx + \int f_2(x) \, dx,$$

which shows that the integral of the sum of two functions equals the sum of the integrals of the two functions. For example,

$$\int (x + \sin x) \, dx = \frac{x^2}{2} - \cos x + C.$$

In this case only one constant is required. The sum of any number of functions can be integrated in a similar manner.

To find the integral of a function of $cx$,

$$\int f(cx) \, dx,$$

where $c$ is a constant, it is useful to make the substitution

$$u = cx$$

and to note that

$$du = c\,dx.$$

Hence,

$$\int f(cx)\,dx = \frac{1}{c}\int f(u)\,du.$$

For example,

$$\int \sin 2x\,dx = -\tfrac{1}{2}\cos 2x + C.$$

**A.6 The definite integral.** Consider a function $f(x)$ of one independent variable $x$, as shown in Fig. A.9, and let the function be single-valued and continuous in an interval $a \le x \le b$. Imagine the interval $a \le x \le b$ to be subdivided into $n$ parts of lengths $\Delta_1 x, \Delta_2 x, \ldots, \Delta_n x$ (not necessarily equal), and let a value $x_i$ of $x$ be selected anywhere in each subinterval $\Delta_i x$, as shown in Fig. A.9. If the value of the function at $x_i$ is $f(x_i)$, then the total area of all the rectangles in Fig. A.9 is

$$\sum_{i=1}^{n} f(x_i)\,\Delta_i x.$$

If the number of subintervals $n$ is now allowed to approach infinity in such a way that the length of the largest one approaches zero, the total area of all the rectangles approaches a definite number which is the same

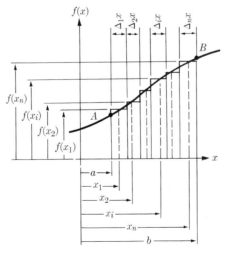

FIGURE A.9

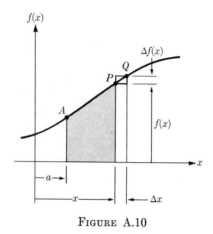

FIGURE A.10

regardless of how the limiting process is carried out. This number, sym-bolized by

$$\int_a^b f(x)\ dx,$$

is called the *definite integral* of the function $f(x)$ between $a$ and $b$. [The values $a$ and $b$ are called the *lower limit* and *upper limit* of the integral, respectively, and $f(x)$ is called the *integrand* as before.] Thus, by definition,

$$\int_a^b f(x)\ dx = \lim_{n\to\infty} \sum_{i=1}^n f(x_i)\ \Delta_i x. \qquad (A.5)$$

This number is also defined as the *area under the curve* between $A$ and $B$.

To evaluate the integral defined by Eq. (A.5), suppose that $g(x)$ is a specific function such that $g'(x) = f(x)$. Let $u(x)$ be the area under the curve of $f(x)$ between $A$ and any point $P$ with abscissa $x$. This area is shown crosshatched in Fig. A.10. An increment $\Delta x$ in $x$ produces an in-crement $\Delta u$ in the area, the latter increment being the area under the curve between $P$ and $Q$. If the increment $\Delta x$ is made small enough, it is intuitively clear from Fig. A.10 that

$$[f(x) + \Delta f(x)][\Delta x] \geq \Delta u \geq [f(x)][\Delta x].$$

Dividing this inequality by $\Delta x$,

$$f(x) + \Delta f(x) \geq \frac{\Delta u}{\Delta x} \geq f(x).$$

Hence,

$$\lim_{\Delta x \to 0} [f(x) + \Delta f(x)] \geq \frac{du}{dx} \geq \lim_{\Delta x \to 0} f(x).$$

Since

$$\lim_{\Delta x \to 0} \Delta f(x) = 0,$$

it follows that

$$\frac{du}{dx} = \lim_{\Delta x \to 0} f(x) = f(x),$$

i.e., the rate of change of the area with respect to $x$ is equal to the function. Therefore,

$$du = f(x) \, dx,$$

and

$$u(x) = \int f(x) \, dx = g(x) + C.$$

Since a small change in $x$ produces only a small change in $u(x)$, never a sudden jump, the function $u(x)$ is continuous, and the last equation indicates that, if $g(x)$ is also a continuous function, the constant $C$ has a single value which holds for any $x$ in the interval $a \leq x \leq b$. To find this value of $C$, the condition that $u(a) = 0$ is used, so that

$$0 = g(a) + C,$$

and

$$C = -g(a).$$

Finally, therefore,

$$u(x) = g(x) - g(a),$$

and

$$u(b) = g(b) - g(a).$$

Since $u(b)$ is the area under the curve between $x = a$ and $x = b$, which is by definition the definite integral, the following important equation results:

$$\int_a^b f(x) \, dx = g(b) - g(a). \tag{A.6}$$

It is customary to write the right-hand side of Eq. (A.6) as

$$g(x) \Big|_a^b ,$$

so that

$$\int_a^b f(x) \, dx = g(x) \Big|_a^b .$$

The following examples illustrate the evaluation of the definite integral by means of Table A.1:

$$\int_a^b 2x \, dx = x^2 \Big|_a^b = b^2 - a^2;$$

$$\int_1^2 9x^2 \, dx = 3x^3 \Big|_1^2 = 3(8 - 1) = 21;$$

$$\int_0^\pi -\sin x \, dx = \cos x \Big|_0^\pi = (-1 - 1) = -2.$$

If the upper limit of the definite integral is taken as the variable $x$, then, by Eq. (A.6),

$$\int_{x_0}^x f(x) \, dx = g(x) - g(x_0),$$

which is the same as the indefinite integral

$$\int f(x) \, dx,$$

except that a specific value is assigned to the constant of integration.

For two successive intervals $a \le x \le b$ and $b \le x \le c$, as shown in Fig. A.11, the total area under the curve between $A$ and $C$ is obviously equal to the sum of the area between $A$ and $B$ and the area between $B$ and $C$. Hence, the integral of $f(x)$ from $a$ to $c$ is the sum of the integral of $f(x)$ from $a$ to $b$ and the integral of $f(x)$ from $b$ to $c$, that is,

$$\int_a^c f(x) \, dx = \int_a^b f(x) \, dx + \int_b^c f(x) \, dx. \tag{A.7}$$

This can be proved (without reference to areas) by using the definition of Eq. (A.5). From Eq. (A.7) it follows, if $g(x)$ is continuous between $a$ and $c$, that

$$\int_a^c f(x) \, dx = [g(b) - g(a)] + [g(c) - g(b)] = g(c) - g(a).$$

If there is a discontinuity in $g(x)$ at a point $x = b$ in an interval $a \le x \le c$, then the mathematical expression for $g(x)$ changes at $x = b$, so that

$$g(x) = g_1(x) \qquad \text{if} \quad a \le x < b,$$
$$g(x) = g_2(x) \qquad \text{if} \quad b < x \le c.$$

A simple illustration of this is shown in Fig. A.12. Equation (A.7) is still valid, and hence

$$\int_a^c f(x) \, dx = [g_1(b) - g_1(a)] + [g_2(c) - g_2(b)].$$

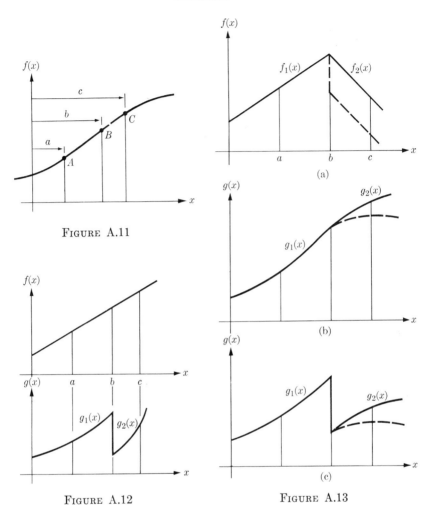

FIGURE A.11

FIGURE A.12

FIGURE A.13

In this case, however,

$$\int_a^c f(x)\, dx \neq g(c) - g(a),$$

inasmuch as

$$g_1(b) \neq g_2(b).$$

Another irregularity which may occur at a point $x = b$ in an interval $a \leq x \leq c$ is a change in the mathematical expression for $f(x)$. One example of this is a point of nondifferentiability of $f(x)$ at $x = b$, a simple illustration of which appears in solid lines in Fig. A.13(a). The solid lines in Fig. A.13(b) show a continuous function $g(x)$ corresponding to the given function $f(x)$, and the solid lines in Fig. A.13(c) show a discontinuous one.

In these situations the mathematical expressions for both $f(x)$ and $g(x)$ usually change at $x = b$, so that

$$\left.\begin{array}{l} f(x) = f_1(x) \\ g(x) = g_1(x) \end{array}\right\} \text{ if } a \leq x < b,$$

$$\left.\begin{array}{l} f(x) = f_2(x) \\ g(x) = g_2(x) \end{array}\right\} \text{ if } b < x \leq c.$$

Hence,

$$\int_a^c f(x)\,dx = \int_a^b f_1(x)\,dx + \int_b^c f_2(x)\,dx$$

$$= [g_1(b) - g_1(a)] + [g_2(c) - g_2(b)],$$

and

$$\int_a^c f(x)\,dx = g(c) - g(a)$$

only if $g(x)$ is continuous.

If there is a discontinuity in $f(x)$ at $x = b$, as represented by the dashed lines in Figs. A.13(a), (b), and (c), the integral

$$\int_a^c f(x)\,dx$$

is not defined, although it may still be necessary to find the area under $f(x)$ between $x = a$ and $x = c$. The total area is found by adding the area between $a$ and $b$ to that between $b$ and $c$, so that, if $u(c)$ is the total area between $a$ and $c$,

$$u(c) = \int_a^b f_1(x)\,dx + \int_b^c f_2(x)\,dx = [g_1(b) - g_1(a)] + [g_2(c) - g_2(b)],$$

and, again,

$$u(c) = g(c) - g(a)$$

only if $g(x)$ is continuous.

All the foregoing difficulties can be avoided if the interval of the definite integral is subdivided at every point where there is an irregularity in either $f(x)$ or $g(x)$ and a separate integral is written for each subinterval.

In addition to the important property of Eq. (A.7), there are the following other useful properties of the definite integral which can be verified by assuming $f(x)$ and $g(x)$ to be continuous and using Eq. (A.6) and Table A.1:

(1) $\displaystyle\int_a^b cf(x)\,dx = c\int_a^b f(x)\,dx.$

(2) $\int_a^b [f_1(x) + f_2(x)]\, dx = \int_a^b f_1(x)\, dx + \int_a^b f_2(x)\, dx.$

(3) $\int_a^b f(x)\, dx = -\int_b^a f(x)\, dx.$

(4) If $f(x) > 0$ everywhere between $a$ and $b$, then $g(x)$ is increasing everywhere in the interval, and

$$\int_a^b f(x)\, dx > 0, \qquad \int_b^a f(x)\, dx < 0.$$

If $f(x) < 0$ everywhere between $a$ and $b$, then $g(x)$ is decreasing everywhere in the interval, and

$$\int_a^b f(x)\, dx < 0, \qquad \int_b^a f(x)\, dx > 0.$$

If $f(x)$ changes sign in the interval, as shown in Fig. A.14, and if the integral is taken from left to right, then the area under the positive portion of the curve is positive, and the area over the negative portion is negative, which means that areas below the $x$-axis cancel those above and an integral over the entire interval gives the net area rather than the total area.

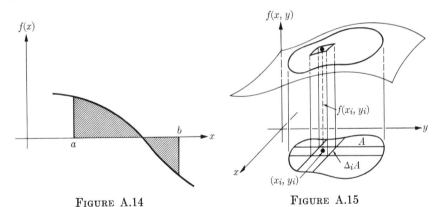

FIGURE A.14          FIGURE A.15

**A.7 Double and triple integrals.** Consider a function $f(x, y)$ of two independent variables $x$ and $y$. Such a function can be imagined plotted on a three-dimensional graph as shown in Fig. A.15. To each set of two values for $x$ and $y$ there corresponds one value of the function $f(x, y)$, and all such values of the function define a surface of the type shown in Fig. A.15. Let the function $f(x, y)$ be continuous (i.e., small changes in either $x$ or $y$ produce only small changes in the function) over a region $A$ of the $xy$-plane. Imagine the region $A$ to be subdivided by a group of lines parallel to the $x$-axis and another group parallel to the $y$-axis, the spacing of the lines being not necessarily uniform. The region $A$ is thus divided into a number of rectangles and a number of irregular figures adjoining the boundary of the region, and it is permissible to ignore the latter portions and consider only the perfect rectangles. (This is justified below.) If the rectangles are numbered in any order and their areas called $\Delta_1 A$, $\Delta_2 A$, ..., $\Delta_n A$, then values $x_i$, $y_i$ of the independent variables can be selected anywhere in each subregion $\Delta_i A$, as shown in Fig. A.15. If the value of the function at $(x_i, y_i)$ is $f(x_i, y_i)$, then $f(x_i, y_i) \Delta_i A$ is the volume of a rectangular prism of height $f(x_i, y_i)$. The total volume of all such rectangular prisms is

$$\sum_{i=1}^{n} f(x_i, y_i) \Delta_i A.$$

The number of subregions $n$ can now be allowed to approach infinity in such a way that the area of the largest one approaches zero. For each successive subdivision of the region by two groups of lines, all the perfect rectangles in $A$ are retained, so that the portion of $A$ being neglected in the irregular figures becomes less and less significant, and, in the limit, the entire region $A$ is taken into account. The limiting process causes the total volume of all the prisms to approach a definite number which is the same regardless of how the limiting process is carried out. This number, symbolized by

$$\iint_{A} f(x, y) \, dA,$$

is called the *double integral* of the function $f(x, y)$ over the region $A$. Thus, by definition,

$$\iint_{A} f(x, y) \, dA = \lim_{n \to \infty} \sum_{i=1}^{n} f(x_i, y_i) \Delta_i A. \tag{A.8}$$

This number is also defined as the *volume under the surface* over the region $A$.

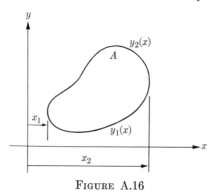

FIGURE A.16

Figure A.16 is a view of the $xy$-plane which shows the region $A$. It is possible to prove that the double integral defined in Eq. (A.8) can be evaluated by taking two successive definite integrals, the first,

$$\int_{y_1(x)}^{y_2(x)} f(x, y) \, dy,$$

being taken as if $x$ were constant and using limits expressed as functions of $x$, and the second being an ordinary definite integral with the result of the first integration as an integrand and $x_1$ and $x_2$ as limits. That is,

$$\iint_A f(x, y) \, dA = \int_{x_1}^{x_2} \left[ \int_{y_1(x)}^{y_2(x)} f(x, y) \, dy \right] dx. \qquad (A.9)$$

The same result is obtained if an $x$-integration is performed first, i.e.,

$$\iint_A f(x, y) \, dA = \int_{y_1}^{y_2} \left[ \int_{x_1(y)}^{x_2(y)} f(x, y) \, dx \right] dy,$$

where $y_1$ and $y_2$ are now the extreme values assumed by $y$ in the region.

In the special case where $f(x, y) = 1$ over the entire region of integration, the double integral becomes

$$\iint_A dA,$$

and, by Eq. (A.9),

$$\iint_A dA = \int_{x_1}^{x_2} \left[ \int_{y_1(x)}^{y_2(x)} dy \right] dx = \int_{x_1}^{x_2} [y_2(x) - y_1(x)] \, dx$$

$$= \int_{x_1}^{x_2} y_2(x) \, dx - \int_{x_1}^{x_2} y_1(x) \, dx.$$

Using the definition from Art. A.6 of the area under a curve, we see that the last pair of integrals is the difference between the area under the upper curve of Fig. A.16 and the area under the lower curve. This difference is defined as the area of the region $A$, the area also being designated by the symbol $A$. Hence,

$$A = \iint_A dA, \qquad (A.10)$$

and this general formula for the area of a plane region covers all the familiar formulas for areas of elementary figures such as circles, triangles, etc. Equation (A.10) simply states that the total area $A$ is the limit of the sum of all the elemental portions $\Delta_i A$ of the area as the number of these portions approaches infinity.

Consider a function $f(x, y, z)$ of three independent variables $x$, $y$, $z$. The plotting of such a function is impossible to visualize, since it requires a four-dimensional graph. A region $V$ over which the function is single-valued and continuous, however, can be shown in three dimensions. (See Fig. A.17.) This region is subdivided by three sets of planes parallel to the coordinate planes into a number of rectangular parallelepipeds and a number of irregular shapes adjoining the boundary of the region. Numbering the perfect parallelepipeds in any order and calling their volumes $\Delta_1 V$, $\Delta_2 V$, . . . , $\Delta_n V$, we can select values $x_i$, $y_i$, $z_i$ of the independent variables in each subregion $\Delta_i V$, as shown in Fig. A.17. The sum

$$\sum_{i=1}^{n} f(x_i, y_i, z_i)\, \Delta_i V$$

does not have the geometrical significance possessed by its one- and two-dimensional counterparts, but its behavior as $n$ approaches infinity is similar to that of the others, and the number that the sum approaches, symbolized by

$$\iiint_V f(x, y, z)\, dV,$$

is called the *triple integral* of the function $f(x, y, z)$ over the region $V$. Thus, by definition,

$$\iiint_V f(x, y, z)\, dV = \lim_{n \to \infty} \sum_{i=1}^{n} f(x_i, y_i, z_i)\, \Delta_i V. \tag{A.11}$$

This integral is evaluated by taking three successive definite integrals, the first,

$$\int_{z_1(x,y)}^{z_2(x,y)} f(x, y, z)\, dz,$$

being taken as if $x$ and $y$ were both constant and using limits which are functions of both $x$ and $y$. The resulting function of $x$ and $y$ is then integrated twice in exactly the same way as for the double integral. Hence,

$$\iiint_V f(x, y, z)\, dV = \int_{x_1}^{x_2} \left\{ \int_{y_1(x)}^{y_2(x)} \left[ \int_{z_1(x,y)}^{z_2(x,y)} f(x, y, z)\, dz \right] dy \right\} dx. \tag{A.12}$$

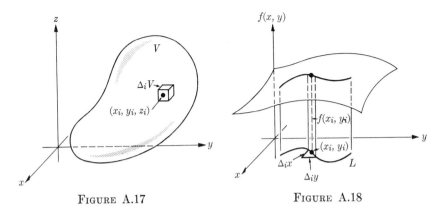

FIGURE A.17  FIGURE A.18

The same result is obtained by integrating with respect to $x$, $y$, and $z$ in any other order.

In the special case where $f(x, y, z) = 1$ over all of $V$, the triple integral becomes

$$\iiint_V dV,$$

and, by Eq. (A.12),

$$\iiint_V dV = \int_{x_1}^{x_2} \left\{ \int_{y_1(x)}^{y_2(x)} \left[ \int_{z_1(x,y)}^{z_2(x,y)} dz \right] dy \right\} dx$$

$$= \int_{x_1}^{x_2} \left\{ \int_{y_1(x)}^{y_2(x)} [z_2(x, y) - z_1(x, y)] \, dy \right\} dx.$$

The last expression is significant as the difference between the volumes under the two surfaces bounding the region $V$ of Fig. A.17. This difference is defined as the volume of $V$, the volume also being designated by the symbol $V$. Hence,

$$V = \iiint_V dV, \tag{A.13}$$

and this general formula for the volume of a three-dimensional region covers all the familiar formulas for volumes of elementary shapes such as spheres, cylinders, etc. Equation (A.13) simply states that the total volume $V$ is the limit of the sum of all the elemental portions $\Delta_i V$ of the volume as the number of these portions approaches infinity.

One other important type of integral is the *line integral*. The two-dimensional line integral can be introduced by considering a function $f(x, y)$ and a curved line $L$ in the $xy$-plane, as shown in Fig. A.18. Subdividing the line $L$ into $n$ parts and denoting by $\Delta_i x$ and $\Delta_i y$ the increments of $x$ and $y$ corresponding to each part, a point $(x_i, y_i)$ is selected in each part. (In this case, $y_i$ is a function of $x_i$, whereas previously they were both independent.) By definition,

$$\int_L f(x, y)\, dL = \lim_{n \to \infty} \sum_{i=1}^{n} f(x_i, y_i)\sqrt{(\Delta_i x)^2 + (\Delta_i y)^2}. \qquad (A.14)$$

The length $L$ of the line is defined by letting $f(x, y) = 1$, so that

$$L = \int_L dL, \qquad (A.15)$$

and this general formula for the length of a curved line in a plane covers formulas such as that for the circumference of a circle. Other types of line integrals are also defined as follows:

$$\int_L f(x, y)\, dx = \lim_{n \to \infty} \sum_{i=1}^{n} f(x_i, y_i)\, \Delta_i x,$$

$$\int_L f(x, y)\, dy = \lim_{n \to \infty} \sum_{i=1}^{n} f(x_i, y_i)\, \Delta_i y.$$

For a given curve $L$ and a given function $f(x, y)$, these two line integrals, in general, have values different from each other and different from the integral of Eq. (A.14).

In three dimensions,

$$\int_L f(x, y, z)\, dL = \lim_{n \to \infty} \sum_{i=1}^{n} f(x_i, y_i, z_i)\sqrt{(\Delta_i x)^2 + (\Delta_i y)^2 + (\Delta_i z)^2}, \qquad (A.16)$$

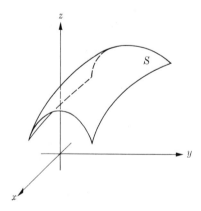

FIGURE A.19

and Eq. (A.15) again gives the length of the line.  The other line integrals
in this case are

$$\int_L f(x, y, z) \, dx = \lim_{n \to \infty} \sum_{i=1}^{n} f(x_i, y_i, z_i) \, \Delta_i x,$$

$$\int_L f(x, y, z) \, dy = \lim_{n \to \infty} \sum_{i=1}^{n} f(x_i, y_i, z_i) \, \Delta_i y,$$

$$\int_L f(x, y, z) \, dz = \lim_{n \to \infty} \sum_{i=1}^{n} f(x_i, y_i, z_i) \, \Delta_i z.$$

Other types of integrals, such as the *surface integral* over the surface $S$
of Fig. A.19, designated by

$$\iint_S f(x, y, z) \, dS,$$

can also be defined as limits of summations, but the definitions become
complicated, and, since such integrals arise only in advanced mechanics,
they are not discussed further in this introduction to scalar calculus.

**A.8 Partial derivatives.**  By definition, the *partial derivatives* $\partial z/\partial x$ and
$\partial z/\partial y$ of a function

$$z = f(x, y) \tag{A.17}$$

are the functions obtained by taking the ordinary derivatives of $z$ with
respect to $x$ (holding $y$ constant) and $y$ (holding $x$ constant), respectively.
For example, if

$$z = \sin (x \cos y),$$

then

$$\frac{\partial z}{\partial x} = \cos y \cos (x \cos y), \qquad \frac{\partial z}{\partial y} = -x \sin y \cos (x \cos y).$$

A function of two variables is said to be *differentiable* at a point $(x, y)$
if both of its first partial derivatives exist and are continuous at the point.
*Higher partial derivatives*, e.g.,

$$\frac{\partial^2 z}{\partial x^2} = \frac{\partial}{\partial x} \left( \frac{\partial z}{\partial x} \right),$$

and *mixed partial derivatives*, e.g.,

$$\frac{\partial^2 z}{\partial x \, \partial y} = \frac{\partial}{\partial x} \left( \frac{\partial z}{\partial y} \right),$$

may also exist for a function of two variables.  If the derivatives

$$\frac{\partial^2 z}{\partial x\, \partial y}$$

and

$$\frac{\partial^2 z}{\partial y\, \partial x}$$

are continuous, it can be shown that

$$\frac{\partial^2 z}{\partial x\, \partial y} = \frac{\partial^2 z}{\partial y\, \partial x}. \qquad (A.18)$$

By definition, the *total differential dz* of a differentiable function $z(x, y)$ is given by

$$dz = \frac{\partial z}{\partial x}\, dx + \frac{\partial z}{\partial y}\, dy,$$

so that $dz$ is a function of four variables, the coordinates $x$ and $y$ and the two arbitrarily chosen increments $dx$ and $dy$ of the coordinates.  In some cases $dz$ is an approximation to $\Delta z$ (the actual change in $z$ corresponding to $dx$ and $dy$).

### Problems

A.1  Two sides of a triangle have a length of 10 in. each and an included angle $\gamma$.  Plot a graph of the length of the third side vs. $\gamma$ for values of $\gamma$ between 0 and 180°.

A.2  A rectangle of base length $b$ and height $h$ is inscribed in a circle of given radius $c$.  Are $b$ and $h$ independent variables?  Is $h$ a function of $b$?  Express the area $A$ of the rectangle as a function of $b$.

[*Ans.:* $A = b\sqrt{4c^2 - b^2}$.]

A.3  Using the $\Delta$-process, verify that

$$\frac{d}{dx}\, (x^2) = 2x.$$

A.4  Using the formula for the derivative of a quotient of two functions and the formulas for the derivatives of $\sin x$ and $\cos x$, verify that

$$\frac{d}{dx}\, (\tan x) = \sec^2 x.$$

A.5  Find the derivative of each of the following functions:

(a)  $y = ax^2 + bx + c,$           (b)  $y = \dfrac{ax + b}{cx + d},$

(c) $y = 2 \sin x \cos x$, \qquad\qquad (d) $y = \dfrac{\sin 2x}{x}$.

A.6 Find the derivative of each of the following functions:

(a) $y = (x - 2)^3$, \qquad\qquad (b) $y = (ax^2 + bx + c)^n$,

(c) $y = x^2 \sin \dfrac{1}{x^2}$, \qquad\qquad (d) $y = \sqrt{\tan x}$,

(e) $y = \tan \sqrt{x}$.

$\left[ \text{Ans.: (a) } 3(x - 2)^2; \quad \text{(b) } n(2ax + b)(ax^2 + bx + c)^{n-1}; \right.$

$\left. \text{(c) } -\dfrac{2}{x} \cos \dfrac{1}{x^2} + 2x \sin \dfrac{1}{x^2}; \quad \text{(d) } \dfrac{1}{2} \dfrac{\sec^2 x}{\sqrt{\tan x}}; \quad \text{(e) } \dfrac{\sec^2 \sqrt{x}}{2\sqrt{x}}. \right]$

A.7 Find the second derivative of the functions of Problems A.5(a), A.5(c), and A.6(b).

A.8 Find the differential $dy$ of the functions of Problems A.6(a) and A.6(c).

$\left[ \text{Ans.: (a) } 3(x - 2)^2 \, dx; \text{ (c) } \left( -\dfrac{2}{x} \cos \dfrac{1}{x^2} + 2x \sin \dfrac{1}{x^2} \right) dx. \right]$

A.9 Evaluate each of the following indefinite integrals:

(a) $\displaystyle\int -\sec^2 x \, dx$, \qquad\qquad (b) $\displaystyle\int (ax^2 + bx + c) \, dx$,

(c) $\displaystyle\int 32x^{15} \, dx$, \qquad\qquad (d) $\displaystyle\int \dfrac{1}{6x} \, dx$,

(e) $\displaystyle\int (\sec 2x)^2 \, dx$.

A.10 Evaluate each of the following definite integrals:

(a) $\displaystyle\int_0^3 4 \, dx$, \qquad\qquad (b) $\displaystyle\int_{-2}^4 (5 + x - 3x^2) \, dx$,

(c) $\displaystyle\int_{-c}^c (c^2 - x^2) \, dx$, \qquad\qquad (d) $\displaystyle\int_{-\pi/4}^{\pi/4} 2 \sec^2 x \, dx$,

(e) $\displaystyle\int_0^\pi \left( 3 - 2 \sin \dfrac{x}{2} \right) dx$.

[Ans.: (a) 12; (b) $-36$; (c) $\frac{4}{3}c^3$; (d) 4; (e) 5.425.]

A.11 Find the area under the curve $y = x^2$ between $x = 0$ and $x = 1$.

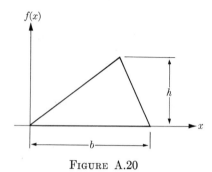

$f(x)$

$h$

$x$

$b$

FIGURE A.20

A.12 Find the area under the parabola $y = 2x^2 - 4x + 4$ between $x = -1$ and $x = 3$.

[*Ans.*: $\frac{56}{3}$.]

A.13 Find the area enclosed by the parabola $y = \frac{1}{2}x^2$ and the straight line $x - 2y + 2 = 0$.

A.14 Use the definite integral of the function $f(x)$ to prove that the area of the triangle in Fig. A.20 is given by $A = \frac{1}{2}bh$.

# SUGGESTED READING

CRANDALL and DAHL, *An Introduction to the Mechanics of Solids*, McGraw-Hill Book Company, Inc., New York, 1959.

DERESIEWICZ, *Elements of Engineering Statics*, Columbia University Press, New York, 1957.

HOUSNER and HUDSON, *Applied Mechanics—Statics* (1949) and *Applied Mechanics—Dynamics* (Second Edition, 1959), D. van Nostrand Company, Inc., Princeton, New Jersey.

INGARD and KRAUSHAAR, *Introduction to Mechanics, Matter, and Waves*, Addison-Wesley Publishing Company, Inc., Reading, Massachusetts, 1960.

KANE, *Analytical Elements of Mechanics*, Volume 1, Academic Press, New York, 1959.

McCUSKEY, *An Introduction to Advanced Dynamics*, Addison-Wesley Publishing Company, Inc., Reading, Massachusetts, 1959.

SEELY and SMITH, *Advanced Mechanics of Materials*, Second Edition, John Wiley & Sons, Inc., New York, 1952.

SHAMES, *Engineering Mechanics—Statics* (1959) and *Engineering Mechanics—Dynamics* (1960), Prentice-Hall, Inc., Englewood Cliffs, New Jersey.

SHANLEY, *Strength of Materials*, McGraw-Hill Book Company, Inc., New York, 1957.

SYNGE and GRIFFITH, *Principles of Mechanics*, Third Edition, McGraw-Hill Book Company, Inc., New York, 1959.

TIMOSHENKO, *Strength of Materials*, Part I (Third Edition, 1955) and Part II (Third Edition, 1956), D. van Nostrand Company, Inc., Princeton, New Jersey.

YEH and ABRAMS, *Principles of Mechanics of Solids and Fluids*, Volume 1, McGraw-Hill Book Company, Inc., 1960.

# INDEX

# INDEX

# INDEX TO USEFUL TABLES AND FIGURES